NOBEL PRIZE LIBRARY

———

REYMONT

ROLLAND

RUSSELL

Nobel Prize Library

PUBLISHED UNDER THE·SPONSORSHIP OF THE

NOBEL FOUNDATION & THE SWEDISH ACADEMY

Ladislas Reymont

Romain Rolland

Bertrand Russell

ALEXIS GREGORY, *New York*, AND

CRM PUBLISHING, *Del Mar, California*

CONTENTS

Ladislas Reymont

1924

"For his great national epic,

The Peasants"

Illustrated by STANISLAS LEPRI

SINCE NO OFFICIAL CEREMONY TOOK PLACE IN 1924, THE FOLLOWING
CRITICAL ESSAY ON *The Peasants,* THE WORK FOR WHICH REYMONT WON
THE PRIZE, WAS PREPARED BY PER HALLSTRÖM IN LIEU OF
A PRESENTATION ADDRESS

LADISLAS REYMONT AND
THE PEASANTS

By *PER HALLSTRÖM*

CHAIRMAN OF THE NOBEL COMMITTEE
OF THE SWEDISH ACADEMY

––––––––––

THIS POLISH WORK of imagination has its starting point in the natural-istic novel, especially in the form which that genre received from Zola in France. Reymont has acknowledged that the idea of his book was evoked by *La Terre,* not through his admiration of it, but through the indignation and opposition it provoked. He found in it a conventionalized, distorted, and coarse characterization of the class of society in which he had grown up and which he loved with all the warmth that had been cherished by his childhood memories. He knew this class of society from abundant experi-ence, from within, and with full understanding—not, like Zola, merely through hasty journalistic studies made in accordance with a program mapped out beforehand with preconceived results; and he wished to de-scribe it in its reality, without any distortion through theories. But Zola had a decisive influence on the work in a quite different and more posi-tive fashion. *Chlopi (The Peasants,* 1904–09), in the final form in which we have it, would hardly be conceivable without the lessons that Reymont learned from Zola's work as a whole—its searching description of the environment, its orchestral mass effects, its uncompromising verity, and the harmonious working together of external nature and hu-man life. Nevertheless *Chlopi,* rather than turning out to be a naturalistic novel, has taken on epic proportions—certainly naturalistic in method but epic in scope.

For us moderns, that which most profoundly marks a narrative poem as an epic, is a certain completeness and harmony, a general impression of rest, however the various episodes may be charged with suffering and struggle. It is not easy to express this effect in a conceptual form, for it is our feelings that perceive it. It achieves its results mainly from the fact that all the elements of strife and unrest are gradually smoothed out before us, like waves that wrestle with one another; the circles never reach as far as the tranquil horizon that bounds the poem; the unrest puts no question and sends no lament beyond that limit. The world that we have before our eyes is a definite one and is unshakable in its foundations; but it is not a world of compulsion and imprisonment. It is wide enough for human beings to express themselves in action according to the measure of their powers. Hence the harmony of the poem. Whatever happiness is recorded, the most irremediable suffering—the disparity between given reality and ideal requirements—is not to be found there, or at least it does not reach consciousness. The most permanently bitter tragedy, that which from within shatters a being to fragments, has not yet been created; the figures we see are entire and simple and move in *one* piece. Whether the figures be large or small, whether their features be fair or foul, they assume a kind of plastic beauty and monumentality.

It is this that the Polish writer has attained in *Chlopi;* and that he achieved it, in spite of a quite modern training which scarcely promised to lead to such a goal, is surely due to the fact that his chosen subject moved of itself toward this happy form. He probably did not seek the form himself—that is evidenced by the rest of his very different production; but when it offered itself to him in the course of his work, he understood it and followed its laws. This is surely merit enough and worthy of great honor.

His Polish peasants possess in their primitive conditions, and perhaps only in consequence thereof, the simple nature, the archaism in their contours, demanded by epic art—a great esthetic value which, however, has been obtained at the expense of being defective in other ways. This throng of figures has extremely little of what is ordinarily called character. Among the men only few have even the raw material of character in mental energy and firmness; and their working up of this material inspires but little respect. The manliness which consists in self-discipline, a sense of responsibility, and a personal grasp of the idea of right has barely attained any development beyond collective and vague mass feeling. What we see of the life of conscience is the common ground of the village, not the guarded estate of the individual. Consequently one must not expect more from the women: hence it is much that in one figure, the sorely tried Hanus, the pliant forces of her nature become welded together into a stubborn sense of duty.

There is really hardly any moral backbone to be found in this low-lying tract round the sluggishly flowing river. Passion bounces in men's wills like a storm in the reeds, and they bend before every breath of wind, and a spark sets everything ablaze. The sense of honesty is uncertain, perhaps chiefly because it has not had free air to grow in. From time immemorial this people has had to protect itself against oppression by those who owned the soil—which was all they had to subsist on. And when the soil at last became theirs, the gift came from foreign masters, who grudged them a soul of their own. The passivity, fatalism, and naive good humor, which under similar circumstances were developed in their Slavonic brethren to the east, held no power in the Polish temperament. Here we meet instead a peculiar nervousness which is not elsewhere a characteristic of the peasant, and which readily expresses itself in anger and violent deeds. All their ill-treatment has not sufficed to crush their pride, but that pride is abundantly mixed with vanity: it is touchy, lacking in balance, and gives no trustworthy support to human dignity. Their virtues have as little root as those of children. They consist in directness, in easily stirred susceptibility, in inflexible and lively spirits: they point to a superfluity of unexhausted gifts; and over the whole there extends a never-failing charm, a certain glamour of nobility. But above all, these people appeal to us through their strong imaginative life. In their poverty and frailty they have windows opened to the world of dreams; and all that is tender and good and beautiful in them flourishes there.

The Church has preserved for them this city of refuge, and to her they are attached with a deep love, piety, and reverence; through her, they expect someday atonement and transfiguration; and in a poetical sense they are already partaking of these good things. By constantly returning to this feature Reymont has contrived to keep the air of beauty over his epic.

Without effort, he has found the gleam of heroism which an epic needs, although his subject matter did not provide him with heroic figures. Heroism was to be found only in their primitively strong, deep attachment to the soil, which gives and takes their lives and lends to their struggle and their love something of the greatness of the forces of nature. Epic breadth and greatness have been attained, too, through the simple touch of genius in the composition of the work, which has been cast in the form of a cycle of the seasons. Autumn, winter, spring, and summer, in symphonically balanced parts, give their contrasts and their harmony in a mighty hymn to life; and when the year has swung full circle in the vicissitudes of human fate, it continues in our imagination in constant novelty and constant recurrence. The episodes in the richly developed action do not occur once only: they have a typical validity. Whether they are idyllic or passionate, tragically wild or merrily diverting, they have all been turned to a rhythm of "Works and Days" in a kind of Hesiodic peasant-world: they have in them a dash of the eternal youth of the earth.

The monotony which usually tends to threaten the peasant novel through its diffuseness of detail has here generally been avoided by the range and the mobility of the material. Unity of style has been combined with an uncommon power and delight in color in the painting of the several parts; and the characterization of the figures, in their dramatic working, has received due attention within the given frame. Everything gives the impression of a reality faithfully described—with possibly one exception, the chief female character Jagna, who is quite as much a symbol as a type. But the symbol is poetically justified. In fact, it is the poetry of the Polish soil and the Polish peasant woman, all the natural magic, the blind working of natural impulses, the pliancy and imaginativeness, the hunger for beauty, and the absence of responsibility, which flourish and intoxicate and are smirched and trampled in times of trouble and guilt. She is the embodiment of all the flaws that Reymont has revealed in his people, despite his love for them; yet she also represents all those qualities which are rich and splendid in human nature. He has made her the tragic heroine of his work; and if, here as elsewhere (and perhaps in consequence of a weakness he shares with the circles he describes), he has passed no clear judgment, he has not allowed any lessening of the tragic tension.

To sum up, this epic novel is characterized by an art so grand, so sure, so powerful, that we may predict a lasting value and rank for it, not only within Polish literature but also within the whole of that branch of imaginative writing which has here been given a distinctive and monumental shape.

THE PEASANTS

By LADISLAS REYMONT

Translated from the Polish by Michael H. Dziewicki

[Excerpt from Volume 4: "Summer"]

CHAPTER I

Thus did Matthias Boryna die.

With dreadful yelps and howls, and leaps against the door to be let in, Lapa awoke the sleepers in the cabin, who were enjoying their Sunday rest; and then he pulled them by their clothes, and ran out a little, looking back again to see if they followed him, till Hanka took notice.

"Go, Yuzka, and see what that dog would have us do."

She ran out after him in good spirits, skipping along the road.

He led her to her father's body.

On beholding it, she uttered such awful shrieks that they all came out at once, and found him cold, rigid, lying on his face just as when he had passed away, his arms stretched out crosswise in a last fervent prayer.

Still attempting to revive him, they bore the body to the hut.

All their endeavors were fruitless: what lay before them was a corpse, and nothing more.

A bitter lamentation rose up: Hanka rent the air with cries; Yuzka cried not less wildly, and dashed her head against the wall; Vitek and the little ones wailed aloud, and Lapa howled and barked outside. Pete alone, who had been coming and going about the yard, glanced at the sun, and went back to his bed in the stable.

Matthias now lay on his couch, stiff and stark, as lifeless as a sun-dried earth-clod or a felled trunk. He still held a little sand fast in his clenched fist. In his wide-open eyes, gazing afar into some heavenly region, there was a look of wondering rapture.

Nevertheless, there emanated from that body an effluence of mortality so somber, so profoundly sad, that they had to cover it with a sheet.

His death was immediately known throughout the village; and barely had the sun appeared over its roofs, when visitors came pouring in one after another, raised the sheet, looked into his eyes, and knelt down to say a prayer for him. Others, stricken with awe at this example of God's dominion over human life, stood wringing their hands in mournful silence.

Meanwhile the mourners' lamentations continued resounding unceasingly.

And now Ambrose came, turned away the crowd outside, closed the cabin door, and, together with Yagustynka and

[7]

Agata (the latter having crept in to pray beside the body), set about rendering the last services to the deceased, which he always did willingly, and in general with plenty of witticisms; but this time he felt somehow heavy at heart.

"So much for the happiness of any man!" he muttered, as he undressed the body. "Dame Crossbones, as often as she has a mind, will clutch you by the throat, slap you in the face; and ye, turning up your toes, are borne away to the 'Priests' Cow-byre'; and is there any able to resist her?"

Even Yagustynka was grieved, and said, in no merry mood: "Poor man! they neglected him so in this world that 'twas better for him to die!"

"Indeed? And who, then, did him any harm?"

"Nay, were they so very good to him?"

"And who on earth has all to his liking? Why, even a squire, even a king, must suffer trouble and pain."

"He had not to bear either hunger or cold: we can say no more."

"Ah, good Mother, what is hunger? The heart-ache gnaws far worse."

"True. I have felt it. And Yagna cut him to the heart: nor did his own children spare him."

"But," Agata put in, interrupting the prayers she was saying, "he had children that were good, and did him no wrong."

Yagustynka turned snappishly upon her. "Say your prayers, you! ye were best. What? will she drone dirges for the dead man, and listen all the time to the talk?"

"Well, but if his children were bad, would they mourn for him so? Only hark to them!"

"Had he but left you so much, ye would move heaven and earth with your lamentations!"

Here Ambrose interfered. "Be quiet," he said; "here comes Yagna."

She rushed in, but stood transfixed in the middle of the room, unable to speak.

They were then attiring the body in a clean shirt.

"What! . . . gone?" she said at last, with eyes fixed on him. Fear was gripping at her throat and her heart; her blood ran cold and she could scarcely breathe.

"Did they not tell you?" Ambrose inquired.

"I was asleep at Mother's: Vitek came to call me but now.—Is he dead truly and indeed?" she asked suddenly, approaching him.

"Surely 'tis for a coffin, not for a wedding, that I am attiring him."

She could not make it out, and staggered up against the wall; she fancied herself in a deep sleep, the prey of some nightmare.

Several times she quitted the room, but always returned: to keep her eyes away from the body was impossible. Now and again she would start up to go out, and yet stayed on; at times she went out as far as the stile, and looked far across the fields with unseeing gaze; or she would seat herself outside, but close to the room and to Yuzka, who was weeping, tearing her hair, and forever crying:

"Oh my father, my lost father! lost!"

There was great wailing and sobbing, not only in, but also around, the cabin. Of the mourners, Yagna alone, though quaking in every limb, and stirred to the inmost depths of her being, could not shed one tear, could not utter one cry. She only walked to and fro with eyes gloomily bright, with an expression of stern awe.

It was a good thing that Hanka presently recovered herself and, though tearful yet, was able to see to everything, and felt quite calm on the arrival of the blacksmith and his wife.

Magda wept; the smith asked for particulars, which Hanka gave him.

" 'Tis well that the Lord Jesus has sent him so easy a death!"

"Poor man! Running out afield to flee Dame Crossbones' embrace!"

"Yestereve I went to look at him; he was as quiet as usual."

"And did he not speak? Not a word?" the smith asked, wiping tearless eyes.

"Not a word. So I pulled the down covering over him, gave him to drink, and came away."

"What? and so he got up alone! Per-adventure, then, he might not have died, had any been there to watch over him," said Magda, between her sobs.

"Yagna was sleeping at her mother's. She always does so, now the old dame is so very ill."

"It was to be!—And it has been!" said the blacksmith. "These three months and over he has been a-dying. Whoso cannot be healed, better let him die quickly. Let us thank the Lord God that he suffers no longer."

"Aye, and well ye know how much the physicians and medicines cost us in the first days . . . and all to no purpose."

"Ah!" Magda lamented; "how good a farmer he was! how able a man!"

"What grieves me is that Antek should not find him alive, when he comes back."

"He is no child, nor likely to weep on that account.—Rather bethink yourself of the funeral."

"True, true.—Oh, what a pity that Roch is away just now!"

"We can do without him. Be not troubled: I will see to all," the smith replied.

He showed a sorrowful face, but was evidently masking some hidden thought as he set to help Ambrose to fold up the dead man's clothes. For a long time he ferreted in the store-room among hanks of spun wool and odds and ends; then he went up the ladder—for the boots which hung there, he said. The fellow panted as loud as a pair of bellows, pattered prayers for the dead man louder than Agata, and was continually recalling the good actions of the deceased. But his eyes were meanwhile wandering about the room, and his hands gliding about under the pillows, or groping in the straw of the mattress.

At length Yagustynka said tartly: "Are ye looking for aught in particular?"

"One cannot find, unless one seeks!" he answered. And then he began to search quite openly; nor did the arrival of Michael from the organist's, in hot haste for Ambrose, hinder him in the least.

"Come at once, Ambrose: four babies wait in church to be christened."

"Let them wait; I must first of all get him neat and tidy."

"Nay, ye had better go, Ambrose," said the smith, who wanted to get rid of him.

"What I have offered to do, I will do. I shall not soon lay out such another as he. Take my place in church, Michael," he added, turning to the lad, "and let the godfathers and godmothers go round the altar with lighted tapers: they will drop you kopeks in plenty.—What!" disparag-ingly; "ye are to be an organist, yet cannot serve at a simple christening?"

Hanka now brought in Matthew, to measure Boryna for his coffin.

"Do not grudge him room in this last dwelling of his," said Ambrose, in a sad tone; "let the poor man have some com-fort, at least after death!"

"Lord, Lord!" Yagustynka whispered; "when he lived, he had not enough with all his many acres; and now four boards will suffice him amply!"

Agata, interrupting her prayers, here faltered tearfully:

"He was a landowner, and shall be buried as such; but some poor creatures know not under which hedge they are to die. . . . May light perpetual shine upon you! May——" And here she broke down again.

Matthew said nothing, but nodded, and after taking the measure, said a prayer and went out. Though it was Sunday, he set to work directly. All the necessary tools were in the hut, and some seasoned oaken planks that had long been in readiness lay upstairs. He had presently set up his workshop in the orchard, and was hard at work—and making Pete, who had been told to assist him, work hard too.

The day had dawned long ago, and the sun was shining with jocund burning rays. It had been quite hot ever since breakfast-time; all the fields and orchards were being slowly plunged in a vapor-bath of whitish simmering air.

In some places, the languishing trees stirred their leaves, as birds overwhelmed by heat might flutter their wings. The lull of the day of rest had pervaded all the village; nothing moved but the swallows darting over the pond, and the carts bearing people to church from some neighboring hamlet, with clouds of dust in their wake. . . . Every now and then one of them stopped in front of Boryna's, where the disconsolate family were sitting, to greet them and sigh heavily, looking in through the open windows and door.

Ambrose made good speed, and hastened the preparations: soon the bed was out in the orchard, and the bedding spread on the hedge to air; and now he called upon Hanka to bring him juniper-berries with which to fumigate the mortuary chamber.

But just then she heard nothing. She had wiped the last tears from her eyes, and was looking down the road, in the hope that she might at any moment see her Antek.

But, as the hours passed, and he did not come, she wanted to send Pete to town for news of him.

"Nay," objected Bylitsa, who had just come in from Veronka's hut; "he will bring no news and only tire the horse."

"But they must know something at the police bureau."

"No doubt; but it is closed on Sundays. Besides, they will tell you naught, if their palms be not greased."

"Alas!" she complained to her sister, "I can bear this no longer."

"Oh, he will yet be a thorn in your side," hissed the blacksmith, darting a glance at Yagna, who was sitting under the eaves. And, his fruitless search for the money having stirred his bile, he added spitefully: "His legs must be stiff with the irons he wore; how, then, can he make haste home?"

She replied nothing, and went to look out upon the road again.

As the Mass-bells were ringing, Ambrose made for the church after ordering Vitek to grease the dead man's boots well, for they had got so dry that they could not be put on him.

The smith, together with Matthew, went off to the village; and now there remained no one in the cabin but the women and Vitek, busily greasing the boots, softening them over the fire, and at times casting a look in the direction of Yuzka, whose sobs were growing fainter.

There was now no movement at all upon the road, the people being in church; nor was anything to be heard in Boryna's cabin but the voice of Agata within, saying the litany for the dead. It rose up like the chirruping of a bird, along with the volumes of juniper smoke, with which Yagustynka was perfuming the hut and the passage.

They heard the service begin. Audible in the noonday hush, the chants wafted from the church, and the sound of the organ came to them in high-pitched undulations, pleasant and remote.

Hanka could find no rest within doors, so she went to the stile, to get through her prayers there.

"Dead, dead, dead!" she thought, as the beads slipped slow through her fingers.—But she prayed with her lips only; her brain, her heart, were full of manifold puzzling thoughts, and not a few misgivings.

"Thirty-two acres. Also pastures. And a bit of forest. And the outhouses, and the livestock!" She sighed and cast a look of affection on the broad acres before her.

"If we could but pay them off, and keep all the land together!—And be just what his father has been!"

Pride and ambition filled her heart; she gazed sunwards, smiled fearlessly, and went on telling her beads, her bosom swelling with agreeable hopes.

"No, I will not give up even half the land. Half the cabin is mine, too. Nor shall the others get a single one of my milch-kine!"

She went on very long in this way, saying her prayers, flinging tearful glances over those lands, clad with sunshine, as if it were a tissue of gold, where the rye, in its growing luxuriance, waved its rusty-red drooping ears; where the darker barley-patches stood shining in the light, glossy and shimmering; where the bright green oats, thickly sprinkled with yellow-flowering weeds, stirred and quivered in the parching heat; where over the blossoming clover that lay spread out on the hill-slope, like a blood-red kerchief, a great bird was hovering, balanced on its outstretched wings, and where the broad beans stood, with their thousands of snowy flowers, keeping watch and ward over the young potato-plants, and a few plots of flax in the

hollows gleamed blue with delicate flowers—childlike eyes that seemed blinking in the glare.

All was so wondrously beautiful! The sun grew hotter and hotter meanwhile; and the warm breeze, laden with the scents of the blossoms that glowed in countless numbers, breathed from the fields with delicious life-giving might, dilating the souls of men.

"O native soil, O holy soil, most holy!" she said, bending down to kiss it.

She heard the church-bells tinkling, twittering in the air.

"O my dear Jesus! all's for Thee—yea, all things in the world!" she murmured fervently, and again betook herself to prayer.

But close to her she heard a rustling noise, and looked around her cautiously. Beneath the cherry-trees, leaning against the trellised fence, Yagna stood, absorbed in unpleasant thought.

"What, never one moment of peace!" Hanka complained; for, at the sight of her, ·sharp memories arose—sharp as stinging nettles.

"Yes, there's the donation made to her. 'Tis a fact! Aye, six whole acres! Oh, that thief!" She turned her back upon her, but could not take up her prayers again. Like hounds that not only barked but bit deep, the wrongs and outrages of former days came back and beset her.

Noon had passed; the shrunken shadows were beginning to creep out once more from under the trees and the houses. In the corn which bent slightly towards the sunbeams, the grasshoppers played their faint shrill music, a beetle hummed by at intervals, or a quail piped. And the weather was all the time growing more and more intolerably hot.

High Mass was now ended, and the women came out of church to take off their shoes by the pond, and there was no more solitude for Hanka; the roads swarmed so with men and wagons that she went home.

Boryna was at last lying in state.

In the middle of the room he lay, on a wide bench, with a cloth over it and burning tapers around. He had been washed, combed, and clean-shaved, but his cheek bore a deep gash from Ambrose's razor, which a bit of paper concealed. He was arrayed in his very best clothes: the white capote that had been made for his wedding with Yagna, striped breeches, and all but quite new boots. In his over-worked withered hands he held the image of Our Lady of Chenstohova.

A large barrel of water stood by to keep the air cool; and upon earthenware tiles there lay juniper-berries, smoldering and exhaling their aromatic smoke, that filled the whole cabin with a bluish haze, through which the awful majesty of death was mistily visible.

So lay, then, in silent state, the body of Matthias Boryna, an upright and an able man, a thorough Christian, a farmer and the son and descendant of farmers—the foremost man in Lipka.

He was in readiness, about to depart, to bid farewell to his kinsfolk and all that knew him, and set out on the Great Journey!

His soul had already passed before the Judgment-seat: it was but his worn-out body, the empty shell his soul had once inhabited, that lay there, feebly smiling, among lights and smoke-wreaths and unceasing prayers.

In came the people then, in an interminable procession, sighing, beating their breasts, musing profoundly, or weeping; and the sounds of their stifled sobs and faint whispers was like the pattering of autumnal rain. They came and went without end: all Lipka came, rich and poor, young and old, men and women.

In spite of the magnificent weather,

his death made the whole village gloomy and wretched; everyone was in deep sadness, everyone greatly given to moralize over "the unhappy fate of mortal man."

Many of the dead man's friends lingered about the hut, and some of the goodwives remained to attempt consoling Hanka and Magda and Yuzka in words of homely comfort, condoling and weeping heartily along with them.

To Yagna nobody said one word. Though indeed she cared little for their pity, she felt nevertheless pained at being so pointedly left alone; so she went out into the garden, where she sat listening to Matthew at work hammering the coffin.

"That creature!" the Voyt's wife hissed after her. "To dare show her face at all!"

"Oh, let her be!" said another; "it is no time now to think of her misdeeds."

"Aye, leave them to the Lord Jesus, who will judge them hereafter," Hanka added mercifully.

"And for the bitter things ye say, the Voyt will reward her abundantly," the smith remarked, with a sneer, and went away, the miller having sent for him. Luckily; for the goodwife was swelling with rage like a turkey, and ready to fly out at him.

He broke into a croaking laugh, and hurried off. The others lingered on to talk, but the talk flagged, partly through their sorrow, partly on account of the intense heat. It was indeed so hot that all the flowers and plants were fading, and the walls shedding tears of resin.

Of a sudden a bellow, long-drawn and plaintive, was heard, and a peasant, driving a cow, passed by on the farther side of the pond.

He pulled her hard by the rope, while they looked on in dull silence.

"Taking her to the priest's bull, I suppose," Yagustynka said; but no one took any interest in her remark.

The bells rang for Vespers and they

took leave of Hanka, who then sent Vitek to ask the smith to go with her and arrange with the priest for the funeral expenses. He presently returned, saying that the smith was in conference with the Squire and the miller, and taking afternoon tea together; his stallions were outside, pawing the ground in the shade.

"He with the Squire!—How strange!" But she could not wait, and accompanied by Magda, dressed in her best, she went to the priest's house.

He was in the farm-yard, and sent them word he would see them there.

He sat in the shade, close to the fence. In the middle of the yard, not far from a rather fine cow that a peasant held fast with a rope, a powerful dappled bull was turning round and round her, kept back with difficulty by the priest's farm-servant, pulling at the end of his chain.

"Valek! Just wait a little: he is not ready yet," the priest called out. Then, mopping his bald head, he called the women to him, and asked about Boryna's death, and consoled and comforted them with the greatest kindness. But when they inquired about the funeral fees, he stopped them short, saying impatiently:

"Of those things later. I am no extortioner. Matthias was the biggest farmer in the village; he cannot have a mean funeral. No, I tell you, he cannot," he repeated fiercely, as was his way.

They embraced his feet, not venturing to insist.

"Ah!" he cried suddenly. "You little blackguards! I'll give it you! Look at them, those bad boys!" He was addressing the organist's sons, peeping surreptitiously over the hedge.—"Well, and what think ye of my bull, hey?"

"A splendid beast!" Hanka replied. "Finer than the miller's."

"The two differ as much as a bull differs from a wagon! Only look at him!" And he came nearer with them, and

patted the flanks of the animal, that now was approaching closer to the cow.

"Oh, what a neck! what a back! what a splendid chest! what a dewlap!" he cried, breathless with enthusiasm. "Why, 'tis no bull, 'tis a bison!"

"Indeed, I never saw so fine a one."

"No, ye never did. It is a thoroughbred Hollander. Cost me three hundred roubles."

"So great a sum as that?" they exclaimed in amazement.

"Not one kopek less. Valek, let him go . . . but cautiously now; the cow is but a puny thing.—She will be mated in an instant. . . . Aye, the bull is exceeding dear. But then the Lipka folk—if they want to have a breed of first-rate kine, will have to pay not less than one rouble, and ten kopeks for my man besides!—the miller is wroth, but I was disgusted with the miserable beasts his bull is accountable for.—Now then, run away!" he said, noticing that the women averted their faces with shame. As they went, he called after them: "Tomorrow we bring the body to the church!" and set to helping the peasant, who had much ado to hold his cow.

"You'll very soon thank me for a calf such as you did never yet see in your life.—Valek, take him away to rest awhile. Though indeed he can scarcely be in need of any rest at all . . . Such a trifle!" he boasted.

The women had repaired to the organist's, because they had to make a separate agreement with him. And as they had to take coffee there, and talk for some time afterwards, the cattle were coming home when they returned to their huts.

Mr. Yacek puffed at his pipe, standing in the porch with Matthew, whom he tried to engage to build Staho's hut, but who seemed hardly pleased at the offer, and would say nothing definitive.

"As to cutting up the timber, that's no

great affair; but as to building the hut . . . Do I know? I have enough of the country and may be going somewhere far away.—No, I cannot say for sure." As he spoke thus, he glanced at Yagna, who was milking her cow outside the byre.

"Well, well, I shall finish the coffin tomorrow morning, and then we may talk the matter over," he concluded, and hurried away.

Mr. Yacek, entering the room where Boryna lay, prayed for him long and fervently, wiping away many a tear. He said to Hanka afterwards: "May his sons but resemble him! He was a good man, a true Pole; was with us in the insurrection; came of his own accord, and did not spare his blows: I have seen him in action. Alas! it is through us he has perished! . . . There's a curse upon us," he added, as if speaking to himself. Though Hanka could not make out well all he said, yet his words were so full of kindness that she fell at his feet and embraced them out of gratitude.

"Never do that!" he exclaimed angrily. "What am I more than one among you?"

Once more he cast a look a Boryna, lit his pipe at the taper, and left the place, without answering the salutations of the blacksmith, just then entering the passage.

"What, so proud today?" the smith cried; but as he was in good spirits this vexed him but little. Seating himself by his wife's side, he talked to her very low:

"You must know, Magda, that the Squire is seeking to come to terms with our village—and looks for me to help him. Of course I shall make a good thing of it. But mum! not a whisper of this, wife of mine: 'tis a big affair."

And he went off to the tavern, inviting men to come there and confer with him.

Along the western horizon the sky looked like a sheet of rusted iron, but a few clouds still glowed above in golden light.

When all the evening duties had been done, the people assembled around the dead body. More and more tapers were lit about Boryna's head; Ambrose snuffed the wicks again and again, and chanted out of a book; and all present joined in the responses, weeping and lamenting one after another.

The neighbors came too, but, as it was very close within, stayed outside, droning out the long sorrowful notes of the Litany as they knelt.

This continued till late at night, when they retired, leaving only Ambrose and Agata to watch the body till morning.

This they did, at first chanting in a loud voice. But when all noise and movement around had ceased, they felt drowsy, and even Lapa, coming in and licking the grease off his master's boots, failed to wake them up.

About midnight, all became extremely dark, not a single star shone. Withal, there was a deep dead stillness, unbroken save by the faint whispering of a tree, or some eerie far-off sound—neither a shout, nor a crash, nor a call—remote and fading away in the distance.

No house in Lipka had any light at all now, save Boryna's, with the pallid illumination of the tapers, and the dead body just visible in the yellow flames, only blurred by the smoke of the perfumes, and seen as in a cloud of bluish fog. But Ambrose and Agata, with their heads pressed against the body, were both sound asleep and snoring loud.

The short summer night was soon over, as if hurrying to depart before the first cock-crow. One after another, all the tapers went out except the largest, which still sent up its long waving flame, like a blade of gold.

At last the gray mist-clad dawn looked into the room and into Boryna's face, who seemed somehow to have awaked from his heavy sleep, and to be listening to the first twitterings of the nestling birds, and through discolored lids eyeing the still remote daybreak.

Now the mill-pond sighed, with drowsy undulations; now the forest began to loom out darkly, looking like a range of black earth-hugging clouds, as the fading night grew phosphorescent, and the trees scattered here and there stood out distinct like tufts of swarthy plumes on the brightening skyline while the first morning breeze sprang up, playing with the orchard trees and murmuring in the ears of the sleepers outside the huts.

Few, however, opened their eyes as yet, being somewhat languid, as is usual after Sunday or a fair.

Then came the day, misty before sunrise, but with the lark chanting his matins, the waters bubbling their joyful carol, the corn giving forth its melodious many-sounding voices; and presently with the plaintive bleating of the sheep, the screaming of the geese, human calls resounding, gates creaking, horses neighing, and all the bustle and movement of those rising to their daily work. But everything was still and quiet yet in Boryna's hut.

They were sleeping, overcome by the grief that had wrung their hearts so sorely.

In came the wind through open windows and doors, whistling and blowing the old man's hair about, and tossing the flame of the last taper in every direction.

And he lay still as a stone, no longer ready to rush to work himself, nor to urge others to toil: deaf to every call now for evermore!

The wind was rising higher, streaming through the orchard with great force, making the trees shake and rustle and sway and toss, and seem peeping in through the windows at Boryna's ashen face. So did the tall slender hollyhocks, bending and bowing at the windows, not unlike red-cheeked country lasses. Now and then a bee from the Manor hives looked in, or a butterfly, glancing in the light; a swallow would dart in and out with a hesitating twitter; and flies and cockchafers, and every kind of living creature came likewise: so that the room was filled with a quiet buzz and drone and whirring hum—the voices of all these things, repeating:

"Dead—dead—he is dead!"

The sun rose—a huge red-hot globe, stilling all those voices; and then it suddenly veiled its glorious all-powerful and life-giving face, now hidden behind dense-volumed vapors.

The world grew gray; in a minute it began to rain abundantly in warm tiny drops, and soon their fall was heard through every field and orchard, pattering continually.

The roads cooled and exhaled the peculiar smell of rain; the birds sang loud and lustily to welcome it; the world was bathed in its grayish tremulous spray; and the thirsty cornfields, and the shriveling leaves, and the trees, and the rills with their dry parched throats, and the baked clods of earth—all drank deep and heartily, uttering, as it were, a silent thanksgiving.

"Thanks, Brother Rain! Thanks, Sister Cloud! We all thank you!"

Hanka, who slept by the open window, was waked first by the rain driving in her face, and ran at once to the stable.

"Up, Pete! the rain has come.—Run and heap the clover in cocks—quick, or it will mowburn and rot!—And you, Vitek, lazy boy! drive our kine afield.— All the other folk's kine are out by now."—As she spoke, she let the geese out of the fowl-house, and they hastened to splash joyfully in the pools of water.

While she was thus engaged, the smith came, and they settled together what would have to be purchased in town for the funeral feast next day. He took the money; but on starting in his britzka, he called her and whispered:

"Hanka, let me have one-half, and I'll never breathe a word about your robbing the old man!"

She flushed red as a beet-root, and cried out in a passion:

"Say what ye will, and to the whole world!—Look at that man! He thinks that all are like himself!"

He glared at her, pulled at his moustache, and drove off.

Hanka was very busy indeed, and her voice was soon heard giving orders everywhere.

Two fresh tapers having been lit at Boryna's side, a sheet was spread over the body. Agata went on praying, and every now and then putting more juniper-berries on the hot coals.

After breakfast, Yagna came from her mother's, but was so frightened of the dead man that she never went in, and only wandered outside, watching Matthew as he worked at the coffin. He had done hammering now, and was just painting a white cross upon the top, when he saw her at the stable-door, silent and looking upon the black coffin-lid with a great sinking at heart.

"Yagna!" he whispered compassionately, "you're a widow now—a widow!"

"Yes, yes, I am!" she returned in a sad subdued voice.

He felt much pity for her; so worn, and pale, and unhappy-looking, and like a child that has been ill-used.

" 'Tis the common lot!" he told her, gravely.

"A widow! a widow!" she repeated. Tears welled up to her dark-blue eyes; a deep sigh burst from her bosom. She ran out into the rain and wept there so plentifully that Hanka came to bring her within doors.

"Of what use is weeping? We too have much to bear. But to you, forlorn one, it is in truth a still greater blow," she said kindly.

Yagustynka, always the same, here observed:

"Weep away! But ere the year be out, I'll sing you such a new wedding-song as will make you dance like mad."

"Such jests are ill-timed now!" Hanka said reproachfully.

"I say true; 'tis no jest! Why, is she not wealthy and lovely and young? She will need a stout stick to keep the men away from her!"

Hanka, going out to take the pigs their mash, looked along the road.

"What," she thought with misgiving, "can the matter be? He was to be set free on Saturday: it is Monday now, and there's no news of him!"

But she had no time for brooding. Her assistance was wanted to make the rest of the hay and all the clover just mown into cocks, for the rain never left off, and was falling in torrents.

In the evening, the priest came with the organist and the Confraternity, bearing lighted tapers, to lay Boryna in his coffin. Matthew nailed it down, the priest recited some prayers, sprinkled holy water over it, and it was taken to church in procession, Ambrose tolling the funeral bell the while.

How empty, how fearfully quiet the hut seemed on their return! Yuzka quite broke down. Hanka said:

"He was just like a corpse for so many a day, yet we felt there was a master among us!"

"But Antek will come," Yagustynka assured her, "and there will then be another master!"

"Would it were soon!" she sighed.

But as in this rainy weather there was a great deal of work to do, she dashed her tears away. "Come, good people!" she cried. "Should the greatest man in the world die, he is like a stone in the depths of the sea—never to be fished up again; and the land will not wait, and we must toil and till it."

Then she took them all to earth up the potato-plants, Yuzka alone staying at home to take care of the babies, and because the sorrow, which she had not yet got over, had made her ill. Lapa was constantly by her side, watching over her, and also Vitek's stork, that stood on one leg in the porch, as if on guard.

When the downpour, heavy and warm as it was, had lasted for some time, the birds ceased from singing, and all the beasts listened in silence to the purl and gurgle and drumming of the torrential rain. Only the geese made a riotous noise, swimming merrily about in the frothy pools.

"Tomorrow we shall surely have fine weather," people said, on coming back from the fields, seeing the sun shine bright at evening, and peer out with his fiery eye over the country-side.

"Would it might still rain tomorrow! it will be worth much gold to us!"

"Aye, our potatoes were all but destroyed."

"And how dried up the oats were!"

"Things will look better now."

"If it could but rain for three days running!"

And so on.

It had kept pouring steadily till nightfall, and the peasants had the pleasure of standing outside their huts to breathe the cool and deliciously fragrant air. Meanwhile the Gulbas lads were urging all the boys and girls to sally forth and kindle the "Sobotki"[1] fires on a neighboring eminence. But the weather was far from pleasant, and only a few bonfires gleamed that evening along the skirts of the forest.

Vitek wished very much for Yuzka to

go with him to the Sobotki. But she said: "No, I will not. What care I for amusements now . . . or for anything in the world?"

Still he pressed her to go. "We will only light a bonfire, leap over it . . . and come home again."

"No! And you too shall stay at home: else Hanka shall know of it," she said, threatening him.

He went notwithstanding—and came back too late for supper, famished, and most shockingly bespattered with mud; for the rain had been falling all the time. Indeed, it only gave over the next day, at the time of the funeral service.

Even then the weather was cloudy and foggy, setting off still better the bright green of the fields, threaded with silver brooklets everywhere. It was fresh, cool, pleasant: the lands, all drenched and soaked, seemed fermenting with intense life.

A votive Requiem Mass was celebrated by the parish priest, who afterwards, in company with his Reverence of Slupia, and the organist, seated in pews on either side of the sanctuary, chanted the *Officium Defunctorum* in Latin. High on a catafalque lay Boryna, amid a grove of burning tapers. Around him the whole village knelt humbly, praying and giving ear to the long-drawn, melancholy dirge, that now sounded like a cry of terror, making their flesh creep and wringing their hearts; now gave out subdued murmuring syllables, low thrilling moans, that caused the tears to start unwilled; and now again would soar on high in unearthly rapture, like the hymns of angels in everlasting bliss; and the hearers would wipe away their tears, or burst into uncontrollable fits of weeping.

This lasted a full hour. At last Ambrose took the tapers out of their sockets to distribute them among the congregation; and the priest, having prayed before the body, gone round it, swinging his

---

[1] The "Sobotki" correspond to the St. John's Eve fires.—*Translator's Note.*

silver thurible until all the air around was blue with incense-smoke, and sprinkled it with holy water, walked forward to the door, the cross preceding him.

Then was there within the church a confused din of cries and wailing and sobbing, as several husbandmen of the highest standing, shouldering the coffin, bore it to the cart outside, the basket-work of which was crammed with straw. Yagustynka (furtively, lest the priests should see and prevent this superstitious act) thrust under it a big loaf, wrapped up in clean linen.

The dismal knell burst forth, the black banners were raised and the lights flared and flickered. Staho having lifted the cross, the two priests intoned:

"Miserere mei, Deus . . ."

The dread strains, the chant of death—the dirge of infinite sorrow—began to sob forth, and they wended their way towards the burying-ground.

In front of the procession, the black flag bearing the skull and crossbones, fluttered like a bird of horror: following in its wake came the silver cross, a long line of taper-bearers, and the priests, arrayed in black copes.

Then appeared the coffin, high in view, and the loudly lamenting mourners, and all the village in the rear, walking in sad dreary silence. Even the sick and the crippled had come.

The gray clouds hung low in the sky, almost resting on the tops of the poplars, and motionless, as if intent on the chants that were sung. When a breeze arose, the trees shed their tears over the coffin, while the corn in the fields bent low as though to salute their master, leaving them forever.

Floating through the air with the voices of the groaning bells, the dirge rolled a stillness as of death on the hearts of the listeners; while the mourners wailed, and the banners flapped, and the cart-wheels creaked—and the lark sang, far away in the fields.

And once again the *Miserere* resounded, with a magical effect on the feelings of those present.

Their hearts were as dying within them; their eyes strayed over the land and up to the gray sky, begging for mercy. Their faces had grown pale with the strain on their emotions; trembling had taken hold of them; and more than one whispered his prayers out of livid lips, with fervent sighs and beatings of the breast, and hearty repentance of sin. And over them all loured that heavy sense of irreparable loss, and a feeling of immense woe, bringing forth most searching desolating thoughts, so that they could not but give way and mourn aloud.

They mused on the inevitable fate of man; on the fruitlessness of all his endeavors; on the utter vanity of his life, his joys, his possessions, his hopes—all mere smoke, dust, illusion, nothingness!—on his folly in setting himself above any creature whatsoever—he that is a mere whiff of wind that comes none knows whence, blows none knows why, goes none knows whither; or the impossibility—were a man lord of the whole world, and enjoying all imaginable pleasures—of avoiding death: and wherefore, then, doth the soul of man drag with it this torpid body? To what purpose doth man live?

Such were the meditations of the people, as they walked in procession, gazing around upon the verdant fields with looks of sorrow unutterable, faces set hard and souls shuddering within them.

But nevertheless, they knew well that

their refuge—their sole refuge—was in the infinite goodness and mercy of the Lord.

"Secundum magnam misericordiam tuam!" . . .

The mysterious Latin words fell upon their hearts like clods of frost-baked earth; and as they walked on, they bowed their heads instinctively to the sounds, as men must bow to the inexorable scythe of death. Now they felt absolutely resigned to all that might come—as indifferent as those rocks they saw cropping out of the fields close by them, in their hard gray strength; or the fallows and flowery meadows, and the mighty trees which may at any time be blasted by the thunderbolt, and yet which raise their heads to Heaven boldly, with a silent song of gladsome life!

Thus they traversed all the village, each one so lost in serious thoughts that he felt as if alone in a boundless desert, and seeing with his mind's eye all his forefathers borne to the churchyard, visible through the great poplar trunks.

And now, to the dreary tolling of the bells, it came in full sight, rising out of the corn with its clumps of trees, its crosses and its graves, opening before them that terrible insatiable abyss into which all the generations were slowly dropping. Peering through the air, dim with rain, they fancied they could see coffins borne from every hut, funeral trains crawling along every road, and everybody weeping, lamenting, sobbing for the loss of some dear one, till the world was full of mourning, and drowned in bitter tears.

They were already turning off to the churchyard lane, when the Squire came up with them, got down from his carriage, and accompanied the coffin on foot—a thing of some difficulty, because the road was narrow, and planted thickly with birch-trees on either side of the surrounding cornfields.

When the priests had done chanting, Dominikova, who was led by Yagna, and walked bent down, almost blind, struck up as well as she could the psalm: "He that dwelleth . . . ," which they all sang with great fervor, relieving their depressed spirits with this declaration of unbounded trust in God.

And thus they entered the burial-ground.

The foremost husbandman now carried the coffin, the Squire himself lending a hand to hold it up as they went along the yellow pathway, past grass and crosses and graves, till beyond the chapel they came to the tomb just dug among hazel-trees and elder-bushes.

At the sight, the wailing broke forth again, and still louder. The tomb was surrounded with banners and lights, and the people thronged with sinking hearts to gaze into that empty pit of sand.

Now the priest mounted a heap of sand thrown up, and he turned round and lifted up his voice, saying to the people:

"Christian folk and men of Lipka!"

Every sound was instantly hushed, save the distant tolling of the bells, and the sobbing of Yuzka, who had put her arms round her father's coffin and held it embraced.

The priest took snuff, wiped the tears from his eyes, and spoke thus:

"Brethren, who is it ye are burying this day? who, I ask?

"Matthias Boryna, ye will answer.

"And I will tell you, it is also your foremost husbandman, and an honest man, and a true son of the Church, that ye are now burying.

"I, who have known him this many a year, can testify how exemplary and religious his life was, how regularly he confessed and went to Communion, and how he helped the poor.

"How he helped the poor, I say," the priest repeated with emphasis, and stopping to draw a long breath.

As he paused, the crying broke out again more loudly. And now he resumed in a sad voice:

"Poor Matthias! And he is with us no longer!

"Gone!—Taken by death, that wolf that chooses for himself the goodliest ram in the flock—in broad day, unhindered by any.

"Like the lightning that strikes a lofty tree and cleaves it in twain, so the cruel hand of death has struck him down.

"But, as Holy Scripture saith, he has not died altogether.

"For behold him, a wanderer from this earth, standing at the gate of Paradise, and knocking, and crying pitifully to be let in, till at last Saint Peter asks him:

" 'Who, then, art thou, and what wouldst thou have?'

" 'I am Boryna of Lipka; and I pray God in His mercy . . .'

" 'What! have thy brethren tormented thee so that thou couldst live no longer?'

" 'I will tell thee all, Saint Peter,' quoth Matthias; 'but prithee set the gate ajar, that I may warm me a little in the heat of God's mercy, for I am icy cold after my sojourn upon earth.'

"So Saint Peter set the gate ajar, but did not let him enter yet, saying:

" 'Now speak the truth to me, for there is none whom lies can deceive here.—Speak hardily, good soul, and say wherefor thou hast left this earth.'

"Then did Matthias drop down on his knees; for he heard the Angels singing, and the little bells ringing, as during Mass at the Elevation; and answered with tears:

" 'I shall speak the truth, even as in confession. Lo, I could not stay upon earth any more. Men are there like wolves to one another, and quarrels are rife, and dissensions, and sins against our Lord.

" 'They are not men, Saint Peter, not human creatures, but mad dogs, as it were. . . . Behold, they are so evil that I cannot say all the evil they do. . . .

" 'Gone is obedience, gone is honesty, gone is all mercy as well! The brother rises up against his brother, and the child against his father, and the wife against her husband, and the serving-man against his master. They respect nothing any more—neither old age, nor dignity of station, nor even the very priesthood itself.

" 'The Evil One now reigns in every heart; under his rule lasciviousness and drunkenness and spite now flourish daily more and more.

" 'Knaves, ridden by knaves whom knaves drive: such are they all!

" 'Trickery is everywhere, and fraud, and cruel oppression, and such thieving! Set but down what ye hold in your hand, they will snap it up at once!

" 'They will graze their beasts, or trample down the grass, on your very best meadow.

" 'If you possess but a strip of land, they will take it and plough it for their own!

" 'Let but a fowl run forth from your garden: they'll instantly seize it!

" 'All they do is to swill vodka, commit uncleanness, and neglect God's service. They are heathens, Christ-murderers, and the Jews their accomplices are scores of times more honest and God-fearing than they.'

"Here Saint Peter interrupted him: 'Oh, is it thus in your parish of Lipka?'

" ' 'Tis no better elsewhere perchance, but nowhere is it worse.'

"Then Saint Peter smote his hands together, and his eyes flashed. And, stretching down his fist towards the earth, he said:

" 'Men of Lipka, are ye then such? Such loathsome wretches, heathens worse even than Germans? Ye possess goodly fields, a fertile soil, pastures and meadowlands, and also portions of the forest: and 'tis thus that ye demean yourselves? O knaves that ye are, waxed fat with too much bread!—Most surely will I tell our Lord of your misdeeds, and He will henceforth keep a tighter hand upon you!'

"Matthias, good man as he was, tried hard to plead for his people; but Saint Peter grew wroth, and cried out, stamping his foot:

" 'Say not one word in their favor: they are villains, all of them! This one thing do I tell thee: let those sons of Judas repent and do penance ere three weeks are past . . . or if not, I will afflict them bitterly, with hunger, and fire, and sickness; and the scoundrels shall remember me well!' "

The priest went on preaching in the same unsparing fashion, and dealing out menaces of God's anger against them, with such effect that the whole congregation burst into sobs of contrition, and beat their breasts in token of repentance.

Then, after a breathing-space, he again spoke of the deceased, and pointed out how he had fallen for their sakes. And he wound up with an appeal to them all to live in concord and avoid sin, since no one knew whose turn it would be next to stand before God's awful judgment-seat.

Even the Squire was seen to brush away a tear.

The priest went off with him, when the funeral came to a close. And as the coffin descended with a thud into the grave, and the sand began to stream down upon it with a hollow rumbling, there arose such a tempest of cries, such a din of tumultuous lamentations, as might well have softened the hardest heart.

Yuzka wept clamorously, and Magda, and Hanka, and all the relations, near or distant, and even many that were not related at all. But not less loud than the loudest rang the shrieks of Yagna, who felt something clutch and tear at her heart, and made her as one beside herself.

"Yes, yes! She is bellowing now: yet what pranks she used to play upon her husband!" someone muttered aside; and Ploshkova, wiping her eyes, remarked:

"She would fain find grace in their eyes, and not be expelled from the cabin."

"Does she think them such fools that they can be cozened so?" was the outspoken comment of the organist's wife.

Yagna was completely unmindful of them all. Stretched out on a mound of sand, she lay crying wildly, with a feeling as if it were she herself upon whom those heavy reverberating torrents of earth were now pouring down, for whom the bells were tolling so mournfully, and over whom the people were so sorrowfully lamenting.

They now began to disperse: some, as they went, stopping to kneel and pray for some dear departed, others wandering about the tombs in dreary meditation, and others again lingering here and there, as they saw Hanka and the smith giving invitations to the customary funeral feast.

The earth was now beaten down over the grave; a black cross had been stuck in; and all went to the cabin with the mourners in several groups, talking low, condoling with them, and at times shedding tears.

The cabin was ready for them, with tables and settles ranged along the walls; and the company, when seated, was offered bread and vodka.

They drank at first with quiet decorum, and broke a little bread. The organist read suitable prayers, and a litany was sung for the deceased, with pauses when the blacksmith went round with drinks, and Yagustynka with more bread.

The women gathered in the other apartment with Hanka, and took tea and sweet cakes; and, the organist's wife leading off, they sang strains so plaintive and piercing that hens about the orchard began to cackle. Thus did the company eat, drink, and weep to the honored memory of him who had died, and sing pious hymns for his soul, as befitted such an occasion and such a man.

Hanka grudged neither food nor drink, and generously pressed them all to partake. When, at noon, many of them expected to depart, a dish of *kluski* boiled in milk was served, followed by broiled meat with cabbage and pease.

"Other folk," Boleslaus' wife whispered, "have not such dainties even at their weddings."

"True; but what a goodly inheritance he leaves them!"

"And no doubt a large hoard of ready money."

"The blacksmith talked of its having been in the cabin—and vanished somewhere."

"Aye, he complains, but knows full well where he has hidden it."

The organist, who by this time was somewhat flustered, now stood up, and, glass in hand, set to extolling the late Boryna in such high-flown terms and such a wealth of Latin quotations that, little as they understood, they wept copiously, as they did at a sermon hard to make out.

The noise increased, the faces grew flushed, the glasses clinked in fine style: some were groping for these with one hand and, with the other arm round their neighbor's neck, babbled and stammered pitiably. Some still attempted to keep up the sad tone due to such an occasion; but no one paid any heed to them. Each turned to the companions he preferred, talking with them most affectionately, and drinking to them again and again.

Ambrose alone was that day unlike his usual self. He had indeed drunk as much as any, nay, perhaps more, having taken all that he possibly could get; but he sat moping in a corner now, wiping his eyes and sighing heavily.

Some of them endeavored to put him in a gay humor.

"Draw me not out, I am in no mood," he growled. "I am soon going to die. To die! Over me there will be only the dogs to whine; or perhaps an old woman may clink a broken pot for me," he mumbled, whimpering.

"Yea, I was at Matthias' christening, and made merry at his first wedding, and buried his father. Oh, well I remember that day! O Lord! And how many others I have laid in their graves, and sounded their funeral knell. Now 'tis time for me to go!"

And getting up suddenly, he went out into the orchard. Vitek afterwards said that the old man had sat down behind the cabin and wept for ever so long.

But he was not one to trouble much about. Besides, just as twilight was at hand, the priest, accompanied by the Squire, came in unexpectedly.

His Reverence consoled the orphans, patted the childrens' heads, and drank some tea, made for him by Yuzka; while the Squire, after some words exchanged with various people, took a glass which the smith offered him, drank to them all, and said to Hanka:

"If anyone has cause to regret Matthias, it is surely I. Were he living now, I might come to an agreement with Lipka. And perchance," he added in a louder tone, glancing round, "I might even agree to all your demands. But with whom am I to make terms? With the

Commissioner[1] I can have naught to do, and there is no man among you now who can represent Lipka."

They listened with deep attention, weighing every one of his words.

He talked on for some time, and put a few questions; but he might have spoken to a wall with as much effect. No one thought of letting his tongue run freely, or so much as opening his mouth.

They only nodded and scratched their heads, and looked at one another. . . . At length, seeing that he could not break down that barrier of suspicious caution, he went out along with the priest, and all the visitors saw him to the gate.

It was only afterwards that their surprise and bewilderment found tongue.

"Well, well! The Squire himself coming to a peasant's burial!"

"He fawns on us; therefore he has need of us," Ploshka said.

Klemba took his part. "Wherefore should he not have come as a friend?"

"Years have brought you no wisdom. When did ever a Squire come to the peasants as a friend? Say when!"

"Since he seeks an agreement, there must be something kept back."

"Only this: that he needs it more than we do."

"And that we are able to hold off!" cried Sikora, who was tipsy.

"Ye may be able: not all of us are!" angrily exclaimed Gregory, the Voyt's brother.

They began to quarrel, each man airing his own view.

"Let him give up both timber and forest-land, and then we'll come to terms."

"We need not do so at all. There will be a sentence, and all will be ours by law."

---

[1] The representative of the Russian Government.—*Translator's Note.*

"Mother of dogs! let him go a-begging; 'twill serve him right!"

"Because the Jews have got hold of him, lo, he comes whining to us peasants for help!"

"And once his only cry was: 'You peasant! get out of my way, or 'ware my horse-whip!' "

Here some one quite drunk cried out: "Never trust him, I tell you; he and his likes only plot the ruin of us peasants."

Then the blacksmith shouted: "Farmers, hear my words—words of wisdom! If the Squire wants to make an agreement, make one by all means, taking what ye can get, and not seeking pears of willow-trees, as the saying is."

Gregory seconded him strongly.

" 'Tis God's truth!—Come with me to the tavern, all of you, and let us talk the matter over."

And presently they all left the premises together, accompanied (as it was late) by the gaggling of geese and lowing of herds coming back from the fields, and many a shepherd, playing on the flute.

They went along noisily, more than one screaming at the top of his voice, merely to give vent to his satisfaction after the feast and (so to speak) blow off the steam.

Meantime, at the Borynas', when the hut had been tidied up, all was silent and dreary and eerie.

Yagna was bustling about in her own room, like a bird beating its wings in the cage: but marking how stupefied with grief all the others were, she went out and said no word to them.

The place then became still as a tomb. Supper over, and the evening household duties performed, they all felt oppressed with sleep; but no one cared to leave the big room. Sitting by the fire, they looked into the dying embers, and gave a timorous ear to every sound they heard. It was quiet outside; only the wind whistled at times, and made the trees rustle, the fences creak, and a pane jingle now and again. Or Lapa would growl, his hair stiffening all down his back with terror; and then the dull interminable stillness would once more come over them.

There they sat, shivering with ever-increasing fear, and so scared that more than one crossed himself and said his prayers with chattering teeth. All felt sure that Something was moving about, walking in the loft above, making the rafters creak, fumbling at the door, peeping in at the windows as it passed, rattling at the latch, and going round the whole cabin with a heavy tread.

On a sudden, a neighing was heard in the stable. Lapa, barking violently, flung himself against the door, while Yuzka cried out in uncontrollable anguish: " 'Tis Father! O God! 'tis Father!" in an outburst of affrighted tears.

Thereupon Yagustynka thrust her fingers forth three times, and said gravely:

"Do not weep. Weeping only keeps a soul longer upon this earth: you would prevent him from departing in peace. Open ye the door, and let the wanderer flee away to the fields of the Lord Jesus.—May he go, and peace be with him!"

They threw the door open, and presently all was as still as death. Only reddened eyes glanced about in fear, while Lapa smelt in every corner, with a whine from time to time, and a wag of his tail, as though fawning on someone . . . someone unseen. They felt now, more strongly than ever, that the dead man's soul was straying somewhere about in their midst.

At last Hanka thought of the Evening Hymn, and intoned, in a trembling husky voice:

"All our actions, done this day,
At Thy feet, O Lord, we lay!" . . .

which the others took up heartily, and to their great relief.

CHAPTER II

It was an ideal summer's day.

About ten in the morning: for the sun stood half-way between east and south, and ever with hotter fires. And all the bells in Lipka belfry had begun to peal with might and main.

The loudest was the one they named Peter. It boomed full-throated: as when a peasant, somewhat in his cups, goes swaying from side to side of the roadway, and his deep roar tells all the world how merry he is.

The second, a little smaller, that (according to Ambrose) had been christened Paul, took up the strain with livelier and more high-pitched tones, ringing long and clangorously, in ecstasies of joy, like a maiden in the glow of love on a spring day, who runs out afield and, darting through the rye, sings from a full bosom to the winds, to the lands, to the clear sky, and to her own joyful heart.

And the third, the *Sygnaturka*, which announces that Mass begins, poured out its notes, like a bird, doing all that it could (though in vain) to outvie the other two with a hurried babbling tinkle.

All three, sounding together, formed a grand orchestra—a roaring bassoon, a warbling violin, and a jingling cymbal, with shrill quivering notes: their music was very solemn and very pleasant to the ear.

It was the day of the local Feast—Saint Peter and Paul—and it was for this that they called the people so joyfully.

In the bright dazzling sunshine and the burning heat, the dealers had ever since dawn been setting up their shady booths, and the tables and counters beneath them, on the large open space in front of the church.

And no sooner had the bells sent their merry peals over the country-side than all sorts of vehicles came rolling in through clouds of dust from as far as the eye could reach, with great crowds of people on foot. All the roads, lanes and field-paths were red with women's dresses or white with men's capotes.

Still from the brazen throats of those bells did the notes pour forth, and they roll sunward their chants and their loud invocations:

"*Kyrie!—Kyrie!—Kyrie eleison!*"

"Madonna!—Madonna!—Most holy Madonna!"

"To Thee, O God!—To Thee I cry—I cry—I cry aloud!"

All the huts were decorated with greenery; and in the whole aspect of the village, on this noted day of high solemnity, there was an atmosphere that lifted up the heart and filled it with rapture.

Every thoroughfare was soon encumbered with foot-passengers, horses and wagons: the travelers within these gazing about them in wonder at the scenery, so beautifully adorned by nature for so great a festival.

All the landscape was given over to an inundation of wild flowers. Along every pathway there reigned a wonderful profusion of soft white and gold and violet hues. The larkspur and the convolvulus put their perfumed heads forth from their hiding-places in the cornfields: bluebells and corn-flowers were seen in every patch, and the hollows where water had been now teemed with forget-me-nots, making the dells look like bits of blue, fallen from the sky. There were clumps of vetches without end, buttercups and dandelions innumerable, and the purple flowers of the thistle and clover, and daisies with camomiles—and countless others, of which only our Lord knows the names, since they were blooming for Him alone. And as sweet a perfume came up out of the fields as when his Reverence in church offers incense to the Holy Sacrament!

The newcomers smelled all those perfumes with intense pleasure, but nevertheless hurried on, not sparing the whip; for the heat was too great to bear, and simply overwhelming.

And shortly all Lipka was crowded, even to the skirts of the forest.

Whenever there was the slightest shadow, wagons were drawn up, horses unharnessed; and as to the space in front of the church, it was all but impassable.

The pond was lined with women come to wash their feet clean from the dusty road, put their shoes on, and make themselves fit for church. Mature peasants were exchanging neighborly greetings; and the younger generation—lads and lasses—went together with wistful looks past the booths, or thronged very thick around a barrel-organ player, on whose instrument sat a strange little beast from beyond the seas, clad all in red. It had a snout not unlike the face of an old German, and leaped about so, and performed such antics, that they all held their sides with the fun of it.

The music played was so merry, they could scarce hold back from dancing where they stood. But then it was accompanied by a very different tune at the same time: the begging hymns droned out by the *Dziads,* who formed a double row, from the church-porch to the lich-gate, where sat another of them, a fat man, always led by a dog. He it was who sang most fervently, and dragged out the words with the slowest drawl of them all.

At the signal for High Mass, the whole assembly rushed to the church like a torrent in spate; in an instant it was full—so terribly full that the people felt their ribs crack. There was an awful crush indeed, and even a few sharp words, and the greater part of those come had to stay outside, by the walls, or under the trees.

Several priests had come over from the nearer parishes. They at once took their places in confessionals, set up beneath the trees, and began to shrive the people.

It was most fearfully sultry weather, the wind having died away, but the multitudes thronged patiently round the confessionals or swarmed in the church-yard, seeking in vain some protection against the extreme heat.

Mass had just begun when Hanka came along with Yuzka. But to get even so far as the church-door was out of the question; so they stood out in the full blaze, not far from the churchyard-wall.

The organ pealing announced that High Mass was in progress. All knelt down piously, or seated themselves on the grass to pray. It was just noon now, and the heat in the still air was tremendous. The sky hung overhead like a white-hot oven tile, so dazzling that it plucked the eyes out. The earth, too, underfoot, and the walls around, glared with heat; and the poor people knelt motionless, hardly able to breathe—baked, as it were, in the sun's pitiless glow.

From within came the music of the organ, mingling with the pattering of their prayers; now and then rose a distant voice from the altar; or the tiny bells were rung or the organist sang loud and hoarsely. Then came long intervals of relative silence in this furnace, while the incense-smoke came out by the church-door, weaving bluish odoriferous festoons round the kneelers' heads.

But in the bright incandescence of the day, this open space and the churchyard, strewn with garments of many a dazzling hue, had the air of a great garden of flowers. And so they were—these worshipers, humbly prostrate at this hallowed hour before their Lord, hidden beneath the veils of that burning sun, and of the sacred silence which enveloped them!

Even the *Dziads* had ceased from their importunate begging. Only from time to time one of them would wake up from somnolence, say a "Hail Mary" and ask alms in a louder key.

The heat was now almost that of a conflagration: the fields and orchards seemed ready to burst into white flames.

The hush, too, was yet more slumber-compelling than before; some nodded, falling asleep as they knelt; others withdrew, no doubt to refresh themselves, for a well-sweep was heard to creak.

They only quite woke up when the church rang to the tones of the whole congregation, singing within; when the banners came out waving, followed by the priest beneath the crimson baldachin, holding the Monstrance aloft, and supported only by the Squires of the parish as he went forth for the procession, with all his parishioners behind him. Slowly, to the sound of the chants that rose up to Heaven with grand and mighty fervor, the procession—a river of humanity rolling in full flood—flowed round the church-walls, resplendently white, and radiant in the sun. And thereon floated the crimson baldachin, quite hidden in the smoke from the thuribles: only now and then did a rift in those clouds give a glimpse of the sun-like ostensory, with its golden rays. The banners, like huge birds, flapped their wings over the heads of the swarming multitudes, the fere-tories, wrapped in mist-like gauze, tottered forward with their bearers; and the organ thundered, and the glad bells boomed, and the whole people sang together from the bottom of their hearts, enchanted, carried away—far away—towards Heaven, towards Him, the Sun of Righteousness!

. . . .

The service was over at length. The Squires had come out of church, seeking in vain a little shade, until Ambrose made room for them under one of the trees, and brought them chairs for their greater convenience.

The Squire of Vola had also come, but did not sit down with them, and was perpetually moving about. Whenever he saw a known face of some Lipka villager, he went up and spoke to him as a friend. Happening to meet Hanka thus, he pushed his way to her through the crowd.

"Is not your goodman back yet?"

"Alas! no."

"Ye went to bring him, of course?"

"I went directly after Father's funeral, but was told he was only to be released in a week: that is, on Saturday next."

"And the bail—what of the bail? Have ye paid the money in?"

"Roch is seeing to that," she replied, with cautious reserve.

"If ye cannot pay, I am willing to vouch for Antek."

"Thanks, most heartily," she said, bending down to his feet. "It may be that Roch can arrange all things by himself, if not, he will be forced to take other measures."

"But remember: should need arise, I'll vouch for him."

He went farther, and perceived Yagna, sitting close to the wall near her mother, and deep in prayer; unable to invent any topic or pretext of conversation, he only smiled at her, and returned to his own people.

Her eyes followed them, she being very much interested in the young ladies, who were clad in such sort that she could not but wonder, marveling also at the whiteness of their faces and the slimness of their waists. Lord! and they breathed forth such sweet fragrance, sweet as the perfumed whorls from a censer!

And the thing they flirted to cool their cheeks! why, it was just like a turkey's tail!—And how those young Squires came and ogled them! And they laughed so loud that the people around were shocked!

Then, from the end of the village, perhaps from the bridge near the mill, there came a sudden clattering and rumbling, while volumes of dust rose above the trees.

"Come too late for Mass!" Pete whispered to Hanka.

"Just in time to put out the candles!" someone said with a laugh.

Others peeped over the wall to look out on the road that skirted the pond.

Very soon, in a tempest of noisy barking, a long line of great white-tilted vans came in sight.

"The Germans! The Germans from Podlesie!" was the cry.

It was true. There were fifteen of these vans, more or less, drawn by stout draught-horses. Women and children, sitting within, and a complete assortment of domestic furniture, were visible under the canvas coverings. Beside these vans marched a lot of burly red-headed Germans, puffing at their pipes. Great dogs ran by their sides, often showing their teeth and barking back at the Lipka dogs, which attacked them furiously.

The people drew near to look at them, several even leaving the churchyard to see them closer.

They drove by slowly, making their way with difficulty through the jumble of wagons and horses; but, on passing in front of the church, not one of them so much as doffed his cap. Their eyes were glaring, their beards bristling—with hatred, no doubt. And they eyed the people with murderous looks.

"Ha!   ha!   Long-Trousers!   . . . Carrion!"

"Ye horse-begotten ones!"

"Droppings of swine!"

And other epithets fell, thick as hail.

"Well?" Matthew called out to them. "Who has won the day, O Father-landers?"

"Who is forced to leave, you or we?"

"Our fists are too heavy; is it not so?"

"Come, stay awhile; 'tis our local feast.—We'll make merry with you in the tavern."

They replied nothing, but lashed their horses to urge them on.

"Not so fast, or your breeches will come tumbling down!"

Here a boy threw a stone at them, and several seized bricks to follow up the blow, but were stopped in time.

"Let them alone, lads, and allow this plague to go from us."

"A sudden death carry you off, ye ungodly hounds!"

And a Lipka woman stretched out her fist, screaming after them:

"May all of you perish like mad dogs!"

So they passed by, and vanished on the poplar road, as the clattering of their carts faded away with the column of dust they had raised.

The people of Lipka were overjoyed, and could pray no more, but came clustering around the Squire in increasing numbers. This pleased him vastly, and he talked gaily with them and offered them snuff.

"Ah!" he said at length; "so you have smoked them out and the swarm has flown, hey?"

Gregory replied, in tone of mock pity: "Our sheepskins do not delight their nostrils. And then they are too delicate folk to dwell nigh us: if we come to loggerheads with any of them, why, down he goes straightway."

The Squire asked with curiosity: "What, have you fought together at any time?"

"Why, no . . . not a fight exactly . . . but Matthew here just gave one of them a tap for not returning his greeting, 'Praised be Jesus Christ!' And behold, the fellow was at once covered with blood, and well-nigh gave up the ghost!"

"They are a soft-limbed people," Matthew explained blandly. "To the eyes they look strong as oak-trees; but put forth your fist, 'twill feel as though it had struck a feather-bed!"

"And in Podlesie they had no chance. Lost their kine, it is said."

"True, they have not brought even one away with them now!"

"Kobus might tell us something . . ." one of them was beginning, when Klemba cut in sharply:

"They died—as all know—of rinderpest."

The men shook with suppressed laughter, but kept it down well, while the smith pressed forward, and said: "If the Germans have gone, we owe it to his Honor the Squire."

"Because I prefer to sell my land to my own countrymen, no matter on what terms," the latter asserted with great energy; and went on to assert that his grandfather and great-grandfather had always held with the peasants.

Sikora grinned to hear this, and said in a lower tone: "Aye, 'tis a fact, and the Squire his father scored it on my back with a horse-whip to remember! I bear the marks yet!"

But the other had apparently not heard him, and was telling what trouble he had had to get rid of the Germans. The peasants listened with civil assent; but, as to his kind feelings, they kept their own opinion.

"Surely butter would not melt in our benefactor's mouth," Sikora sneered; and Klemba bade him hold his tongue.

While they were thus complimenting one another, a clergyman in surplice, with a plate in his hand, pushed his way into the group.

"If 'tis not Yanek, the organist's son!"

It was he, but now wearing the priest's cassock, and making the collection. He greeted everyone, and collected with great success; for they knew him, and it was impossible to let him pass without offering something. So each man undid the bundle his money was knotted in, and often a silver *zloty* jingled among the coppers on the plate. The Squire flung down a rouble, the young ladies of Vola small silver coins in plenty. Yanek, streaming with perspiration, red as fire, but happy and radiant, went on collecting indefatigably all through the churchyard, passing no one by, and saying a good word to everybody. He met Hanka, and saluted her so cordially that she gave twenty kopeks. But when he came face to face with Yagna, clinking the money in his plate before her, she raised her eyes—and was struck dumb with amazement. He too was so taken aback by her confusion that he at once and without a word passed on farther.

She had even forgotten to make an offering, lost as she was in the contemplation of the young man—the very image, she thought, of the saint painted above one of the side-altars: so young, so slender, so beautiful to look upon! Oh, what a spell those gleaming eyes of his had cast on her! . . . Vainly she rubbed her eyes, and crossed herself again and again to get rid of it.

Around her ran whispers:

"Only an organist's son, yet how well he is clad!"

"And his mother is as vain as a turkey about him."

"Ever since Eastertide, he has been at the school for priests."

"His Reverence sent for him to make the collection today."

"For his son, at least, the grasping old skinflint is liberal enough."

"Surely, for will not the glory of the priesthood do honor to him too?"

"Aye, and no small profit will be his likewise."

But Yagna, following him with fascinated eyes, heard no word of what they said.

The service being quite at an end, the congregation was now dispersing, and Hanka was moving towards the gate, when Balcerkova came up to her with important news.

"Know ye that, between Simon, son of Dominikova, and the girl Nastka, the banns have just been published?"

"Oh, but what will Dominikova say to that?"

"There will, of course, be another quarrel."

"She cannot do anything to prevent it: Simon is in the right—and of age besides."

"There will be a perfect hell in the hut," Yagustynka observed.

Hanka sighed: "Are there too few quarrels and sins against God as it is?"

"Have ye heard," Ploshkova asked her, "the news about the Voyt?" And she brought her large belly and bloated face unpleasantly close.

"I have had so much trouble with the funeral, and so many other cares of late, that I know naught of what goes on in the village."

"Well, the head man at the office told my goodman that the village accounts were short by a great sum. And now the Voyt is going about everywhere and whining to get money lent to him; for there may be an investigation any day."

"Father-in-law used to say it would surely end in that wise."

"Aye, he was puffed up, and proud, and played the great man; now he must pay for his greatness."

"Can his land be taken from him?"

"Of course it can; and if it should not suffice, he must go to jail," Yagustynka said. "The rogue has had his fling: let him have his punishment!"

"I could not understand why of late he never showed his face at our cabin, even for the funeral."

"Oh, 'twas not Boryna but Boryna's widow he cared for!"

But Yagna, holding her mother by the hand, was passing by, and they held their peace. Nevertheless, and though the old dame walked stooping and with eyes still bound, Yagustynka could not refrain from a hit at her.

"When is Simon's wedding to be? What we heard today from the pulpit was so unexpected! . . . Though indeed, now the lad is tired of doing a girl's work, it is hard to forbid him his manhood. And," she added mockingly, "Nastka will do that work now for him."

Dominikova drew herself up suddenly, and addressed Yagna in a hard voice:

"Take—take me away, else that viper will sting me again."

She went sobbing away, and Ploshka chuckled.

"Blind as she was, she knew well who you were!"

"She's not so blind but that she can see to tear Simon's hair out!"

"Ah, God grant she may harm no one else besides!"

There was no more talking; they were in the great crush close to the gate, and Hanka was separated from the others: not much grieved to be spared that cruel backbiting they enjoyed so. To each of the *Dziads* she gave a kopek, and five to the blind one with the dog, saying: "Come and dine with us, *Dziad!*—At the Borynas'!"

He lifted his head, and rolled his sightless eyes. "I think ye're Antek's wife.— God reward you!—Surely I shall come . . . and speedily."

Without the gates, the throng was less dense; but there too sat more *Dziads*, in two parallel rows, uttering various complaints. At the very end was a young man, with a green shade over his eyes, singing to the accompaniment of his fiddle ballads about the "kings of olden time," and surrounded by a large audience: coins were frequently dropped into his cap, his performance being a decided hit.

Hanka, who stood close to the churchyard, looking for Yuzka, most unexpectedly happened to see her father.

He was among the *Dziads,* holding out his hands for alms, and begging with the usual whine of the class!

At first she thought her eyes were mistaken, and rubbed them, and looked again. No! it was—it was—he himself!

"My father a *Dziad!* O Lord!" She flushed burning red with the shame of it, drew her kerchief far over her brows, and crept round to him from behind the wagons by which he was sitting.

"What, oh, what do ye here?" she groaned, crouching behind him lest she should be seen.

"Hanka! . . . Yes . . . it is I."

"Come with me!—Come home!—Instantly!—O Lord Jesus, such a disgrace to us all! Come."

"I will not . . . long have I thought to do this. . . . Why should I burden you, if kindly folk will come to my aid . . . I will go along with the others . . . see the world . . . visit the sanctuaries . . . hear about new things.—Aye, and I will bring money home to you. See, here's a *zloty:* buy a toy for little Peter therewith.—Here!"

She seized him firmly by the coat-collar, and almost by main force dragged him out of the jumble of wagons.

"Home with me this instant, I say!— What, have ye no shame?"

"Unhand me, or I shall be angry with you!"

"That wallet, throw it away! And quickly, lest any behold it!"

"Look ye, I will do just as I choose.

Wherefore should I be ashamed? 'The wallet's his mother, who has Hunger for brother.'" At those words he jerked himself free from her, darted away among the horses and carts, and disappeared.

It was out of the question to think of following him in such a crowd as there was all round the church.

There the people, though drenched with perspiration, half choked with dust, half roasted by the heat, were all the same enjoying themselves to their heart's content, in this seething cauldron!

The barrel-organ played lustily, the *Dziads* cried aloud, the little ones whistled in the earthenware birds they had bought; horses were biting each other and squealing, being more than usually tormented with flies that day; and men talked with their friends, or went in company to look at the booths, besieged especially by girls, who were swarming there like bees about a hive.

The articles sold were more or less those on sale at the annual fairs: pictures of saints, victuals and homely dainties, clothing, ribbons, beads, etc.; and at every booth there was a great concourse of people, stopping there on their way from church.

Some went afterwards to the tavern, some straight home. Others, overcome with sleep and weariness, just laid themselves down under the wagons or about the orchards and farm-yards to refresh themselves and to rest.

In so intense a heat that they could scarcely breathe, few cared much to chat, or even to move: many felt stupefied, almost swooning. And as just then the villagers sat down to their meal, the place grew quieter at last.

At the priest's house, they had made a grand dinner for the clergymen and the Squires, whose heads were to be seen through the open windows, out of which floated the noise of talk and the clinking of glasses, together with such delightful aromas as made the mouths of them that passed by to water.

Ambrose, arrayed in his very best, and wearing all his military decorations, was continually moving about the passages, and heard frequently crying out in the porch: "You riff-raff away, or I thrash you within an inch of your lives!"

But his threats served him in no way; the urchins were like sparrows, perched all over the fences; and the boldest even crept under the windows. He could only scold, and threaten them with his Reverence's stick.

Hanka, in search of her father, came to him just then, and asked whether he had not seen him.

"Bylitsa?—Why, 'tis so tremendously hot, he must be asleep somewhere in the shadow.—Ah! ye little wretches!" he cried, and went stumping after the urchins.

Greatly upset, Hanka returned home, and told the occurrence to her sister, who had come to dine with her.

But Veronka only gave a shrug.

"His having joined the *Dziads* will not cost him a kingdom, and it will make things easier for us. Better men than he have ended likewise!"

"But, good God! what a disgrace to us, to let our own father go a-begging!—And what will Antek say?—And the others, our neighbors, will they not cry out that we have turned him out to beg?"

"Let them yelp as they please! Anyone can wag his tongue; but who will offer help? No one."

"And I—I will not allow my father to beg."

"So high and mighty? Then take him and feed him yourself."

"So will I!—You, you grudge him a few spoonfuls of food.—Oh, I see now! . . . 'tis you that have driven him to this!"

"What? what? is there too much of aught in my home? Am I to take the food out of my children's mouths, and give it to him?"

"Yet remember: he has a legal claim to be fed by you for the land he made over."

"To give what I have not, I will not rend my bowels."

"Rend them, but give: Father comes first! He has more than once complained to me that you starve him, and care less for him than for your swine."

"Most true. I starve my father, and live myself like a rich lady! So stout am I that my petticoat slips off my hips, and I have hardly strength to crawl."

"Do not talk so: folk might think ye spoke the truth."

"But I do! Were it not for Yankel, we should not even get the potatoes and salt we eat.—Ah, 'tis a true saying: 'Good-man Bellyful thinks no one is hungry.'"

She was going on in this way, and growing more and more querulous, when the blind man, led by his dog, appeared on the premises.

"Sit ye down here by the hut," Hanka said, and hurried away to get him his dinner.

Dinner had been already served under the trees, and the smell of the dishes came to his nostrils.

"Groats and fat bacon: very good indeed. May it profit you!" the beggar muttered, sniffing the scent of it, and smacking his lips.

His dog sat close to the house-wall, panting with wide-open jaws, and tongue lolling out; for the heat was so great as to melt them all to nothing. In the hot sleepy stillness, only the scraping of the spoons was heard, with (at times) a swallow twittering under the eaves.

"Oh, how cooling would a little dish of sour milk be!" sighed the *Dziad*.

Yuzka answered at once: "Be easy, I shall fetch you some."

"Well, has your whining brought you in much today?" Pete asked, tapping the dish lazily with his spoon.

"Lord have mercy on all sinners, and remember not their ill-treatment of the *Dziads!*—Brought me in much, quotha! —Whoso sees a *Dziad* must needs stare into the sky, or turn down another road. Or, drawing forth some miserable small coin, he will wish he had change for a five-kopek piece. We shall die of starvation!"

"But," Veronka objected, "this year the hard times before harvest press sorely on all of us."

"They do; but for all that, no man goes short of vodka."

Yuzka here put a porringer in his hands, and he began to sup it eagerly.

Presently he said: "They tell us the Lipka folk are to come to terms with the Squire today: is it so?"

"They may do so," Hanka said, "if they get their rights granted."

"And do ye know," Vitek put in, "that the Germans have gone from among us?"

"Oh, may the plague stop their breath!" the *Dziad* burst out, clenching his fist with fury.

"Have they, then, injured you too?"

"I went to them last evening: they set their dogs at me! . . . Scum of the earth, dog-begotten miscreants! . . . I hear the men of Lipka have made it too hot for them to stay. . . . Ha! I would flay them alive, leave not a rag of skin upon any of them!" he said, as he emptied the porringer, and, after feeding his dog, prepared to depart.

"'Tis your harvest now, and ye must go and gather it in," Pete said sarcastically.

"I must, indeed. Last year we were only six in all here; now we are four times as many, and my ears tingle with the din we make."

Yuzka said: "Pray spend the night with us."

"May our Lord give you health, O you that remember the poor starveling!"

"A fine starveling indeed! With such a belly that he can hardly drag it!" sneered Pete, seeing him waddle ponderously in the middle of the road, groping for obstacles with his staff.

And then they all went out again: to hear Vespers, and enjoy the sweet tones of the organ, and weep their fill in church, and then visit the booths once more, were it only to feast their eyes on the splendors they displayed.

Simon had bought a string of amber beads for his Nastka, and ribbons, and a bright scarlet kerchief: all of which she immediately put on. And then they went from booth to booth, arms round waists, overflowing with gladness and intoxicated with joy.

Yuzka followed them, trying here and there to cheapen some article for sale, and ever more ruefully counting her money—only one wretched *zloty* in all!

Yagna, not far from them, affected not to see her brother, and walked alone, sorrowful and forlorn. All those fluttering ribbons now failed to rejoice her; and the barrel-organ's tunes, and the crowd and the hubbub, failed too.

She walked along, carried on by the multitudes, and stopping where they stopped, knowing neither why she had come nor whither she was drifting.

Matthew glided up to her, and whispered softly:

"Do not drive me away from you!"

"And have I ever done that?"

"Once surely. And with words of upbraiding!"

"Because you had said what you should not—and I had no choice.—Someone had——"

She broke off suddenly; Yanek was slowly pushing through the crowd towards her.

"He's here, then?" whispered Matthew, pointing to the young cleric, whose hands

people wanted to kiss, and who smilingly refused the honor.

"He behaves like the son of a Squire! And how well I remember him, not so long since, running after the kine!"

"He, tending kine?—Never!" she exclaimed, hurt by the very thought.

"I have said. I recollect perfectly how the organist thrashed him one day for letting the kine graze in Prychek's oatpatch, he asleep under a pear-tree the while."

Yagna left him, and timidly made her way towards the young cleric, who smiled at her, but (finding himself the observed of all observers) turned his eyes away at once; and having purchased some tiny engravings of saints at a booth, he set about distributing these to anyone who cared to get them.

She stood rooted to the spot, gazing on him with ardent eyes. And to her vermilion lips there came a smile—bright, calm, and very sweet, like honey.

"Here is your holy patron, Yagna," he said, handing her a picture of St. Agnes.—Their hands just touched, and fell apart, as from the smart of a burn.

She, shaking all over, durst not utter one syllable. He added a word or two, but she remained speechless, her eyes drowned in his.

The crowd drove them asunder. She placed the engraving in her bodice, and looked about her for some time. He was not visible any more, having entered the church, where another service was going on. But still she saw him in fancy.

"How like he is to that saint above the altar!" she said, uttering her thoughts aloud.

"And that's why all the girls stare at him so!—They are foolish. 'Not for dogs, I'm afraid, are sausages made.'"

She looked round quickly: Matthew was by her side!

Murmuring some inarticulate words, she tried to get away from him, but in vain; he followed her step by step. It was some time, however, before he ventured on putting this question:

"Yagna, what says your mother about Simon's banns?"

"What can she say? Let him marry, if he choose: his will is his own."

He made a wry face, and asked hesitatingly:

"But tell me, will she make over to him his portion of land?"

"How should I know? She has said naught to me. He can ask her himself."

Simon and Nastka then joined them, with Andrew, who appeared suddenly, the five thus forming quite a group. Simon spoke first:

"Yagna, do not take Mother's part; she would do me an injustice."

"No, it is your part I am taking.—But, good heavens! how you have changed in these last few days! . . . 'Tis wonderful!" And, indeed, the brother she now saw before her was quite a dashing young fellow—clean-shaven, straight-backed, with a hat tilted on one side, and a snow-white capote!

"Because I am my mother's drudge no longer."

"And are you better off in your freedom?" she inquired, pleased at his spirit.

"Ask the bird you let go out of your hand: ye will see! . . . Did you hear the banns published?"

"And when is the wedding to be?"

Here Nastka answered, nestling tenderly to his side, and passing her arm round his waist:

"In three weeks, before harvest-home." And she blushed deeply.

"And the wedding shall take place, were it in the tavern: I will not beg to use Mother's cabin."

"But have you a place for your wife?"

"Certainly; I shall remove to the side of our cabin opposite Mother's. I shall not seek lodgings among the villagers.

Let her but give me the land that's my due—I shall do well!" he said, swelling with self-confidence.

"And we," Matthew declared, "are not going to send Nastka away empty-handed. She will get one thousand *zloty* in cash!"

Here the smith came up, took him aside, whispered a word, and hurried away.

They went on talking, and filling up imaginary details. Simon thought with sparkling eyes what a good farmer he would be, once come into his own, and how he would settle down to work. Oh, they would soon see what a man he was!—Nastka gazed on him, open-mouthed in wonder. Andrew talked in the same sense; Yagna alone was absent-minded, hearing barely half of what they said. It did not interest her.

"Yagna!" Matthew cried. "Come over to the tavern; the band will be playing."

"I care no more for such amusements," she replied, sadly.

Her eyes were dimmed. He shot a glance into them, pulled his cap down, and rushed off, jostling those in his way. In front of the priest's house he met Teresa.

"Whither away?" she asked him timidly.

"To the tavern. A meeting has been called by the smith."

"I should go with you gladly."

"I neither thrust you aside, nor is there lack of space. But take heed lest they speak evil of you for the glances of your eyes!"

"They speak as it is, and tear me to pieces, as dogs tear a dead sheep."

"Then wherefore give them occasion?" he asked, now growing impatient.

"Wherefore? Well, you know wherefore!" she replied in a husky voice.

He walked forward, and so fast that she could hardly keep up with him.

Suddenly turning round on her, "Now then!" he cried; "there ye are, shedding tears like a calf!"

"Nay, nay! 'twas but a little dust in mine eyes," she returned.

Unexpectedly, he moderated his pace, and, walking by her side, spoke to her with much gentleness:

"Here is a little money: purchase something for yourself at one of these booths.—And come ye to the tavern: we will dance together."

She would fain have fallen at his feet to thank him.

"For the money I care not; but your kindness, how great it is!" she faltered, her face red as fire.

"Well, come then; but later. Until the evening I shall be much engaged."

And with a farewell smile on the tavern door-step, he went in.

There were plenty of people there, and it was stifling hot. The great room was full of people, drinking and chatting with one another; but the private parlor contained the best youth of Lipka, with the smith and Gregory, the Voyt's brother, at their head. There were several of the older farmers, too: Ploshka, the Soltys, Klemba, and Adam, cousin to Boryna. Even Kobus, though uninvited, had found means to enter.

When Matthew came in, Gregory was speaking very earnestly, and writing with chalk on the table.

By the proposed agreement, the Squire promised to give four acres of the Podlesie farm for each one of the forest they made over to him; also to let them have as much more land, to be paid by instalments. Moreover, he was to give them timber on credit for building the huts.

All this Gregory set forth, article by article, calculating in figures how the land should be divided, and how much each was to get.

" 'A promise is a toy made to give fools joy!' " grumbled Ploshka.

"But this—this is a fact, not a promise. He is to sign everything at the notary's—and do not forget it! So much land for us folk! Each family in Lipka will have an additional holding: think of that, my masters!"

The blacksmith here repeated what the Squire had directed him to say.

They listened attentively, in silence, looking hard at the white figures on the table, and reflecting.

" 'Tis all right—a golden opportunity; but will the Commissioner give his consent to it?" asked the Soltys, first to speak, and running his fingers through his shock of hair.

"He must!" Gregory thundered. "When our assembly has decided, we shall ask no official's leave: he cannot help himself! We will have it so!"

"Leave or no leave, there's no need to shout so loud. Will one of you see whether the policeman is not listening, close outside the wall?"

"I saw him drinking at the bar this minute," Matthew affirmed.

"And when," someone asked, "has the Squire said he would sign?"

"Tomorrow, if ye will," was the answer. "Let us but accept, he will sign at once, and we can measure the ground out afterwards."

"Then, directly after harvest-home, we might enter into possession?"

"And give it proper tilling in autumn?"

"Ah! splendid! . . . How the work will go on then!"

All began talking excitedly together. They were full of joy; their eyes shone with the consciousness of success, and they stretched their arms forth as if to seize upon the long-wished-for holdings.

Some fell to humming tunes, some to calling on the Jew for vodka, out of sheer gladness. Some talked no little nonsense about the division of the portions they were to have, and everyone had visions of the new lands and riches and happiness that were to be theirs.

They were like men drunk: they babbled, they drummed on the table with their fists, on the floor with their feet: the uproar was tremendous.

"Ah! then—then the local feast at Lipka will indeed be a grand affair!"

"And how many weddings we shall have every Carnival!"

"Why, all the Lipka girls will not suffice!"

"We shall send to town for more, hey?"

"Be quiet, boys!" old Ploshka exclaimed, thumping on the table for silence. "Ye make such a hullabaloo as do the Jews in their synagogue on the Sabbath.—What I would say is this: is there not some trick in the Squire's offer?"

They all became silent suddenly; it was a bucket of cold water thrown over their enthusiasm. At last the Soltys spoke:

"I too can in no wise understand what makes the man so very lavish."

"Aye," one of the older men chimed in; "there must be something wrong about it: else how could he give up so much land almost for nothing?"

Gregory flew into a passion, and cried out:

"This I say: ye are a lot of driveling fools!"

And once more he set to explain everything, till he was all in perspiration. The blacksmith, too, put things as strongly as he could: but there was no convincing old Ploshka. He only wagged his head and smiled sceptically, till Gregory leaped at him with fists clenched and trembling with restrained fury.

"Say your say, then, since you think ours to be worthless!"

"So will I.—Well do I know that set of

hounds; and I tell you: believe naught till ye see it down in black and white. They have from all time grown fat by wronging us; and now they mean to make money by some other wrong."

"If ye think thus, ye may withhold your vote; but do not prevent the others!" Klemba cried.

"And you—you, one of them that went up against him to the forest: do you now take his part?"

"As I went then, so will I go once more, if needful! I take not his part, but am only for a just agreement that shall advantage us all. Only a fool cannot see that such a contract is for the good of Lipka. Only a fool will refuse what is offered him."

" 'Tis ye that are all fools! Ye would sell your breeches for a pair of braces.— Aye, and doubly fools! for if the Squire will give so much, he will perchance give yet more."

They went on disputing, while others took Klemba's part, and the noise grew so deafening that Yankel came in, putting a bottle of vodka on the table.

"Come, come, good farmers all!" he cried. "Here's to Podlesie—a new Lipka! —And be ye all masters there!" And he passed the vodka from one to another.

This caused a still greater din; but everyone was now in favor of the agreement—except old Ploshka.

The smith—he must have been well paid for his good offices—spoke the loudest of all, extolling the Squire, and his honorable intentions; and he stood drinks to the whole company—now vodka, now beer, now rum with so-called "essence."

They had thus enjoyed themselves a good deal—some indeed too well—when suddenly Kobus, who had hitherto not uttered one single word, started up and attacked them all with a savage onslaught of abuse.

"And where do we *Komorniki* come

in?" he shrieked. "Are we mere cat's-paws? We all who are not landowners stand up against this agreement. What, shall one have a belly so great he can hardly walk, and another die of starvation? The lands must be meted out equally to all.—Ye are all of you carrion and Squires!—Look at them, those bare-backed ones, who yet hold their heads as high as if they sneezed at us all!" He screamed so loud, and with such foul language, that they put him out of doors; but outside the tavern he still continued his invectives and imprecations.

They then separated, some to go home, and some to enjoy the dance, for the music had just struck up.

Evening was falling now. The sky, all in flames, tinged the orchard tree-tops and the ears of corn with crimson and gold. A soft damp wind had sprung up, and the croaking of frogs and the piping of quails resounded; the grasshoppers' shrill notes were heard in the fields, mingling with the everlasting rustling of the cornstalks, the rumbling of the carts driving off, and now and then the drunken song of a man on his way home.

These noises gradually subsided. The villagers sat outside their huts, enjoying the quiet and the cool of the evening.

Boys were bathing near the mill, splashing and bawling; in the enclosures, the lasses were singing country songs.

There was next to no one at the Borynas'. Hanka had gone out with the children; Pete had absented himself somewhere, and Yagna had been away since Vespers.

Only Yuzka, busied with the evening household cares, was there with the blind *Dziad*. He, sitting in the porch, inhaled the cool breeze and, while mumbling a prayer, lent an attentive ear to the approaches of Vitek's stork, that was sidling up for a surprise attack on his legs with its beak.

"Ah, you villain, a murrain on you!—

How hard it pecks!" he grumbled, drawing his feet under him, and waving his long rosary. But the stork only retreated a few paces, and again, with its long stretched-out beak, advanced in another direction.

"Oh, I hear you well! You shall not get at me this time.—A clever fowl, though!" he muttered. But just then he heard someone fiddling in the yard; so he drove the stork away with several cuts of his rosary, in order to listen with more pleasure to the sounds.

"Yuzka, who is it playing so featly?"

"Only Vitek! He has learned to play from Pete; and now he is forever playing, till one's ears tingle.—Vitek, have done, and give the colts their clover now!" she called to him.

The fiddle was silent. But a thought had struck the *Dziad* and when Vitek came in, he said to him in a most friendly tone:

"Here's for you. Such good playing is well worth a five-kopek piece."

Vitek was immensely gratified.

"Can you play pious tunes as well?"

"Whatsoever I hear, I can play."

"Ah, but 'every fox praises its own tail.'—Now, prithee, play this air." And he bleated out something in his professional line, shrill, slow, and quavering.

Vitek brought his fiddle before the *Dziad* had done, and after first imitating him exactly, then repeated the tune with such variations as he had heard in church. The *Dziad* was astounded.

"Why, lad, you could even become an organist!"

"Oh, I can play anything—from the music heard in the Manors to the songs they sing in the taverns." So Vitek boasted, and went on playing snatches of what he had heard, till the fowls at roost set to cackling, and Hanka, who had come back, sent him off to help Yuzka with her work.

Hanka then sat down in the porch,

suckling her little ones, and conversing with the *Dziad,* who spun incredible yarns for her all the time; which she did not call in question, but listened, with sad eyes looking out into the night.

Yagna was not back yet. She had gone out to see some girl friends; but, agitated by the spirit of unrest, she could stay nowhere. Again and again she had felt forced to leave their huts, and in the end she wandered alone about the village. She gazed long upon the waters, now dark, yet visible as they trembled to the breeze; on the gently stirring shadows; on the cottage lights that shot over the surface of the pond and died away in the distance. Then, impelled onward, she cast a glance beyond the mill at the meadows, wrapped in warm white mist, while the lapwings flapped about, flying over her head.

There she gave ear to the waters that rolled through the sluices down the river's murky throat, beneath the lofty slumberous alder-trees; and she fancied the sound was a mournful call—a tearful melodious complaint.

From one end of Lipka to the other she wandered, lost like those waters that can find no outlet, and beat forever sadly between impassable rocky walls.

Something was gnawing at her heart. It was not sorrow, not yearning, nor the sensation of love. Her eyes were burning with an arid glow, and she felt an awful sob swelling her bosom as if about to tear it asunder.

Now, after a time—she knew not how—she found herself close to the priest's house. A carriage and horses were outside the porch; she heard them pawing restlessly. There was a light in one room only, where the visitors were playing at cards.

On all this she gazed idly to her heart's content; then passed along the fence between Klemba's lands and the priest's large garden. She slipped close to the quickset hedge, in great nervous agitation: the overhanging boughs dashed the dew from their leaves into her face. On she moved mechanically, never thinking where her steps were leading her . . . till the organist's one-storied house rose up barring the way.

The four front windows were all open and lighted.

She crept along, hugging the shadow of the hedge, till close enough to look in.

A lamp hung from the ceiling; under it the father and mother were taking tea with their children; but Yanek was walking about the room, and talking to them.

She could catch every one of his words, every creak of the boarded floor, the ceaseless tick of the clock, and even the organist's heavy breathing.

Yanek was speaking of things so much beyond her that she could not make out one word.

But, fixing her eyes on him as on the picture of some saint, she drank in every sound of his voice, sweeter to her than the sweetest honey. As he walked, he at times was unseen, towards the end of the room: then again he reappeared, coming into the lamp-lit circle. Several times he stopped by the window, and she shrank back, fearing to be seen; but he always looked only up into the star-besprinkled sky, saying a few pleasant words that brought a laugh to the others' lips and bright looks into their eyes. At last he sat down by his mother's side, and his little sisters climbed upon his knees, clinging to his neck, while he hugged them fondly and caressed them, and played with them till the cabin echoed to their innocent laughter.

The clock struck. His mother rose, saying:

"You are forever chattering, but 'tis bedtime; and you have to start by daybreak tomorrow."

"True, Mother dear.—Alas! how short this day has seemed to me!" he complained.

Yagna's heart was wrung so sorely that the tears welled up to her eyes.

"But," he added, "our vacation is nigh; and the Rector has promised to let me go home sooner, if his Reverence will but write to ask him."

"I shall beg him to do so; fear naught, he will write," said his mother, who was making a bed for him just opposite the window.

Their farewells were long and loving; his mother held him to her breast, as she kissed him.

"To bed now, my dearest, and sleep sound."

And now at last he was alone!

Yagna saw how they walked on tiptoe in the other rooms, and spoke in whispers, not to disturb him. They closed the windows, and soon the whole house was noiseless, that Yanek might sleep more soundly.

Yagna too would have gone home, but for something that kept her rooted to the spot; and she stood spellbound, staring into that last open lighted window.

Yanek read for some time out of a great book; then, kneeling down by the window, he crossed himself, clasped his hands in prayer, raised his eyes to Heaven, and began in an impressive whisper.

It was dead of night. Silence reigned; the stars were twinkling in the heights of heaven. A warm fragrant breath came from the fields, and at intervals there sounded the rustling of a bough, the faint warbling of a bird.

Yagna was now growing more and more beside herself. Her heart throbbed madly, her eyes glowed with fire, her full lips were burning hot. Instinctively, she stretched her arms out to him; though at the same time she was shrinking back within herself, she felt a strange resistless agitation take hold of her, and had to lean against the fence that creaked again to her trembling.

Yanek looked out of the window and around, then went on with his prayer.

What then took place within her, she was never able to understand. Such a fire ran through all her limbs, and with such penetration, that she was ready to cry aloud with the delicious pain of it. Shudders came over her like swift lightning flashes; she felt a burning whirlwind rushing away with her; wild cries, impatient to break forth, thronged all her being, tense with an unspeakable longing. She wanted to crawl towards him— nearer—nearer—but only to lay her lips on his white hands—kneel to him—gaze on him close at hand—pray to him as to some holy image! Yet she held back, deterred by a feeling of mystic dread, and the vague fear of some horrible evil.

"O Jesus! O merciful Jesus!" escaped her lips in a stifled moan.

Yanek rose, bent out of the window, and said, as though he had perceived her:

"Who is there?"

In mortal alarm, she held her breath. Her heart stopped beating, she was paralyzed with a sort of sacred terror. Her soul, as it were, fluttered in her throat, as it fluctuated in the throes of suspense— and rapturous disquiet!

But Yanek saw nothing save the fence. He shut the window, undressed quickly, and put out the light.

Then the night fell upon her. She still remained there a long time, gloating upon the blackness of the silent window. The chill of the darkness struck through her, sprinkling its silver dew over her hot desires, quenching the ardor in her blood, and shedding over her a sense of unutterable happiness! A sweetly solemn calm pervaded her soul—the calm of the flowers which dream before sunrise—and she burst forth into a wordless prayer of bliss—the marvelous sweetness of that ecstasy which the mind's unsullied dreams bring forth—unspeakable joy like that of a spring day which dawns—and with it came glad tears in big beads— beads from the rosary of thanksgiving offered to the Lord!

CHAPTER III

"Pray, Hanka, may I go home?" Yuzka entreated, laying her head down upon the pew-seat.

"Aye, do: run about everywhere like a silly calf!" said Hanka, rebuking her, and looking up from her rosary.

"But I feel so faint, so weary!"

"Do not be so restless: it will be over soon."

His Reverence was just ending a low Mass for Boryna's soul, which the family had retained for the octave of his death.

All his nearest relations sat in the side-pews. Yagna and her mother alone were kneeling in front of the altar. Somewhere in the choir, Agata was pattering prayers aloud.

The church, cool and quiet, was dark, except for one streak of light that shot in through the open door, and lit up the place as far as the pulpit.

Michael, the organist's pupil, served Mass, jingling the tiny bells very loud, as usual, and also as usual continually turning his head about after the swallows which were darting in and out of the place.

The priest having ended Mass, they all went out to the churchyard; but as they were going past the belfry, Ambrose called them.

"His Reverence wishes to speak to you."

And he came up almost at once, with his breviary under his arm, and wiping his bald crown. Having welcomed them kindly, he said:

"My friends, I want to say how well you have acted in having a Mass said for the deceased: it will help his soul towards its eternal rest. It will, I assure you."

He then took snuff, sneezed violently, and asked them if they intended dividing the property that day. And, on receiving the answer that this was the date after the funeral on which the division was usual, he continued:

"Then I may say a few words about it to you. In dividing the property, remember to do all things by common consent, and to act justly. Let me hear of no quarrels, no dissensions. If Boryna knew that you tore—as wolves tear a sheep—that estate to the prosperity of which he gave his whole life, he would turn in his grave. Moreover, God forbid that ye wrong any one of the orphans! Yuzka is but a simple child as yet; Gregory is far away. Let each have his own, even to the uttermost kopek!—Also, when making the division, have a care to respect his known will. His soul, peradventure, sees you at this very moment! . . . As I am always telling you in my sermons, concord is the great thing—it upholds all in the world: naught was ever done with discord— naught but sin and the transgression of God's law.—Further, ye should not forget the church. He was always liberal, and neither for lights nor for Masses, nor for any other need, did he ever grudge his money. Wherefore did God bless the work of his hands."

He continued for some time in this strain. They embraced his knees with grateful thanks. Yuzka, weeping loudly, fell on her knees to kiss his hand. He took her to his bosom, kissed her on the crown of her head, and said soothingly:

"To weep is foolish, little one: the orphan is God's especial care."

Hanka, deeply touched, whispered: "Her own father could not have been more loving." He was very much moved himself, for he hastily brushed a tear away, offered snuff to the blacksmith, and changed the conversation.

"Well, are ye coming to terms with the Squire?"

"We are; five of us go to the Manor this very day."

"God be praised! I will say a Mass to that intention on my own account."

"I think the village ought to have a Votive Mass sung with the greatest solemnity. What! Does not each of us get a new farm—as it were for nothing?"

"You are right, Michael. And I have said a good word for you to the Squire. —Now, go your ways, and remember: Concord and justice!"

"And—hist, Michael!" he called after the smith, who was leaving; "come ye round later to see about my curricle; the right spring is bent and grazes the axle-tree."

"Oh, the bulky priest of Laznov has weighed it down; 'tis very like."

And so they all went to Boryna's, Yagna the last, going with her mother, who could scarcely drag herself along.

It being a work-day, there were but few people on the mill-pond road: only a few children playing about. Though early in the morning, the sun was hot, but agreeably tempered by the wind, which blew hard enough to make the orchards toss their branches about, laden with ripe red cherries, and the corn beat against the fences in boisterous waves.

The huts stood open, and their gates as well; the bedding lay spread upon the hedgerows, and everybody was out in the fields. Some were bringing in the last of the hay, which filled the nostrils with aromatic scent, and left long strips that waved like streaming Jews' beards, from the trees the heaped-up wagons passed under.

They walked along, pondering the question of how the property should be divided.

A ditty rose, wafted on the wind—possibly from the fields where they were at work on the potatoes; from the mill came the beating of the water-wheels, mingling with the strokes of a washerwoman's batlet hard by.

"The mill is continually grinding now," Magda remarked.

"Aye, the days before harvest are the miller's harvest."

Hanka sighed. "Times are much harder this year than last. Everyone complains bitterly, and the *Komorniki* are really starving."

"And the Koziols," the blacksmith added, "are prowling about to snap up anything they can lay hands on!"

"Say not that. The poor creatures keep themselves alive as best they can. Yesterday Koslova sold her ducklings to the organist's wife, and got some money thereby."

"They will soon drink it all," Magda returned. "I will say no word to their hurt; but 'tis strange that my boy found the feathers of the drake I lost during father's funeral, behind their cow-byre."

"And who was it," Yuzka asked, "that made off with our bedding that very same day?"

"When is their suit against the Voyt to come off?"

"Not so soon. But Ploshka is for them, and they will make things hot for the Voyt and his wife."

"Ploshka was ever a meddler with other folk's matters."

"Our friend, hoping to become Voyt, is currying favor everywhere."

Here Yankel passed by, dragging and pulling at the mane of a hobbled horse, that lashed out and resisted with all its might and they laughed and made merry at his expense.

"Oh, 'tis well for you that ye can

laugh! What trouble I have with the beast!"

"Stuff it with straw, fix a new tail on it, and take it to some fair: it will never do as a horse, but ye may sell it for a cow!" the smith bawled. Their laughter became a roar, for the horse had jerked himself free, leaped into the pond, and, in spite of threats and entreaties, lain down wallowing in the water.

"A remarkable brute. Bought of a gipsy, no doubt?"

"Set a pail of vodka before it: ye may then perhaps tempt it out!" joined in the organist's wife, who sat by the pond, watching a flock of ducklings, as downy as yellow catkins, while a hen ran cackling along the bank in dismay.

" 'Tis a fine lot.—From the Koziols, I suppose?"

"Yes. But they are always running away to the pond." And she tried to call them back, flinging them handfuls of Turkish wheat into the water.

Seeing them, however, making for the other bank, she went after them in a hurry.

As soon as they had arrived, and Hanka was busy over the breakfast, the blacksmith set to prowl about every corner of the cabin and all the premises, even exploring the potato-pits. At last Hanka could not help observing:

"Think ye any potatoes are missing?"

"I never," he answered, "buy a pig in a poke."

"Ye know the place of everything better than I do myself," she said, stiffly, pouring out the coffee. "Come, Dominikova! Come, Yagna! Come and join us!"

For those two had, on arriving, shut themselves up in the opposite room.

No one was at first willing to open the conversation. Hanka, extremely cautious and guarded, pressed them all to eat, and poured out coffee abundantly, but kept her eyes carefully all the time on the smith, who was prying about from his

place, darting glances in every direction, and clearing his throat again and again. Yagna sat louring and mournful, her eyes glistening as if they had been quite recently full of tears. At her side, Dominikova talked in whispers. Yuzka was the only one to chatter freely, which she did just as usual, as she flew from one pot to another, full of boiling potatoes.

After a long tedious pause, the smith broached the subject.

"Well. How shall we divide the property?"

Hanka gave a start; but she at once recovered herself, and replied with calm and evidently after having thought it out well:

"How are we to divide it at all? I am here only to watch over my goodman's estate, and have no power to decide aught. When Antek returns, he will see to the division."

"But when will he come back? And things cannot drag on so."

"They must! As they did during Father's illness, so they shall until Antek's return."

"But he is not the only inheritor."

"But, he being the eldest son, the land comes down to him from his father."

"He has not more right to it than any of us."

"Ye also may have your share of the land, if Antek prefers it so. I shall not quarrel over this with you: the decision is not mine."

"Yagna!" her mother urged; "say a word about your claim."

"Why should I? They know of it well enough."

Hanka turned a deep red, and kicked Lapa, that had curled up beneath her feet. She hissed between her clenched teeth:

"Aye, the wrong done to us, we remember it well!"

"As you say. Wild words are of no account here, but the six acres are—

those made over to Yagna by her late goodman."

"If the deed of gift is in your hands, none can snatch it away," Magda growled angrily. She had hitherto been sitting speechless and giving suck to her baby.

"True; and we have it duly signed and attested."

"Well, all must wait, and Yagna with the rest."

"Of course. But she may take away her personal belongings at once: her cow, her calf, her swine, her geese . . ."

"No!" the smith interrupted in a hard voice. "All those things are common property, and to be shared equally by all."

"By all? Is that your will? No one can take from her my wedding-present!" And, raising her voice, "Perchance," she cried, "ye would likewise divide her petticoats among you—and her feather-bed likewise . . . eh?"

"I did but jest; and ye fly out at me at once!"

"Because I know you to the bottom of your heart!"

"But now," he went on, "to what purpose is all this prating? You are right, Hanka; we must needs wait till Antek comes back.—And I have presently to go in haste and meet the Squire: I am stayed for." And he rose.

But, having caught sight of his father-in-law's sheepskin, hanging in the corner, he offered to pull it down.

"This would be just the thing for me."

"Touch it not: it is hanging there to dry," Hanka said.

"Well, then, let me have those boots. Only the uppers are in good condition, and they too are patched," he pleaded, trying to get them down.

"Not one thing is to be touched. Should you take aught, they will say that half of the household goods have been carried off. Let an inventory be made

first, and officially. Till then, I will not allow one stake to come out of a hedge."

"Ha!" said Magda; "but Father's bedding is gone, and will not be down in the inventory."

"I have told you what came to pass. Directly after his death, I spread it on the hedge to air; and one came by night and stole it. . . . I could not see to everything, all alone."

"Strange that a thief should have been so ready at hand!"

"Do you mean by that I am lying now, and stole it then?"

"Be quiet, Magda, no quarreling. . . . He that stole it, let him have his winding-sheet cut out of it!"

"Why, the feathers alone weighed thirty pounds!"

"Hold your tongue, I say!" the black-smith shouted at his wife, and asked Hanka to come out with him into the farm-yard: he wished, he said, to look at the swine.

She went with him, but well on her guard.

"I would fain give you good advice."

She listened attentive, wondering what it could be.

"Ye must, one of these evenings, and ere the inventory is made, drive two of the kine to my byre. We can entrust the sow to our cousin, and stow away all we can at our acquaintances'.—I will let you know with whom.—Ye will declare in the inventory that the corn has all been sold to Yankel: give him a couple of bushels, and he will bear witness to anything. The miller will take one colt, and it may feed in his paddock. Of the vessels and implements, some may be hidden among the potatoes, some in the rye-fields. . . . 'Tis friendly advice I am giving you! . . . They all do the same—all that are not fools. . . . You have been working to death: 'tis just ye should get a larger share. . . . To me you need only give a few crumbs. And fear noth-

ing: I will help you through the whole
business; aye, and make it my affair, too,
that ye shall get all the land for your
own! . . . Only hearken to me: none
can give better advice than I.—Why,
even the Squire takes mine gladly.—
Well, what say you?"

She answered in slow tones, looking at
the man steadfastly and with scorn:

"Thus much: even as I will give up
naught that's mine, so too am I not
covetous of aught else!"

He staggered as if from a stunning
blow—then glared at her in fury and
hissed:

"Besides, I would not breathe a word
to anyone of how ye despoiled the old
man!"

"Breathe what ye choose to whom ye
choose!—But I will tell Antek of your
advice, and he shall speak to you on the
matter!"

He scarcely could swallow down an
imprecation. But he only spat on the
ground, and walked off hurriedly, calling
to his wife through the open window:

"Magda, have an eye to all things, lest
there be yet more thefts here!"

But as he passed, with what disdain
Hanka eyed him!

Maddened by her scorn, he made off,
but meeting the Voyt's wife, who just
entered the enclosure, stopped to confer
with her for some time, angrily and with
clenched fists.

She came bringing an official document with her.

" 'Tis for you, Hanka: the policeman
has brought it in from the bureau."

"About Antek, perchance!" she thought
in great trepidation, taking the paper in
her apron-covered hand.

"I think it concerns Gregory. My
goodman is out—gone to the District
office—and the policeman only said there
was something about Gregory being
dead, or . . ."

"Jesu Maria!" Yuzka shrieked, and
Magda started to her feet in horror.

Helplessly, seized with overwhelming
fear, they turned the ominous paper
about.

"You perhaps, Yagna, could understand it," Hanka said beseechingly.

They stood round her, choking with
suspense and dread; but Yagna, after a
long try at spelling it out, gave up the
attempt.

"I cannot read it: 'tis not written in
our language."

"Nor penned in her presence either!"
the Voyt's wife sneered. "Other things
there are, however, in which she is more
learned!"

"Go ye your ways," Dominikova
snarled, "and let quiet folks be."

But the Voyt's wife would not miss the
opportunity to strike a blow at her.

"Ye are good at rebuking your neighbors. But ye had better have kept your
daughter from lying in wait for other
women's husbands!"

"Peace, peace, good woman," Hanka
interfered, foreseeing what was coming;
but the Voyt's wife only grew more en-
raged.

"Oh, I will say my say now, if never
again!—Her, who has poisoned my life
so, I never will forgive till my dying
day!"

"Well, then, say your say! A cur will
bark louder than you can!" Dominikova
growled. She took it coolly, but Yagna
flushed red as a beet-root. Yet, though
overwhelmed with shame, she nevertheless took refuge in reckless stubbornness;
and as if to spite the other, she held her
head up, and fastened her eyes upon her
enemy with a taunting expression and a
malicious smile.

The look, the smile, infuriated the
other, and she denounced her lubricity in
a torrent of invectives.

"Your words are frenzy, you are drunk

with hate!" the old dame said, to draw her anger away; "your husband will answer grievously before God for my daughter's misfortune."

"Misfortune!—Aye, 'tis an innocent young maiden he has seduced! . . . Ha, such a maiden that with everyone and under every green bush . . ."

"Hold your wicked tongue, or—blind as I am—my hands will surely find their way to your hair!" the old woman cried threateningly, her hand tightening its grasp on her stick.

"Oh, will you try?—Only touch me! Only dare!" she repeated, with a defiant scream.

"Ha! will she, who has waxed fat upon wrongs done to her neighbors, venture now to beset and pester them—as hard to shake off as a bur?"

"Say, you, in what thing have I ever done you wrong?"

"That you will know, when your husband shall be condemned to jail!"

The Voyt's wife rushed at her with lifted fists; but Hanka caught her back, and said sternly to them both:

"Women, for God's sake!—Would ye turn my cabin into a tavern?"

This instantly put a stop to their brawl. Both breathed hard and were panting. Tears came streaming from under the bandages that covered Dominikova's eyes, but she was first to come back to her senses, and say, sitting down with hands clasped and a deep sigh:

"God be merciful to me a sinner!"

The Voyt's wife had rushed out in a fury; but, returning, she put her head in at the window, crying out to Hanka:

"I tell you, drive that wanton from your house! And do so while there yet is time, lest you rue it sorely! Let her not stay one hour more beneath your roof, or that hell-born pest will make you go yourself! O Hanka, defend yourself—and for that, be merciless, be without pity for

her. She is only lying in wait to entrap your Antek. . . . Don't you see what a hell she now prepares for you?" She leaned further into the room and, stretching her fist towards Yagna, shouted with the most intense hatred:

"Yet a little, yet a little, you devil from hell! I shall not die in peace, I shall not go to Holy Confession, until I have seen you driven with cudgels out of Lipka!— Oh, get you away to the soldiers, you drab, you swinish jade! Your place is with them!"

She was gone, and over the cabin there came a silence like that of the grave. Dominikova shook with a dumb passion of weeping; Magda rocked her little one; Hanka, plunged in torturing thought, looked into the fire; and Yagna, though she still had on her face the same hardened reckless expression, the same wicked smile, had turned as white as a sheet. Those last words had cut deep into her soul; she felt stabbed as though by a hundred knives, each stab streaming with her life-blood: an inhuman torment that was impelling her to shriek out at the top of her voice, or even dash her brains out against the wall. But she controlled herself, pulled her mother by the sleeve, and said in an agonized whisper:

"Mother, come away. Let's flee this place. And quickly!"

"Right; for I am broken and shattered. But you must return and watch over what is yours."

"I will not stay here! I so loathe the place that to stay is beyond me.—Why did I ever darken these doors? Better have broken a limb than have ever come here!"

"Were you, then, so evilly dealt with?" Hanka asked quietly.

"Worse than a chained-up dog! Even in hell there must be less pain than I have suffered here!"

"Strange, then, that you could bear it

[45]

so long: no one imprisoned you here. You were free as air to go!"

"So I will. And may the plague choke you, for being—what you are!"

"Curse not, or I may cast my own wrongs in your teeth!"

"Why are ye all—as many as dwell in Lipka—all of you against me?"

"Live rightly: none will say one word of bitterness to you!"

"Peace, Yagna, peace; Hanka bears you no malice!"

"Let her too howl with the rest. Aye, let her! As dogs, dirt to me is all their howling. And what have I done to them? Whom have I robbed or slain?"

"What have ye done? Have you the front to ask?" Hanka exclaimed, in stupefaction, standing up opposite her. "Do not drive me too far, or I may speak!"

"Speak, prithee! I dare you to speak! What do I care for you?" Yagna vociferated, now in a towering passion, that spread within her like a conflagration; and she was ready to do anything—even the very worst that offered.

The tears had instantly sprung to Hanka's eyes at the remembrance of Antek's infidelity, that rose up before her with a pang so acute that she could hardly stammer out:

"What have ye done with him—with my husband, say? Ye never would let him be, but followed him everywhere, like the rampant piece of lust ye are!" . . . Her breath failed her, and she broke into sobs.

Like a she-wolf set upon in her den, at bay, and ready to tear anything she meets with to pieces, Yagna sprang up. Burning with the most furious hate, and frenzied to the uttermost extreme of rage, she lashed her adversary with stinging words, that came each of them from her lips like the strokes of a whip.

"Indeed?—So 'twas I who pursued your man, was it? Yet there is none but knows how I always drove him from me! How, like a cur, he would whine outside my door, that he might have but the mere sight of a shoe of mine!—Yes, and he took hold of me by force, till I was bereft of sense, and let him do all his will, for my brains whirled.—And now will I tell you all the truth . . . but you will rue the telling! He loved me—loved me more than tongue can tell! And you he shrank from, even to loathing; his gorge, poor man! rose at the thought of your love; 'twas in his throat, as rancid reasty fat, ancient and musty and unbearable; and at the memory of you, he would spit with sheer disgust! Nay, not to see you any more, he willingly would have done himself a harm. . . . You sought the truth; you have it now!—And, moreover, I will tell you—and do not forget it—if I should but say the word, when you would kiss his feet, he'd spurn you from him, and go following me throughout the world!—So weigh my words, and never dare to think yourself my equal.—Have you understood?"

Towards the end, though loud and passionate in speech, she had become mistress of herself, fearless, and more beautiful than ever. Even her mother listened to her with astonishment, mingled with dread; for now another woman stood revealed before her, as terrible, as evil, and as dangerous as the dark cloud that bears the lightning within it.

Her words pierced Hanka, wounded her almost to death. They struck her without mercy, crushed and trampled her down. She felt strengthless, mindless, almost as unconscious as a tree that falls struck by the thunderbolt. She was scarcely able to breathe; her lips grew very white, and she sank back on a bench. Her anguish, it seemed to her, was rending her to pieces—nay, crushing her to grains of barren sand: even the tears had vanished from her face, grown ashy with the throes of that fierce ordeal, though her bosom still was shaken with deep dry sobs. She stared out into space as if in terror—into the abyss which had opened suddenly before her eyes; and she trembled as trembles an ear of corn, that the wind whirls on to destruction.

Yagna had long ago gone with her mother to the other side of the house; Yuzka was with the ducklings at the mill-pond; but Hanka still sat motionless in the same place, like a bird bereft of her fledglings, unable to scream out, to defend itself, to flee anywhither, only now and then stirring its wings, and uttering a mournful cry.

But Heaven had pity on her and granted her a little relief. She came to herself again, knelt down before the holy pictures, and with abundant tears made a vow to go on pilgrimage to Chenstohova, if what she had heard should prove untrue.

She was not even angry with Yagna any more; she only dreaded her; and, hearing her voice now and then, crossed herself, as if to keep off a fiend.

Then she set to work. Her experienced hands worked almost as deftly as usual, little as her thoughts accompanied them; but she never remembered that she took the children out of doors and set the cabin in order that day.—At length, having prepared dinner and placed it in vessels for the field-laborers, she sent it to them by Yuzka.

And now, being quite alone, and no longer agitated, she sat down to reflect over every word said. Intelligent and kind-hearted though she was, she could not put from her mind the blows dealt at her self-respect as a wife; more than once their memory made her burn with indignation, and her heart writhed under the torment it gave her; more than once the thought of some awful revenge filled her

mind. But at last she came to this conclusion:

"Truly, as to good looks, there is no comparison between me and her. But I am his wedded wife; I am the mother of his children"; and her confidence returned at the thought.

"And should he even go astray after her, he will return again to me!—And at any rate," she added to comfort herself, looking out of the window, "he can never marry her!"

Afternoon was melting into evening, when the thought of a step that must be taken flashed suddenly across Hanka's mind. She considered for a minute or two, leaning against the wall; then, wiping her eyes, she strode out into the passage, flung open the door of Yagna's room, and said, loud but calmly:

"Get out, out!—Out of this cabin instantly!"

Yagna, starting up from her settle, faced her for many seconds with a steady look. Then Hanka, taking a step or two back from the threshold, repeated in a hoarse voice:

"Take yourself away this instant, else will I have you thrown out by our farm-servant!—This instant!" she said once more, with stern emphasis.

Here the old dame would have interfered, eager to bring forward explanations and excuses; but Yagna merely shrugged her shoulders.

"Not a word to her—to that wretched wisp of straw! We know what she would have."

She took a paper out of the bottom of a chest.

" 'Tis the donation you'd have back, and the six acres therewith: take them, eat them, fill your belly with them!"

Flinging the paper in her face, she added scornfully:

"And choke yourself to death in the eating!"

Then, paying no heed to her mother's remonstrances, she speedily set about packing up all her things and carrying them outside.

Hanka felt dizzy, as if she had received a blow between the eyes; but she picked up the paper, and said, threatening her: "Quicker than that, or I will set the dogs on you!"

Meanwhile, she nevertheless felt overwhelmed with amazement. What! throw away six whole acres of land as one might cast away a broken pot?—How could she? The woman must be moon-struck, she thought, and eyed her over with astonishment.

Yagna, paying no more attention to her, was now taking down her own pictures, when Yuzka entered with a loud outcry.

"Give up the coral necklaces: they are mine from my mother—mine—mine—mine!"

Yagna was just unfastening them, but stopped.

"No," she answered, "I will not. Matthias gave them to me: mine they are!"

Yuzka shrieked and stormed, until Hanka was forced to silence her. Then all became calm again; Yagna seemed to have become deaf and dumb. After having taken all her things out, she hurried away to get her brother's help.

Dominikova made no further opposition, but replied to no word either from Hanka or from Yuzka. Only, when all her daughter's things were on the cart, she rose and shook her fist, and said:

"May the worst of all possible fates not pass you by!"

Hanka winced under the curse, but took it quietly, and called after her: "When Vitek brings the cattle home, he'll drive your cow to your hut. And send someone for all the rest in the evening, to drive them home to you."

She gazed for a long time upon them as they departed in silence, wending their way round the pond. She had no leisure for reflection, for the hired laborers came in presently: so she stowed the deed away carefully in her chest, under lock and key. But she was subdued and depressed the whole evening, and it was with but small pleasure that she listened to Yagustynka's praises of what she had done.

Then, after the men had returned once more to their work, she took Yuzka with her to weed the flax, which was in places quite yellow with wild flowers. She worked with great diligence to shake off old Dominikova's menaces from her mind; but unsuccessfully; and she was especially uneasy about what Antek would say on his return.

"How he will knit his brows when I show him the deed!—Oh, the fool!—Six whole acres! 'tis all but a farm by itself."

"Ah! Hanka," Yuzka cried, "we have forgotten the letter about Gregory!"

"Aye, so we have.—Yuzka, leave off your work: I shall go to the priest and ask him to read it."

The priest, however, was not within doors, and when she saw him at a distance among the field-workers, with his cassock taken off, she felt afraid he might rebuke her publicly for her act. "For no doubt," she thought, "he must know about it by this time." So she went to the miller, who was just then trying how the sawmill worked, along with Matthew.

"My wife told me just how ye have smoked out your stepmother. Ha, ha! Ye look like a wagtail, but have the claws of a hawk!" Laughing, he set to read the letter, but at the first glance at it, he cried out: "Oh, what awful news!—Your Gregory has been drowned.—'Twas as far back as Eastertide. . . . They write that ye can get his things by applying at the District Office."

"Gregory dead!—So strong a man!—

And so young!—He was not over twenty-six.—And was to have come back this harvest-time.—Drowned! O merciful Jesus!" she moaned, wringing her hands at the mournful news.

"Well," Matthew remarked, with bitter animosity, "heritages seem to be coming your way. Ye have but now to turn Yuzka out upon the world, and the whole estate will be yours and the blacksmith's!"

"Are ye already off with the old love of Teresa, and on with Yagna's new love?" she interrupted him; and thereupon he was suddenly absorbed in the machinery, while the miller burst into a loud guffaw.

"Oh, what a good tit for tat!—And what a brave little woman!"

On her way home, she dropped in to tell Magda, who wept copiously, and uttered many an ejaculation of grief:

"'Tis the will of the Lord. . . . Ah! a man like an oak-tree. . . . Few his equals in all Lipka! . . . Oh, lot of man, oh, unhappy lot!—Here today, gone tomorrow! . . . Then his belongings go to his family: Michael will go to the office tomorrow and fetch them. . . . Poor fellow! and he so eager to be home again!"

"All is in God's hands. . . . He was always unlucky with water. Remember how once he was near drowning in the pond, and was saved by Klemba. . . . Surely it was written that he should die no other death!"

They mourned together, and wept—and parted; for they both, and Hanka especially, had plenty of work to do.

The news spread about very fast. The men who came back from the fields were already talking about Gregory and Yagna: all heartily sorry for the one, but not all for the other: concerning her, opinions were divided. The women (the older ones in particular) were very decidedly on Hanka's side, and violently hostile to Yagna; while the men, though

hesitatingly, inclined to take the other's part. This even gave rise to some disputes.

Matthew, on his way home from the sawmill, heard them talk. At first he merely spat in token of contempt, or let out a curse under his breath; but, hearing what they said outside Ploshka's hut, he could not help crying out indignantly:

"Hanka had no right to expel her: she has property there of her own."

Here Ploshka's wife, red-faced and stout of figure, turned upon him.

"Nay," she cried, " 'tis well known that Hanka does not deny her right to the land. But she has other fears, for Antek may come home any day. Who can watch a thief living in the house? Was she to sit still and take no heed of their doings? Was she?"

"Fiddlesticks! all that has naught to do with the case. Your unbridled tongues are wagging, not for the sake of justice, but from envy and spite!"

When you thrust a stick into a wasps' nest, they all fly out at you: so did the women at him.

"Oh, indeed! what is there in her to envy, say? That she's a light-o'-love and a wanton? That ye all run after her like dogs? That you long for her, every one of you? That she is a cause of sin and a shame to all the village? Shall we envy her those things?"

"Perchance ye do: ye are beyond man's understanding. Worn-out old besoms ye are, who would hate the very light of the sun! Had she but been like that Magda, the tavern wench, and done the worst of things, you would have forgiven her; but simply because she is the fairest of all, you'd all like to drown her—aye, and in a spoonful of water too!"

This caused such a storm that he was glad to make his escape, crying as he went:

"Ye foul jades, may your tongues rot in your heads!"

Passing by Dominikova's house, he looked in at the open window. The room was lit, but Yagna could not be seen, and he was unwilling to go in; so he regretfully passed on to his own hut, on his way to which he was met by Veronka.

"Ah, I was at your home just now.—Staho has dug the new foundations and made the trunks ready, so that you might cut them into shape now: when are ye coming?"

"On Tib's eve perhaps. I am disgusted with this village, and may any day throw everything up—and go over the hills and far away!" he cried angrily, as he went past.

"Something," she wondered, as she went her way to Boryna's, "must have stung the man pretty sharply: what can it be?"

Supper was done, and Hanka told her all at leisure. Yagna's expulsion interested her deeply; but on hearing of Gregory, she only observed:

"His death will make one the fewer to share the property."

"It will.—I never thought of that."

"And with what the Squire has to give for the forest, you will get hard upon seventeen acres apiece! . . . To think of it! Even other folk's death is a gain to those already rich!" she sighed ruefully.

"What care I for wealth?" said Hanka. But when she went to bed, and thought the matter over, she felt a secret joy in her heart.

And afterwards, kneeling down for her evening prayer, she said resignedly:

"Since he has died, it is the will of our Lord." And she prayed fervently for his eternal rest.

The next day, about noon, Ambrose came to her cabin.

"Where have ye been?" she inquired.

"At the Koziols'. A child there has been scalded to death. She called me in, but there is naught needed for it save a coffin and a few clods."

"Which of them is it?"

"The younger of the two that she brought from Warsaw this spring. It fell into a tub of boiling water, and was all but boiled."

"Those foundlings, as it seems, do not get on with her."

"They do not.—But she is no loser: the funeral expenses are paid.—I came to you on another business, however."

She looked at him uneasily.

"Dominikova, you must know, has gone to the law court with Yagna—to complain of your having turned her out, I suppose."

"Let her. I do not care."

"They went to confession this morning, and had later a long conference with the priest. I could not catch half they said against you, but what they said made him shake his fist with anger!"

"A priest—to poke his nose into other folk's business!" she blurted out. All day long, however, the tidings stuck in her memory painfully; she was full of fears and evil surmises, and quite at a loss what to do.

At nightfall, a cart stopped in front of her cabin. She ran out, breathless and terrified; but it was only the Voyt, sitting there behind his horses.

"You know about Gregory already," he began. " 'Tis a calamity; but there's nothing to be said.—Now I have also some good news for you. Today—or tomorrow at the latest—ye shall see Antek again."

"Are ye not beguiling me?" she asked; the news was too good to believe.

"When the Voyt tells you so, ye may believe him. They informed me in the Bureau."

" 'Tis well he comes back; it was high time indeed," she returned, coolly; it seemed, with no joy at all. And then the Voyt, after a moment's reflection, began talking to her as a friend.

"That's a bad business ye have made with Yagna! She has laid a complaint against you, and may make you smart for having used violence and taken the law into your own hands. Ye had no right to expel her from her own apartment.—A pretty thing it will be, when Antek comes back, and ye are thrown into jail for it, both of you!—Now take my sincere friendly advice: make matters up. I'll do all I can to get the complaint withdrawn; but ye must yourself make amends for the injury done."

Hanka stood erect before him, and told him her mind thus:

"Are you speaking as the defender of my victim, or of your mistress?"

His whip struck the horses so hard that they bounded away at a gallop.

CHAPTER IV

Hanka could not sleep a wink that night, after such manifold and painful experiences. She continually thought that she heard someone creeping about the premises, along the road, or even close to the cabin. She listened. All the inmates were sleeping sound. The night was still, though the trees murmured; but not very dark, for the stars gave a dim light.

It was stiflingly close within. The ducklings, put to rest under the bed, smelled unpleasantly, but Hanka would not throw the window open. Her bed and pillows were hot beneath her, burning hot; she tossed from side to side, more and more agitated, full of multitudinous thoughts swarming in her brain, and drenching her with streaming sweat. At last, her fears growing uncontrollable, she started out of bed, and went out barefoot, in her shift, and bearing a hatchet that she had snatched up at random—out into the yard.

Everything stood wide open there. Pete lay sprawling outside the stable, snoring hard. The horses were munching their provender and clinking their halter-chains; the cows, that had not been tethered for the night, either wandered about the yard or lay chewing the cud with moist dripping muzzles, and lifting towards Hanka their ponderous horned heads and the dark balls of their unfathomable eyes.

She went back to her bed and lay down open-eyed, listening attentively, and at times quite sure that she could hear voices and distant steps.

"Peradventure the folk of some cabin hard by are awake and talking," she said, attempting to explain matters; but no sooner had the panes turned gray from black than she rose and went out again, this time with Antek's sheepskin thrown over her.

In the porch, Vitek's stork was standing asleep, with one leg drawn up under him, and his head thrust beneath his wing; and their flock of geese, huddled together in the enclosure, formed a dim white mass.

The fields beyond were flooded with low-lying grayish fogs, out of which only the highest tree-tops surged, like pillars of thick black smoke.

The pond glistened in the darkness like a huge sightless eye, fringed with lashes of alders that rustled around it, while all the neighborhood slept, wrapped in the fog's opaque invisibility.

Hanka sat down close to the house, leaned back against the wall, and fell into a doze. When she again opened her eyes, she saw with astonishment that the night had gone; the clouds were all burning red like a distant conflagration.

"If he has but started early enough, he will be here directly," she said to herself, looking down the road. Her short spell of slumber had so much refreshed her that, to while the time away till sunrise, she took out the children's clothes to wash in the pond, while the light grew stronger and stronger.

The first cock crowed, quickly followed by others, making a loud noise throughout the village. Some larks too were heard, but at rare intervals, while the whitewashed walls and the empty dew-drenched roads gradually became distinct.

Hanka was busy washing, when a sound of stealthy steps drew her attention; and as she looked around curiously, a shadow passed out of Balcerek's enclosure and slung away among the trees.

"Yes—'tis a visitor to Mary! who can it be?" She could by no means make sure, for the shadow had vanished directly. "Ah! So proud a girl! One so vain of herself and her beauty—to let in a sweetheart by night!—Who would have thought it?"

She was scandalized. On looking about her again, she perceived the miller's man, gliding by, at the other end of the village.

"He is coming home, no doubt, from the tavern where his Magda lives!— Those men! like wolves prowling in the night!—What doings, alas!" She sighed, but a restless feeling quickened her senses now and stirred her blood. This, however, presently passed away as she went on washing in the cool water; and in a voice which, though subdued, thrilled with intense fervor, she began the hymn:

"Soon as dawn blushes in the sky,
To Thee, O God, my voice shall cry!"

And the chant rolled over the fallen dew, and made one with the approaching daybreak.

It was time now to rise: opening windows, clattering clogs, and loud cries showed that the villagers were awakening.

Hanka spread out upon the fence all the things she had washed, and ran to wake her people. But they were so heavy with sleep that their heads but just rose and fell back on the pillow.

To her intense indignation, Pete shouted at her:

"Mother of dogs!—'Tis too early! I'll sleep till sunrise!" And he refused to stir.

The babies were crying, and Yuzka whined:

"Yet a little, Hanka dear! I went to bed but a minute ago!"

She then lulled the little ones to rest, drove the poultry into the yard, waited patiently for a few minutes more, and then—just before the sun had risen, when the heights of heaven were one mass of flame, and the mill-pond reddened in the dawn—she returned to the charge, and made such a din and uproar that the sleepers could not but get out of bed. And when Vitek came scratching himself drowsily, and rubbing his back against the corner of the hut, she chastised him well with sharp words.

"You'll wake up fast enough with a first-rate drubbing!—Aye, and why, you young hound! why did you not fasten the kine to the mangers last night? Would you have them gore each other's bellies in the dark, hey?"

He answered her back, but whipped out of sight in time, for she made a fierce rush at him. Then, looking again into the stable, she set upon Pete:

"The horses are mumbling their empty racks!—And you! you are lying abed even till sunrise! O you idle one!"

"Ye scream as a magpie ere it is to rain," he growled back. "Why, all the village can hear your noise!"

"Let them hear! Let them all know what a sluggard, what a lazy drone, what a dawdler you are!—Oh, but the master will be back now, and he'll keep you in order, I promise you!"

"Yuzka!" she now shouted from the other end of the yard. "Spotted One's udders are swollen hard: milk her carefully, and let not half the milk remain, as you did last time.—Vitek! take your breakfast and be off; and if you let the sheep stray—as you did yesterday—I'll know the reason why!" . . . So she went about, giving orders, bustling everywhere, and all the time hard at work herself: feeding the fowls, and the swine that were standing close to the cabin; giving a pail of thin batter to drink to the calf just weaned; throwing the ducklings boiled groats, and driving them off to the mill-pond. Vitek received a slap on the back, and his food in a wallet. Nor was the stork forgotten; she set a pipkin before him, full of potatoes cooked the day before; and he *klek-kleked,* plunged his beak in, and ate with a hearty appetite. Hanka was everywhere, and seeing to everything, and managing all in the best way.

As soon as Vitek had gone off with the cows and sheep, she went over to Pete, whom she could not bear to see idling about.

"Take all the dung out of the byre!" she ordered; "it is bad for the cows at night, and fouls them all over: they're as filthy as swine."

Just then the sun's red burning eye peeped at them from afar, and the *Komorniki* arrived to pay with their work for the flax and potato-fields they had rented.

She set Yuzka to peeling potatoes, gave suck to her babies, put her apron on over her head, and said:

"Keep an eye on everything here! And should Antek come, let me know: I shall be in the cabbage-field.—Come, good folk, while it is still cool and dewy. We shall first earth up the cabbages, and set

to yesterday's work again after breakfast."

As they walked on down by the old disused peat-diggings, a few lapwings circled over their heads and some storks were wading about the low marshy ground, stepping carefully, and thrusting their heads forward. In the air there was a marshy smell, mixed with that of the sweet flag and the sedges, with clumps of which the old peat-diggings were overgrown.

Then they set to work, beginning their talk (of course with the inexhaustible topic of the weather) while they earthed up the cabbage-plants, that had grown well, but were greatly infested with weeds —towering dandelions, rank duckweeds, and even forests of thistles.

" 'What man needs not nor sows, most abundantly grows,' " said one woman, knocking the earth from the roots of a weed.

"And all evil things likewise," said another; "sin is sown by none, yet the world is full thereof."

"Because its life is sturdy!" Yagustynka struck in, to air her peculiar views. "My dear! so long as man lives, sin shall live. Do they not say: 'If sin you destroy, you kill all our joy'? and again: 'But for sin dearly cherished, long ago man had perished.'—It must, then, be good for something, just as this weed is: our Lord made them both!"

This theology was sternly rebuked by Hanka. "What! . . . Our Lord make evil? It is only man that, like a swine, mars all things with his rooting snout." And they said no more.

The sun was up in the sky now, and the mists had all disappeared, when troops of other women came along from the village.

Hanka laughed at them.

"Fine workers! Waiting till the dew shall dry, lest they wet their feet!"

"Not all are so eager for work as you are."

"And not all are forced to work so hard," she answered with a sigh.

"Well, your goodman is coming back: then will ye rest."

"I have vowed, if he returns, to go to Chenstohova for the day of Our Lady of Angels. And the Voyt tells me he is coming today."

"The folk at the Bureau must know: so the news will be true.—But what a number of people are off to Chenstohova on foot this year! The organist's wife is to be a pilgrim too, they say; and she tells me that the priest is to come with the pilgrimage."

Yagustynka made fun of the idea. "Who will carry his guts for him? He will never do so by himself.—Nay, 'tis only a promise, as usual with him."

"I have been there several times, with the others, and should long to go every year," sighed Filipka—she from over the water.

"Everyone longs for a spell of idleness."

"Oh, heavens!" she went on, paying no attention to the jeer; " 'tis all delight: everything along the road is so pleasant, so sweet to look on! And ye gaze out upon the world, and hear so much, and pray so much besides! . . . And one thinks for a few weeks that one has got rid of all woes and all cares. One feels as though born again!"

"True, and many have told me the same," said Hanka. "One is specially under the loving influence of God's grace."

A girl was hastening towards them, slipping along between the bulrushes and the thick clumps of alder. Hanka shaded her eyes, looked, saw it was Yuzka, and heard her from afar crying, as she waved her arms:

"Hanka, Hanka! Antek is home!"

She flung down her hoe, and sprang up

as if about to fly away like a bird; but she mastered her feeling, let down her skirt which she had tucked up, and, in spite of her rapture and her throbbing heart that made her almost unable to speak, said as quietly as if she had not heard any news at all:

"You will go on working without me, and come round to the cabin for breakfast."

The women looked at one another.

"Her calm," Yagustynka said, "is only outside, lest folk should laugh at her for wanting her goodman so badly.—I could not have mastered myself so!"

"Nor I!—But God grant that Antek do not go wrong any more!"

"As he will now no longer have Yagna at close quarters, it may be that he will keep straight."

"O my dear! when a man scents a petticoat, he'll follow it all over the world!"

" 'Tis a truth. There's no beast so greedy to its own hurt as some men are."

So they talked, letting the work flag and all but come to a standstill. Hanka meanwhile went on, conversing both with Yuzka and everyone she met, though she knew but little of what either she said to them or they to her.

"Has Roch come with him?" she would ask again and again.

"How many a time have I told you yes?"

"And how is he looking?—How?"

"How can I tell you that?—In he came and asked at the very threshold: 'Where's Hanka?' So I told him and ran to fetch you—and that's all."

"And he asked after me!—May the Lord . . .! May he . . ." She was incoherent, beside herself with gladness.

From a distance she perceived him, sitting with Roch in the porch, and as soon as he saw her, he went out to meet her in the enclosure.

She advanced more and more slowly,

catching at the roadside fence not to fall, for her legs were giving way under her. She felt choked with sobs, and her brain whirled so, she could only utter these words:

"You here!—Here at last!"—And she could speak no more for the tears of joy that choked her.

"Here at last, Hanka dear!" He clasped her to his breast in a mighty hug, full of the deepest affection and love. She nestled to his side with an uncontrollable impulse, while her happy tears went streaming down her pale cheeks, and her lips trembled, and she surrendered herself all to him with childlike simplicity.

It was long before she could speak at all; but, indeed, how could any speech ever express what she felt? She would have knelt to him, kissed the dust at this feet; and when a word or two burst from her lips, they were but like flowers falling before him as an offering, fragrant with happiness, bedewed with her heart's blood; and these her faithful eyes, brimming over with illimitable love, would lay down at his feet, with the fidelity of a dog that lives only in his master's will and favor.

"You do look poorly, dearest Hanka!" he said, stroking her face with the tenderest affection.

"No wonder, having suffered so much and waited so long!"

"Poor woman!" Roch here observed; "she has been worked sadly beyond her strength."

"Ah! and ye too are here, Roch! How could I forget you so?" And she welcomed him, and kissed his hands, while he said, with a smile:

"Very easily!—Well, I wished to bring you your goodman home; and now here he is!"

"Aye, here he is!" she cried, standing up before Antek and eyeing him in admiration. For he was so much whiter now—so much more refined in his strength—so beautiful, so lordly—as if he were someone else! She looked at him in bewilderment.

"Have I changed in aught, that your eyes examine me so?"

"No, not changed . . . and yet somehow not the same at all!"

"Oh, when I set to field-work again, I shall soon be once more just as I was!"

And now, making a dart into the hut, she came out, bearing her youngest-born.

"You see him for the first time, Antek!" she cried, as she lifted up the boy, roaring lustily. "Just look: he is as like you as two peas."

"A fine youngster!" He wrapped him up in the skirt of his capote, and rocked him to and fro.

"I have given him the name of Roch!—Here, Peter, go to Father"; and she pushed forward the other boy, who clambered on to Antek's knee, prattling childishly the while. Antek caressed him as tenderly as the other.

"Dear little things! darling mites!— How Peter has grown!—And he talks a little already . . ."

"Oh, and he takes such notice, and he's so clever! Can he but get hold of a whip, he wants at once to crack it at the geese!" She came kneeling down beside them. "Peter! Come! Try to say 'Dad'!"

He indeed said something dimly resembling the word, and continued cooing to himself, and pulling his father's hair.

"Yuzka," Antek said, "why do you eye me askant so? Come hither."

"But I dare not," she said.

"Come to me, silly one, come to me!" And he folded her in a kind brotherly embrace.

"And now you will obey me in all things, even as you did once obey Father. Fear not: I shall never be harsh to you, and from me you shall suffer no wrong."

The girl burst into a flood of tears, remembering her lost father and her brother who was drowned.

"When the Voyt told me of his death," Antek said, "I was quite stunned with grief. How dear he was to me! I never dreamed . . . And I had already arranged how we should divide the land; I had even thought of a wife for him!" he said, sorrowfully; when Roch, to turn away their thoughts from so sad a subject, exclaimed, rising from his seat:

"Talking is all very well, but not when the stomach cries famine!"

"Dear, dear! I had forgotten all about that.—Yuzka, just catch me those two yellow cockerels. . . . *Tsip, tsip, tsip!* come along! . . . Will you not begin with eggs? Or a bit of new bread, and butter made but yesterday?—Yes, cut off their heads and scald them in boiling water! . . . I shall have everything ready in a moment. . . . What a ninny I was to forget!"

"Let be, Hanka; the cocks will come in later. I would have something more homely just now; something of the country, I am so fed up with town food: give me potatoes and *barszcz* of all things!" And he laughed merrily. "Only get something else for Roch!"

"Thanks heartily; but both you and I have the same tastes as to that."

Hanka went off to get things ready. But the potatoes were on the boil by now, and she had only to fetch from the larder a huge sausage for the *barszcz.*

"This I was keeping on purpose for you, Antek. 'Tis from the pig ye sent me word to kill for Easter."

"And a splendid festoon it makes, too; though with the Lord's help, we shall get through it!—But where are the presents, Roch, say?"

The old man hauled forward a large bundle, out of which Antek took a variety of articles.

"Here's for you, Hanka, whenever you would fare anywhither." And he handed her a woolen shawl—just like the one the organist's wife had!—a black ground, with red and green chequers.

"For me! O Antek, how good of you not to forget!" she cried, overwhelmed with gratitude.

"Roch reminded me," he confessed, "or I should have forgotten. We went together to make our choices and purchases."

They had bought a great many things: he had shoes for her besides, and a silk kerchief for a head-dress: azure-blue, with tiny yellow flowers. Yuzka got another just like it, but green; also a frill and several rows of beads, with a long ribbon to tie them. There were gingerbread cakes for the children, and mouthorgans as well; and there was even something that he set apart unopened, for the blacksmith's wife. Nor had he forgotten either Vitek or the farm-servant.

And how they all exclaimed with admiration at each new marvel as it came forth, and looked it over, and measured its size! How the tears of joy ran down Hanka's cheeks! and how Yuzka caught her head in her hands with bewildered amazement!

"Well have you deserved all these presents. Roch told me how perfectly everything has been managed on the farm.—Be quiet now, I did not come to be thanked!" he cried, for they were all crowding to embrace him in their gratitude.

"I should never have dreamed of buying any such beautiful things," Hanka said, still in the melting mood, as she tried on her new shoes. "They are a little tight for me, now I go barefoot; but in winter they will be just the thing."

Roch asked her about the doings in the village. She answered, but in a desultory way, being very busy with the food. In a short time she had set before them a large dish of boiled potatoes, plentifully seasoned with fat bacon, and another one, not a whit smaller, of *barszcz,* in which there swam a huge sausage, looking for all the world like a floating wheel.

And they fell to with an excellent appetite.

"That's the food I like," he cried, merrily; "lots of garlic to give the sausage a taste! After that, a man feels he has something inside him. But there, in jail . . . they fed me so—devil take them all!"

"Ah! poor dear! how famished you must have been!"

"Aye, aye! towards the end I had no taste for anything!"

"The boys told us only a starving dog could eat what they gave them: it is so?"

"There's some truth in that; but the worst was staying locked up. In the cold weather it was still bearable; but when the sun shone warm, and I smelled the smell of the land—oh, then, how I raged! I even tried to tear out the window-bars; but they prevented me."

"Is it true," Hanka asked in a trembling voice, "that they beat folk there?"

"No doubt. But then the place is full of such villains, 'twere but justice to flog them daily.—Oh, no one ever dared to lay a finger on me! If anyone had . . . well, I'd have made short work of him."

"Yea, in truth! Who on earth could overcome you, you mighty one?" she said, with eyes gloating over him, and attentive to the least signal he should give.

They had soon finished their meal, and went out to sleep in the barn, where Hanka had already carried them beds and pillows.

"I declare," Antek said, laughing, "we shall both melt away like dripping in that place!"

She closed the great barn-door upon them, and then gave way to her feelings: to hide them, she went and weeded the parsley-bed, every now and then looking around her, while the tears welled up.

They were tears of joy, shed—why? Because the sun beat hot upon her shoulders; because the green leaves were fluttering over her; because the birds sang, and fragrance filled her senses; and she felt so happy, so serene, so blissful within her soul!—As if she had just returned from confession—perhaps happier still!

"Thou, O Lord Jesus, hast done all this," she murmured, raising her moist eyes to Heaven, her soul filled with the deepest and most ineffable gratitude for the great boon she had received.

"And all things have changed so wonderfully!" she sighed in ecstasy.—All the time they slept, she remained as in a sweet trance. She watched over them, as a hen does over her chickens; took the children far out into the orchard, lest they should awaken the sleepers; and drove all the animals out of the farmyard, heedless if the pigs should root up the new potatoes, or the fowls go scratching over the sprouting cucumber-plants.

The day was painfully long, but there was no help for that. Breakfast-time, dinner-time passed: still they slept. She sent all the people to work, caring little whether they should or should not be lazy, with her not by, and stood continually on the watch, or continually tripping between cabin and barn.

And many, many a time did she take out the things he had brought her, and try them on, and cry out:

"Is there in all the world another man so kind and so thoughtful as he is?"

At last, however, she sped away to the village; and every woman she saw she accosted with:

"Do ye know, my goodman has come back! He is sleeping in the barn now!"

Her eyes and face were radiant with smiles; everything in her breathed such joy and exhilaration that they were all astounded.

"What spell can that jail-bird have

thrown over her? Why, she is beside herself about the man."

"She will grow proud and stuck-up in a very short time: you will see!"

"Oh, but let Antek go back to his old ways again, and she will be taken down finely!" So they gossiped.

Of all they said, she heard not one word.—She was back home presently, and preparing a first-class dinner. But hearing some geese scream in the pond, she ran out to silence them with a volley of stones; which nearly brought about a quarrel with the miller's wife, their owner.

She had scarcely sent the field-laborers their afternoon meal, when the two men came out of the barn. Dinner was spread for them in the cool shadow in front of the house. Beer and vodka were not lacking there, nor even a dessert—half a sieve full of ripe red cherries, brought from the priest's house.

"A noble dinner!" Roch said smiling; "quite a wedding-feast!"

"And should the Master's return be a second-rate festival?" she answered, busily serving them, and eating very little herself.

Dinner was hardly over, when Roch went out into the village, promising to look in again in the evening; and Hanka said to her husband:

"Will you look at the farm?"

"Certainly! My 'holidays' are over; I must buckle to work now.—God! how little did I think I should inherit my father's land so soon!"

He sighed, and followed her. She took him first to the stable, where three horses and a colt were snorting and stamping; then to the empty cow-byre, and the granary, full of new-mown hay. He looked into the sties too, and into the shed where all the various implements and tools were stored.

"That *britzka* must be taken in to the threshing-floor: its paint is peeling off with the heat here."

"So I told Pete more than once; but the fellow does not mind me."

She called the pigs and poultry round her, priding herself on their numbers; and then she told him about the field-work; what had been sown, and where, and how much of each crop. When she had finished, he said:

"I can hardly think that you have done all this by yourself."

"For your sake, I could have done still more!" she whispered, overjoyed at his praise; and the whisper came hot from her heart.

"You have backbone, Hanka . . . and plenty of it too!—I did not expect it of you."

"I had to, and needs must when the devil drives."

After looking about the orchard, with its half-ripe cherries, and the plots of parsley and onions, and the young cabbage-plants, they came back; and as they passed the side where his father had lived he peeped in at the window.

"And where's Yagna?" he asked, seeing with surprise that the room was empty.

"At her mother's. I turned her out," she replied in a firm voice, looking him full in the face.

He knit his brows, pondered awhile, then lit a cigarette, and said quietly and with seeming indifference:

"Dominikova is a bad animal; she will not be ousted without a lawsuit."

"I hear they both went to lodge a complaint yesterday."

"Well, well, 'between complaint and sentence, there is a good long distance'; but we must consider things well, and not let her play us any tricks."

She told him how it had all come about—of course, omitting many a detail. He heard her out, put no question,

and only frowned heavily. But when she handed him the paper, he gave a sarcastic laugh.

"With that paper ye may as well . . . why, 'tis worth absolutely naught!"

"How so!—It is the very same paper your father gave her!"

"What's the use of a broken stick?— Had she annulled the deed at the notary's, that would have been something. It was in mockery she flung it to you!"

He gave a shrug, took little Peter on his arm, and made for the stile.

"I am going to look at the fields and come back," he said over his shoulder, and at the hint she stopped short, much as she had longed to go with him. As he passed the stack, now repaired and filled with new hay, he glanced at it from under heavy eyelids.

"It was repaired by Matthew!" she called out to him from the stile where she stood. "The roof alone required some scores of straw trusses."

"Good, good!" he grunted in reply, and strode away through the potatoes along the pathway, uninterested in such trifles.

The fields on that side of the village nearly all bore autumn-sown crops this year: so he met but few people, and those he met he saluted curtly, and passed on. But soon he walked more slowly, for Peter was beginning to feel heavy, and the hot still weather acted strangely upon him. He stopped to examine almost every field in particular.

"Ha! that weed is simply choking the flax!" he cried, observing the patches of flax, azure-blue with flowers, but thickly strewn with the yellow blooms of some weed.

"She bought her linseed unsifted, and sowed it unsifted too!"

Then he stopped close to the barley, stunted, parched and scarce visible for the thistles, and camomile plants, and sorrels which grew there.

"They have sown in too wet soil.— That swine! he has ruined the field! The rascal ought to have his neck twisted for tilling the land so. And how it has been harrowed! Dog-grass and couch-grass everywhere!" He was much displeased.

But presently he came to a vast expanse of rye, waving in the sunshine, with heavy billowy ears of corn, sounding and rustling. This was a set-off: it had grown magnificently, the straw was thick in the stem, and the ears were full.

"It grows like a forest of pines! Ah, that was Father's sowing. . . . Even the Manor could show naught better!"—He plucked an ear, and rubbed it in his hands. The grain was full and fine, but soft as yet, liable to be ruined by a hailstorm.

But where he stopped longest to admire and feast his eyes was over the wheat. The growth was not quite regular—in clumps here, in hollows there— but the ears were all glossy, darkish in hue, dense-growing, and large in size.

"A first-rate crop! And, though on rising ground, it has suffered not at all from the drought. . . . 'Tis a harvest of pure gold!"

On arriving at the boundary, he gazed back. Away by the churchyard they were mowing the clover, and the scythes moved flashing over the meadows, like gleams of lightning. On the fallows flocks of geese were feeding; men swarmed about like ants; and higher and farther still he could descry lonely houses, trees hunched up, gnarled and drooping over the roads; and again more and more vast lands fading into the distance, as into a flood of bluish trembling water.

All was hushed in profound silence; the sultry air vibrated; it was, as it were, an atmosphere of white flame, through which a stork might be seen walking up and down, or poising itself on dropping wings; or a crow flying past, with beak wide open, gaping with the heat.

On high there was but the intense dark azure, with a few white clouds straying across it. But below, the dry burning wind made sport: now whirling and staggering about like a drunken man; now starting up with a sudden loud whistle; or, again, lurking somewhere away out of sight, and then bursting out unexpectedly in the corn, which it teased and dashed to and fro, and drove hither and thither in lofty billows—to disappear again as suddenly, no one knew where, while the cornfields murmured in low voices, as if complaining of its rough behavior.

Antek, having reached his fallow at the skirt of the forest, had another burst of indignation.

"Not yet ploughed up or manured! Our horses stand idle, the dung is wasted in heaps . . . and what does it matter to him, the dirty scamp?—May all . . ." he swore fiercely, drawing nigh to the cross by the poplar road.

But here, tired, slightly dizzy, and with his throat full of dust, he sat down in the shadow of the birch-trees by Boryna's Cross. Little Peter had gone to sleep: he laid him down on his capote; and then, wiping away streams of sweat from his brow, he looked out upon the landscape, and fell into a reverie.

The first afternoon shadows of the forest were hesitatingly creeping down to the corn. The tree-tops, glowing in the sun, were conversing one with another, while the thickets of hazel and aspen below shook like men sick with an ague. Woodpeckers pecked on incessantly; magpies were shrieking somewhere unseen. And at times a bee-eater would flash athwart the old moss-grown oak-trees—a flying fragment of rainbow!

A cool breath was wafted from within the quiet woodland recesses, into which the sun but rarely shot his keen darts; it came, redolent of mushrooms, of resin, of pools simmering in the hot blaze.

Suddenly a hawk was seen above the forest, circled over the fields, and, poising itself for an instant, swooped down into the corn.

Antek sprang forward to balk it, but too late: a stream of feathers was floating down, and the robber fleeing through the air, while below partridges piped plaintively, and a terrified hare fled at random, its white scut bobbing up and down.

" 'Twas most featly done! A bold thief!" Antek thought, returning to his seat. "Well, hawks too must get their food somehow. Such is the law of the world!" he reflected, as he covered little Peter with his capote; for there were numberless black wild bees and bumble-bees buzzing around them.

He recalled those days of the near past, when he was longing so fiercely, with such insatiable thirst, to be back in his fields once more.

"How they tormented me, the villains!" he said with a curse. Then he became quite motionless.—Just in front of him, a few quails, calling to each other, put their heads timorously out of the rye, but popped back at once, on hearing a band of sparrows alight upon a birch-tree, fluttering, bickering, fighting, and flying down into the sand beneath, with a great racket and hubbub . . . when suddenly they all were silent, as if rooted to the spot.—The hawk flew past again, so near them that its shadow glided over the field beneath!

"Little brawlers! he has struck you dumb pretty quickly!" Antek mused. " 'Tis just the same with men. How many need only a threat, and are hushed at once!"

Some wagtails came out upon the road, hopping so near that with a sweep of his hand he almost caught one of them.

[60]

"I but just missed getting one of the silly creatures for the boy."

And now crows came, one after another, flocking out of the forest, pecking at anything they could find. Scenting a man, they began, cautiously and holding their heads awry, to peer about and go round him, hopping ever nearer and nearer, and opening their gruesome beaks.

"Oh, no! I am not to be a feast for you," he laughed, throwing a clod at them; and they, like thieves found out, fled away in silence.

But after a time, while thus gazing out on the countryside, his whole soul attentive to every one of its sounds and sights, all the creatures about him began to draw near him boldly. Ants ran over his back, butterflies again and again settled in his hair, lady-birds walked about his face, and great green caterpillars of the wood explored his boots with lively interest; squirrels too, peeping forth from the forest, their brownish-red tails high in air, seemed deliberating whether they should not approach him. He, however, noticed none of them, plunged as he was in a sort of dreamy state, which the sight of the country had caused in his mind, and that filled him with indescribable sweetness.

He felt as though he were himself the very waft of the wind through the corn, the very gleam of the soft green fleece of the grass, the rolling of the streamlets over the heated sands, athwart the meadows redolent of new-mown hay; he felt himself one with the birds flying high above the earth, and crying to the sun with the great incomprehensible clamor of Life: as if he had become the murmur of the fields, the tossing of the pine-forest, the rush and mighty impetus of all growing things; also the mysterious potency of that hallowed Mother, the Earth, who brings forth all in joy and gladness. And he knew himself, knowing that he was all these things in one—both what he saw and what he felt, what he touched and understood, and what he could not even seize but by the merest glimmering—that which many a soul will only see clearly at the instant of death—besides that which only looms vaguely within the human soul, and gathers and lifts it up to the unknown region where it weeps tears of ineffable sweetness, and yet is weighed down as with a stone by an insatiable craving.

But all these thoughts passed through his mind like clouds: before he could grasp one clearly, another had taken its place, as absorbing as the former and yet harder to understand.

He was awake, and yet he had a drowsy sense as of sleep coming to his eyes; he was led somehow into a land of ecstasy, where he felt as one feels at the most holy moment of the Holy Mass: when the soul floats away in adoration, towards some garden where angels dwell, some happy land—Paradise, or Heaven!

Though his was a hard tough nature, by no means given to sentiment, he was nevertheless, during those unearthly moments, ready to fall prostrate on the earth, kiss her with burning kisses, and take her to himself in the most loving embrace.

"What is it that has wrought upon me so? It must be the change of air—nothing else," he grunted to excuse his feelings, rubbing his eyes and knitting his brows. But indeed an overwhelming Power had seized upon him: it was by no means possible to crush down that jocund serenity which now flooded all his being.

He knew himself back in the land—*his* land—yea, the land of his father, of his forefathers: was it strange that he should feel his soul glad, and that every throb of his heart should cry out aloud and joyfully to the whole world: "Here I am once more, and here do I remain!"?

He pulled himself together, bracing himself to take up this new life, to walk in his father's ways and those of his ancestors before him: like them, he bowed his shoulders to the yoke of heavy toil, to be borne bravely, unweariedly, until little Peter should step into his place.

"It is the order of things that the young should succeed the old and the sons the fathers, one by one, continually, so long as it shall be Thy will, O merciful Jesus," he thought, in deep meditation.

He bent his head over his hands, bowing it low; for many and various thoughts had now come into his mind, mournful recollections which the accusing voice of conscience now brought before him—bitter painful truths that humbled him in the dust, as he acknowledged his multitudinous transgressions and sins.

It was a hard thing, this confession of his, and he found it no easy matter to appease his conscience; but he fought down his stubbornness, conquered his pride, and looked back on his past life with true repentance, examining every act with the utmost severity and fairness of judgment.

"I have been naught but an infamous fool!" he thought with deep sadness, while a bitter smile writhed his lips. "All in the world must take place in due order. Aye, my father spoke wisely: 'When all carts go the same way, woe to him that falls from one; he will be crushed under the wheels.'—But every man has to realize this by himself, with his own reason; and this may cost very dear indeed."

Sounds of lowing now floated from the wood; the cattle were coming home amid great volumes of dust; oxen, sheep with their attendant dogs, careful to keep them away from the corn; squealing herds of pigs, driven home with many a blow; calves plaintively seeking their lost mothers; a few herdsmen on horseback, and the others on foot with the flocks, striking, shouting, and keeping up a stream of noisy talk.

Antek had remained with Peter on one side to let them pass, when Vitek saw him and came up to kiss his hand.

"I see you have grown pretty well in these last times."

"I have in truth. The trousers I got in autumn now come but just beyond my knees."

"All will be well; be sure that Mistress will give you a new pair.—Is there grass enough for the kine?"

"Alas! no, it is all sere and drying up. If mistress had not fodder for them at home, they could give no milk at all.—Pray let me have Peter, for a little ride," he added pleadingly.

"But surely he will fall off the horse!"

"Why, no: how often and often have I taken him about on our filly! Besides, I shall be there to hold him.—How he loves riding and crying out at the horse!" —He took the boy and set him on an old jade that was plodding along with drooping head. Peter clutched at her mane with his tiny hands, smote her flanks with his bare heels, and screamed aloud with pleasure.

"A fine little fellow! O you dear boy of mine!" Antek exclaimed admiringly.

And he at once turned off from the road, taking a short cut that led straight to his barn, as the descending sun painted the sky with gold and pale emerald-green, and the wind went down, and the falling dew made the ears of corn to droop.

He walked slow, with many memories at his heels: Yagna among them, as vivid as in life. He rubbed his eyes to get rid of the vision; but in vain. In spite of him, she walked on by his side, as she once had done; and as then, she seemed to shed around her such a delightful glow that it made the blood rush to his head.

"Peradventure 'twas well Hanka drove her away! She is to me as an ulcer in the flesh—a rankling ulcer!—But the past will never be again," he said, a strange pain gnawing at his heart; and he added, with stern reproof: "My wild oats are all sown!" as he entered the enclosure.

In the yard they were busy over their evening labors, Yuzka milking the cows outside the byre and singing a shrill ditty, while Hanka made *kluski* in the porch.

As Antek went in to look over his father's apartments, his wife followed him.

"After we have set things in order here, we shall remove to this side.—Is there any lime to be had?"

"Yes, I bought some at the fair, and shall call Staho in tomorrow: he will whitewash the place.—Certainly, we shall be more comfortable here."

He peered awhile into every corner, thinking.

"Were you in the fields?" she asked him timidly.

"I was. All is in good order. Hanka, I could not have done better myself."

She colored deeply with the pleasure of hearing him praise her.

"Only," he went on to say, "let that Pete go and feed swine, not till my ground! The good-for-nothing oaf!"

"I know him well, and have even been looking out for another farm-servant."

"Well, I shall tackle him, and—should he not be obedient—send him flying!"

Hearing the children cry, she ran to them. Antek went into the yard to continue his inspection of everything. He was so severely masterful of aspect, that —though he only threw out a word here and there—Pete felt alarmed, and Vitek, afraid to come near him, slunk about at a respectful distance.

Yuzka was milking her third cow, and bawling ever louder and louder:

"Still, Pretty One, be still,
  And let me fill
    The pail!"

"Why," he called out to her, "you screech as if flayed alive!"

She was dumb for an instant; but, bold and daring by nature, she soon struck up again, though in a less high-pitched key this time:

"My mother begs of thee
  This evening not to fail:
Still, Pretty One, be still!"

"Can you not be quiet? Master is present!" Hanka said, reprovingly, carrying some water for the cow to drink.

Antek took the vessel from her hands, and set it before the cow, saying with a laugh:

"Screech away, Yuzka, screech away; you'll drive all the rats off the premises in no time!"

"I shall do just as I please!" she answered back sulkily, in a mood to quarrel. But as soon as they had gone by, she ceased her song, though she still eyed her brother askance, with a resentful sniff.

Hanka, busy with the pigs, carried them so many heavy tubs of mash that he was sorry for her.

"That is too hard work for you; let the lads carry them," he said. "And I shall get you a wench besides; Yagustynka is of no more use to you than the whining of a dog!—Where is she now?"

"Gone to her children, to make it up with them!—A wench? Well, one would be handy; but the expense!—I could manage things by myself. But let it be as you will have it." It was surprising (so grateful she felt) that she did not kiss her husband's hand. In great glee, she added: "And then I should be able to breed yet more geese, and fatten yet another swine for sale."

After revolving the matter in his mind, he came to this conclusion:

"Now we have a farm of our own, we must behave as becomes our condition, and as our fathers have always done!"

After supper, he went outside the hut, to receive his friends and acquaintances, who had come to welcome him back with great joy.

"We were looking out for you," Gregory said, "even as the kite looks out for rain."

"Ah, well, they kept me there, they kept me, that pack of wolves! and there was no getting away from them!"

All sat down in the shadow of the hut. There were lights on every side, and bright stars overhead; the mill-pond murmured, moaning now and then; and all around it the people were enjoying the cool of the evening.

Roch interrupted some commonplace talk with: "Know ye that the head official has decided there is to be an assembly here in a fortnight, to vote for a school?"

"Is that our business?" young Ploshka cried. "Let our fathers see to it."

Gregory took him up sharply. " 'Tis easy enough to lay all on our fathers' backs, and lie lazily on our own! The reason things go so ill in the village is that none of us younger men will trouble about them."

"Let them make over their lands to us, and we will!"

This was an opening for a dispute, when Antek suddenly interposed.

"We certainly do need a school here; but we ought not to vote half a kopek for such a one as the head official would give us."

Roch seconded him strongly, urging them all to resist.

"Ye will each vote a *zloty,* and have to pay a rouble. . . . What about the vote for the Law-Court Building, eh? They

have fattened finely on your money; their bellies protrude with a vengeance!"

"I am decidedly against the vote," said Gregory, and, taking up some books, he went to study quietly by Roch's side.

There was little further talk after that; even Matthew spoke but few words, only keeping his eye upon Antek; and they were about to go home, when the blacksmith appeared. He had but just come back from the Manor, he said, and fell a-cursing both village and villagers.

"And what ails you now?" asked Hanka, peeping out of the window.

"What, indeed?—I shame to tell it: our peasants here are all louts and boobies! They don't know their own mind.—The Squire behaved to them as to men and landholders; and they, they acted like mere gooseherds. The agreement had been made: naught was required but to sign it. Then one of them scratches me his head and grunts: 'Shall I . . . or shall I not?' Another would fain still consult his goodwife anew; a third sets to whining for a bit of meadow adjacent to his land, that he wants given him.—What can be done with such fellows?—The Squire is raging—will not hear of the agreement any more, nor let any of the cattle from Lipka graze on his lands, and will make anyone smart that sends them there."

This unforeseen calamity dismayed them all, and they had no words too strong for the guilty. Matthew said with sorrow:

"All this comes from the people's having no leader. We are like stray sheep!"

"Has not Michael pointed this out to them clearly enough?"

"Oh, Michael! He goes where gain is to be had, and holds with the Manor: none therefore will trust him. They listen; but as to following what he says . . . !"

Here the smith swore he cared only for

the public good, even to giving time and trouble gratis, that the agreement might be made!

"And if ye should swear that in church," Matthew growled, "they still would not believe you."

"Let someone else, then, try," he retorted; "we shall see how he succeeds."

"Yes, someone else ought certainly to try."

"And who? The priest? Or the miller perhaps?" several men asked ironically.

"Who?—Why, Antek Boryna! If he cannot bring folk to their senses, we must give them up as a bad job."

"I?—I?" Antek faltered, in confusion. "Will anyone hearken to me?"

"All will! You are an able man, and the foremost among us."

"True it is!—Aye, aye!—You and none other!—We'll follow you!" were the cries that arose—not much to the smith's taste, seemingly. He twisted about, scratched his moustache, and grinned maliciously when Antek said:

"Well, well, they say: 'Pot-making is for others than saints.'—I can but try; and we'll talk the matter over another time."

Several, as they went away, took him aside, urging him to accept, and promising their support. Klemba said:

"We must have someone to lead us, who has wits and a strong hand, and honesty into the bargain."

"And," Matthew added, laughing, "who can command, and use a cudgel if needful."

Antek now remained alone with the smith; Roch had gone aside to pray earnestly in the porch.

They talked matters over very quietly and very long. Hanka meantime went about the hut, shaking up the bedding, providing the pillows with clean slips, and making her ablutions as for some great solemnity; combing her hair by the window, and peeping out at the two men

with growing impatience. She listened attentively, too, to the smith, who dissuaded Antek from taking up such a burden, since he never could manage the peasants, and the Squire was against him.

"That's false!" she called out to him through the window. "He offered to stand bail for you in court."

"If ye know so much more about it, then let's drop the matter," he cried, surly as a dog.

Antek rose, yawning drowsily.

"But," his visitor concluded, "I'll just wind up with this: you are only at liberty till your trial; and who knows how things will go with you then? In such a position, how can you meddle with other folk's affairs?"

Antek sat down again, and was lost in a brown study. The smith did not wait for his answer, but went home.

Hanka more than once looked out at Antek, but he did not notice her. She at last called him in a tone of timid pleading:

"Come, Antek, 'tis bedtime; you must be very weary."

"Coming, Hanka, coming!" he said, rising heavily.

She began to say her evening prayers with tremulous lips, while she undressed in haste.

But he went in, sorely troubled, and thinking: "What shall I do if I am sent to Siberia?"

CHAPTER V

"Pete, bring firewood in!" Hanka called out from the cabin-door. She was covered with flour and very untidy with bread-making.

A big fire roared in the baking-oven. She raked the coals to spread them out, and hastened to roll the dough and shape it into loaves, which she carried out into the passage upon a board that she set in the sunshine, for them to rise more quickly. She bustled about in a great hurry, for the dough was almost over-brimming the big kneading-trough, covered with bedding for warmth.

"Yuzka! more wood on the fire; one end of the oven is almost black!"

But no Yuzka was at hand, and Pete did not hasten to obey. He was loading dung on a cart, heaping and pressing it down, keeping up meanwhile a conversation with the blind *Dziad,* who was occupied in making ropes of straw outside the barn.

The afternoon sun was so hot that the walls exuded liquid resin, and the wind blew like the blast from an oven, making every movement wearisome. The flies, too, hummed in myriads over the cart, and the horses, assailed, and maddened by them, came near breaking their halters, and perhaps their legs, in pulling and straining to avoid their bites.

The yard was so flooded with the heat, together with the pungent effluvium of the dung, that even the birds in the orchard close by could sing no longer; the hens had lain down half dead under the hedge, and the pigs wallowed squealing in the mud by the well. All at once the *Dziad* fell a-sneezing furiously: a whiff yet more noisomely offensive had reached him from the cow-byre.

"God bless you, *Dziad!*"

"That's no incense-smoke, I wot; and used though I am to the smell, it is stronger than snuff in my nostrils."

"But use makes all things pleasant."

"Fool! don't you think I ever smell aught but dung?"

"I was but repeating what my old grandsire told me when my drill-sergeant gave me slaps in the face."

"Ha, ha, ha!—Did you get used to that, pray?"

"I soon had enough of such drilling, and meeting the ruffian one day in a quiet corner alone, I made his face swell like a pumpkin . . . and he never slapped mine any more!"

"Did you serve long?"

"The whole of my five years! I could not purchase my discharge; so I had to—shoulder arms.—At first, ere I knew a thing or two, anyone who would could ill-treat me, and I had to suffer want . . . till my comrades taught me to snap up anything I needed . . . or get some maidservant to give it me, whom I promised to marry. And what nicknames those Russian soldiers gave me! and how they laughed at my speech and at my manner of prayer!"

"Did they dare laugh at that, the plague-spotted heathen?"

"Aye, till I punched their ribs for them, one after another, and made them leave off!"

"You must be a strong fighter!"

"Not especially," he answered with a boastful smile; "but I could drub any three of them at a time!"

"Have you seen warfare?"

"Of course. Against the Turks. We thrashed them soundly, we did!"

"Pete!" Hanka called out to him; "where's the wood?"

"Where it was," he muttered inaudibly.

"Your mistress is calling you," the *Dziad* said.

"Let her call! What, am I to wash up the pots for her?"

"Are you deaf?" she shouted, running out of the house towards him.

"I shall not feed the fire; 'tis no duty of mine!" he shouted back.

She began thereupon to rail at him to the best of her ability.

He, on his side, railed back at her, nothing loath, and when she presently gave him a harder home-thrust, he planted his pitchfork in the dung and cried angrily:

"Ye have not to do with Yagna now: your screaming will not scare me away."

"But what I will do, you shall see . . . and remember!"

She went on scolding the insolent fellow, while she carried the loaves of dough into the porch, or flung the logs into the oven, or looked after the children. But the labor and the intense heat were wearing her out terribly; for it was stiflingly hot within and in the passage on account of the fire in the oven. The flies, too, that swarmed on every wall, were so insupportable that she almost wept with rage as she beat them off with a branch, all streaming with perspiration, exasperated, and ever more impatient and slower at her work.

She was just patting the last loaf into shape for the oven, when Pete prepared to drive out of the yard.

"Wait a moment and take your afternoon meal!"

"Whoa!—Yes, I may as well: my stomach is empty enough after dinner."

"Had you too little to eat?"

"The food is so wretched, it goes through the bowels as through a sieve."

"There's insolence for you! What, you must have meat? And am I munching sausages in corners, say? No other farmers can at this season give their men what you get. Look at the *Komorniki,* how they feed!"

She set down in the porch a pot of sour milk and a loaf, and he began to cram himself gluttonously, now and again flinging a morsel of bread to the stork, that had hurried in from the orchard, and stood now, like a dog, watching him eat.

"Poor stuff.—As thin as buttermilk," he grumbled, when pretty well filled.

"Naught less than cream would do for you, belike? Wait till you get some!"

When he could eat no more and had taken the reins to start, she said to him sarcastically: "Take service with Yagna; she will fatten you!"

"Surely. When she ruled here, no one starved in the hut!" And he gave the horse a stroke with the whip, and the cart a push with his shoulder, to set it in motion.

He had wounded her to the quick, but was off before she could find words to answer him.

The swallows were twittering under the thatch, and a flock of pigeons alighted cooing in the porch. She drove them away; and then, hearing a grunt, rushed out, fearing her pigs were at the onion-bed. Fortunately, it was but the neighbor's sow, rooting beneath the fence.

"Just put your snout inside our enclosure, and I shall dispose of you in a fine way!"

But no sooner was she returning to work than the stork hopped on to the porch, lurked about there for a moment, cocked first his right eye at the loaves, then his left . . . and set to dig into the dough, swallowing it by large morsels!

Uttering a loud cry, she rushed at him.

He fled away with wide-open beak, making frantic efforts to get the dough down; but when she caught up with him to give him a beating, he flew up and alighted on the top of the barn, where he remained for a long time, rapping out his *klek-klek* and wiping the dough from his beak on the thatch.

"O you thief! let me but catch you, and I'll shatter you to bits!" she threatened, filling up the hollows the stork's beak had made.

Yuzka came in then, and all Hanka's anger was poured forth on her.

"Where have you been, you gadabout? —Always running hither and thither, like a cat with a bladder tied to its tail!—I'll tell Antek what a worker you are!—But get the embers out now, and quickly!"

"I was only at the Ploshkas' with their Kate. All are afield, and the poor girl has no one to fetch her water even!"

"What ails her, then?"

"The small-pox, I think; she is flushed and burning hot."

"And if you have caught it from her, I will take you off to the hospital."

"Is it likely? I have sat by a sick-bed already, nor ever got any hurt. Have ye no mind how I tended you, when you were lying in?" And so she went on after her fashion, prattling away in her absurdly thoughtless fashion, driving the flies off meantime and preparing to take the embers out of the oven.

Hanka interrupted her as she worked: "Ah! you must take the food to the people in the field."

"Instantly, instantly!—Shall I fry some eggs for Antek?"

"Do; but take heed not to put in too much fat!"

"Oh, do ye grudge it him?"

"How could I? But it might not agree with him."

Yuzka loved a run; so she did her work quick, and was off, before Hanka had closed the oven, with three vessels of sour milk, and bread done up in her apron.

Hanka cried to her from the window: "See whether the linen spread to bleach is dry, and wet it on your return: it is sure to be dry before sunset."

But the little chit was over the stile by then; the song she was singing floated back, and her hemp-colored hair was seen bobbing along through the rye.

On the arable land, by the forest, the *Komorniki* were scattering the dung brought previously by Pete, while Antek was ploughing it in. The stiff clay soil, though it had been harrowed not long ago, was hard as stone and baked in the sun; the horses had to pull with such

mighty efforts as to strain their harness to breaking-point.

Antek, seemingly glued to his plough-handles, drove his way on with dogged pertinacity, his mind concentrated on his work: now and then clacking the whip on the horses' hind quarters, but mostly encouraging them with a smack of his lips; for the work was really very wearisome. With a firm steady hand he directed the plough, cutting furrow after furrow, in long straight strips, such as it is the custom to make for wheat-land.

Crows hopped along by the furrows, picking up earthworms; and the bay colt, that had been out to graze on the field pathway, again and again pressed to its mother's side, eager to suck her milk.

"Milk at its age! What can have come over the greedy thing!" Antek growled, striking at its legs with his whip. It ran off, tail in the air, while he went on ploughing patiently, only at times breaking the silence with a word or two to the women. He was cross and tired out, and, when Pete arrived, gave vent to his feelings.

"These women," he cried, "have been fain to stop working because of you; and you come on now slow as a ragpicker!—Wherefore have ye stopped so long at the edge of the forest? I saw you!"

"The 'wherefore' is there still; ye can see it; it will wait."

"A curse on your saucy tongue!—Vee-o, old fellow, Vee-o!"

But now the horses went slower, foam-flecked and worn out. He himself, stripped to his shirt and drawers, was perspiring profusely, and his hands too were feeling the stress of the work. So that, on perceiving Yuzka, he cried out very heartily:

"Good now, 'twas high time ye came; we are all famishing!"

He finished the furrow up to the pine-wood, took the horses from the plough and turned them loose to graze on the verdant road by the forest: then, flinging himself down at the border of the wood, ate like a ravenous wolf, Yuzka all the time chattering away until he had enough of it.

"Let me be.—I care naught for your tittle-tattle," he said peevishly, and she, answering as peevishly back, ran off to pluck berries in the wood.

The pine-forest was quiet, dried up, aromatically scented, and, as it were, dying in the sun's fierce outpour. Only a very little verdure was to be seen, and out of its depths there blew a breeze laden with resinous fragrance, and carrying on its wings the warbling of birds.

Antek, stretched out on the grass, lit a cigarette and, looking into the distance, saw, as through a thickening fog, the Squire on horseback, leaping across the Podlesie fields; and some men with him, bearing poles for land-measuring.

Huge pines, with trunks as of red copper, rose above him, flinging down wavy and slumberous shadows. He would presently have fallen fast asleep, had it not been for the quick clatter of a wagon—the organist's servant, carting trunks to the sawmill—and then the sound of the familiar greeting: "Praised be Jesus Christ!"

One by one, the *Komorniki* were coming home from the forest, each with a load of firewood on her shoulders. At the very end of the file, Yagustynka dragged herself along, bowed almost to the ground beneath her burden.

"Rest ye here.—Why, your eyes are almost starting from their sockets."

She seated herself opposite him, leaning her load against a tree, and scarce able to breathe.

"Such labor is not for you," he told her with compassion.

"Yes: I feel quite crushed now," she replied.

"Lay those heaps closer, closer!" he cried to his farm-servant Pete, and went

on: "Why does not someone take your place?"

She answered only with a surly look, and turned away her red eyes full of anguish.

"Ye are now so changed!—Ye give way so. . . . Quite another woman."

" 'Even a flint will break under the hammer,' " she moaned, hanging her head. "And: 'Suffering consumes man faster than rust eats iron.' "

"The present season is hard even for well-to-do farmers."

"Hard! Let none talk of times being hard, so long as he has wild marjoram to eat, cooked with bran."

"Good heavens! come round this evening: we shall find two or three bushels of potatoes for you still. When harvest comes, ye can work the price out."

She broke down in a fit of crying, and could hardly speak to thank him.

"Perchance, too," he added kindly, "Hanka may have something else for you besides."

"Had it not been for her, we should have died of starvation!" she declared, sobbing. "Yes, I'll work for you whenever you may want me. May God reward you! I am not speaking for myself; I am accustomed to hunger. But my dear little mites are crying out: 'Grandam, give us to eat!'—and there is naught for them! I tell you: to feed them, I would cut off my own arms, or steal things from the altar, and sell them to the Jew."

"Then do ye live once more with your children?"

"Am I not their mother? Can I leave them in such misery? Every misfortune seems to have fallen on them this year. Their cow has died; all their potatoes have rotted (they even had to buy seed-potatoes); the gale blew their barn down; and, to crown all, my daughter-in-law has been ailing ever since her last child was born. They are all left to God's mercy."

"Aye, but why? Because your Voytek always reeks of brandy and only cares for the tavern."

"If at times he has taken too much, 'twas misery drove him that way," she said, eager in defense of her son. "Never, while he had work to do, did he even look in at the Jew's. But to a poor man, every glass is reckoned as a crime.—Alas! the Lord has dealt with them bitterly, very bitterly.—Is it right He should thus dog the steps of a poor foolish lout? And for what? What harm has he done?" she muttered, raising to Heaven her eyes, full of indignant challenge.

"But what! have ye not laid your curse on them?" Antek said, with strong significance. "Often and often ye have!"

"Ah, was it possible that our Lord should ever have listened to my senseless outcries?" But she added, in a tone of secret uneasiness: "Even when a mother curses her children, her heart never really wishes them evil.—'Wrath and woe make tongues go!' Aye, indeed. . . ."

"Has your Voytek farmed out his meadow yet?"

"The miller offered a thousand *zloty* for it, but I would not allow it. What that wolf has once got in his grip, not the devil himself could wrest out of it!—And perhaps someone else might be found with the cash?"

"It is surely a lovely meadow—can be mown twice a year. Had I only ready money just now!" He sighed, licking his lips with strong desire.

"Matthias would have been glad to get it: it lies so close to Yagna's land."

The name uttered gave him a start. He paused, however, and then inquired, with an indifferent look, his eyes wandering over the country-side:

"How are they getting on at Dominikova's?"

But she guessed what was in his mind, and smiled with thin lips, drawing closer:

"The place is a hell for them all! All there have funeral faces: they are chilled to the marrow with the gloom which fills it. They cry their eyes out, and live on, waiting upon God's Providence. Yagna especially——"

And she set to weave him a story about Yagna's sufferings and miseries and lonely life—adding all kinds of flattering things besides, to draw him out. But he remained mute, though such a raging desire for Yagna had sprung up within him that he was quivering all over.

Luckily Yuzka, coming back from the forest, made a diversion. She poured out into his hat the berries she had plucked, took up the empty vessels, and scampered away home. And Yagustynka, without waiting for any confidences, rose to go away, moaning with pain.

"Pete!" he ordered curtly. "Take her back with you in the cart!"

Once more he grasped the plough-handles and set patiently to cleave the baked and stubborn clay, bending forward like an ox under the yoke, and putting his whole soul into the work, but unable to stifle the desire that surged up.

The day seemed very long to him. Many a time he looked to see the sun's height, and measure the length of the fields, of which much still remained to be ploughed. His trouble of mind increased, and he beat the horses, and cried furiously to the women to work faster. His agitation, too, was getting beyond bearing; and his brain swarmed so now with countless thoughts that his hands could no longer drive the plough steadily, and it would deflect against the stones. Hard by the forest, it went so deep under a root that the coulter was wrenched off.

To do any more work was out of the question. He took the plough away on a light sledge, to which he put one of the horses, and made for home.

The cabin was empty, and everything there untidy and soiled with flour: Hanka, in the orchard, quarreled with a neighbor.

"The woman! She has always time enough for brawling!" he growled, on entering the farm-yard. There he grew still more angry: the other plough, which he took out of the shed, was quite out of gear. He worked at it a long time, losing his patience as he heard the quarrel going on, and Hanka raising her voice to a scream.

"If ye pay for the damage done, I'll give you back your sow: if not, I'll bring an action! Pay for the linen she tore in spring on the bleaching-ground; pay for my potatoes she has eaten now! I have witnesses to prove what has been done.— Oh, a clever woman this is!—Thinks to fatten her sow at my expense, does she? But I will not give up my rights!"

So she went on, and the neighbor giving her as violent language in return, the quarrel was waxing venomous, both of them stretching out their fists over the hedge.

"Hanka!" shouted Antek, heaving the plough on to his shoulders.

She at once ran to him, out of breath, and ruffled like an angry hen.

"Why, what a din you do make! All the village can hear you."

"I'm standing up for my rights!" she cried out. "What, shall I suffer another man's swine to root in my garden? So much harm done—and am I to say no word?" But he stopped her short, with a sharp sentence.

"Dress yourself, and try to look like a creature of God."

"What now? Must I dress up for work as for church?"

He eyed her with disdain, for she looked as though someone had swept the cabin floor with her. Then he walked away.

The smith was busy at work; his hammers were heard from a distance, loudly and tunefully clinking; and the forge, hot as hell, was uproarious with the tempestuous streams from the bellows that puffed in cadence.

Michael himself was working with his assistant, forging long bars of iron; and his face looked like a blackamoor's, and he beat on the anvil, as it were, out of sheer spite against it, smiting unweariedly.

"And for whom are those thick axletrees?"

"For Ploshka's wagon. He is to cart timber for the saw-mill."

Antek rolled a cigarette and sat down by the door-step. The hammers went on with pertinacious fury, smiting rhythmically again and again on the red-hot iron, slowly changing its shape beneath their strokes, as they bent it to the will of those who wielded them; and the smithy vibrated.

"Would ye not like to cart timber as well?" asked Michael, thrusting the bar deep into the flame, and working the bellows.

"I suppose the miller would not be willing. I hear he is the organist's partner, and hand in hand with the Jews."

"But you have horses," he said with bland friendliness; "horses and all that is needful. And your Pete does naught but lounge about your farm-yard.—And they pay pretty well."

"No doubt a little money before the harvest would be a good thing; but then, am I to go and beg the miller to do me a service?"

"No: arrange matters direct with the dealers."

"Whom I do not know!—If you would speak for me . . ."

"Since you ask me, I am willing—and shall go to them this very day."

Antek went out hurriedly; for now the

hammers were playing, and a deluge of sparks of fire flew on every side.

"I shall be back this instant, and am only going to look what kind of timber they are bringing in."

At the sawmill, likewise, the workers were lively; the logs were being hewn into shape one after another; the saws rasped harshly through the great trunks, while the water, pouring out of the wheels into the river, boiled and bubbled and foamed, swirling along the narrow mill-tail banks. Rough pine-logs, with their boughs scarcely lopped off, thundered down out of the carts, till the earth shook; while half a dozen workmen were busy with their axes, squaring them for the mill; and others were carrying the sawn boards out into the sunshine. Matthew was foreman there, and Antek could see him busily engaged, both working himself and directing the work of the others.

They met with hearty good-fellowship.

"Why, what's become of Bartek?" Antek asked, looking round him.

"He had enough of Lipka, and is gone from us."

"Some folk must needs be always on the move!—Ye seem to have work for a long time in advance, with so much timber here!"

"For a year, perchance, or yet longer. If the Squire come to terms with all us, he is going to cut down and sell the half of his woods."

"Ah! I saw them measuring the land out again on the Podlesie farm."

"Yes: someone comes to terms every day.—The silly sheep! They would not make an agreement one and all together, because they hoped the Squire would offer more. And now they make it apart and in secret from the others, each one striving to be first!"

"Some men are like donkeys, which, if you would have them go forward, you have to pull their tails. Yes, indeed, they are silly sheep.—And of course the Squire makes a good profit out of this state of things."

"Have ye taken possession of your property as yet?"

"No, it is too soon after Father's death, and we may not divide the land; but I have already overhauled the whole property carefully."

A face just then appeared among the alders on the farther bank of the river. Antek fancied it might be Yagna. The thought made him restless, and though the talk continued, his eyes wandered a good deal towards the bank of the stream.

"Now," he said presently, "I must go and bathe: the heat is unbearable"; and with that he went away down-stream, making as if in search of a convenient place. But as soon as he was out of sight, he mended his pace to a run.

Yes, it was she herself, with a hoe on her shoulder, going out to work on her cabbage-plot.

He soon reached and greeted her.

She looked round cautiously and, recognizing him as he bent forward among the parted sedges, stopped short, alarmed, bewildered, and uncertain what to do.

"What! don't you know me?" he whispered eagerly, trying at the same time, though unsuccessfully, to pass the river.

"Was it possible not to know you?" she answered low, looking apprehensively behind her towards the cabbage-plot, on which several women made red splashes afar.

"Where are you in hiding? I cannot find you anywhere."

"Where? Your woman drove me from the cabin: I am staying with Mother."

"Concerning that matter, I desire speech with you. Come, Yagna, and meet me by the churchyard this evening. I have something to say to you. Do come!" And he begged her very earnestly.

"Yes?—And what if someone should see me with you once more?—Of what has been I have enough already!" she answered. But he begged and entreated so hard that she felt her heart melting, and was sorry for the man.

"What new thing can you say? and wherefore do you call me?"

"Am I, Yagna, so altogether a stranger to you now?"

"No stranger; but yet not mine! I think no more of such things."

"But come only, and you'll not rue it!—Do you fear the burying-ground? Then come to the priest's orchard. . . . Have you forgotten where, Yagna? Have you forgotten?"

Yagna averted her head, for her face was suffused with crimson.

"Talk not foolishly; you shame me!" She was exceedingly confused.

"Come—come—come! I shall be waiting till midnight!"

"Wait, then!" And she turned away and fled to the cabbage-field.

He gazed after her greedily, full of such craving, and burning with such fire in every vein, that he longed to pursue and seize her in the presence of all—and could barely hold back from doing so.

" 'Tis naught—only the great heat has inflamed me mightily," he thought, and undressed quickly to take a bath.

The cool water calmed him down; its chill brought him to his senses, and he began to reflect.

"How miserably weak I am, for a trifle to upset me so!"

He felt humiliated and looked round, fearing lest someone might have seen him with her; and then he carefully passed in review all he had heard said against Yagna.

"A pretty creature you are, indeed!" he thought, in contempt not unmingled with sorrow. But suddenly, as he stopped be-neath a tree, a vision of her came before his eyes, in all her dazzling and marvelous beauty. And he cried:

"There's not another like her in the whole wide world!"

This he said to himself with a groan, yearning terribly to see her but once again, to gather her in his arms, to press her to his breast, and take his full of those red lips of hers, and suck her sweet honey to the very last drop!

"Only, O Yagna! for this one last time! this once, this once only!" he cried aloud to her as if she had been present. For some time afterwards he rubbed his eyes, and gazed upon the trees around him, before he could muster sufficient strength to go back to the forge. Michael was alone, working at Antek's plough.

"Will your cart," he asked him, "be able to bear such a great weight of timber?"

"Let there be but the timber for it to bear!"

"I have promised: 'tis just as if you had it on your cart already."

Antek set to ciphering on the door with a bit of chalk.

"I find," he said with much pleasure, "that I may earn about three hundred *zloty* ere harvest-time."

"It will," the smith remarked casually, "come in handy for that affair of yours."

Antek's face clouded over at once, and his eyes looked gloomy.

"Say that nightmare of mine! When I but think of it, I feel all broken, and care no more even for my life."

"That I can well understand; but not your having failed as yet to seek some means to preserve yourself."

"But what can I do?"

"Something must be done. What, man! the calf gives its throat to the butcher: will you do so too?"

"None can butt through a stone wall with his head," Antek returned, sighing bitterly.

[73]

Michael went on working with great energy; Antek sat plunged in disquieting and fearful thoughts, which made his face dark with changing expressions, till he started up and looked out in dismay. His brother-in-law let him suffer so for a considerable time, watching him with eyes full of cunning; but he finally said in a low voice:

"Casimir of Modlitsa found a way."

"He that fled to 'Hamerica'?"

"The same. A clever dog!—Aye, and a resolute one: who knew what he had to do, and did it!"

"Did they ever prove that he slew the gendarme?"

"He did not wait so long. No fool he, to submit to rot in prison!"

"He could flee: he was single."

"A man saves himself as he can. See, I do not advise you in any wise: I only say what others have done. But Voytek Gayda of Volitsa came back from penal servitude only last Eastertide.—Ten years. Well, 'tis not a whole lifetime, and one can survive it."

"Ten years! O Lord God!" Antek murmured, clutching at his hair.

"Yes; it was hard labor for that space of time."

"I could bear anything but that! God! I was there but for a few months, and came near losing my wits."

"Whereas ye could be beyond the seas in three weeks: ask Yankel."

"But it is so horribly far! How can I go—throw up everything—leave home, children, land, my village, and flee so awfully far—and forever?"

He was absolutely panic-stricken.

"But yet so many have gone there of their own accord; and none of these ever dreamed of returning to this Paradise of ours."

"And I cannot bear even to think of it!"

"True. But take a look at Voytek, and

hear what he tells about his penal servitude: ye will find it still more unbearable to think of. Why, the man is not forty yet, but quite hoary, and bent, and tottering: he spits blood, and can hardly move, and all can see he is bound for the 'priest's byre' soon.—But I need say no more: ye have your reason, and must decide."

And for the time he was silent; having sown trouble in the man's mind, he could safely leave it to grow up in time, and bring forth the harvest he expected. So, having repaired the plough, he said lightly:

"And now I am off to the dealers. Have your cart ready to carry the timber.—As for that other business, do not trouble. What is to be—is to be; and God is merciful.—I shall see you tomorrow evening."

Antek, however, could not forget his words. He had swallowed the bait of friendship, and it stuck in his throat, just as a hook sticks in the poor fish that has taken it and chokes. What pangs he felt —what sufferings he had to bear!

"Ten years! Ten years! Oh, how can I ever bear ten years!" The very thought palsied and benumbed him.

Arriving at his home, he trundled the cart into the barn, to have it in readiness for the next morning; but feeling a deep sense of weariness come over him—of the utter inutility of all his efforts—he only called to Pete, who was watering the horses at the well.

"Grease the cart's axle-trees, and have it in readiness for tomorrow. Tomorrow you'll have to bring timber from the forest to the sawmill here."

Pete, who cared but little for such hard work, swore violently when he heard the order.

"Keep a civil tongue in your head, and do as I tell you.—Hanka, give the horses three measures of oats for provender tomorrow, and you, Pete, get them fresh clover from the meadow: they must have plenty to eat."

To Hanka's questionings he gave only a mumbled answer, and presently went round to Matthew, with whom he was now on a very friendly footing.

The latter, who had but just come home from his work, was supping a dish of sour milk outside his cabin, to cool him after the heat of the day.

Antek could hear, somewhere near, a sort of trickling sound—a querulous heart-broken wailing.

"Who is making that noise?"

"Who but my sister Nastka? I have enough of her love affair!—Her banns are all published now, her wedding is to take place next Sunday—and lo! Dominikova has sent word to us through the Soltys that the holding had been left to her alone; that she will not let Simon have a single strip of land, nor even enter her cabin! And the old woman will keep to what she says: I know her well, that creature!"

"And Simon? What has he to say to that?"

"What should he say? Ever since the morning, he has been sitting in the orchard as dumb as a post, and says not one word even to Nastka. I am afraid his mind must have given way!"

"Simon!" he cried out into the orchard. "Come this way. Boryna is here to see us; perchance he can give some good advice."

After a minute, he came and sat down, without any word of greeting to either of them. He looked very much broken down, and as thin as a plank of aspen wood. Only his eyes burned; and on his thin face there was a look of desperate resolve, from which nothing on earth could turn him away.

"Well," Matthew asked him in a kindly tone, "what have you made up your mind to do?"

"To take an ax and kill her like a dog!"

"Fool! keep such wild talk for the tavern!"

"As there's a God in heaven, I will kill her. What—what else remains for me to do? She drives me off my father's land, turns me out of my hut, gives me no money whatever—what am I to do? I am an orphan, cast destitute on the world; and whither shall I go—whither? My own mother has wronged me so awfully!" he groaned, brushing away a tear with his sleeve. Then, suddenly starting up: "No!" he cried out; "in the name of all mothers of dogs, I will not forgive this, I will not—not if I should rot in jail for it!"

They quieted him. He sat still, but somber, and in such a state of dumb fury that he would not so much as answer Nastka's sobbing whispers. The others conferred together, thinking how they could be of use to him; but they found no means, because Dominikova, with her hopeless obstinacy, blocked the way. But at last Nastka took her brother aside, and pointed out a plan to him.

"She has hit on an excellent thing!" he exclaimed in great joy, on returning. "She says: Let him purchase six acres of the Podlesie farm from the Squire, to be paid by installments.—Is't not a good thought?"

"As good as any, indeed.—But . . . whence shall the money come?"

"In any case, for the outset, and as an earnest, Nastka has her thousand *zloty* of ready money."

"True; but whence will the livestock come, and the cabin, the implements and the seed to sow?"

"Whence?—From these!" Simon cried suddenly, springing up and waving both his arms.

"'Tis good talk, that; but can you accomplish it?" Antek asked, in doubt.

"Let me but have it—the land to work

on . . . and ye shall see!" he exclaimed with great energy.

"Then we have but to talk with the Squire and buy the land."

"Wait a little, Antek, wait a little; let us consider this in all its bearings."

"Ye will see how well I shall do everything!" said Simon, speaking hurriedly. "Who was it ploughed Mother's ground? Who reaped for her?—I alone! And was it work badly done? Am I a sluggard, tell me? Let the whole village answer—nay, let even Mother bear witness! . . . Oh, if I only have the land! . . . Help me to get that, O ye my dearest of brethren, and I shall thank you to the day of my death!" he cried, weeping and laughing by turns—intoxicated, as it were, with the joy of the hope which had come to him.

As soon as he was a little calmed, they set to deliberate and to talk over the idea and see what was to be done.

"Provided," Nastka said, with a sigh of fear, "provided the Squire be willing to accept installments."

"I think he will, if Matthew and I guarantee their being paid."

Nastka, for his kindness, was ready to kiss his hands.

"I myself have had sufferings, and know how they taste to other folk," he said, rising to take leave; for it was dark upon the earth: only the sky was yet alight, and the evening glowed in the West.

Antek hesitated awhile in which direction to turn his steps, but at last bent them towards home.

He walked on very leisurely, and at length was close to his cabin. The windows were open and alight, the children wailing within, Hanka raising her voice and Yuzka retorting shrilly. He could not quite make up his mind, till Lapa came joyfully whining and leaping up. Then—following a sudden impulse of ill humor —he gave the dog a kick and walked

back to the village, going down the lane that led to the priest's orchard. He passed along the organist's premises so silently that not even a dog gave tongue; and gliding on outside the priest's garden, he was presently on the wide field-pathway which divided Klemba's land from that of his Reverence.

He was completely hidden in the dark shadow of the trees.

The moon, a sharp thin sickle, already glittered in the shadowy sky. Stars peeped out in ever greater and greater numbers; and the evening, though hot, was shedding dew upon the earth. Quails flew out of the rye; droning beetles whizzed over the fields, and the scent and silence of the meadows made the brain whirl in a sort of stupor.

Yagna was not in sight.

Instead, about half a furlong away, the parish priest, clad in a white dust-coat, walked about saying his prayers, and apparently so intent upon them that he took scant notice how his horses, from grazing on his own miserable fallow land, had crossed to Klemba's rich clover meadow, that rose high and dark, with lush growth and countless flowers, on the other side of the path.

The priest walked on, now whispering his prayers, now looking up to the stars, now stopping to listen intently. And whenever he heard any the faintest murmur in the direction of the village, he would turn round quickly, in seeming anger against his horses.

"You Gray One, whither have you wandered? Into Klemba's good clover, hey? Fond of other folk's property, are you not? What, shall I baste your flanks soundly, will you have me do it, hey!" And his voice sounded very stern.

But the priest's horses were eating with so good an appetite that he could not find it in his heart to stop them, in spite of the harm they were doing: so, looking round him, he reasoned thus with himself:

"Let them take a little, each one of them, poor creatures! I shall put up some prayers for old Dame Klembova's everlasting rest—or make the loss up in some other way!—Oh, the greedy beasts! how fond they are of that clover!"

And once more he paced back and forth, and said his prayers and kept watch, never dreaming that Antek was watching him, and listening, and ever awaiting Yagna more eagerly.

Some time passed thus. At last it occurred to Antek to go and confide his troubles to the priest.

"So learned a man must surely know some way out of them!" he thought, slipping away in the shadow of the barn, to appear thence boldly round the corner, and step out into the field-way, clearing his throat noisily.

The priest, hearing someone come near, called out to his horses:

"You mischievous creatures! You foul beasts! Cannot I take my eye off you for one instant, but ye must be at once on my neighbor's land? O ye swine!—Off with you, Chestnut!" And plucking up his long skirts, he drove them away very speedily.

"Oh! Boryna!" he cried, when the man was near enough. "Well, how goes the world with you?"

"I came to speak with your Reverence, and had been at your house already."

"Yes, I had strolled out to say my prayers and look after the horses: Valek has gone to the Manor house. But those misbegotten beasts of mine—Heaven save the mark!—I can do nothing with them.—Look how magnificently Klemba's field of clover has grown. . . . Like a forest! And from the very same seed as my own. . . . And mine has been so frost-bitten that there's naught in my fields but camomile weeds and thistles." He sighed heavily, seating himself on a stone.

"Sit down; we'll talk together. What splendid weather we have!—In three weeks we shall hear the sickles clinking. I tell you we shall."

Antek sat down and tried to unburden his mind, while the priest listened attentively, now shouting at the horses, now taking pinch after pinch of snuff, and sneezing with great violence.

"Whither! Whither!—'Tis not our land!—Behold what perverse swine they are!"

But Antek did not make any headway; he stammered and wandered a good deal in his explanations.

"I see you're in evil case.—Now tell me—tell me all frankly: it will ease your heart! To whom can one speak openly, if not to a priest?"

He stroked his head, and offered him snuff; and Antek, encouraged, at last made a clean breast of it.

The priest heard him out, and then said with a deep sigh:

"For the slaying of the forester, I should have given you only a canonical penance. You were fighting to save your father; and, moreover, the man—a libertine and an unbeliever—is no very great loss. But the courts will not let you off so. Ye will get at least four years of hard labor! As to escaping . . . True, men can live in America. And they get out of jail likewise.—But, between the two evils, the choice is a hard one!"

And now he was for Antek's escaping instantly; now he advised him to stay and work his time out; and said in conclusion: "One thing is undoubtedly to be done: have trust in God's Providence and wait upon His mercy."

"But they will put me in irons and drive me to Siberia!"

"Well, men come back thence: I myself have seen some."

"Aye, but in what state shall I find my farm—after so many a year? How will my wife be able to keep things going?—All will go to rack and ruin!"

"With all my heart I wish I could do something for you; but what can be done?—Wait a little: I shall say Mass for you at the altar of the Transfiguration here!—Pray drive me these horses into the stable; it is high time—yes, yes, it is high time to go to bed."

Antek was so greatly upset that he had forgotten all about Yagna, whom he did not remember till he left the priest's yard, and hastened to find her.

She was awaiting him, crouched in the shadow of the granary.

"Oh, the time has been long—how long!"

Her voice was changed and hoarse . . . perhaps with the falling dew.

"How could I slip away from his Reverence?" he asked, with an attempt to embrace her; but she thrust him away.

"I am in no mood now for that sort of thing!"

"You are so changed, I know you no longer!" Her behavior hurt him.

"As ye left me, so I am!"

"Were you another, you could not be more different!" He pressed closer to her.

"Can you marvel, after such long neglect?"

"Never did I neglect you; but could I fly to you out of prison?"

"I was alone—alone with my remorse and with a living corpse!" And she shuddered with cold.

"And did you never think to come and visit me? Oh, no, your head was full of other thoughts!"

"O Antek, Antek!" she exclaimed incredulously; "did you ever expect my coming?"

"Can I say how much?—Like an idiot, I was hanging at the bars every day, looking out for you." He stopped, shaken with sudden anguish.

"My God!—And your curses on me—there, beyond the haystack? And your rancor of old days? And when they took you away, did you speak to me—look at

me even? Ye had a kind word for all, even for the dog—I marked it well—but none for me!"

"Yagna, I bore you no grudge whatsoever. But a man whose soul is tortured forgets both himself and the whole world." They were speechless awhile, standing shoulder to shoulder, hip to hip, the moon shining straight into their faces. Both breathed heavily; both were torn with memories that seared them, and their eyes brimmed with unshed tears of agony.

"Not so did ye receive me, once upon a time," he said gloomily.

All at once she fell a-weeping with abundant tears, like a little child.

"And how shall I receive you, pray? Have you blasted my life and wronged me too little as yet, now that all men look upon me as on a dog?"

"I blasted your life?—Was't through me?" He was hot with anger.

"Yea, through you! On your account did that harridan—that offal—drive me from your door! And on your account have I become the laughing-stock of all Lipka!"

"Oh, and do ye no longer meet the Voyt? and the others besides? Ha?" he broke out grimly.

"All that—all!—came about because of you!" she hissed, pierced by his words to her inmost heart. "Wherefore did you force your will on me as on a dog? Had you no wife of your own? I was senseless; you had so befooled me that I saw no one in the world but you. And why did you leave me then, a prey to all men?"

But he, in a frenzy of bitterness, muttered between his set teeth:

"Did I constrain you, forsooth, to become my stepmother? And did I force you to be afterwards the prize of any that cared?"

"Ah! why did you not lift a finger to prevent me? Had you loved me, you would never have left me to myself, but saved me . . . as others would have done!" Her regret was so clear, so sincere and unfathomably deep, that he found no word to defend himself. All his former acrimony vanished from his soul, and he again felt love stirring there.

"Hush, my Yagna, hush, my little one!" he whispered tenderly.

"And this wrong besides have I suffered, that you—you, of all men!—should rise up against me with the others!" she sobbed, her head against the barn.

He led her away to the field-path, gathered her to his bosom, fondled her, caressed her silky locks, and wiped her wet cheeks, and kissed her trembling lips, and her eyes, welling with briny tears—those dear sorrowful eyes of hers! He showered every endearment on her, and presently her weeping grew fainter; she leaned her drooping head upon his breast, and put her arm round his neck with childlike trust.

But Antek's blood was by now all on fire; his kisses grew fierce and stormy, his embraces tightened to a crushing hug.

She at first did not realize what was coming on, nor what was passing in herself. It was only when she felt completely helpless, and knew again the power of his hot kisses, that she attempted to break loose, begging him in terror, almost with tears:

"Let me go! Antek, for God's sake, let me go!—I shall cry out!"

But escape was impossible: his wild impetuosity crushed all resistance down, and prevailed utterly.

"For the last—the very last, last time!" he ejaculated, in a hoarse breathless voice.

And the world turned round them both, and they both went down headlong into the boiling whirlpool. Both loved passionately, as they once had loved be-fore—fainting, swooning, near to death. As once—as of old—as in the past!

They forgot all—all save the tempest of fire that was carrying them away—all save their own insatiable desire. As the thunderbolt unites with the tree which quenches its fire and is itself consumed, so they each destroyed the other's passion in the tempest of their own. And for that one short minute of a rapture soon to expire forever, after this last exuberant outburst, their former love had revived.

A moment afterwards, they were again seated side by side, feeling their souls very dark within them. Each glanced at the other by stealth, and as if in terror: each shunned meeting the other's eyes that spoke of shame and regret.

Once more, with lips eager for kisses, he sought her lips, but without success: she turned away from him with aversion.

In vain he whispered in her ear the sweet names of endearment he had once given her. She looked up at the moon, and replied not a word. In him, this bearing of hers aroused resentment, cooled passion down, and brought petulance and ill humor in its stead.

They sat together, unable to speak, each impatient of the other's presence, each waiting for the other to rise and go.

Yagna's flame was out to the last spark; nothing was there but ashes now; and she spoke first, with barely concealed animosity.

"In truth, ye did take me like a robber —by sheer might and main."

"Well, Yagna, and are you not mine— mine?" He would have embraced her again, but she pushed him violently from her.

"Neither yours nor anyone's!—Understand that!—No, nor anyone's!"

She fell a-crying once more, but this time he neither fondled nor soothed her.

After some time, however, he asked her very seriously:

"Yagna, will you flee with me?"

"And whither?" she returned, her wet eyes looking him full in the face.

"Why not to 'Hamerica'? Would you go, Yagna?"

"But what would ye do with your wife?"

He started as though stung.

"Tell me true: will you give her poison?"

He caught her round the waist, showered kisses over all her face, and begged and entreated her to run away with him—somewhere—and be with him forevermore. He spoke a long while of his plans and hopes; he had suddenly caught hold of that idea—flight with her—as a drunken man catches at a fence to steady himself. He talked, too, like a drunken man, for he was carried away by his feverish excitement. She heard him out, and then said, with frigid scorn:

"Because ye have forced sin upon me, do ye think me such a fool as to believe this nonsense?"

And though he swore he was but telling her the truth, and swore it by all holy things, she would not even listen, but shook herself free of him, and said:

"Not even do I dream of going. Why should I? Am I so ill off, though alone?" Throwing her apron over her head, she looked cautiously round. " 'Tis late; I must hurry away."

"Wherefore in such haste? Will anyone come from your home for you?"

"But for you 'tis time: Hanka has made the bed, and yearns sorely!"

The words made him snarl like a dog.

"Of him that is waiting for you down there at the tavern," he said venomously, "I do not remind you."

"Know, then," she said, with biting emphasis, "that more than one is waiting: aye, and are ready to wait even till

morning! You would have it you are the only one, forsooth! You are too saucy!"

"Then off with you—go! Go, even to that old Jew!" he almost spat the words at her.

But she stood there still. They were both together, panting heavily, staring one at the other out of eyes full of hate, each seeking what words might wound the other most deeply.

"Ye had something to say to me: say it now, for never will I meet you again."

"Fear not: never will I ask you!"

"I would not, were you to come whining at my feet!"

"Without doubt; you are too busy, having to meet so many every night."

At that, crying: "May you die the death of a dog!" she leaped over the stile and into the field.

He did not follow, nor call after her, but looked on as she ran through the fields and disappeared like a shadow among the orchards; rubbed his eyes, as if only just waking, and grumbled in sullen ill humor:

"My wits are clean gone from me! Lord! how far astray a man can be led by a woman!"

On his return to the hut, he somehow felt extremely ashamed. He could not pardon himself for what he had done: it obsessed and haunted him cruelly.

His bed—made in the orchard, the heat and flies within doors being intolerable—was awaiting him.

But he could not sleep. He lay looking up at the stars that twinkled overhead, and listening to the quiet footsteps of the night . . . and . . . making up his mind about Yagna.

"Neither with nor without her can I live!" He cursed her under his breath, and sighed in pain, turning from side to side, throwing off his covering, and wetting his feet to cool them in the long dewy grass. But no sleep came, and his thoughts persecuted him as before.

In the hut, one of the children set up a wail, and Hanka murmured some words. He lifted his head; but soon all was still again. And then his mind began to swarm with thoughts; the memories of past joys came floating about him, like fragrant spring breezes. But he was not now to be their slave any more; now he could resist their charms, and contemplate them with calm deliberation, and in their very presence take a firm resolve, as solemn as if he were at Holy Confession.

"This must cease—and forever!—'Tis a foul offense against God!—Would I have folk speak about me anew?—Am I not a landed man, a father?—Aye, I must—I must—end all this now."

He felt the resolve to be unutterably painful to keep; but he took it nevertheless.

And a bitter but deep reflection occurred to him: "Let a man but once go wrong, he may come to cling so to iniquity that even death itself will not part them!"

It was dawn now, and the sky seemed covered with a mantle of gray cloth, but Antek was yet waking: and as soon as the daylight had come, Hanka appeared at his side. He looked at her with eyes full of sadness, but wonderfully gentle; and when she told him what the smith had called to let her know late the evening before, he passed his hand kindly over her unkempt hair.

"If the carting pays, I'll buy you something at the fair."

Such gracious behavior on his part made her radiant with joy, and she pressed him hard to get her a glazed sideboard, "such as the organist possessed."

"And soon ye'll be thinking of a sofa like those at the Manor!" he said, laughing; but, promising her all she wanted, he rose early, to put his neck under the yoke again, and take up the work which waited for him at all times.

He had a further talk with the blacksmith, and directly after breakfast sent Pete to cart dung afield, while he himself went to the wood with a couple of horses.

In the clearing, the work was going on with great alacrity. Many men were busy shaping the wood cut down in wintertime; the ceaseless strokes of the axes and rasping of the saws put one in mind of woodpeckers, tapping everlastingly. In the long grass of the glades, the horses of Lipka were grazing, and the smoke of their fires curled upward.

He recalled the scene which had taken place there, and, seeing the men of Lipka now working together in amity with the "nobles" of Rzepki and the others, he nodded his head.

"Misery has taught them its lesson: a needful one, was it not?" he said to Philip, Yagustynka's son, who was squaring a pine-log.

"But who was at fault save the Squire and the farmers?" the man growled sullenly, continuing to lop off the boughs.

"Rather, much rather, foolish spite and bad blood!" said Antek.

He stopped at the place where he had killed the forester, and swore softly to himself; for he felt the passion of yore stirring within him anew.

"The wretch! it is he that has brought me to this!—If I could, I would serve him worse still!"—He spat angrily, and set to work.

All day long he went on carting timber to the sawmill, working as if for dear life: yet he could neither drive from his mind the remembrance of Yagna nor of his impending trial.

A few days after, he heard from Matthew that the Squire was willing not only to accept installments, but to let them have other wood in addition to the big timber; and so Nastka's wedding had been put off until such time as Simon should be settled on his own land.

But other folk's affairs interested him little now; and the blacksmith, who visited him almost every day, was constantly terrifying him, speaking about his unhappy position, and promising him pecuniary help to escape, should he be in sore straits.

Antek was at such moments quite ready to throw everything up and flee; but again, looking round him at the countryside, and reflecting that flight would mean leaving all that forever, he was panic-stricken, and would have preferred even the worst of prisons.

Yet the thought of a prison, too, filled him with despair.

All these inward struggles weighed him down, made him grow haggard and bitter, and harsh and fierce with those at home. What had come over him? Hanka did her very utmost, but to no purpose, to find this out. She had instantly suspected him of renewing relations with Yagna. But her own close scrutiny, and that of Yagustynka (whose fidelity was well paid) and others besides, assured her that the two were quite apart now, and never met: so she was at ease on that score. And yet, no matter how faithful a servant she proved herself, giving him the best food with the most exact punctuality, making the cottage a pattern of neatness and cleanliness, and the farm stock the very perfection of success—all would not do. He was always sullen, morose, ready to upbraid her for the slightest cause, and more than miserly of kind words. And it was worse still when he went about speechless, dreary, sad as an autumn night—not angry, not ill-tempered—only sighing deeply; often spending his whole evening with his acquaintances in the tavern.

She durst not question him openly; and Roch vowed that he was aware of nothing wrong. It might well be the truth. The old man was now seen at their cottage only at night. The whole day he was going about with his books, teaching the peasants to pray to the Sacred Heart of Jesus—a devotion which the Russian Government had severely forbidden in church.

One evening, all being together at supper, the dogs set to barking furiously along the mill-pond. Roch laid his spoon down and listened attentively.

"Some stranger.—I'll go and see who it is."

He returned in a minute, very pale, and saying:

"Sabers are flashing along the road.— If I should be asked after, I am in the village." And he slipped away among the orchard-trees.

Antek, white as a corpse, started to his feet. Dogs barked outside the fence; and men, heavily tramping, were heard in the porch.

"Have they come to fetch me?" he faltered, terror-struck.

They were all petrified: the gendarmes appeared on the threshold.

Motionless, Antek glanced at the open doors and windows. Luckily, Hanka had presence of mind enough to offer them settles and beg them to be seated.

They answered with civility enough, and at once threw out hints about supper, so that she had to prepare some scrambled eggs for them.

"Where are ye going so late?" Antek at length made bold to ask them.

"On duty! We have much to do," their leader returned, with a glance round him.

"After thieves, no doubt!" he continued, with more assurance, bringing a bottle out of the store-room.

"After thieves—and others. . . . Drink to us, goodman."

He did so. And then they set to upon the scrambled eggs, till their spoons scraped together the empty dish.

The inmates sat silent, like terror-stricken rabbits.

After cleaning the platter, they took took another glass of vodka; and their leader, wiping his moustaches, said impressively: "Is it long since ye were let out of prison, say?"

"Surely your Honor can answer that best."

He stirred impatiently; then, on a sudden:

"Where is Roch?" he asked.

"Which Roch?" was Antek's reply, who had understood on the spot, and felt much more at his ease.

"A certain Roch, I am told, is living with you."

"Can your Honor be speaking of that beggar who haunts our village?—'Tis true, his name is Roch."

The gendarme fidgeted again, and said with a threatening look:

"Play me no tricks, he is known to dwell with you!"

"Surely, he had his abode here at times, but elsewhere likewise. Where he happens to find himself, there he spends the night: 'tis his way. Now in the cabin, now in the byre, and oft beneath the hedges.—Is your Honor in any wise interested in the man?"

"I? In no wise: I ask to be informed."

"A good honest man he is," Hanka put in here; "nowhere does he trouble the waters."

"We know, we know well what manner of man he is!" he grumbled emphatically, and continued to seek for information about him by various arts—even going the length of offering them snuff. But they all answered so that he was just as wise as before; and in the end, finding himself no farther on the trail, he got up in a rage, crying:

"And I declare that the man dwells in your cabin!"

Here Antek blurted out: "Think ye I have him in my pocket?"

"Boryna!" the gendarme returned fiercely; "I am here on duty: understand

that!"—But he took leave in more friendly fashion, carrying with him as a present a dozen eggs and a very large pat of fresh butter.

Vitek followed them on their way step by step, and said afterwards how they had been at the Soltys's and the priest's, and had also tried to look in at several windows yet alight; only they could make no discoveries for the barking of the dogs, and had gone away as they came.

Now this incident had upset Antek to such a degree that, no sooner was he alone with his wife, then he told her his trouble.

She did not interrupt him by one single word, until at last he told her there remained nothing for him to do but to sell everything and go abroad—even to "Hamerica."

Then she stood up before him, pallid, ashen-white.

"I will not go!" she cried, with a dark frown. "No, nor let my children go either, to destruction! Not I! And if you think to force me, I'll cleave their skulls with an ax and leap down the well myself. And I am speaking the truth, so help me, O Lord God!" she screamed, kneeling down before the holy images, as one does to take a solemn vow.

"Hush, hush, dear!" Antek said. "I never meant it!"

She caught her breath, and continued, with difficulty restraining her tears:

"You will work out your time and come back. Fear nothing: I will manage all, and not lose one strip of land. Ye know me not as yet!—No, I will keep a firm grip on everything. And our Lord will help me to pull through with this affliction too." Then she wept silently.

He too was mute for a long while. At last he said: "God's will be done! I must await my trial here."

And thus did all the blacksmith's scheming and treachery prove a dead failure.

THE LIFE AND WORKS OF
LADISLAS REYMONT

By JOZEF TRYPUCKO

THE Swedish Academy voted the Nobel Prize for Literature to the Polish author, Ladislas Stanislas Reymont mainly for his novel in four volumes, *Chlopi* (*The Peasants*) (1904–1909). To authorities on European literature the decision was not surprising; Reymont's *Peasants* is a great national epic, written in a modern spirit. Yet the award was the culmination of one of the most curious careers in world literature.

Reymont's youth and his first literary efforts were curiously similar to those of the Russian novelist Maxim Gorki. Like Gorki, he passed his early years in the lower depths of society, and never completed his studies. Born in 1867 in the Polish village of Piotrków (now Kobielo Wielkie), Reymont could have had a modest and respectable life. His father, originally the village organist, became the owner of some sixty acres of land and a mill. Attempts were made to school young Ladislas, but he resisted; he rebelled constantly, and when he was sent away from home to train for business he took the chance to escape from his family and try his own way of life. First he joined a traveling theatrical troupe, then got a minor job in the railway system; next he toured Germany as assistant to a roaming professional spiritual-

ist, only to return to the theater. After a period of novitiate with the Paulist Fathers in Czestochowa, he returned to the railways as a poorly paid helper, living in a peasant's cottage on tea and bread. After two years of solitary misery he drew up a balance sheet of his life, and declared: "I saw that, in spite of my struggles and efforts of every description, I had reached bottom."

It was at this point that Reymont embarked on a literary career. He had written six stories on the subjects he knew best—farmers, wandering actors, corrupt officials. When, in 1893, the stories were published, he packed his bags and, with three rubles and fifty kopecks in his pocket, settled in Warsaw. There he lived in a room with a mason, a shoemaker, and a tailor. Since he was the poorest member of the group, his place was in the darkest corner of the room, and he could not write at home. But he spent much time at St. John's Church, where there was light enough for him to see his pen and paper. This was a period of feverish work for Reymont; it was also the time when he broke completely with his family. He read and wrote unceasingly, through moods of deep depression and thoughts of suicide. "The more profound my faith became," he wrote, "the more violent my fascination with annihilation, and then incessant hunger pushed me toward the abyss."

At the beginning of April, he joined a group of pilgrims going to the holy city of Czestochowa. A Warsaw journal advanced him twenty-five rubles to write the story of the pilgrimage, and for eleven days he walked in the sun and through the green forests. *Pielgrzymka do Jasney Góry* (Pilgrimage to the Mountain of Light, 1895), Reymont's account of the journey attracted the attention of the critics. Writing at top speed, he published two important books on the lives of strolling actors, *Komedjantka* (*The Comedian*), in 1896, and *Fermenty* (Ferments), in 1897; in the latter year he also assembled all his previously published stories in a single volume, *Spotkanie* (Encounters). In 1899 he published a two-volume novel, *Ziemia obiecana* (The Promised Land), dealing with the industrial world of Lodz, and two shorter stories, *Lili* and *Sprawiedliwie* ("In the Light of Justice"). But in spite of his success with the critics, Reymont remained in financial difficulty; ironically, it was not until 1902, when he was injured in a railway accident and received a large sum in compensation, that he was freed from money worries.

The four volumes of *The Peasants* appeared separately between 1904 and 1909. They were followed by an account of the Chelm region, *Reportaz z Ziemi Chelmskiey* (The Apostolate of the Knout) in 1910; a novel, *Marzyciel* (The Dreamer), in the same year; *Wampir* (The Vampire) in 1911; the trilogy *Rok 1794* (The Year 1794), which appeared between 1913 and 1918; and finally four more books of short stories. After World War I, Reymont visited Polish immigrants in America and recorded his impressions of the journey in several narratives. His final completed work was an allegorical story of the lives of animals,

Bunt (Defiance), published in 1924. After his death in December 1925, a selection of his stories was published under the title of *Krosnowa i swiat* (Krosnowa and the World).

Life itself served Reymont as school and university. He never formally studied the art of writing, and belonged to no school. But he was a man of his time, subject to its currents and its literary fashions. He was, in fact, part of the great post-Romantic period that produced a new flowering of Polish literature. Behind him there was the rich literary tradition of Positivism; at his side there were numerous examples to follow. He was aware of French naturalism and Symbolism, of German Expressionism, and of Gorki's and Andreyev's Russian pessimism.

Reymont wrote what he saw and heard; he wrote from nature. He knew village life from top to bottom, and that subject makes up a major part of his work. His knowledge of the strolling actor's life provided the substance of two novels and several short stories. For two years he studied the industrial world of Lodz, and he painted a vivid picture of that octopuslike city, in which machines had precedence over men, and the lust for wealth over every other aspiration. He traveled through Western Europe and gained some knowledge of America; his journeys provided him with the material for a number of stories on both Polish and foreign themes. With all other Poles, he witnessed the 1905 Revolution in Russia, and the subsequent weakening of the Czarist government in Poland; under this stimulus, he wrote stirring accounts drawn from his nation's history. He lived in Warsaw during World War I, and that experience was given artistic expression in a collection of long stories, *Za frontem* (Behind the Front).

In all this varied work, Reymont relied

upon an amazing visual and auditory memory. His eye, like a photographer's film, caught and recorded every detail of the most trivial scene; his characters do not speak in a language imposed upon them but in their own words, reproduced from living models. Reymont profited from his theatrical apprenticeship: he trained himself to visualize his characters in action, and presented them as if he himself were an eyewitness to their acts and were transmitting the living image directly to his readers. For the most part, he did not describe or analyze what was taking place in his characters' minds. Reymont was no philosopher, and had no talent for plumbing the mazes of the human soul. This is not to say that his characters are mere marionettes, capable of no more than gesticulating and mouthing. At its best, Reymont's art consisted in endowing his heroes with words and actions sufficiently expressive to make up for the lack of analysis.

Reymont's earliest writings were marked by the influence of Émile Zola's naturalism. He described the lives of the homeless and the hungry—people who had reached the depths of suffering and who committed crimes for a loaf of bread. The details of these outcasts' lives are terrible in their realism. A starving unemployed man without a job kills his ailing benefactor and friend to get his job. A girl locks her old father into the cellar to freeze because he is leaving his land to another of his children. A ruined girl is driven out into an autumn night, her child in her arms, by her seducer; a merciless sentence is imposed on a horse thief. In Reymont's hands these brute sufferings become major problems for which society must find effective remedies.

Another problem that dominated the author at this period was the destruction of artistic talents simply because society is not aware that they exist.

The story of a talent destroyed is told in the two novels *Komedjantka* and *Fermenty.* Here Reymont takes us into the world of the traveling theatrical troupe, masterfully portraying a group of meticulously observed characters and obviously profiting from his memories of the time when he himself was one of these actors. But the actors' world is only one element of these novels, and not the most important. Both books are important documents on the whole of society in their period, a society that now belongs to a dead past.

Because Reymont was so closely associated with the Polish countryside and peasantry, *The Promised Land,* set in the industrial city of Lodz, sometimes called the Manchester of Poland, represents a turning point in his work. In *The Promised Land* the city as a whole, with all its social divisions, plays the major role. The cast of characters is large, but all these people have one overweening desire: to grow rich at all costs; the moral sense does not exist among them. As Reymont saw it, a modern industrial city presents a kind of Apocalypse. It is a Moloch that crushes everything by its weight, and the individual is as powerless against the force that pulverizes him as the heroes of antiquity were powerless in the face of fate.

After painting this grim scene, Reymont returned to the countryside to fashion his epic of peasant life. He deliberately set out to portray the peasant not as a depraved brute but as a man who, despite his vices, is at all times a human being and can rise to nobility and heroism.

The plot of *The Peasants* is exceptionally simple. Within a single year, divided into four seasons that correspond to the four parts of the novel, Reymont encompasses the life of the village of Lipce. He presents not only the people who make up all the classes of this miniature republic, but also the settings and events that constitute their lives: domestic existence and work in the fields, weddings, baptisms and funerals, run-of-the-mill days and days of crisis, joys and dramas, prose and poetry, passion and resignation—and the natural setting that provides a backdrop for these lives and forms an integral part of their being.

The peasant who figures in this novel had never before appeared in Polish literature, though that literature had devoted much attention to problems of the lower classes. Reymont's peasant is not an outcast from society, persecuted and exploited by everyone, enduring hardship and hunger, arousing pity and compassion. He is aware of his place and function in society, aware of his dignity as a human being. He has forgotten a humiliating past and has embarked with confidence on a new life. He has his own ethic, his consciousness of his importance to the nation, his pride, his serenity, and even his own laws. Though he plays no part in political and cultural life—he is not yet ready for that—he senses the future that belongs to him. He is free of all feelings of inferiority, for he is the master on his own land and he has no feeling of being at another's mercy. He loves his land with passion, for he was born there and he is its product. Besides the land he has one other great love: the religion and rites of his forebears—a very special religion, steeped not only in the teachings of the church but also in many primitive and even pagan sources.

Patriotism plays a relatively minor part in the peasant's mentality. Barely thirty years had passed since the distribution of land to the peasants in 1864; the old relations between landowners and peasants were unchanged, and this fact is stressed in the novel. Neither the Russian nor the Polish governments was deeply concerned with improving the peasant's condition or dissipating old prejudices. Under such conditions it would have been absurd to ascribe an intense national sentiment to the peasant; and Reymont presented his peasants as loving their soil rather than their country. Reymont's peasants have not yet entered history; they remain outside historical events, keeping their primitive vitality and thin reserves of energy and hope untouched for the future. In the era of the cult of the superman, of pessimism, of *fin de siècle* decadence, the peasant remained a sort of virgin soil, beneath which a future life was pulsing.

This does not mean that Reymont's peasants did not care what government ruled them or what language they spoke. The national sentiment dormant in them came to life when German colonizers established themselves in the village or when the Czar's government attempted to force a Russian school on them. At such times the Polish peasant recognized that he was a Pole. "Every animal has its own language," one of the novel's characters proclaims. "We are the only ones who speak a foreign language on order." The peasants championed their ancestral spoken language, not the written language of the school, for in matters of education (as the result of a deliberate Czarist policy) they had still a long way to go; many of them were barely able to read the public documents issued by local authorities.

The Peasants is an ethnographic document from which nothing that concerns rural life has been omitted, in which everything is completely authentic, drawn directly from nature and presented in all its details. It is a prose encyclopedia of peasant life, just as *Pan Tadeusz*, by the greatest of all Polish poets, Adam Mickiewicz (1798–1855), is a poetic encyclopedia of the life of the nobility. Mickiewicz captured this life just as it was entering into history and preserved it for posterity. Reymont did the same thing with the life of the peasantry, catching it almost at the last moment, just before new farming methods and rapid industrialization destroyed the village and the peasants began to move to the cities or emigrate across the sea. Reymont's novel portrays the village of a bygone era, an era of which virtually no trace remains today. It is a unique historical document.

But *The Peasants* is also a masterpiece of world literature. It is hard to tell as one reads it where the novel ends and the prose poem begins. The descriptions of nature are unmatched; no one in Polish literature since Mickiewicz had been able to evoke so much beauty from landscapes. Reymont's visual memory, particularly his sensitivity to colors, makes this novel a magnificent, vivid fresco. And he creates such musical effects with language that certain pages are veritable symphonies. The peasants themselves speak their own dialect, and this dialect penetrates the narrative passages as well, heightening the novel's sense of authenticity. Nor is it a matter of language alone. *The Peasants* is so saturated with folk elements that it has become a treasure trove to the student of Polish folklore.

For Poles, 1905 marked a turning point in the policy of the Russian government. The revolutions of that year in both Russia and Poland led, among other things, to a relaxation of official censorship and to greater freedom of expression for national themes. Reymont took advantage of the new climate to write *Z Dni konstytucyjnych* (Days of the Constitution, 1905) in which he depicted Warsaw's martyrdom during the uprising against the Czar's police. His second work in this vein was the disturbing

document on the "land of Chelm," *Reportaz z Ziemi Chelmskiey,* written after the Czar's government had proclaimed a law of religious toleration, and published abroad as *The Apostolate of the Knout.* Some historical background is necessary for an understanding of this book.

After the union of Poland and Lithuania in 1386, there were many Orthodox Catholics in the new state; like the church of the Grand Duchy of Moscow, these communicants were directly subordinate to the Patriarch of Constantinople. But the rupture between Moscow and Constantinople and the grant of independence to the Russian church confronted Polish and Lithuanian Orthodox Catholics with a dilemma: to remain under the jurisdiction of Constantinople or to accept the authority of the Patriarch of Moscow. In the end they chose a third solution: they recognized the authority of the Pope, who, under the Union of Brzesc (Brest-Litovsk) in 1595, permitted them to retain the Greek liturgy and the Julian calendar. This was the origin of the Uniate Rite.

After the Russian conquest of Poland, the Russian authorities resolved to annihilate these Uniates at the earliest opportunity. To begin with, they ordered the liquidation of the Uniate church on Russian-Lithuanian soil. All that survived was a tiny enclave in the area of Chelm, in the region known as the "Kingdom of Poland," but after the defeat of an insurrection of January 1863, it became possible to liquidate the rest of the little group. In 1874 and 1875 every means from persuasion to violence and cruelty was invoked against them. It was the story of these years on which Reymont built his book.

After the epic surge of his previous work, Reymont surprised his readers with an unaccustomed economy in his choice of style and scene. The theme he had chosen was more than adequate for another great popular epic, yet he deliberately avoided all literary effect and did not even exploit all the material that was available to him. He used only a few episodes—told by the heroes themselves —of the religious persecutions, describing them without any lyric note, without declamatory devices, without any cry to God for justice and vengeance. But he distilled an irrefutable testimony of truth from the raw facts. This direct statement, made in the manner of an eyewitness no longer surprised by anything that happens in the world, make a powerful impression on the reader. There are, for example, many descriptions of the celebration of mass in literature, but none so moving as the one in Reymont's little book. Before dawn, in the heart of the forest, well hidden from the Czar's police, before thousands of humbly kneeling worshipers, among the plaintive notes of the plover and the cries of wild birds, the bloodless sacrifice is celebrated: "The forest poised for a moment —gathered its forces—and then grew calm, bending down as if to turn an eager ear to the murmur of the fervent prayers in the chant so filled with tears held back, with mourning and with sobs."

Reymont rarely expressed his views on social questions. He was above all an artist, and an impartial observer of life. What chiefly interested him was not so much the individual as the element in the individual that provides an insight into all mankind. The everyman sprung from the soil of Poland bore within him the seeds of vice and virtue that characterize every human being, regardless of class and nationality. By reproducing his image and defending his ideal, Reymont, a sorcerer of words, transcended the limits of his nation and his time. He is as alive today as he was when he received the Nobel Prize in 1924.

Jozef Trypucko is a professor at the University of Uppsala in Sweden. Translated by Charles Lam Markmann.

THE 1924 PRIZE

By KJELL STRÖMBERG

THE Nobel Prize for 1924 was given to a Polish writer, Ladislas Stanislas Reymont "for his great national epic, *The Peasants.*" As had already been the case with Knut Hamsun, the laureate for 1920, it is clearly stated in the account of the reasons which moved the Swedish Academy to make this choice, that it was this work alone which won the Prize for the writer who was later described as "the Slavic Hesiod."

Among the eighteen candidates who were nominated there was, however, a compatriot who could have claimed the honor with just as much if not more right, and for his work as a whole: Stefan Zeromski. He was looked on as the incarnation of the national conscience by general opinion in his own country, which had at last been liberated from foreign domination and re-established behind its old frontiers. Zeromski, supported by a strong press campaign, was the "official" candidate for resuscitated Poland, whereas Reymont, even before the liberation, had been proposed only by the philological section of the Academy of Science of Cracow, which still masqueraded under its former Austrian title of "imperial."

One can hardly question the justice of the Swedish Academy's choice, if one takes exclusively into account the purely artistic and literary value of the works submitted to its judgment. Reymont's rustic tetralogy, even though it may not quite have the character of a national epic, remains a masterpiece and it would be difficult to challenge it with any of the works of Zeromski, in spite of their lofty patriotic inspiration. All of the experts on Slavic literature agree on this point.

Of course it would have been possible to split up the reward and divide the Prize between Reymont and Zeromski, as had been done for the two Danish laureates, Gjellerup and Pontoppidan in 1917, and this solution would doubtless have given greater satisfaction to public opinion in Poland. But the Swedish Academy preferred to follow the advice of its experts, and would not allow its award to be made dependent on considerations of political expediency. Still less would it allow itself to be beguiled by the proposition of an expert who recommended dividing the Prize between Reymont and a Czech writer, Aloïs Jerasek.

Certainly the Prize was not awarded to Reymont without opposition. Important competitors included several future laureates, including George Bernard Shaw, Grazia Deledda, and Thomas Mann.

Reymont was an invalid when he was awarded the Prize, and he was unable to travel to Stockholm to receive it from the hands of the King. He died the following year, in 1925, before reaching the age of sixty.

Translated by Camilla Sykes.

Romain Rolland

1915

"As a tribute to the lofty idealism of
his literary production and to the sympathy
and love of truth with which he has
described different types of human beings"

Illustrated by *GUSTAVE NEBEL*

BECAUSE OF WORLD WAR I, NO NOBEL
PRIZE CEREMONIES WERE HELD IN 1915

JEAN-CHRISTOPHE

By ROMAIN ROLLAND

Translated by Gilbert Cannan

[Excerpts]

THE DAWN

Dianzi, nell'alba che precede al giorno,
Quando l'anima tua dentro dormìa. . . .
Purgatorio, ix.

I

Come, quando i vapori umidi e spessi
A diradar cominciansi, la spera
Del sol debilemente entra per essi. . . .
Purgatorio, xvii.

From behind the house rises the murmuring of the river. All day long the rain has been beating against the windowpanes; a stream of water trickles down the window at the corner where it is broken. The yellowish light of the day dies down. The room is dim and dull.

The new-born child stirs in his cradle. Although the old man left his sabots at the door when he entered, his footsteps make the floor creak. The child begins to whine. The mother leans out of her bed to comfort it; and the grandfather gropes to light the lamp, so that the child shall not be frightened by the night when he awakes. The flame of the lamp lights up old Jean Michel's red face, with its rough white beard and morose expression and quick eyes. He goes near the cradle. His cloak smells wet, and as he walks he drags his large blue list slippers. Louisa signs to him not to go too near. She is fair, almost white; her features are drawn; her gentle, stupid face is marked with red in patches; her lips are pale and swollen, and they are parted in a timid smile; her eyes devour the child—and her eyes are blue and vague; the pupils are small, but there is an infinite tenderness in them.

The child wakes and cries, and his eyes are troubled. Oh! how terrible! The darkness, the sudden flash of the lamp, the hallucinations of a mind as yet hardly detached from chaos, the stifling, roaring night in which it is enveloped, the illimitable gloom from which, like blinding shafts of light, there emerge acute sensations, sorrows, phantoms—those enormous faces leaning over him, those eyes that pierce through him, penetrating, are beyond his comprehension! . . . He has not the strength to cry out; terror holds him motionless, with eyes and mouth wide open and he rattles in his throat. His large head, that seems to have swollen up, is wrinkled with the grotesque and lamentable grimaces that he makes; the skin of his face and hands is brown and purple, and spotted with yellow. . . .

[95]

"Dear God!" said the old man with conviction: "How ugly he is!"

He put the lamp down on the table.

Louisa pouted like a scolded child. Jean Michel looked at her out of the corner of his eye and laughed.

"You don't want me to say that he is beautiful? You would not believe it. Come, it is not your fault. They are all like that."

The child came out of the stupor and immobility into which he had been thrown by the light of the lamp and the eyes of the old man. He began to cry. Perhaps he instinctively felt in his mother's eyes a caress which made it possible for him to complain. She held out her arms for him and said:

"Give him to me."

The old man began, as usual, to air his theories:

"You ought not to give way to children when they cry. You must just let them cry."

But he came and took the child and grumbled:

"I never saw one quite so ugly."

Louisa took the child feverishly and pressed it to her bosom. She looked at it with a bashful and delighted smile.

"Oh, my poor child!" she said shame-facedly. "How ugly you are—how ugly! and how I love you!"

Jean Michel went back to the fireside. He began to poke the fire in protest, but a smile gave the lie to the moroseness and solemnity of his expression.

"Good girl!" he said. "Don't worry about it. He has plenty of time to alter. And even so, what does it matter? Only one thing is asked of him: that he should grow into an honest man."

The child was comforted by contact with his mother's warm body. He could be heard sucking her milk and gurgling and snorting. Jean Michel turned in his chair, and said once more, with some emphasis:

"There's nothing finer than an honest man."

He was silent for a moment, pondering whether it would not be proper to elaborate this thought; but he found nothing more to say, and after a silence he said irritably:

"Why isn't your husband here?"

"I think he is at the theater," said Louisa timidly. "There is a rehearsal."

"The theater is closed. I passed it just now. One of his lies."

"No. Don't be always blaming him. I must have misunderstood. He must have been kept for one of his lessons."

"He ought to have come back," said the old man, not satisfied. He stopped for a moment, and then asked, in a rather lower voice and with some shame:

"Has he been . . . again?"

"No, father—no, father," said Louisa hurriedly.

The old man looked at her; she avoided his eyes.

"It's not true. You're lying."

She wept in silence.

"Dear God!" said the old man, kicking at the fire with his foot. The poker fell with a clatter. The mother and the child trembled.

"Father, please—please!" said Louisa. "You will make him cry."

The child hesitated for a second or two whether to cry or to go on with his meal; but not being able to do both at once, he went on with the meal.

Jean Michel continued in a lower tone, though with outbursts of anger:

"What have I done to the good God to have this drunkard for my son? What is the use of my having lived as I have lived, and of having denied myself everything all my life! But you—you—can't you do anything to stop it? Heavens! That's what you ought to do. . . . You should keep him at home! . . ."

Louisa wept still more.

"Don't scold me! . . . I am unhappy

enough as it is! I have done everything I could. If you knew how terrified I am when I am alone! Always I seem to hear his step on the stairs. Then I wait for the door to open, or I ask myself: 'O God! what will he look like?' . . . It makes me ill to think of it!"

She was shaken by her sobs. The old man grew anxious. He went to her and laid the disheveled bedclothes about her trembling shoulders and caressed her head with his hands.

"Come, come, don't be afraid. I am here."

She calmed herself for the child's sake, and tried to smile.

"I was wrong to tell you that."

The old man shook his head as he looked at her.

"My poor child, it was not much of a present that I gave you."

"It's my own fault," she said. "He ought not to have married me. He is sorry for what he did."

"What, do you mean that he regrets? . . ."

"You know. You were angry yourself because I became his wife."

"We won't talk about that. It is true I was vexed. A young man like that—I can say so without hurting you—a young man whom I had carefully brought up, a distinguished musician, a real artist— might have looked higher than you, who had nothing and were of a lower class, and not even of the same trade. For more than a hundred years no Krafft has ever married a woman who was not a musician! But, you know, I bear you no grudge, and am fond of you, and have been ever since I learned to know you. Besides, there's no going back on a choice once it's made; there's nothing left but to do one's duty honestly."

He went and sat down again, thought for a little, and then said, with the solemnity in which he invested all his aphorisms:

"The first thing in life is to do one's duty."

He waited for contradiction, and spat on the fire. Then, as neither mother nor child raised any objection, he was for going on, but relapsed into silence.

. . .

They said no more. Both Jean Michel, sitting by the fireside, and Louisa, in her bed, dreamed sadly. The old man, in spite of what he had said, had bitter thoughts about his son's marriage, and Louisa was thinking of it also, and blaming herself, although she had nothing wherewith to reproach herself.

She had been a servant when, to everybody's surprise, and her own especially, she married Melchior Krafft, Jean Michel's son. The Kraffts were without fortune, but were considerable people in the little Rhine town in which the old man had settled down more than fifty years before. Both father and son were musicians, and known to all the musicians of the country from Cologne to Mannheim. Melchior played the violin at the Hof-Theater, and Jean Michel had formerly been director of the grand-ducal concerts. The old man had been profoundly humiliated by his son's marriage, for he had built great hopes upon Melchior; he had wished to make him the distinguished man which he had failed to become himself. This mad freak destroyed all his ambitions. He had stormed at first, and showered curses upon Melchior and Louisa. But, being a good-hearted creature, he forgave his daughter-in-law when he learned to know her better; and he even came by a paternal affection for her, which showed itself for the most part in snubs.

No one ever understood what it was that drove Melchior to such a marriage —least of all Melchior. It was certainly not Louisa's beauty. She had no seductive quality: she was small, rather pale, and delicate, and she was a striking contrast to Melchior and Jean Michel, who were both big and broad, redfaced giants, heavy-handed, hearty eaters and drinkers, laughter-loving and noisy. She seemed to be crushed by them; no one noticed her, and she seemed to wish to escape even what little notice she attracted. If Melchior had been a kind-hearted man, it would have been credible that he should prefer Louisa's simple goodness to every other advantage; but a vainer man never was. It seemed incredible that a young man of his kidney, fairly good-looking, and quite conscious of it, very foolish, but not without talent, and in a position to look for some well-dowered match, and capable even—who knows?—of turning the head of one of his pupils among the people of the town, should suddenly have chosen a girl of the people—poor, uneducated, without beauty, a girl who could in no way advance his career.

But Melchior was one of those men who always do the opposite of what is expected of them and of what they expect of themselves. It is not that they are not warned—a man who is warned is worth two men, says the proverb. They profess never to be the dupe of anything, and that they steer their ship with unerring hand towards a definite point. But they reckon without themselves, for they do not know themselves. In one of those moments of forgetfulness which are habitual with them they let go the tiller, and, as is natural when things are left to themselves, they take a naughty pleasure in rounding on their masters. The ship which is released from its course at once strikes a rock, and Melchior, bent upon intrigue, married a cook. And yet he was neither drunk nor in a stupor on the day when he bound himself to her for life, and he was not under any passionate impulse; far from it. But perhaps there are in us forces other than mind and heart, other even than the senses—mysterious forces which take hold of us in the moments when the others are asleep; and perhaps it was such forces that Melchior had found in the depths of those pale eyes which had looked at him so timidly one evening when he had accosted the girl on the bank of the river, and had sat down beside her in the reeds—without knowing why—and had given her his hand.

Hardly was he married than he was appalled by what he had done, and he did not hide what he felt from poor Louisa, who humbly asked his pardon. He was not a bad fellow, and he willingly granted her that; but immediately remorse would seize him again when he was with his friends or in the houses of his rich pupils, who were disdainful in their treatment of him, and no longer trembled at the touch of his hand when he corrected the position of their fingers on the keyboard. Then he would return gloomy of countenance, and Louisa, with a catch at her heart, would read in it with the first glance the customary reproach; or he would stay out late at one inn or another, there to seek self-respect or kindliness from others. On such evenings he would return shouting with laughter, and this was more doleful for Louisa than the hidden reproach and gloomy rancor that prevailed on other days. She felt that she was to a certain extent responsible for the fits of madness in which the small remnant of her husband's sense would disappear, together with the household money. Melchior sank lower and lower. At an age when he should have been engaged in unceasing toil to develop his mediocre talent, he just let things slide, and others took his place.

But what did that matter to the unknown force which had thrown him in with the little flaxen-haired servant? He had played his part, and little Jean-Christophe had just set foot on this earth whither his destiny had thrust him.

. . .

Night was fully come. Louisa's voice roused old Jean Michel from the torpor into which he had sunk by the fireside as he thought of the sorrows of the past and present.

"It must be late, father," said the young woman affectionately. "You ought to go home; you have far to go."

"I am waiting for Melchior," replied the old man.

"Please, no. I would rather you did not stay."

"Why?"

The old man raised his head and looked fiercely at her.

She did not reply.

He resumed.

"You are afraid. You do not want me to meet him?"

"Yes, yes; it would only make things worse. You would make each other angry, and I don't want that. Please, please go!"

The old man sighed, rose, and said:

"Well . . . I'll go."

He went to her and brushed her forehead with his stiff beard. He asked if she wanted anything, put out the lamp, and went stumbling against the chairs in the darkness of the room. But he had no sooner reached the staircase than he thought of his son returning drunk, and he stopped at each step, imagining a thousand dangers that might arise if Melchior were allowed to return alone. . . .

In the bed by his mother's side the child was stirring again. An unknown sorrow had arisen from the depths of his being. He stiffened himself against her. He twisted his body, clenched his fists, and knitted his brows. His suffering increased steadily, quietly, certain of its

strength. He knew not what it was, nor whence it came. It appeared immense,—infinite, and he began to cry lamentably. His mother caressed him with her gentle hands. Already his suffering was less acute. But he went on weeping, for he felt it still near, still inside himself. A man who suffers can lessen his anguish by knowing whence it comes. By thought he can locate it in a certain portion of his body which can be cured, or, if necessary, torn away. He fixes the bounds of it, and separates it from himself. A child has no such illusive resource. His first encounter with suffering is more tragic and more true. Like his own being, it seems infinite. He feels that it is seated in his bosom, housed in his heart, and is mistress of his flesh. And it is so. It will not leave his body until it has eaten it away.

His mother hugs him to her, murmuring: "It is done—it is done! Don't cry, my little Jesus, my little goldfish. . . ." But his intermittent outcry continues. It is as though this wretched, unformed, and unconscious mass had a presentiment of a whole life of sorrow awaiting him, and nothing can appease him. . . .

The bells of St. Martin rang out in the night. Their voices are solemn and slow. In the damp air they come like footsteps on moss. The child became silent in the middle of a sob. The marvelous music, like a flood of milk, surged sweetly through him. The night was lit up; the air was moist and tender. His sorrow disappeared, his heart began to laugh, and he slid into his dreams with a sigh of abandonment.

The three bells went on softly ringing in the morrow's festival. Louisa also dreamed, as she listened to them, of her own past misery and of what would become in the future of the dear little child sleeping by her side. She had been for hours lying in her bed, weary and suffering. Her hands and her body were burning; the heavy eiderdown crushed her; she felt crushed and oppressed by the darkness; but she dared not move. She looked at the child, and the night did not prevent her reading his features, that looked so old. Sleep overcame her; fevered images passed through her brain. She thought she heard Melchior open the door, and her heart leaped. Occasionally the murmuring of the stream rose more loudly through the silence, like the roaring of some beast. The window once or twice gave a sound under the beating of the rain. The bells rang out more slowly, and then died down, and Louisa slept by the side of her child.

All this time Jean Michel was waiting outside the house, dripping with rain, his beard wet with the mist. He was waiting for the return of his wretched son: for his mind, never ceasing, had insisted on telling him all sorts of tragedies brought about by drunkenness; and although he did not believe them, he could not have slept a wink if he had gone away without having seen his son return. The sound of the bells made him melancholy, for he remembered all his shattered hopes. He thought of what he was doing at such an hour in the street, and for very shame he wept.

.   .   .

The vast tide of the days moves slowly. Day and night come up and go down with unfailing regularity, like the ebb and flow of an infinite ocean. Weeks and months go by, and then begin again, and the succession of days is like one day.

The day is immense, inscrutable, marking the even beat of light and darkness, and the beat of the life of the torpid creature dreaming in the depths of his cradle—his imperious needs, sorrowful or glad—so regular that the night and the day which bring them seem by them to be brought about.

The pendulum of life moves heavily, and in its slow beat the whole creature seems to be absorbed. The rest is no more than dreams, snatches of dreams, formless and swarming, and dust of atoms dancing aimlessly, a dizzy whirl passing, and bringing laughter or horror. Outcry, moving shadows, grinning shapes, sorrows, terrors, laughter, dreams, dreams. . . . All is a dream, both day and night. . . . And in such chaos the light of friendly eyes that smile upon him, the flood of joy that surges through his body from his mother's body, from her breasts filled with milk—the force that is in him, the immense, unconscious force gathering in him, the turbulent ocean roaring in the narrow prison of the child's body. For eyes that could see into it there would be revealed whole worlds half buried in the darkness, nebulæ taking shape, a universe in the making. His being is limitless. He is all that there is. . . .

Months pass. . . . Islands of memory begin to rise above the river of his life. At first they are little uncharted islands, rocks just peeping above the surface of the waters. Round about them and behind in the twilight of the dawn stretches the great untroubled sheet of water; then new islands, touched to gold by the sun.

So from the abyss of the soul there emerge shapes definite, and scenes of a strange clarity. In the boundless day which dawns once more, ever the same, with its great monotonous beat, there begins to show forth the round of days, hand in hand, and some of their forms are smiling, others sad. But ever the links of the chain are broken, and memories are linked together above weeks and months. . . .

The River . . . the Bells . . . as long as he can remember—far back in the abysses of time, at every hour of his life—always their voices, familiar and resonant, have rung out. . . .

Night—half asleep—a pale light made white the window. . . . The river murmurs. Through the silence its voice rises omnipotent; it reigns over all creatures. Sometimes it caresses their sleep, and seems almost itself to die away in the roaring of its torrent. Sometimes it grows angry, and howls like a furious beast about to bite. The clamor ceases. Now there is a murmuring of infinite tenderness, silvery sounds like clear little bells, like the laughter of children, or soft singing voices, or dancing music—a great mother voice that never, never goes to sleep! It rocks the child, as it has rocked through the ages, from birth to death, the generations that were before him; it fills all his thoughts, and lives in all his dreams, wraps him round with the cloak of its fluid harmonies, which still will be about him when he lies in the little cemetery that sleeps by the water's edge, washed by the Rhine. . . .

The bells. . . . It is dawn! They answer each other's call, sad, melancholy, friendly, gentle. At the sound of their slow voices there rise in him hosts of dreams—dreams of the past, desires, hopes, regrets for creatures who are gone, unknown to the child, although he had his being in them, and they live again in him. Ages of memory ring out in that music. So much mourning, so many festivals! And from the depths of the room it is as though, when they are heard, there passed lovely waves of sound through the soft air, free winging birds, and the moist soughing of the wind. Through the window smiles a patch of blue sky; a sunbeam slips through the curtains to the bed. The little world known to the eyes of the child, all that he can see from his bed every morning as he awakes, all that with so much effort he is beginning to recognize and classify, so that he may be master of it—his kingdom is lit up. There is the table where people eat, the cupboard where he

hides to play, the tiled floor along which he crawls, and the wall-paper which in its antic shapes holds for him so many humorous or terrifying stories, and the clock which chatters and stammers so many words which he alone can understand. How many things there are in this room! He does not know them all. Every day he sets out on a voyage of exploration in this universe which is his. Everything is his. Nothing is immaterial; everything has its worth, man or fly. Everything lives—the cat, the fire, the table, the grains of dust which dance in a sunbeam. The room is a country, a day is a lifetime. How is a creature to know himself in the midst of these vast spaces? The world is so large! A creature is lost in it. And the faces, the actions, the movements, the noise, which make round about him an unending turmoil! . . . He is weary; his eyes close; he goes to sleep. That sweet deep sleep that overcomes him suddenly at any time, and wherever he may be—on his mother's lap, or under the table, where he loves to hide! . . . It is good. All is good. . . .

These first days come buzzing up in his mind like a field of corn or a wood stirred by the wind, and cast in shadow by the great fleeting clouds. . . .

The shadows pass; the sun penetrates the forest. Jean-Christophe begins to find his way through the labyrinth of the day.

It is morning. His parents are asleep. He is in his little bed, lying on his back. He looks at the rays of light dancing on the ceiling. There is infinite amusement in it. Now he laughs out loud with one of those jolly children's laughs which stir the hearts of those that hear them. His mother leans out of her bed towards him, and says: "What is it, then, little mad thing?" Then he laughs again, and perhaps he makes an effort to laugh because he has an audience. His mamma looks severe, and lays a finger on her lips to warn him lest he should wake his father: but her weary eyes smile in spite of herself. They whisper together. Then there is a furious growl from his father. Both tremble. His mother hastily turns her back on him, like a naughty little girl: she pretends to be asleep. Jean-Christophe buries himself in his bed, and holds his breath. . . . Dead silence.

After some time the little face hidden under the clothes comes to the surface again. On the roof the weathercock creaks. The rain-pipe gurgles; the Angelus sounds. When the wind comes from the east, the distant bells of the villages on the other bank of the river give answer. The sparrows foregathered in the ivy-clad wall make a deafening noise, from which three or four voices, always the same, ring out more shrilly than the others, just as in the games of a band of children. A pigeon coos at the top of a chimney. The child abandons himself to the lullaby of these sounds. He hums to himself softly, then a little more loudly, then quite loudly, then very loudly, until once more his father cries out in exasperation: "That little donkey never will be quiet! Wait a little, and I'll pull your ears!" Then Jean-Christophe buries himself in the bedclothes again, and does not know whether to laugh or cry. He is terrified and humiliated; and at the same time the idea of the donkey with which his father has compared him makes him burst out laughing. From the depths of his bed he imitates its braying. This time he is whipped. He sheds every tear that is in him. What has he done? He wanted so much to laugh and to get up! And he is forbidden to budge. How do people sleep forever? When will they get up? . . .

One day he could not contain himself. He heard a cat and a dog and something queer in the street. He slipped out of bed, and, creeping awkwardly with his bare feet on the tiles, he tried to go down the stairs to see what it was; but the door was shut. To open it, he climbed on to a chair; the whole thing collapsed, and he hurt himself and howled. And once more at the top of the stairs he was whipped. He is always being whipped! . . .

He is in church with his grandfather. He is bored. He is not very comfortable. He is forbidden to stir, and all the people are saying all together words that he does not understand. They all look solemn and gloomy. It is not their usual way of looking. He looks at them, half frightened. Old Lena, their neighbor, who is sitting next to him, looks very cross; there are moments when he does not recognize even his grandfather. He is afraid a little. Then he grows used to it, and tries to find relief from boredom by every means at his disposal. He balances on one leg, twists his neck to look at the ceiling, makes faces, pulls his grandfather's coat, investigates the straws in his chair, tries to make a hole in them with his finger, listens to the singing of birds, and yawns so that he is like to dislocate his jaw.

Suddenly there is a deluge of sound: the organ is played. A thrill goes down his spine. He turns and stands with his chin resting on the back of his chair, and he looks very wise. He does not understand this noise; he does not know the meaning of it; it is dazzling, bewildering, and he can hear nothing clearly. But it is good. It is as though he were no longer sitting there on an uncomfortable chair in a tiresome old house. He is suspended in mid-air, like a bird; and when the flood of sound rushes from one end of the church to the other, filling the arches, reverberating from wall to wall, he is carried with it, flying and skimming hither and thither, with nothing to do but to abandon himself to it. He is free; he is happy. The sun shines. . . . He falls asleep.

His grandfather is displeased with him. He behaves ill at Mass.

He is at home, sitting on the ground, with his feet in his hands. He has just decided that the door-mat is a boat, and the tiled floor a river. He all but drowned in stepping off the carpet. He is surprised and a little put out that the others pay no attention to the matter as he does when he goes into the room. He seizes his mother by the skirts. "You see, it is water! You must go across by the bridge." (The bridge is a series of holes between the red tiles.) His mother crosses without even listening to him. He is vexed, as a dramatic author is vexed when he sees his audience talking during his great work.

Next moment he thinks no more of it. The tiled floor is no longer the sea. He is lying down on it, stretched full-length, with his chin on the tiles, humming music of his own composition, and gravely sucking his thumb and dribbling. He is lost in contemplation of a crack between the tiles. The lines of the tiles grimace like faces. The imperceptible hole grows larger, and becomes a valley; there are mountains about it. A centipede moves: it is as large as an elephant. Thunder might crash, the child would not hear it.

No one bothers about him, and he has no need of any one. He can even do without door-mat boats, and caverns in the tiled floor, with their fantastic fauna. His body is enough. What a source of entertainment! He spends hours in looking at his nails and shouting with laughter. They have all different faces, and are like people that he knows. And the rest of his body! . . . He goes on with the inspection of all that he has. How many surprising things! There are so many marvels. He is absorbed in looking at them.

But he was very roughly picked up when they caught him at it.

Sometimes he takes advantage of his mother's back being turned, to escape from the house. At first they used to run after him and bring him back. Then they got used to letting him go alone, only so he did not go too far away. The house is at the end of the town; the country begins almost at once. As long as he is within sight of the windows he goes without stopping, very deliberately, and now and then hopping on one foot. But as soon as he has passed the corner of the road, and the brushwood hides him from view, he changes abruptly. He stops there, with his finger in his mouth, to find out what story he shall tell himself that day; for he is full of stories. True, they are all very much like each other, and every one of them could be told in a few lines. He chooses. Generally he takes up the same story, sometimes from the point where it left off, sometimes from the beginning, with variations. But any trifle—a word heard by chance—is enough to set his mind off on another direction.

Chance was fruitful of resources. It is impossible to imagine what can be made of a simple piece of wood, a broken bough found alongside a hedge. (You break them off when you do not find them.) It was a magic wand. If it were long and thin, it became a lance, or perhaps a sword; to brandish it aloft was enough to cause armies to spring from the earth. Jean-Christophe was their general, marching in front of them, setting them an example, and leading them to the assault of a hillock. If the branch were flexible, it changed into a whip. Jean-Christophe mounted on horseback and leaped precipices. Sometimes his mount would slip, and the horseman would find himself at the bottom of the ditch, sorrily looking at his dirty hands and barked knees. If the wand were lithe, then Jean-Christophe would make himself the conductor of an orchestra: he would be both conductor and orchestra; he conducted and he sang; and then he would salute the bushes, with their little green heads stirring in the wind.

He was also a magician. He walked with great strides through the fields, looking at the sky and waving his arms. He commanded the clouds. He wished them to go to the right, but they went to the left. Then he would abuse them, and repeat his command. He would watch them out of the corner of his eye, and his heart would beat as he looked to see if there were not at least a little one which would obey him. But they went on calmly moving to the left. Then he would stamp his foot, and threaten them with his stick, and angrily order them to go to the left; and this time, in truth, they obeyed him. He was happy and proud of his power. He would touch the flowers and bid them change into golden carriages, as he had been told they did in the stories; and, although it never happened, he was quite convinced that it would happen if only he had patience. He would look for a grasshopper to turn into a hare; he would gently lay his stick on its back, and speak a rune. The insect would escape: he would bar its way. A few moments later he would be lying on his belly near to it, looking at it. Then he would have forgotten that he was a magician, and just amuse himself with turning the poor beast on its back, while he laughed aloud at its contortions.

It occurred to him also to tie a piece of string to his magic wand, and gravely cast it into the river, and wait for a fish to come and bite. He knew perfectly well that fish do not usually bite at a piece of string without bait or hook; but he thought that for once in a way, and for him, they might make an exception to their rule; and in his inexhaustible confidence, he carried it so far as to fish in the street with a whip through the grating of a sewer. He would draw up the whip from time to time excitedly, pretending that the cord of it was more heavy, and that he had caught a treasure, as in a story his grandfather had told him. . . .

And always in the middle of all these games there used to occur to him moments of strange dreaming and complete forgetfulness. Everything about him would then be blotted out; he would not know what he was doing, and was not even conscious of himself. These attacks would take him unawares. Sometimes as he walked or went upstairs a void would suddenly open before him. He would seem then to have lost all thought. But when he came back to himself, he was shocked and bewildered to find himself in the same place on the dark staircase. It was as though he had lived through a whole lifetime—in the space of a few steps.

His grandfather used often to take him with him on his evening walk. The little boy used to trot by his side and give him his hand. They used to go by the roads, across plowed fields, which smelled strong and good. The grasshoppers chirped. Enormous crows poised along the road used to watch them approach from afar, and then fly away heavily as they came up with them.

His grandfather would cough. Jean-Christophe knew quite well what that meant. The old man was burning with the desire to tell a story; but he wanted it to appear that the child had asked him for one. Jean-Christophe did not fail him; they understood each other. The old man had a tremendous affection for his grandson, and it was a great joy to find in him a willing audience. He loved to tell of episodes in his own life, or stories of great men, ancient and modern. His voice would then become emphatic and filled with emotion, and would tremble with a childish joy, which he used to try to stifle. He seemed delighted to hear his own voice. Unhappily, words used to fail him when he opened his mouth to speak. He was used to such disappointment, for it always came upon him with his outbursts of eloquence. And as he used to forget it with each new attempt, he never succeeded in resigning himself to it.

He used to talk of Regulus, and Arminius, of the soldiers of Lützow, of Kœrner, and of Frédéric Stabs, who tried to kill the Emperor Napoleon. His face would glow as he told of incredible deeds of heroism. He used to pronounce historic words in such a solemn voice that it was impossible to hear them, and he used to try artfully to keep his hearer on tenterhooks at the thrilling moments. He would stop, pretend to choke, and noisily blow his nose; and his heart would leap when the child asked, in a voice choking with impatience: "And then, grandfather?"

There came a day, when Jean-Christophe was a little older, when he perceived his grandfather's method; and then he wickedly set himself to assume an air of indifference to the rest of the story, and that hurt the poor old man. But for the moment Jean-Christophe is altogether held by the power of the storyteller. His blood leaped at the dramatic passages. He did not know what it was all about, neither where nor when these deeds were done, or whether his grandfather knew Arminius, or whether Regulus were not—God knows why!—some one whom he had seen at church last Sunday. But his heart and the old man's heart swelled with joy and pride in the tale of heroic deeds, as though they themselves had done them; for the old man and the child were both children.

Jean-Christophe was less happy when his grandfather interpolated in the pathetic passages one of those abstruse discourses so dear to him. There were moral thoughts generally traceable to some idea, honest enough, but a little trite, such as "Gentleness is better than violence," or "Honor is the dearest thing in life," or "It is better to be good than to be wicked"—only they were much more involved. Jean-Christophe's grandfather had no fear of the criticism of his youthful audience, and abandoned himself to his habitual emphatic manner; he was not afraid of repeating the same phrases, or of not finishing them, or even, if he lost himself in his discourse, of saying anything that came into his head, to stop up the gaps in his thoughts; and he used to punctuate his words, in order to give them greater force, with inappropriate gestures. The boy used to listen with profound respect, and he thought his grandfather very eloquent, but a little tiresome.

Both of them loved to return again and again to the fabulous legend of the Corsican conqueror who had taken Europe. Jean-Christophe's grandfather had known him. He had almost fought against him. But he was a man to admit the greatness of his adversaries: he had said so twenty times. He would have given one of his arms for such a man to have been born on this side of the Rhine. Fate had decreed otherwise; he admired him, and had fought against him—that is, he had been on the point of fighting against him. But when Napoleon had been no farther than ten leagues away, and they had marched out to meet him, a sudden panic had dispersed the little band in a forest, and every man had fled, crying, "We are betrayed!" In vain, as the old man used to tell, in vain did he endeavor to rally the fugitives; he threw himself in front of them, threatening them and weeping: he had been swept away in the flood of them, and on the morrow had found himself at an extraordinary distance from the field of battle—for so he called the place of the rout.

But Jean-Christophe used impatiently to bring him back to the exploits of the hero, and he was delighted by his marvelous progress through the world. He saw him followed by innumerable men, giving vent to great cries of love, and at a wave of his hand hurling themselves in swarms upon flying enemies—they were always in flight. It was a fairy-tale. The old man added a little to it to fill out the story; he conquered Spain, and almost conquered England, which he could not abide.

Old Krafft used to intersperse his enthusiastic narratives with indignant apostrophes addressed to his hero. The patriot awoke in him, more perhaps when he told of the Emperor's defeats than of the Battle of Jena. He would stop to shake his fist at the river, and spit contemptuously, and mouth noble insults—he did not stoop to less than that. He would call him "rascal," "wild beast," "immoral." And if such words were intended to restore to the boy's mind a sense of justice, it must be confessed that they failed in their object; for childish logic leaped to this conclusion: "If a great man like that had no morality, morality is not a great thing, and what matters most is to be a great man." But the old man was far from suspecting the thoughts which were running along by his side.

They would both be silent, pondering, each after his own fashion, these admirable stories—except when the old man used to meet one of his noble patrons taking a walk. Then he would stop, and bow very low, and breathe lavishly the formulae of obsequious politeness. The child used to blush for it without knowing why. But his grandfather at heart had a vast respect for established power and persons who had "arrived"; and possibly his great love for the heroes of whom he told was only because he saw in them persons who had arrived at a point higher than the others.

When it was very hot, old Krafft used to sit under a tree, and was not long in dozing off. Then Jean-Christophe used to sit near him on a heap of loose stones or a milestone, or some high seat, uncomfortable and peculiar; and he used to wag his little legs, and hum to himself, and dream. Or sometimes he used to lie on his back and watch the clouds go by; they looked like oxen, and giants, and hats, and old ladies, and immense landscapes. He used to talk to them in a low voice, or be absorbed in a little cloud which a great one was on the point of devouring. He was afraid of those which were very black, almost blue, and of those which went very fast. It seemed to him that they played an enormous part in life, and he was surprised that neither his grandfather nor his mother paid any attention to them. They were terrible beings if they wished to do harm. Fortunately, they used to go by, kindly enough, a little grotesque, and they did not stop. The boy used in the end to turn giddy with watching them too long, and he used to fidget with his legs and arms, as though he were on the point of falling from the sky. His eyelids then would wink, and sleep would overcome him. Silence. . . . The leaves murmur gently and tremble in the sun; a faint mist passes through the air; the uncertain flies hover, booming like an organ; the grasshoppers, drunk with the summer, chirp eagerly and hurriedly; all is silent. . . . Under the vault of the trees the cry of the green woodpecker has magic sounds. Far away on the plain a peasant's voice harangues his oxen; the shoes of a horse ring out on the white road. Jean-Christophe's eyes close. Near him an ant passes along a dead branch across a furrow. He loses consciousness. . . . Ages have passed. He wakes. The ant has not yet crossed the twig.

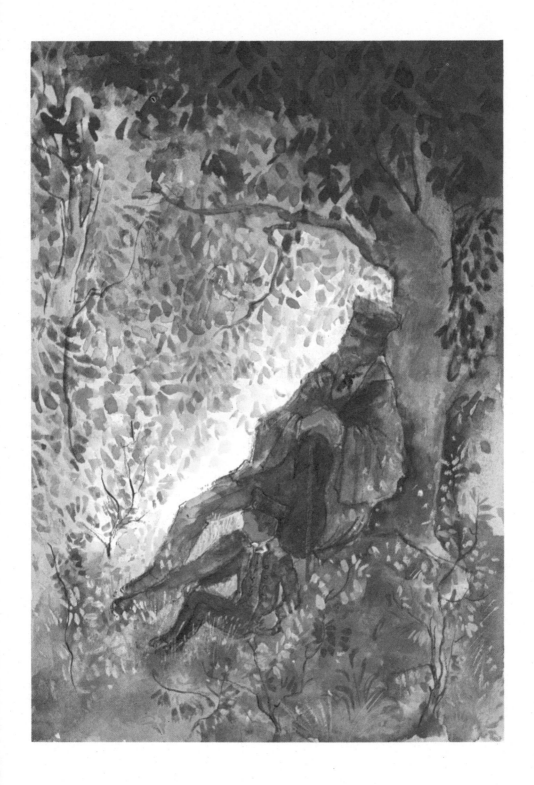

Sometimes the old man would sleep too long, and his face would grow rigid, and his long nose would grow longer, and his mouth stand open. Jean-Christophe used then to look at him uneasily, and in fear of seeing his head change gradually into some fantastic shape. He used to sing loudly, so as to wake him up, or tumble down noisily from his heap of stones. One day it occurred to him to throw a handful of pine-needles in his grandfather's face, and tell him that they had fallen from the tree. The old man believed him, and that made Jean-Christophe laugh. But, unfortunately, he tried the trick again, and just when he had raised his hand he saw his grandfather's eyes watching him. It was a terrible affair. The old man was solemn, and allowed no liberty to be taken with the respect due to himself. They were estranged for more than a week.

The worse the road was, the more beautiful it was to Jean-Christophe. Every stone had a meaning for him; he knew them all. The shape of a rut seemed to him to be a geographical accident almost of the same kind as the great mass of the Taunus. In his head he had the map of all the ditches and hillocks of the region extending two kilometers round about the house, and when he made any change in the fixed ordering of the furrows, he thought himself no less important than an engineer with a gang of navvies; and when with his heel he crushed the dried top of a clod of earth, and filled up the valley at the foot of it, it seemed to him that his day had not been wasted.

Sometimes they would meet a peasant in his cart on the highroad, and if the peasant knew Jean-Christophe's grandfather they would climb up by his side. That was a Paradise on earth. The horse went fast, and Jean-Christophe laughed with delight, except when they passed other people walking; then he would look serious and indifferent, like a person accustomed to drive in a carriage, but his heart was filled with pride. His grandfather and the man would talk without bothering about him. Hidden and crushed by their legs, hardly sitting, sometimes not sitting at all, he was perfectly happy. He talked aloud, without troubling about any answer to what he said. He watched the horse's ears moving. What strange creatures those ears were! They moved in every direction—to right and left; they hitched forward, and fell to one side, and turned backwards in such a ridiculous way that he burst out laughing. He would pinch his grandfather to make him look at them; but his grandfather was not interested in them. He would repulse Jean-Christophe, and tell him to be quiet. Jean-Christophe would ponder. He thought that when people grow up they are not surprised by anything, and that when they are strong they know everything; and he would try to be grown up himself, and to hide his curiosity, and appear to be indifferent.

He was silent then. The rolling of the carriage made him drowsy. The horse's little bells danced—ding, ding; dong, ding. Music awoke in the air, and hovered about the silvery bells, like a swarm of bees. It beat gaily with the rhythm of the cart—an endless source of song, and one song came on another's heels. To Jean-Christophe they were superb. There was one especially which he thought so beautiful that he tried to draw his grandfather's attention to it. He sang it aloud. They took no heed of him. He began it again in a higher key, then again shrilly, and then old Jean Michel said irritably: "Be quiet; you are deafening me with your trumpet-call!" That took away his breath. He blushed and was silent and mortified. He crushed with his contempt the two stockish imbeciles who did not understand the sublimity of his song, which opened wide the heavens! He thought them very ugly, with their week-old beards, and they smelled very ill.

He found consolation in watching the horse's shadow. That was an astonishing sight. The beast ran along with them lying on its side. In the evening, when they returned, it covered a part of the field. They came upon a rick, and the shadow's head would rise up and then return to its place when they had passed. Its snout was flattened out like a burst balloon; its ears were large, and pointed like candles. Was it really a shadow or a creature? Jean-Christophe would not have liked to encounter it alone. He would not have run after it as he did after his grandfather's shadow, so as to walk on its head and trample it under foot. The shadows of the trees when the sun was low were also objects of meditation. They made barriers along the road, and looked like phantoms, melancholy and grotesque, saying, "Go no farther!" and the creaking axles and the horse's shoes repeated, "No farther!"

Jean-Christophe's grandfather and the driver never ceased their endless chatter. Sometimes they would raise their voices, especially when they talked of local affairs or things going wrong. The child would cease to dream, and look at them uneasily. It seemed to him that they were angry with each other, and he was afraid that they would come to blows. However, on the contrary, they best understood each other in their common dislikes. For the most part, they were without hatred or the least passion; they talked of small matters loudly, just for the pleasure of talking, as is the joy of the people. But Jean-Christophe, not understanding their conversation, only heard the loud tones of their voices and saw their agitated faces, and thought fearfully: "How wicked he looks! Surely they hate each other! How he rolls his eyes, and how wide he opens his mouth! He spat on my nose in his fury. O Lord, he will kill my grandfather! . . ."

The carriage stopped. The peasant said: "Here you are." The two deadly enemies shook hands. Jean-Christophe's grandfather got down first; the peasant handed him the little boy. The whip flicked the horse, the carriage rolled away, and there they were by the little sunken road near the Rhine. The sun dipped down below the fields. The path wound almost to the water's edge. The plentiful soft grass yielded under their feet, crackling. Alder-trees leaned over the river, almost half in the water. A cloud of gnats danced. A boat passed noiselessly, drawn on by the peaceful current, striding along. The water sucked the branches of the willows with a little noise like lips. The light was soft and misty, the air fresh, the river silvery gray. They reached their home, and the crickets chirped, and on the threshold smiled his mother's dear face. . . .

Oh, delightful memories, kindly visions, which will hum their melody in their tuneful flight through life! . . . Journeys in later life, great towns and moving seas, dream countries and loved faces, are not so exactly graven in the soul as these childish walks, or the corner of the garden seen every day through the window, through the steam and mist made by the child's mouth glued to it for want of other occupation. . . .

Evening now, and the house is shut up. Home . . . the refuge from all terrifying things—darkness, night, fear, things unknown. No enemy can pass the threshold. . . . The fire flares. A golden duck turns slowly on the spit; a delicious smell of fat and of crisping flesh scents the room. The joy of eating, incomparable delight, a religious enthusiasm, thrills of joy! The body is too languid with the soft warmth, and the fatigues of the day, and the familiar voices. The act of digestion plunges it in ecstasy, and faces, shadows, the lampshade, the tongues of flame dancing with a shower of stars in the fireplace—all take on a magical appearance of delight. Jean-Christophe lays his cheek on his plate, the better to enjoy all this happiness. . . .

He is in his soft bed. How did he come there? He is overcome with weariness. The buzzing of the voices in the room and the visions of the day are intermingled in his mind. His father takes his violin; the shrill sweet sounds cry out complaining in the night. But the crowning joy is when his mother comes and takes Jean-Christophe's hands. He is drowsy, and, leaning over him, in a low voice she sings, as he asks, an old song with words that have no meaning. His father thinks such music stupid, but Jean-Christophe never wearies of it. He holds his breath, and is between laughing and crying. His heart is intoxicated. He does not know where he is, and he is overflowing with tenderness. He throws his little arms around his mother's neck, and hugs her with all his strength. She says, laughing:

"You want to strangle me?"

He hugs her close. How he loves her! How he loves everything! Everybody, everything! All is good, all is beautiful. . . . He sleeps. The cricket on the hearth cheeps. His grandfather's tales, the great heroes, float by in the happy night. . . . To be a hero like them! . . . Yes, he will be that . . . he is that. . . . Ah, how good it is to live!

What an abundance of strength, joy, pride, is in that little creature! What superfluous energy! His body and mind never cease to move; they are carried round and round breathlessly. Like a little salamander, he dances day and night in the flames. His is an unwearying enthusiasm finding its food in all things. A delicious dream, a bubbling well, a treasure of inexhaustible hope, a laugh, a song, unending drunkenness. Life does not hold him yet; always he escapes it. He swims in the infinite. How happy he is! He is made to be happy! There is nothing in him that does not believe in happiness, and does not cling to it with all his little strength and passion! . . .

Life will soon see to it that he is brought to reason.

II

L' alba vinceva l'ora mattutina
Che fuggìa 'nnanzi, sì che di lontano
Conobbi il tremolar della marina. . . .
Purgatorio, i.

The Kraffts came originally from Antwerp. Old Jean Michel had left the country as a result of a boyish freak, a violent quarrel, such as he had often had, for he was devilish pugnacious, and it had had an unfortunate ending. He settled down, almost fifty years ago, in the little town of the principality, with its red-pointed roofs and shady gardens, lying on the slope of a gentle hill, mirrored in the pale green eyes of *Vater Rhein*. An excellent musician, he had readily gained appreciation in a country of musicians. He had taken root there by marrying, forty years ago, Clara Sartorius, daughter of the Prince's *Kapellmeister*, whose duties he took over. Clara was a placid German with two passions—cooking and music. She had for her husband a veneration only equaled by that which she had for her father. Jean Michel no less admired his wife. They had lived together in perfect amity for fifteen years, and they had four children. Then Clara died, and Jean Michel bemoaned her loss, and then, five months later, married Ottilia

Schütz, a girl of twenty, with red cheeks, robust and smiling. After eight years of marriage she also died, but in that time she gave him seven children—eleven children in all, of whom only one had survived. Although he loved them much, all these bereavements had not shaken his good-humor. The greatest blow had been the death of Ottilia, three years ago, which had come to him at an age when it is difficult to start life again and to make a new home. But after a moment's confusion old Jean Michel regained his equilibrium, which no misfortune seemed able to disturb.

He was an affectionate man, but health was the strongest thing in him. He had a physical repugnance from sadness, and a need of gaiety, great gaiety, Flemish fashion—an enormous and childish laugh. Whatever might be his grief, he did not drink one drop the less, nor miss one bite at table, and his band never had one day off. Under his direction the Court orchestra won a small celebrity in the Rhine country, where Jean Michel had become legendary by reason of his athletic stature and his outbursts of anger. He could not master them, in spite of all his efforts, for the violent man was at bottom timid and afraid of compromising himself. He loved decorum and feared opinion. But his blood ran away with him. He used to see red, and he used to be the victim of sudden fits of crazy impatience, not only at rehearsals, but at the concerts, where once in the Prince's presence he had hurled his baton and had stamped about like a man possessed, as he apostrophized one of the musicians in a furious and stuttering voice. The Prince was amused, but the artists in question were rancorous against him. In vain did Jean Michel, ashamed of his outburst, try to pass it by immediately in exaggerated obsequiousness. On the next occasion he would break out again, and as this extreme irritability increased with age, in the end it made his position very difficult. He felt it himself, and one day, when his outbursts had all but caused the whole orchestra to strike, he sent in his resignation. He hoped that in consideration of his services they would make difficulties about accepting it, and would ask him to stay. There was nothing of the kind, and as he was too proud to go back on his offer, he left, brokenhearted, and crying out upon the ingratitude of mankind.

Since that time he had not known how to fill his days. He was more than seventy, but he was still vigorous, and he went on working and going up and down the town from morning to night, giving lessons, and entering into discussions, pronouncing perorations, and entering into everything. He was ingenious, and found all sorts of ways of keeping himself occupied. He began to repair musical instruments; he invented, experimented, and sometimes discovered improvements. He composed also, and set store by his compositions. He had once written a *Missa Solemnis,* of which he used often to talk, and it was the glory of his family. It had cost him so much trouble that he had all but brought about a congestion of the mind in the writing of it. He tried to persuade himself that it was a work of genius, but he knew perfectly well with what emptiness of thought it had been written, and he dared not look again at the manuscript, because every time he did so he recognized in the phrases that he had thought to be his own, rags taken from other authors, painfully pieced together haphazard. It was a great sorrow to him. He had ideas sometimes which he thought admirable. He would run tremblingly to his table. Could he keep his inspiration this time? But hardly had he taken pen in hand than he found himself alone in silence, and all his efforts to call to life again the vanished voices ended only in bringing to his ears familiar melodies of Mendelssohn or Brahms.

"There are," says George Sand, "unhappy geniuses who lack the power of expression, and carry down to their graves the unknown region of their thoughts, as has said a member of that great family of illustrious mutes or stammerers—Geoffrey Saint-Hilaire." Old Jean Michel belonged to that family. He was no more successful in expressing himself in music than in words, and he always deceived himself. He would so much have loved to talk, to write, to be a great musician, an eloquent orator! It was his secret sore. He told no one of it, did not admit it to himself, tried not to think of it; but he did think of it, in spite of himself, and so there was the seed of death in his soul.

Poor old man! In nothing did he succeed in being absolutely himself. There were in him so many seeds of beauty and power, but they never put forth fruit; a profound and touching faith in the dignity of Art and the moral value of life, but it was nearly always translated in an emphatic and ridiculous fashion; so much noble pride, and in life an almost servile admiration of his superiors; so lofty a desire for independence, and, in fact, absolute docility; pretensions to strength of mind, and every conceivable superstition; a passion for heroism, real courage, and so much timidity!—a nature to stop by the wayside.

Jean Michel had transferred all his ambitions to his son, and at first Melchior had promised to realize them. From childhood he had shown great musical gifts. He learned with extraordinary facility, and quickly acquired as a violinist a virtuosity which for a long time made him the favorite, almost the idol, of the Court concerts. He played the piano and other instruments pleasantly. He was a fine talker, well, though a little

heavily, built, and was of the type which passes in Germany for classic beauty; he had a large brow that expressed nothing, large regular features, and a curled beard —a Jupiter of the banks of the Rhine. Old Jean Michel enjoyed his son's success; he was ecstatic over the virtuoso's *tours de force,* he who had never been able properly to play any instrument. In truth, Melchior would have had no difficulty in expressing what he thought. The trouble was that he did not think; and he did not even bother about it. He had the soul of a mediocre comedian who takes pains with the inflections of his voice without caring about what they express, and, with anxious vanity, watches their effect on his audience.

The odd thing was that, in spite of his constant anxiety about his stage pose, there was in him, as in Jean Michel, in spite of his timid respect for social conventions, a curious, irregular, unexpected and chaotic quality, which made people say that the Kraffts were a bit crazy. It did not harm him at first; it seemed as though these very eccentricities were the proof of the genius attributed to him; for it is understood among people of common sense that an artist has none. But it was not long before his extravagances were traced to their source—usually the bottle. Nietzsche says that Bacchus is the God of Music, and Melchior's instinct was of the same opinion; but in his case his god was very ungrateful to him; far from giving him the ideas he lacked, he took away from him the few that he had. After his absurd marriage—absurd in the eyes of the world, and therefore also in his own—he gave himself up to it more and more. He neglected his playing—so secure in his own superiority that very soon he lost it. Other *virtuosi* came to succeed him in public favor. That was bitter to him, but instead of rousing his energy, these rebuffs only discouraged him. He avenged himself by crying down his rivals with his pot-fellows. In his absurd conceit he counted on succeeding his father as musical director: another man was appointed. He thought himself persecuted, and took on the airs of a misunderstood genius. Thanks to the esteem in which old Krafft was held, he kept his place as a violin in the orchestra, but gradually he lost all his lessons in the town. And if this blow struck most at his vanity, it touched his purse even more. For several years the resources of his household had grown less and less, following on various reverses of fortune. After having known plenty, want came, and every day increased. Melchior refused to take notice of it; he did not spend one penny the less on his toilet or his pleasures.

He was not a bad man, but a half-good man, which is perhaps worse—weak, without spring, without moral strength, but for the rest, in his own opinion, a good father, a good son, a good husband, a good man—and perhaps he was good, if to be so it is enough to possess an easy kindness, which is quickly touched, and that animal affection by which a man loves his kin as a part of himself. It cannot even be said that he was very egoistic; he had not personality enough for that. He was nothing. They are a terrible thing in life, these people who are nothing. Like a dead weight thrown into the air, they fall, and must fall; and in their fall they drag with them everything that they have.

It was when the situation of his family had reached its most difficult point, that little Jean-Christophe began to understand what was going on about him.

He was no longer the only child. Melchior gave his wife a child every year, without troubling to think what was to become of it later. Two had died young; two others were three and four years old. Melchior never bothered about them.

Louisa, when she had to go out, left them with Jean-Christophe, now six years old.

The charge cost Jean-Christophe something, for he had to sacrifice to his duty his splendid afternoons in the fields. But he was proud of being treated as a man, and gravely fulfilled his task. He amused the children as best he could by showing them his games, and he set himself to talk to them as he had heard his mother talking to the baby. Or he would carry them in his arms, one after another, as he had seen her do; he bent under their weight, and clenched his teeth, and with all his strength clutched his little brother to his breast, so as to prevent his falling. The children always wanted to be carried—they were never tired of it; and when Jean-Christophe could do no more, they wept without ceasing. They made him very unhappy, and he was often troubled about them. They were very dirty, and needed maternal attentions. Jean-Christophe did not know what to do. They took advantage of him. Sometimes he wanted to slap them, but he thought, "They are little; they do not know," and, magnanimously, he let them pinch him, and beat him, and tease him. Ernest used to howl for nothing; he used to stamp his feet and roll about in a passion; he was a nervous child, and Louisa had bidden Jean-Christophe not to oppose his whims. As for Rodolphe, he was as malicious as a monkey; he always took advantage of Jean-Christophe having Ernest in his arms, to play all sorts of silly pranks behind his back; he used to break toys, spill water, dirty his frock, and knock the plates over as he rummaged in the cupboard.

And when Louisa returned, instead of praising Jean-Christophe, she used to say to him, without scolding him, but with an injured air, as she saw the havoc:

"My poor child, you are not very clever!"

Jean-Christophe would be mortified, and his heart would grow big within him.

Louisa, who let no opportunity escape of earning a little money, used to go out as cook for exceptional occasions, such as marriages or baptismal feasts. Melchior pretended to know nothing about it—it touched his vanity—but he was not annoyed with her for doing it, so long as he did not know. Jean-Christophe had as yet no idea of the difficulties of life; he knew no other limit to his will than the will of his parents, and that did not stand much in his way, for they let him do pretty much as he pleased. His one idea was to grow up, so as to be able to do as he liked. He had no conception of obstacles standing in the way at every turn, and he had never the least idea but that his parents were completely their own masters. It was a shock to his whole being when, for the first time, he perceived that among men there are those who command, and those who are commanded, and that his own people were not of the first class; it was the first crisis of his life.

It happened one afternoon. His mother had dressed him in his cleanest clothes, old clothes given to her which Louisa's ingenuity and patience had turned to account. He went to find her, as they had agreed, at the house in which she was working. He was abashed at the idea of entering alone. A footman was swaggering in the porch; he stopped the boy, and asked him patronizingly what he wanted. Jean-Christophe blushed, and murmured that he had come to see "Frau Krafft"—as he had been told to say.

"Frau Krafft? What do you want with Frau Krafft?" asked the footman, ironically emphasizing the word *Frau*. "Your mother? Go down there. You will find Louisa in the kitchen at the end of the passage."

He went, growing redder and redder. He was ashamed to hear his mother called familiarly *Louisa*. He was humiliated; he would have liked to run away down to his dear river, and the shelter of the brushwood where he used to tell himself stories.

In the kitchen he came upon a number of other servants, who greeted him with noisy exclamations. At the back, near the stove, his mother smiled at him with tender embarrassment. He ran to her, and clung to her skirts. She was wearing a white apron, and holding a wooden spoon. She made him more unhappy by trying to raise his chin so as to look in his face, and to make him hold out his hand to everybody there and say goodday to them. He would not; he turned to the wall and hid his face in his arms. Then gradually he gained courage, and peeped out of his hiding-place with merry bright eyes, which hid again every time any one looked at him. He stole looks at the people there. His mother looked busy and important, and he did not know her like that; she went from one saucepan to another, tasting, giving advice, in a sure voice explaining recipes, and the cook of the house listened respectfully. The boy's heart swelled with pride as he saw how much his mother was appreciated, and the great part that she played in this splendid room, adorned with magnificent objects of gold and silver.

Suddenly conversation ceased. The door opened. A lady entered with a rustling of the stuffs she was wearing. She cast a suspicious look about her. She was no longer young, and yet she was wearing a light dress with wide sleeves. She caught up her dress in her hand, so as not to brush against anything. It did not prevent her going to the stove and looking at the dishes, and even tasting them. When she raised her hand a little, her sleeve fell back, and her arm was bare to the elbow. Jean-Christophe thought this ugly and improper. How dryly and abruptly she spoke to Louisa! And how humbly Louisa replied! Jean-Christophe hated it. He hid away in his corner, so as not to be observed, but it was no use. The lady asked who the little boy might be. Louisa fetched him and presented him; she held his hands to prevent his hiding his face. And, though he wanted to break away and flee, Jean-Christophe felt instinctively that this time he must not resist. The lady looked at the boy's scared face, and at first she gave him a kindly, motherly smile. But then she resumed her patronizing air, and asked him about his behavior, and his piety, and put questions to him, to which he did not reply. She looked to see how his clothes fitted him, and Louisa eagerly declared that they were magnificent. She pulled down his waistcoat to remove the creases. Jean-Christophe wanted to cry, it fitted so tightly. He did not understand why his mother was giving thanks.

The lady took him by the hand and said that she would take him to her own children. Jean-Christophe cast a look of despair at his mother; but she smiled at the mistress so eagerly that he saw that there was nothing to hope for from her, and he followed his guide like a sheep that is led to the slaughter.

They came to a garden, where two cross-looking children, a boy and a girl, about the same age as Jean-Christophe, were apparently sulky with each other. Jean-Christophe's advent created a diversion. They came up to examine the new arrival. Jean-Christophe, left with the children by the lady, stood stock-still in a pathway, not daring to raise his eyes. The two others stood motionless a short distance away, and looked him up and down, nudged each other, and tittered. Finally, they made up their minds. They asked him who he was, whence he came, and what his father did. Jean-Christophe, turned to stone, made no reply; he was terrified almost to the point of tears, especially of the little girl, who had fair hair in plaits, a short skirt, and bare legs.

They began to play. Just as Jean-Christophe was beginning to be a little happier, the little boy stopped dead in front of him, and touching his coat, said:

"Hullo! That's mine!"

Jean-Christophe did not understand. Furious at this assertion that his coat belonged to some one else, he shook his head violently in denial.

"I know it all right," said the boy. "It's my old blue waistcoat. There's a spot on it."

And he put his finger on the spot. Then, going on with his inspection, he examined Jean-Christophe's feet, and asked what his mended-up shoes were made of. Jean-Christophe grew crimson. The little girl pouted and whispered to her brother—Jean-Christophe heard it—that it was a little poor boy. Jean-Christophe resented the word. He thought he would succeed in combating the insulting opinions, as he stammered in a choking voice that he was the son of Melchior Krafft, and that his mother was Louisa the cook. It seemed to him that this title was as good as any other, and he was right. But the two children, interested in the news, did not seem to esteem him any the more for it. On the contrary, they took on a patronizing tone. They asked him what he was going to be—a cook or a coachman. Jean-Christophe revolted. He felt an iciness steal into his heart.

Encouraged by his silence, the two rich children, who had conceived for the little poor boy one of those cruel and unreasoning antipathies which children have, tried various amusing ways of tormenting him. The little girl especially was implacable. She observed that Jean-Christophe could hardly run, because his clothes were so tight, and she conceived the subtle idea of making him jump.

They made an obstacle of little seats, and insisted on Jean-Christophe clearing it. The wretched child dared not say what it was that prevented his jumping. He gathered himself together, hurled himself through the air, and measured his length on the ground. They roared with laughter at him. He had to try again. Tears in his eyes, he made a desperate attempt, and this time succeeded in jumping. That did not satisfy his tormentors, who decided that the obstacle was not high enough, and they built it up until it became a regular break-neck affair. Jean-Christophe tried to rebel, and declared that he would not jump. Then the little girl called him a coward, and said that he was afraid. Jean-Christophe could not stand that, and, knowing that he must fall, he jumped, and fell. His feet caught in the obstacle; the whole thing toppled over with him. He grazed his hands and almost broke his head, and, as a crowning misfortune, his trousers tore at the knees and elsewhere. He was sick with shame; he heard the two children dancing with delight round him; he suffered horribly. He felt that they despised and hated him. Why? Why? He would gladly have died! There is no more cruel suffering than that of a child who discovers for the first time the wickedness of others; he believes then that he is persecuted by the whole world, and there is nothing to support him; there is nothing then—nothing! . . . Jean-Christophe tried to get up; the little boy pushed him down again; the little girl kicked him. He tried again, and they both jumped on him, and sat on his back and pressed his face down into the ground. Then rage seized him—it was too much. His hands were bruised, his fine coat was torn—a catastrophe for him!—shame, pain, revolt against the injustice of it, so many misfortunes all at once, plunged him in blind fury. He rose to his hands and knees, shook himself like a dog, and rolled his tormentors over; and when they returned to the assault he butted at them, head down, bowled over the little girl, and, with one blow of his fist, knocked the boy into the middle of a flower-bed.

They howled. The children ran into the house with piercing cries. Doors slammed, and cries of anger were heard. The lady ran out as quickly as her long dress would let her. Jean-Christophe saw her coming, and made no attempt to escape. He was terrified at what he had done; it was a thing unheard of, a crime; but he regretted nothing. He waited. He was lost. So much the better! He was reduced to despair.

The lady pounced on him. He felt her beat him. He heard her talking in a furious voice, a flood of words; but he could distinguish nothing. His little enemies had come back to see his shame, and screamed shrilly. There were servants—a babel of voices. To complete his downfall, Louisa, who had been summoned, appeared, and, instead of defending him, she began to scold him—she, too, without knowing anything—and bade him beg pardon. He refused angrily. She shook him, and dragged him by the hand to the lady and the children, and bade him go on his knees. But he stamped and roared, and bit his mother's hand. Finally, he escaped among the servants, who laughed.

He went away, his heart beating furiously, his face burning with anger and the slaps which he had received. He tried not to think, and he hurried along because he did not want to cry in the street. He wanted to be at home, so as to be able to find the comfort of tears. He choked; the blood beat in his head; he was at bursting-point.

Finally, he arrived; he ran up the old black staircase to his usual nook in the bay of a window above the river; he hurled himself into it breathlessly, and then there came a flood of tears. He did not know exactly why he was crying, but he had to cry; and when the first flood of them was done, he wept again because he wanted, with a sort of rage, to make himself suffer, as if he could in this way punish the others as well as himself. Then he thought that his father must be coming home, and that his mother would tell him everything, and that his own miseries were by no means at an end. He resolved on flight, no matter whither, never to return.

Just as he was going downstairs, he bumped into his father, who was coming up.

"What are you doing, boy? Where are you going?" asked Melchior.

He did not reply.

"You are up to some folly. What have you done?"

Jean-Christophe held his peace.

"What have you done?" repeated Melchior. "Will you answer?"

The boy began to cry and Melchior to shout, vying with each other until they heard Louisa hurriedly coming up the stairs. She arrived, still upset. She began with violent reproach and further chastisement, in which Melchior joined as soon as he understood—and probably before—with blows that would have felled an ox. Both shouted; the boy roared. They ended by angry argument. All the time that he was beating his son, Melchior maintained that he was right, and that this was the sort of thing that one came by, by going out to service with people who thought they could do everything because they had money; and as she beat the child, Louisa shouted that her husband was a brute, that she would never let him touch the boy, and that he had really hurt him. Jean-Christophe was, in fact, bleeding a little from the nose, but he hardly gave a thought to it, and he was not in the least thankful to his mother for stopping it with a wet cloth, since she went on scolding him. In the end they pushed him away in a dark closet, and shut him up without any supper.

He heard them shouting at each other, and he did not know which of them he detested most. He thought it must be his mother, for he had never expected any such wickedness from her. All the misfortunes of the day overwhelmed him: all that he had suffered—the injustice of the children, the injustice of the lady, the injustice of his parents, and—this he felt like an open wound, without quite knowing why—the degradation of his parents, of whom he was so proud, before these evil and contemptible people. Such cowardice, of which for the first time he had become vaguely conscious, seemed ignoble to him. Everything was upset for him—his admiration for his own people, the religious respect with which they inspired him, his confidence in life, the simple need that he had of loving others and of being loved, his moral faith, blind but absolute. It was a complete cataclysm. He was crushed by brute force, without any means of defending himself or of ever again escaping. He choked. He thought himself on the point of death. All his body stiffened in desperate revolt. He beat with fists, feet, head, against the wall, howled, was seized with convulsions, and fell to the floor, hurling himself against the furniture.

His parents, running up, took him in their arms. They vied with each other now as to who should be the more tender with him. His mother undressed him, carried him to his bed, and sat by him and remained with him until he was calmer. But he did not yield one inch. He forgave her nothing, and pretended to be asleep to get rid of her. His mother seemed to him bad and cowardly. He had no suspicion of all the suffering that she had to go through in order to live and give a living to her family, and of what she had borne in taking sides against him.

After he had exhausted to the last drop the incredible store of tears that is in the eyes of a child, he felt somewhat comforted. He was tired and worn out, but his nerves were too much on stretch for him to sleep. The visions that had been with him floated before him again in his semi-torpor. Especially he saw again the little girl with her bright eyes and her turned-up, disdainful little nose, her hair hanging down to her shoulders, her bare legs and her childish, affected way of talking. He trembled, as it seemed to him that he could hear her voice. He remembered how stupid he had been with her, and he conceived a savage hatred for her. He did not pardon her for having brought him low, and was consumed with the desire to humiliate her and to make her weep. He sought means of doing this, but found none. There was no sign of her ever caring about him. But by way of consoling himself he supposed that everything was as he wished it to be. He supposed that he had become very powerful and famous, and decided that she was in love with him. Then he began to tell himself one of those absurd stories which in the end he would regard as more real than reality.

She was dying of love, but he spurned her. When he passed before her house she watched him pass, hiding behind the curtains, and he knew that she watched him, but he pretended to take no notice, and talked gaily. Even he left the country, and journeyed far to add to her anguish. He did great things. Here he introduced into his narrative fragments chosen from his grandfather's heroic tales, and all this time she was falling ill of grief. Her mother, that proud dame, came to beg of him: "My poor child is dying. I beg you to come!" He went. She

was in her bed. Her face was pale and sunken. She held out her arms to him. She could not speak, but she took his hands and kissed them as she wept. Then he looked at her with marvelous kindness and tenderness. He bade her recover, and consented to let her love him. At this point of the story, when he amused himself by drawing out the coming together by repeating their gestures and words several times, sleep overcame him, and he slept and was consoled.

But when he opened his eyes it was day, and it no longer shone so lightly or so carelessly as its predecessor. There was a great change in the world. Jean-Christophe now knew the meaning of injustice.

There were now times of extremely straitened circumstances at home. They became more and more frequent. They lived meagerly then. No one was more sensible of it than Jean-Christophe. His father saw nothing. He was served first, and there was always enough for him. He talked noisily, and roared with laughter at his own jokes, and he never noticed his wife's glances as she gave a forced laugh, while she watched him helping himself. When he passed the dish it was more than half empty. Louisa helped the children—two potatoes each. When it came to Jean-Christophe's turn there were sometimes only three left, and his mother was not helped. He knew that beforehand; he had counted them before they came to him. Then he summoned up courage, and said carelessly:

"Only one, mother."

She was a little put out.

"Two, like the others."

"No, please; only one."

"Aren't you hungry?"

"No, I'm not very hungry."

But she, too, only took one, and they peeled them carefully, cut them up in little pieces, and tried to eat them as slowly as possible. His mother watched him. When he had finished:

"Come, take it!"

"No, mother."

"But you are ill?"

"I am not ill, but I have eaten enough."

Then his father would reproach him with being obstinate, and take the last potato for himself. But Jean-Christophe learned that trick, and he used to keep it on his plate for Ernest, his little brother, who was always hungry, and watched him out of the corner of his eyes from the beginning of dinner, and ended by asking:

"Aren't you going to eat it? Give it me, then, Jean-Christophe."

Oh, how Jean-Christophe detested his father, how he hated him for not thinking of them, or for not even dreaming that he was eating their share! He was so hungry that he hated him, and would gladly have told him so; but he thought in his pride that he had no right, since he could not earn his own living. His father had earned the bread that he took. He himself was good for nothing; he was a burden on everybody; he had no right to talk. Later on he would talk—if there were any later on. Oh, he would die of hunger first! . . .

He suffered more than another child would have done from these cruel fasts. His robust stomach was in agony. Sometimes he trembled because of it; his head ached. There was a hole in his chest—a hole which turned and widened, as if a gimlet were being twisted in it. But he did not complain. He felt his mother's eyes upon him, and assumed an expression of indifference. Louisa, with a clutching at her heart, understood vaguely that her little boy was denying himself so that the others might have more. She rejected the idea, but always returned to it. She dared not investigate it

or ask Jean-Christophe if it were true, for, if it were true, what could she do? She had been used to privation since her childhood. What is the use of complaining when there is nothing to be done? She never suspected, indeed—she, with her frail health and small needs—that the boy might suffer more than herself. She did not say anything, but once or twice, when the others were gone, the children to the street, Melchior about his business, she asked her eldest son to stay to do her some small service. Jean-Christophe would hold her skein while she unwound it. Suddenly she would throw everything away, and draw him passionately to her. She would take him on her knees, although he was quite heavy, and would hug and hug him. He would fling his arms round her neck, and the two of them would weep desperately, embracing each other.

"My poor little boy! . . ."

"Mother, mother! . . ."

They said no more, but they understood each other.

It was some time before Jean-Christophe realized that his father drank. Melchior's intemperance did not—at least, in the beginning—exceed tolerable limits. It was not brutish. It showed itself rather by wild outbursts of happiness. He used to make foolish remarks, and sing loudly for hours together as he drummed on the table, and sometimes he insisted on dancing with Louisa and the children. Jean-Christophe saw that his mother looked sad. She would shrink back and bend her face over her work; she avoided the drunkard's eyes, and used to try gently to quiet him when he said coarse things that made her blush. But Jean-Christophe did not understand, and he was in such need of gaiety that these noisy home-comings of his father were almost a festival to him. The house was melancholy, and these follies were a relaxation for him. He used to laugh heartily at Melchior's crazy antics and stupid jokes; he sang and danced with him; and he was put out when his mother in an angry voice ordered him to cease. How could it be wrong, since his father did it? Although his ever keen observation, which never forgot anything it had seen, told him that there were in his father's behavior several things which did not accord with his childish and imperious sense of justice, yet he continued to admire him. A child has so much need of an object of admiration! Doubtless it is one of the eternal forms of self-love. When a man is, or knows himself to be, too weak to accomplish his desires and satisfy his pride, as a child he transfers them to his parents, or, as a man who has failed, he transfers them to his children. They are, or shall be, all that he dreamed of being—his champions, his avengers—and in this proud abdication in their favor, love and egoism are mingled so forcefully and yet so gently as to bring him keen delight. Jean-Christophe forgot all his grudges against his father, and cast about to find reasons for admiring him. He admired his figure, his strong arms, his voice, his laugh, his gaiety, and he shone with pride when he heard praise of his father's talents as a virtuoso, or when Melchior himself recited with some amplification the eulogies he had received. He believed in his father's boasts, and looked upon him as a genius, as one of his grandfather's heroes.

One evening about seven o'clock he was alone in the house. His little brothers had gone out with Jean Michel. Louisa was washing the linen in the river. The door opened, and Melchior plunged in. He was hatless and disheveled. He cut a sort of caper to cross the threshold, and then plumped down in a chair by the table. Jean-Christophe began to laugh, thinking it was a part of one of the usual buffooneries, and he approached him. But as soon as he looked more closely at him the desire to laugh left him. Melchior sat there with his arms hanging, and looking straight in front of him, seeing nothing, with his eyes blinking. His face was crimson, his mouth was open, and from it there gurgled every now and then a silly laugh. Jean-Christophe stood stock-still. He thought at first that his father was joking, but when he saw that he did not budge he was panic-stricken.

"Papa, papa!" he cried.

Melchior went on gobbling like a fowl. Jean-Christophe took him by the arm in despair, and shook him with all his strength.

"Papa, dear papa, answer me, please, please!"

Melchior's body shook like a boneless thing, and all but fell. His head flopped towards Jean-Christophe; he looked at him and babbled incoherently and irritably. When Jean-Christophe's eyes met those clouded eyes he was seized with panic terror. He ran away to the other end of the room, and threw himself on his knees by the bed, and buried his face in the clothes. He remained so for some time. Melchior swung heavily on the chair, sniggering. Jean-Christophe stopped his ears, in order not to hear him, and trembled. What was happening within him was inexpressible. It was a terrible upheaval—terror, sorrow, as though for some one dead, some one dear and honored.

No one came; they were left alone. Night fell, and Jean-Christophe's fear grew as the minutes passed. He could not help listening, and his blood froze as he heard the voice that he did not recognize. The silence made it all the more terrifying; the limping clock beat time for the senseless babbling. He could bear it no longer; he wished to fly. But he had to pass his father to get out, and Jean-

Christophe shuddered at the idea of seeing those eyes again; it seemed to him that he must die if he did. He tried to creep on hands and knees to the door of the room. He could not breathe; he would not look; he stopped at the least movement from Melchior, whose feet he could see under the table. One of the drunken man's legs trembled. Jean-Christophe reached the door. With one trembling hand he pushed the handle, but in his terror he let go. It shut to again. Melchior turned to look. The chair on which he was balanced toppled over; he fell down with a crash. Jean-Christophe in his terror had no strength left for flight. He remained glued to the wall, looking at his father stretched there at his feet, and he cried for help.

His fall sobered Melchior a little. He cursed and swore, and thumped on the chair that had played him such a trick. He tried vainly to get up, and then did manage to sit up with his back resting against the table, and he recognized his surroundings. He saw Jean-Christophe crying; he called him. Jean-Christophe wanted to run away; he could not stir. Melchior called him again, and as the child did not come, he swore angrily. Jean-Christophe went near him, trembling in every limb. Melchior drew the boy near him, and made him sit on his knees. He began by pulling his ears, and in a thick, stuttering voice delivered a homily on the respect due from a son to his father. Then he went off suddenly on a new train of thought, and made him jump in his arms while he rattled off silly jokes. He wriggled with laughter. From that he passed immediately to melancholy ideas. He commiserated the boy and himself; he hugged him so that he was like to choke, covered him with kisses and tears, and finally rocked him in his arms, intoning the *De Profundis*. Jean-Christophe made no effort to break

loose; he was frozen with horror. Stifled against his father's bosom, feeling his breath hiccoughing and smelling of wine upon his face, wet with his kisses and repulsive tears, he was in an agony of fear and disgust. He would have screamed, but no sound would come from his lips. He remained in this horrible condition for an age, as it seemed to him, until the door opened, and Louisa came in with a basket of linen on her arm. She gave a cry, let the basket fall, rushed at Jean-Christophe, and with a violence which seemed incredible in her she wrenched Melchior's arm, crying:

"Drunken, drunken wretch!"

Her eyes flashed with anger.

Jean-Christophe thought his father was going to kill her. But Melchior was so startled by the threatening appearance of his wife that he made no reply, and began to weep. He rolled on the floor; he beat his head against the furniture, and said that she was right, that he was a drunkard, that he brought misery upon his family, and was ruining his poor children, and wished he were dead. Louisa had contemptuously turned her back on him. She carried Jean-Christophe into the next room, and caressed him and tried to comfort him. The boy went on trembling, and did not answer his mother's questions; then he burst out sobbing. Louisa bathed his face with water. She kissed him, and used tender words, and wept with him. In the end they were both comforted. She knelt, and made him kneel by her side. They prayed to God to cure father of his disgusting habit, and make him the kind, good man that he used to be. Louisa put the child to bed. He wanted her to stay by his bedside and hold his hand. Louisa spent part of the night sitting on Jean-Christophe's bed. He was feverish. The drunken man snored on the floor.

Some time after that, one day at

school, when Jean-Christophe was spending his time watching the flies on the ceiling, and thumping his neighbors, to make them fall off the form, the schoolmaster, who had taken a dislike to him, because he was always fidgeting and laughing, and would never learn anything, made an unhappy allusion. Jean-Christophe had fallen down himself, and the schoolmaster said he seemed to be like to follow brilliantly in the footsteps of a certain well-known person. All the boys burst out laughing, and some of them took upon themselves to point the allusion with comment both lucid and vigorous. Jean-Christophe got up, livid with shame, seized his ink-pot, and hurled it with all his strength at the nearest boy whom he saw laughing. The schoolmaster fell on him and beat him. He was thrashed, made to kneel, and set to do an enormous composition.

He went home, pale and storming, though he said never a word. He declared frigidly that he would not go to school again. They paid no attention to what he said. Next morning, when his mother reminded him that it was time to go, he replied quietly that he had said that he was not going any more. In vain Louisa begged and screamed and threatened; it was no use. He stayed sitting in his corner, obstinate. Melchior thrashed him. He howled, but every time they bade him go after the thrashing was over he replied angrily, "No!" They asked him at least to say why. He clenched his teeth, and would not. Melchior took hold of him, carried him to school, and gave him into the master's charge. They set him on his form, and he began methodically to break everything within reach—his inkstand, his pen. He tore up his copy-book and lesson-book, all quite openly, with his eye on the schoolmaster, provocative. They shut him up in a dark room. A few moments later the schoolmaster found him with his handkerchief tied round his neck, tugging with all his strength at the two ends of it. He was trying to strangle himself.

They had to send him back.

Jean-Christophe was impervious to sickness. He had inherited from his father and grandfather their robust constitutions. They were not mollycoddles in that family; well or ill, they never worried, and nothing could bring about any change in the habits of the two Kraffts, father and son. They went out winter and summer, in all weathers, and stayed for hours together out in rain or sun, sometimes bareheaded and with their coats open, from carelessness or bravado, and walked for miles without being tired, and they looked with pity and disdain upon poor Louisa, who never said anything, but had to stop. She would go pale, and her legs would swell, and her heart would thump. Jean-Christophe was not far from sharing the scorn of his mother; he did not understand people being ill. When he fell, or knocked himself, or cut himself, or burned himself, he did not cry; but he was angry with the thing that had injured him. His father's brutalities and the roughness of his little playmates, the urchins of the street, with whom he used to fight, hardened him. He was not afraid of blows, and more than once he returned home with bleeding nose and bruised forehead. One day he had to be wrenched away, almost suffocated, from one of these fierce tussles in which he had bowled over his adversary, who was savagely banging his head on the ground. That seemed natural enough to him, for he was prepared to do unto others as they did unto himself.

And yet he was afraid of all sorts of things, and although no one knew it—for he was very proud—nothing brought him so much suffering during a part of his childhood as these same terrors. For two or three years especially they gnawed at him like a disease.

He was afraid of the mysterious something that lurks in darkness—-evil powers that seemed to lie in wait for his life, the roaring of monsters which fearfully haunt the mind of every child and appear in everything that he sees, the relic perhaps of a form long dead, hallucinations of the first days after emerging from chaos, from the fearful slumber in his mother's womb, from the awakening of the larva from the depths of matter.

He was afraid of the garret door. It opened on to the stairs, and was almost always ajar. When he had to pass it he felt his heart beating; he would spring forward and jump by it without looking. It seemed to him that there was some one or something behind it. When it was closed he heard distinctly something moving behind it. That was not surprising, for there were large rats; but he imagined a monster, with rattling bones, and flesh hanging in rags, a horse's head, horrible and terrifying eyes, shapeless. He did not want to think of it, but did so in spite of himself. With trembling hand he would make sure that the door was locked; but that did not keep him from turning round ten times as he went downstairs.

He was afraid of the night outside. Sometimes he used to stay late with his grandfather, or was sent out in the evening on some errand. Old Krafft lived a little outside the town in the last house on the Cologne road. Between the house and the first lighted windows of the town there was a distance of two or three hundred yards, which seemed three times as long to Jean-Christophe. There were places where the road twisted and it was impossible to see anything. The country was deserted in the evening, the earth grew black, and the sky was awfully pale. When he came out from the hedges that lined the road, and climbed up the slope, he could still see a yellowish gleam on the horizon, but it gave no light, and was more oppressive than the night; it made the darkness only darker; it was a deathly light. The clouds came down almost to earth. The hedges grew enormous and moved. The gaunt trees were like grotesque old men. The sides of the wood were stark white. The darkness moved. There were dwarfs sitting in the ditches, lights in the grass, fearful flying things in the air, shrill cries of insects coming from nowhere. Jean-Christophe was always in anguish, expecting some fearsome or strange putting forth of Nature. He would run, with his heart leaping in his bosom.

When he saw the light in his grandfather's room he would gain confidence. But worst of all was when old Krafft was not at home. That was most terrifying. The old house, lost in the country, frightened the boy even in daylight. He forgot his fears when his grandfather was there, but sometimes the old man would leave him alone, and go out without warning him. Jean-Christophe did not mind that. The room was quiet. Everything in it was familiar and kindly. There was a great white wooden bedstead, by the bedside was a great Bible on a shelf, artificial flowers were on the mantelpiece, with photographs of the old man's two wives and eleven children—and at the bottom of each photograph he had written the date of birth and death—on the walls were framed texts and vile chromolithographs of Mozart and Beethoven. A little piano stood in one corner, a great violoncello in another; rows of books higgledy-piggledy, pipes, and in the window pots of geraniums. It was like being surrounded with friends. The old man could be heard moving about in the next room, and planing or hammering, and talking to himself, calling himself an idiot, or singing in a loud voice, improvising a *potpourri* of scraps of chants and sentimental *Lieder,* warlike marches, and drinking songs. Here was shelter and refuge. Jean-Christophe would sit in the great armchair by the window, with a book on his knees, bending over the pictures and losing himself in them. The day would die down, his eyes would grow weary, and then he would look no more, and fall into vague dreaming. The wheels of a cart would rumble by along the road, a cow would moo in the fields; the bells of the town, weary and sleepy, would ring the evening Angelus. Vague desires, happy presentiments, would awake in the heart of the dreaming child.

Suddenly Jean-Christophe would awake, filled with dull uneasiness. He would raise his eyes—night! He would listen—silence! His grandfather had just gone out. He shuddered. He leaned out of the window to try to see him. The road was deserted; things began to take on a threatening aspect. Oh God! If *that* should be coming! What? He could not tell. The fearful thing. The doors were not properly shut. The wooden stairs creaked as under a footstep. The boy leaped up, dragged the armchair, the two chairs and the table, to the most remote corner of the room; he made a barrier of them; the armchair against the wall, a chair to the right, a chair to the left, and the table in front of him. In the middle he planted a pair of steps, and, perched on top with his book and other books, like provisions against a siege, he breathed again, having decided in his childish imagination that the enemy could not pass the barrier—that was not to be allowed.

But the enemy would creep forth, even from his book. Among the old books which the old man had picked up were some with pictures which made a profound impression on the child: they attracted and yet terrified him. There were fantastic visions—temptations of St. Anthony—in which skeletons of birds hung in bottles, and thousands of eggs writhe like worms in disemboweled frogs, and heads walk on feet, and asses play trumpets, and household utensils and corpses of animals walk gravely, wrapped in great cloths, bowing like old ladies. Jean-Christophe was horrified by them, but always returned to them, drawn on by disgust. He would look at them for a long time, and every now and then look furtively about him to see what was stirring in the folds of the curtains. A picture of a flayed man in an anatomy book was still more horrible to him. He trembled as he turned the page when he came to the place where it was in the book. This shapeless medley was grimly etched for him. The creative power inherent in every child's mind filled out the meagerness of the setting of them. He saw no difference between the daubs and the reality. At night they had an even more powerful influence over his dreams than the living things that he saw during the day.

He was afraid to sleep. For several years nightmares poisoned his rest. He wandered in cellars, and through the manhole saw the grinning flayed man entering. He was alone in a room, and he heard a stealthy footstep in the corridor; he hurled himself against the door to close it, and was just in time to hold the handle; but it was turned from the outside; he could not turn the key, his strength left him, and he cried for help. He was with his family, and suddenly their faces changed; they did crazy things. He was reading quietly, and he felt that an invisible being was all *round* him. He tried to fly, but felt himself bound. He tried to cry out, but he was gagged. A loathsome grip was about his neck. He awoke, suffocating, and with his teeth chattering; and he went on trembling long after he was awake; he could not be rid of his agony.

The room in which he slept was a hole without door or windows; an old curtain hung up by a curtain-rod over the entrance was all that separated it from the room of his father and mother. The thick air stifled him. His brother, who slept in the same bed, used to kick him. His head burned, and he was a prey to a sort of hallucination in which all the little troubles of the day reappeared infinitely magnified. In this state of nervous tension, bordering on delirium, the least shock was an agony to him. The creaking of a plank terrified him. His father's breathing took on fantastic proportions. It seemed to be no longer a human breathing, and the monstrous sound was horrible to him; it seemed to him that there must be a beast sleeping there. The night crushed him; it would never end; it must always be so; he was lying there for months and months. He gasped for breath; he half raised himself on his bed, sat up, dried his sweating face with his shirt-sleeve. Sometimes he nudged his brother Rodolphe to wake him up; but Rodolphe moaned, drew away from him the rest of the bedclothes, and went on sleeping.

So he stayed in feverish agony until a pale beam of light appeared on the floor below the curtain. This timorous paleness of the distant dawn suddenly brought him peace. He felt the light gliding into the room, when it was still impossible to distinguish it from darkness. Then his fever would die down, His blood would grow calm, like a flooded river returning to its bed; an even warmth would flow through all his body, and his eyes, burning from sleeplessness, would close in spite of himself.

In the evening it was terrible to him to see the approach of the hour of sleep. He vowed that he would not give way to it, to watch the whole night through, fearing his nightmares. But in the end weariness always overcame him, and it was always when he was least on his guard that the monsters returned.

Fearful night! So sweet to most children, so terrible to some! . . . He was afraid to sleep. He was afraid of not sleeping. Waking or sleeping, he was surrounded by monstrous shapes, the phantoms of his own brain, the larvae floating in the half-day and twilight of childhood, as in the dark chiaroscuro of sickness.

But these fancied terrors were soon to be blotted out in the great Fear—that which is in the hearts of all men; that Fear which Wisdom does in vain preen itself on forgetting or denying—Death.

One day when he was rummaging in a cupboard, he came upon several things that he did not know—a child's frock and a striped bonnet. He took them in triumph to his mother, who, instead of smiling at him, looked vexed, and bade him take them back to the place where he had found them. When he hesitated to obey, and asked her why, she snatched them from him without reply, and put them on a shelf where he could not reach them. Roused to curiosity, he plied her with questions. At last she told him that there had been a little brother who had died before Jean-Christophe came into the world. He was taken aback—he had never heard tell of him. He was silent for a moment, and then tried to find out more. His mother seemed to be lost in thought; but she told him that the little brother was called Jean-Christophe like himself, but was more sensible. He put more questions to her, but she would not reply readily. She told him only that his brother was in Heaven, and was praying for them all. Jean-Christophe could get no more out of her; she bade him be quiet, and to let her go on with her work. She seemed to be absorbed in her sewing; she looked anxious, and did not raise her eyes. But after some time she looked at him where he was in the corner, whither he had retired to sulk, began to smile, and told him to go and play outside.

These scraps of conversation profoundly agitated Jean-Christophe. There had been a child, a little boy, belonging to his mother, like himself, bearing the same name, almost exactly the same, and he was dead! Dead! He did not exactly know what that was, but it was something terrible. And they never talked of this other Jean-Christophe; he was quite forgotten. It would be the same with him if he were to die? This thought was with him still in the evening at table with his family, when he saw them all laughing and talking of trifles. So, then, it was possible that they would be gay after he was dead! Oh! he never would have believed that his mother could be selfish enough to laugh after the death of her little boy! He hated them all. He wanted to weep for himself, for his own death, in advance. At the same time he wanted to ask a whole heap of questions, but he dared not; he remembered the voice in which his mother had bid him be quiet. At last he could contain himself no longer, and one night when he had gone to bed, and Louisa came to kiss him, he asked:

"Mother, did he sleep in my bed?"

The poor woman trembled, and, trying to take on an indifferent tone of voice, she asked:

"Who?"

"The little boy who is dead," said Jean-Christophe in a whisper.

His mother clutched him with her hands.

"Be quiet—quiet," she said.

Her voice trembled. Jean-Christophe, whose head was leaning against her bosom, heard her heart beating. There was a moment of silence, then she said:

"You must never talk of that, my dear. . . . Go to sleep. . . . No, it was not his bed."

She kissed him. He thought he felt her cheek wet against his. He wished he could have been sure of it. He was a little comforted. There was grief in her then! Then he doubted it again the next moment, when he heard her in the next room talking in a quiet, ordinary voice. Which was true—that or what had just been? He turned about for long in his bed without finding any answer. He wanted his mother to suffer; not that he also did not suffer in the knowledge that she was sad, but it would have done him so much good, in spite of everything! He would have felt himself less alone. He slept, and next day thought no more of it.

Some weeks afterwards one of the urchins with whom he played in the street did not come at the usual time. One of them said that he was ill, and they got used to not seeing him in their games. It was explained, it was quite simple. One evening Jean-Christophe had gone to bed; it was early, and from the recess in which his bed was, he saw the light in the room. There was a knock at the door. A neighbor had come to have a chat. He listened absently, telling himself stories as usual. The words of their talk did not reach him. Suddenly he heard the neighbor say: "He is dead." His blood stopped, for he had understood who was dead. He listened and held his breath. His parents cried out. Melchior's booming voice said:

"Jean-Christophe, do you hear? Poor Fritz is dead."

Jean-Christophe made an effort, and replied quietly:

"Yes, papa."

His bosom was drawn tight as in a vise.

Melchior went on:

" 'Yes, papa.' Is that all you say? You are not grieved by it."

Louisa, who understood the child, said:

" 'Ssh! Let him sleep!"

And they talked in whispers. But Jean-

Christophe, pricking his ears, gathered all the details of illness—typhoid fever, cold baths, delirium, the parents' grief. He could not breathe, a lump in his throat choked him. He shuddered. All these horrible things took shape in his mind. Above all, he gleaned that the disease was contagious—that is, that he also might die in the same way—and terror froze him, for he remembered that he had shaken hands with Fritz the last time he had seen him, and that very day had gone past the house. But he made no sound, so as to avoid having to talk, and when his father, after the neighbor had gone, asked him: "Jean-Christophe, are you asleep?" he did not reply. He heard Melchior saying to Louisa:

"The boy has no heart."

Louisa did not reply, but a moment later she came and gently raised the curtain and looked at the little bed. Jean-Christophe only just had time to close his eyes and imitate the regular breathing which his brothers made when they were asleep. Louisa went away on tip-toe. And yet how he wanted to keep her! How he wanted to tell her that he was afraid, and to ask her to save him, or at least to comfort him! But he was afraid of their laughing at him, and treating him as a coward; and besides, he knew only too well that nothing that they might say would be any good. And for hours he lay there in agony, thinking that he felt the disease creeping over him, and pains in his head, a stricture of the heart, and thinking in terror: "It is the end. I am ill. I am going to die. I am going to die!" . . . Once he sat up in his bed and called to his mother in a low voice; but they were asleep, and he dared not wake them.

From that time on his childhood was poisoned by the idea of death. His nerves delivered him up to all sorts of little baseless sicknesses, to depression, to sudden transports, and fits of choking. His imagination ran riot with these troubles, and thought it saw in all of them the murderous beast which was to rob him of his life. How many times he suffered agonies, with his mother sitting only a few yards away from him, and she guessing nothing! For in his cowardice he was brave enough to conceal all his terror in a strange jumble of feeling—pride in not turning to others, shame of being afraid, and the scrupulousness of a tenderness which forbade him to trouble his mother. But he never ceased to think: "This time I am ill. I am seriously ill. It is diphtheria. . . ." He had chanced on the word "diphtheria." . . . "Dear God! not this time! . . ."

He had religious ideas: he loved to believe what his mother had told him, that after death the soul ascended to the Lord, and if it were pious entered into the garden of paradise. But the idea of this journey rather frightened than attracted him. He was not at all envious of the children whom God, as a recompense, according to his mother, took in their sleep and called to Him without having made them suffer. He trembled, as he went to sleep, for fear that God should indulge this whimsy at his expense. It must be terrible to be taken suddenly from the warmth of one's bed and dragged through the void into the presence of God. He imagined God as an enormous sun, with a voice of thunder. How it must hurt! It must burn the eyes, ears—all one's soul! Then, God could punish—you never know. . . . And besides, that did not prevent all the other horrors which he did not know very well, though he could guess them from what he had heard—your body in a box, all alone at the bottom of a hole, lost in the crowd of those revolting cemeteries to which he was taken to pray . . . God! God! How sad! how sad! . . .

And yet it was not exactly joyous to live, and be hungry, and see your father drunk, and to be beaten, to suffer in so many ways from the wickedness of other children, from the insulting pity of grown-up persons, and to be understood by no one, not even by your mother. Everybody humiliates you, no one loves you. You are alone—alone, and matter so little! Yes; but it was just this that made him want to live. He felt in himself a surging power of wrath. A strange thing, that power! It could do nothing yet; it was as though it were afar off and gagged, swaddled, paralyzed; he had no idea what it wanted, what, later on, it would be. But it was in him; he was sure of it; he felt it stirring and crying out. Tomorrow—tomorrow, what a voyage he would take! He had a savage desire to live, to punish the wicked, to do great things. "Oh! but how I will live when I am . . ." he pondered a little—"when I am eighteen!" Sometimes he put it at twenty-one; that was the extreme limit. He thought that was enough for the domination of the world. He thought of the heroes dearest to him—of Napoleon, and of that other more remote hero, whom he preferred, Alexander the Great. Surely he would be like them if only he lived for another twelve—ten years. He never thought of pitying those who died at thirty. They were old; they had lived their lives; it was their fault if they had failed. But to die now . . . despair! Too terrible to pass while yet a little child, and forever to be in the minds of men a little boy whom everybody thinks he has the right to scold! He wept with rage at the thought, as though he were already dead.

This agony of death tortured his childish years—corrected only by disgust with all life and the sadness of his own.

It was in the midst of these gloomy shadows, in the stifling night that every moment seemed to intensify about him, that there began to shine, like a star lost in the dark abysm of space, the light which was to illuminate his life: divine music. . . .

His grandfather gave the children an old piano, which one of his clients, anxious to be rid of it, had asked him to take. His patient ingenuity had almost put it in order. The present had not been very well received. Louisa thought her room already too small, without filling it up any more; and Melchior said that Jean Michel had not ruined himself over it: just firewood. Only Jean-Christophe was glad of it without exactly knowing why. It seemed to him a magic box, full of marvelous stories, just like the ones in the fairy-book—a volume of the "Thousand and One Nights"—which his grandfather read to him sometimes to their mutual delight. He had heard his father try the piano on the day of its arrival, and draw from it a little rain of arpeggios like the drops that a puff of wind shakes from the wet branches of a tree after a shower. He clapped his hands, and cried "Encore!" but Melchior scornfully closed the piano, saying that it was worthless. Jean-Christophe did not insist, but after that he was always hovering about the instrument. As soon as no one was near he would raise the lid, and softly press down a key, just as if he were moving with his finger the living shell of some great insect; he wanted to push out the creature that was locked up in it. Sometimes in his haste he would strike too hard, and then his mother would cry out, "Will you not be quiet? Don't go touching everything!" or else he would pinch himself cruelly in closing the piano, and make piteous faces as he sucked his bruised fingers. . . .

Now his greatest joy is when his mother is gone out for a day's service, or to pay some visit in the town. He listens as she goes down the stairs, and into the street, and away. He is alone. He opens the piano, and brings up a chair, and perches on it. His shoulders just about reach the keyboard; it is enough for what he wants. Why does he wait until he is alone? No one would prevent his playing so long as he did not make too much noise. But he is ashamed before the others, and dare not. And then they talk and move about: that spoils his pleasure. It is much more beautiful when he is alone! Jean-Christophe holds his breath so that the silence may be even greater, and also because he is a little excited, as though he were going to let off a gun. His heart beats as he lays his finger on the key; sometimes he lifts his finger after he has the key half pressed down, and lays it on another. Does he know what will come out of it, more than what will come out of the other? Suddenly a sound issues from it; there are deep sounds and high sounds, some tinkling, some roaring. The child listens to them one by one as they die away and finally cease to be; they hover in the air like bells heard far off, coming near in the wind, and then going away again; then when you listen you hear in the distance other voices, different, joining in and droning like flying insects; they seem to call to you, to draw you away farther—farther and farther into the mysterious regions, where they dive down and are lost. . . . They are gone! . . . No; still they murmur. . . . A little beating of wings. . . . How strange it all is! They are like spirits. How is it that they are so obedient? how is it that they are held captive in this old box? But best of all is when you lay two fingers on two keys at once. Then you never know exactly what will happen. Sometimes the two spirits are hostile; they are angry with each other, and fight; and hate each other, and buzz testily. Then voices are raised; they cry out, angrily, now sorrowfully. Jean-Christophe adores that; it is as though there were monsters chained up, biting at their fetters, beating against the bars of

their prison; they are like to break them, and burst out like the monsters in the fairy-book—the genii imprisoned in the Arab bottles under the seal of Solomon. Others flatter you; they try to cajole you, but you feel that they only want to bite, that they are hot and fevered. Jean-Christophe does not know what they want, but they lure him and disturb him; they make him almost blush. And sometimes there are notes that love each other; sounds embrace, as people do with their arms when they kiss: they are gracious and sweet. These are the good spirits; their faces are smiling, and there are no lines in them; they love little Jean-Christophe, and little Jean-Christophe loves them. Tears come to his eyes as he hears them, and he is never weary of calling them up. They are his friends, his dear, tender friends. . . .

So the child journeys through the forest of sounds, and round him he is conscious of thousands of forces lying in wait for him, and calling to him to caress or devour him. . . .

One day Melchior came upon him thus. He made him jump with fear at the sound of his great voice. Jean-Christophe, thinking he was doing wrong, quickly put his hand up to his ears to ward off the blows he feared. But Melchior did not scold him, strange to say; he was in a good temper, and laughed.

"You like that, boy?" he asked, patting his head kindly. "Would you like me to teach you to play it?"

Would he like! . . . Delighted, he murmured: "Yes." The two of them sat down at the piano, Jean-Christophe perched this time on a pile of big books, and very attentively he took his first lesson. He learned first of all that the buzzing spirits have strange names, like Chinese names, of one syllable, or even of one letter. He was astonished; he imagined them to be different from that: beautiful, caressing names, like the princesses in the fairy stories. He did not like the familiarity with which his father talked of them. Again, when Melchior evoked them they were not the same; they seemed to become indifferent as they rolled out from under his fingers. But Jean-Christophe was glad to learn about the relationships between them, their hierarchy, the scales, which were like a King commanding an army, or like a band of negroes marching in single file. He was surprised to see that each soldier, or each negro, could become a monarch in his turn, or the head of a similar band, and that it was possible to summon whole battalions from one end to the other of the keyboard. It amused him to hold the thread which made them march. But it was a small thing compared with what he had seen at first; his enchanted forest was lost. However, he set himself to learn, for it was not tiresome, and he was surprised at his father's patience. Melchior did not weary of it either; he made him begin the same thing over again ten times. Jean-Christophe did not understand why he should take so much trouble; his father loved him, then? That was good! The boy worked away; his heart was filled with gratitude.

He would have been less docile had he known what thoughts were springing into being in his father's head.

From that day on Melchior took him to the house of a neighbor, where three times a week there was chamber music. Melchior played first violin, Jean Michel the violoncello. The other two were a bank-clerk and the old watchmaker of the *Schillerstrasse*. Every now and then the chemist joined them with his flute. They began at five, and went on till nine. Between each piece they drank beer. Neighbors used to come in and out, and listen without a word, leaning against the wall, nodding their heads, and beating time with their feet, and filling the room with clouds of tobacco-smoke. Page followed page, piece followed piece, but the patience of the musicians was never exhausted. They did not speak; they were all attention; their brows were knit, and from time to time they grunted with pleasure, but for the rest they were perfectly incapable not only of expressing, but even of feeling, the beauty of what they played. They played neither very accurately nor in good time, but they never went off the rails, and followed faithfully the marked changes of tone. They had that musical facility which is easily satisfied, that mediocre perfection which is so plentiful in the race which is said to be the most musical in the world. They had also that great appetite which does not stickle for the quality of its food, so only there be quantity—that healthy appetite to which all music is good, and the more substantial the better —it sees no difference between Brahms and Beethoven, or between the works of the same master, between an empty concerto and a moving sonata, because they are fashioned of the same stuff.

Jean-Christophe sat apart in a corner, which was his own, behind the piano. No one could disturb him there, for to reach it he had to go on all fours. It was half dark there, and the boy had just room to lie on the floor if he huddled up. The smoke of the tobacco filled his eyes and throat: dust, too; there were large flakes of it like sheepskin, but he did not mind that, and listened gravely, squatting there Turkish fashion, and widening the holes in the cloth of the piano with his dirty little fingers. He did not like everything that they played; but nothing that they played bored him, and he never tried to formulate his opinions, for he thought himself too small to know anything. Only some music sent him to sleep, some woke him up; it was never disagreeable to him. Without his knowing it, it was nearly always good music that excited him. Sure of not being seen, he made faces, he wrinkled his nose, ground his teeth, or stuck out his tongue; his eyes flashed with anger or drooped languidly; he moved his arms and legs with a defiant and valiant air; he wanted to march, to lunge out, to pulverize the world. He fidgeted so much that in the end a head would peer over the piano, and say: "Hullo, boy, are you mad? Leave the piano. . . . Take your hand away, or I'll pull your ears!" And that made him crestfallen and angry. Why did they want to spoil his pleasure? He was not doing any harm. Must he always be tormented! His father chimed in. They chid him for making a noise, and said that he did not like music. And in the end he believed it. These honest citizens grinding out concertos would have been astonished if they had been told that the only person in the company who really felt the music was the little boy.

If they wanted him to keep quiet, why did they play airs which make you march? In those pages were rearing horses, swords, war-cries, the pride of triumph; and they wanted him, like them, to do no more than wag his head and beat time with his feet! They had only to play placid dreams or some of those chattering pages which talk so much and say nothing. There are plenty of them, for example, like that piece of Goldmark's, of which the old watchmaker had just said with a delighted smile: "It is pretty. There is no harshness in it. All the corners are rounded off. . . ." The boy was very quiet then. He became drowsy. He did not know what they were playing, hardly heard it; but he was happy; his limbs were numbed, and he was dreaming.

His dreams were not a consecutive story; they had neither head nor tail. It was rarely that he saw a definite picture: his mother making a cake, and with a knife removing the paste that clung to her fingers; a water-rat that he had seen the night before swimming in the river; a whip that he wanted to make with a willow wand. . . . Heaven knows why these things should have cropped up in his memory at such a time! But most often he saw nothing at all, and yet he felt things innumerable and infinite. It was as though there were a number of very important things not to be spoken of, or not worth speaking of, because they were so well known, and because they had always been so. Some of them were sad, terribly sad; but there was nothing painful in them, as there is in the things that belong to real life; they were not ugly and debasing, like the blows that Jean-Christophe had from his father, or like the things that were in his head when, sick at heart with shame, he thought of some humiliation; they filled the mind with a melancholy calm. And some were bright and shining, shedding torrents of joy. And Jean-Christophe thought: "Yes, it is *thus*—thus that I will do by-and-by." He did not know exactly what *thus* was, nor why he said it, but he felt that he had to say it, and that it was clear as day. He heard the sound of a sea, and he was quite near to it, kept from it only by a wall of dunes. Jean-Christophe had no idea what sea it was, or what it wanted with him, but he was conscious that it would rise above the barrier of dunes. And then! . . . Then all would be well, and he would be quite happy. Nothing to do but to hear it, then, quite near, to sink to sleep to the sound of its great voice, soothing away all his little griefs and humiliations. They were sad still, but no longer shameful nor injurious; everything seemed natural and almost sweet.

Very often it was mediocre music that produced this intoxication in him. The writers of it were poor devils, with no thought in their heads but the gaining of money, or the hiding away of the emptiness of their lives by tagging notes together according to accepted formulæ—or to be original, in defiance of formulæ. But in the notes of music, even when handled by an idiot, there is such a power of life that they can let loose storms in a simple soul. Perhaps even the dreams suggested by the idiots are more mysterious and more free than those breathed by an imperious thought which drags you along by force, for aimless movement and empty chatter do not disturb the mind in its own pondering. . . .

So, forgotten and forgetting, the child stayed in his corner behind the piano, until suddenly he felt ants climbing up his legs. And he remembered then that he was a little boy with dirty nails, and that he was rubbing his nose against a whitewashed wall, and holding his feet in his hands.

On the day when Melchior, stealing on tiptoe, had surprised the boy at the keyboard that was too high for him, he had stayed to watch him for a moment, and suddenly there had flashed upon him: "A little prodigy! . . . Why had he not thought of it? . . . What luck for the family! . . ." No doubt he had thought that the boy would be a little peasant like his mother. "It would cost nothing to try. What a great thing it would be! He would take him all over Germany, perhaps abroad. It would be a jolly life, and noble to boot." Melchior never failed to look for the nobility hidden in all he did, for it was not often that he failed to find it, after some reflection.

Strong in this assurance, immediately after supper, as soon as he had taken his last mouthful, he dumped the child once more in front of the piano, and made him go through the day's lesson until his eyes closed in weariness. Then three times the next day. Then the day after that. Then every day. Jean-Christophe soon tired of it; then he was sick to death of it; finally he could stand it no more,

and tried to revolt against it. There was no point in what he was made to do: nothing but learning to run as fast as possible over the keys, by loosening the thumb, or exercising the fourth finger, which would cling awkwardly to the two next to it. It got on his nerves; there was nothing beautiful in it. There was an end of the magic sounds, and fascinating monsters, and the universe of dreams felt in one moment. . . . Nothing but scales and exercises—dry, monotonous, dull—duller than the conversation at mealtime, which was always the same—always about the dishes, and always the same dishes. At first the child listened absently to what his father said. When he was severely reprimanded he went on with a bad grace. He paid no attention to abuse; he met it with bad temper. The last straw was when one evening he heard Melchior unfold his plans in the next room. So it was in order to put him on show like a trick animal that he was so badgered and forced every day to move bits of ivory! He was not even given time to go and see his beloved river. What was it made them so set against him? He was angry, hurt in his pride, robbed of his liberty. He decided that he would play no more, or as badly as possible, and would discourage his father. It would be hard, but at all costs he must keep his independence.

The very next lesson he began to put his plan into execution. He set himself conscientiously to hit the notes awry, or to bungle every touch. Melchior cried out, then roared, and blows began to rain. He had a heavy ruler. At every false note he struck the boy's fingers, and at the same time shouted in his ears, so that he was like to deafen him. Jean-Christophe's face twitched under the pain of it; he bit his lips to keep himself from crying, and stoically went on hitting the notes all wrong, bobbing his head down whenever he felt a blow coming. But his system was not good, and it was not long before he began to see that it was so. Melchior was as obstinate as his son, and he swore that even if they were to stay there two days and two nights he would not let him off a single note until it had been properly played. Then Jean-Christophe tried too deliberately to play wrongly, and Melchior began to suspect the trick, as he saw that the boy's hand fell heavily to one side at every note with obvious intent. The blows became more frequent; Jean-Christophe was no longer conscious of his fingers. He wept pitifully and silently, sniffing, and swallowing down his sobs and tears. He understood that he had nothing to gain by going on like that, and that he would have to resort to desperate measures. He stopped, and, trembling at the thought of the storm which was about to let loose, he said valiantly:

"Papa, I won't play any more."

Melchior choked.

"What! What! . . ." he cried.

He took and almost broke the boy's arm with shaking it. Jean-Christophe, trembling more and more, and raising his elbow to ward off the blows, said again:

"I won't play any more. First, because I don't like being beaten. And then . . ."

He could not finish. A terrific blow knocked the wind out of him, and Melchior roared:

"Ah! you don't like being beaten? You don't like it? . . ."

Blows rained. Jean-Christophe bawled through his sobs:

"And then . . . I don't like music! . . . I don't like music! . . ."

He slipped down from his chair. Melchior roughly put him back, and knocked his knuckles against the keyboard. He cried:

"You shall play!"

And Jean-Christophe shouted:

"No! No! I won't play!"

Melchior had to surrender. He

thrashed the boy, thrust him from the room, and said that he should have nothing to eat all day, or the whole month, until he had played all his exercises without a mistake. He kicked him out and slammed the door after him.

Jean-Christophe found himself on the stairs, the dark and dirty stairs, worm-eaten. A draft came through a broken pane in the skylight, and the walls were dripping. Jean-Christophe sat on one of the greasy steps; his heart was beating wildly with anger and emotion. In a low voice he cursed his father:

"Beast! That's what you are! A beast . . . a gross creature . . . a brute! Yes, a brute! . . . and I hate you, I hate you! . . . Oh, I wish you were dead! I wish you were dead!"

His bosom swelled. He looked desperately at the sticky staircase and the spider's web swinging in the wind above the broken pane. He felt alone, lost in his misery. He looked at the gap in the banisters. . . . What if he were to throw himself down? . . . or out of the window? . . . Yes, what if he were to kill himself to punish them? How remorseful they would be! He heard the noise of his fall from the stairs. The door upstairs opened suddenly. Agonized voices cried: "He has fallen!—He has fallen!" Footsteps clattered downstairs. His father and mother threw themselves weeping upon his body. His mother sobbed: "It is your fault! You have killed him!" His father waved his arms, threw himself on his knees, beat his head against the banisters, and cried: "What a wretch am I! What a wretch am I!" The sight of all this softened his misery. He was on the point of taking pity on their grief; but then he thought that it was well for them, and he enjoyed his revenge. . . .

When his story was ended, he found himself once more at the top of the stairs in the dark; he looked down once more, and his desire to throw himself down was gone. He even shuddered a little, and moved away from the edge, thinking that he might fall. Then he felt that he was a prisoner, like a poor bird in a cage—a prisoner forever, with nothing to do but to break his head and hurt himself. He wept, and he rubbed his eyes with his dirty little hands, so that in a moment he was filthy. As he wept he never left off looking at the things about him, and he found some distraction in that. He stopped moaning for a moment to look at the spider which had just begun to move. Then he began with less conviction. He listened to the sound of his own weeping, and went on mechanically with his sobbing, without much knowing why he did so. Soon he got up; he was attracted by the window. He sat on the window-sill, retiring into the background, and watched the spider furtively. It interested while it revolted him.

Below the Rhine flowed, washing the walls of the house. In the staircase window it was like being suspended over the river in a moving sky. Jean-Christophe never limped down the stairs without taking a long look at it, but he had never yet seen it as it was today. Grief sharpens the senses; it is as though everything were more sharply graven on the vision after tears have washed away the dim traces of memory. The river was like a living thing to the child—a creature inexplicable, but how much more powerful than all the creatures that he knew! Jean-Christophe leaned forward to see it better; he pressed his mouth and flattened his nose against the pane. Where was *it* going? What did *it* want? *It* looked free, and sure of its road. . . . Nothing could stop *it*. At all hours of the day or night, rain or sun, whether there were joy or sorrow in the house, *it* went on going by, and it was as though nothing mattered to *it*, as though *it* never knew sorrow, and rejoiced in *its* strength. What joy to be

like *it*, to run through the fields, and by willow-branches, and over little shining pebbles and crisping sand, and to care for nothing, to be cramped by nothing, to be free! . . .

The boy looked and listened greedily; it was as though he were borne along by the river, moving by with it. . . . When he closed his eyes he saw color—blue, green, yellow, red, and great chasing shadows and sunbeams. . . . What he sees takes shape. Now it is a large plain, reeds, corn waving under a breeze scented with new grass and mint. Flowers on every side—cornflowers, poppies, violets. How lovely it is! How sweet the air! How good it is to lie down in the thick, soft grass! . . . Jean-Christophe feels glad and a little bewildered, as he does when on feast-days his father pours into his glass a little Rhine wine. . . . The river goes by. . . . The country is changed. . . . Now there are trees leaning over the water; their delicate leaves, like little hands, dip, move, and turn about in the water. A village among the trees is mirrored in the river. There are cypress-trees, and the crosses of the cemetery showing above the white wall washed by the stream. Then there are rocks, a mountain gorge, vines on the slopes, a little pine-wood, and ruined castles. . . . And once more the plain, corn, birds, and the sun. . . .

The great green mass of the river goes by smoothly, like a single thought; there are no waves, almost no ripples— smooth, oily patches. Jean-Christophe does not see it; he has closed his eyes to hear it better. The ceaseless roaring fills him, makes him giddy; he is exalted by this eternal, masterful dream which goes no man knows whither. Over the turmoil of its depths rush waters, in swift rhythm, eagerly, ardently. And from the rhythm ascends music, like a vine climbing a trellis—arpeggios from silver keys, sorrowful violins, velvety and smooth-sounding flutes. . . . The country has disappeared. The river has disappeared. There floats by only a strange, soft, and twilight atmosphere. Jean-Christophe's heart flutters with emotion. What does he see now? Oh! Charming faces! . . . A little girl with brown tresses calls to him, slowly, softly, and mockingly. . . . A pale boy's face looks at him with melancholy blue eyes. . . . Others smile; other eyes look at him—curious and provoking eyes, and their glances make him blush—eyes affectionate and mournful, like the eyes of a dog—eyes imperious, eyes suffering. . . . And the pale face of a woman, with black hair, and lips close pressed, and eyes so large that they obscure her other features, and they gaze upon Jean-Christophe with an ardor that hurts him. . . . And, dearest of all, that face which smiles upon him with clear gray eyes and lips a little open, showing gleaming white teeth. . . . Ah! how kind and tender is that smile! All his heart is tenderness from it! How good it is to love! Again! Smile upon me again! Do not go! . . . Alas! it is gone! . . . But it leaves in his heart sweetness ineffable. Evil, sorrow, are no more; nothing is left. . . . Nothing, only an airy dream, like serene music, floating down a sunbeam, like the gossamers on fine summer days. . . . What has happened? What are these visions that fill the child with sadness and sweet sorrow? Never had he seen them before, and yet he knew them and recognized them. Whence come they? From what obscure abyss of creation? Are they what has been . . . *or what will be?* . . .

Now all is done, every haunting form is gone. Once more through a misty veil, as though he were soaring high above it, the river in flood appears, covering the fields, and rolling by, majestic, slow, almost still. And far, far away, like a steely light upon the horizon, a watery plain, a line of trembling waves—the sea. The river runs down to it. The sea seems to run up to the river. She fires him. He desires her. He must lose himself in her. . . . The music hovers; lovely dance rhythms swing out madly; all the world is rocked in their triumphant whirligig. . . . The soul, set free, cleaves space, like swallows' flight, like swallows drunk with the air, skimming across the sky with shrill cries. . . . Joy! Joy! There is nothing, nothing! . . . Oh, infinite happiness! . . .

Hours passed; it was evening; the staircase was in darkness. Drops of rain made rings upon the river's gown, and the current bore them dancing away. Sometimes the branch of a tree or pieces of black bark passed noiselessly and disappeared. The murderous spider had withdrawn to her darkest corner. And little Jean-Christophe was still leaning forward on the window-sill. His face was pale and dirty; happiness shone in him. He was asleep.

III

E la faccia del sol nascere ombrata.
Purgatorio, xxx.

He had to surrender. In spite of an obstinate and heroic resistance, blows triumphed over his ill-will. Every morning for three hours, and for three hours every evening, Jean-Christophe was set before the instrument of torture. All on edge with attention and weariness, with large tears rolling down his cheeks and nose, he moved his little red hands over the black and white keys—his hands were often stiff with cold—under the threatening ruler, which descended at every false note, and the harangues of his master, which were more odious to him than the blows. He thought that he hated music. And yet he applied himself to it with a zest which fear of Melchior did not altogether explain. Certain words of his grandfather had made an impression on him. The old man, seeing his grandson weeping, had told him, with that gravity which he always maintained for the boy, that it was worth while suffering a little for the most beautiful and noble art given to men for their consolation and glory. And Jean-Christophe, who was grateful to his grandfather for talking to him like a man, had been secretly touched by these simple words, which sorted well with his childish stoicism and growing pride. But, more than by argument, he was bound and enslaved by the memory of certain musical emotions, bound and enslaved to the detested art, against which he tried in vain to rebel.

There was in the town, as usual in Germany, a theater, where opera, opéra-comique, operetta, drama, comedy, and vaudeville are presented—every sort of play of every style and fashion. There were performances three times a week from six to nine in the evening. Old Jean Michel never missed one, and was equally interested in everything. Once he took his grandson with him. Several days beforehand he told him at length what the piece was about. Jean-Christophe did not understand it, but he did gather that there would be terrible things in it, and while he was consumed with the desire to see them he was much afraid, though he dared not confess it. He knew that there was to be a storm, and he was fearful of being struck by lightning. He knew that there was to be a battle, and he was not at all sure that he would not be killed. On the night before, in bed, he went through real agony, and on the day of the performance he almost wished that his grandfather might be prevented from coming for him. But when the hour was near, and his grandfather did not come, he began to worry, and every other minute looked out of the window. At last the old man appeared,

and they set out together. His heart leaped in his bosom; his tongue was dry, and he could not speak.

They arrived at the mysterious building which was so often talked about at home. At the door Jean Michel met some acquaintances, and the boy, who was holding his hand tight because he was afraid of being lost, could not understand how they could talk and laugh quietly at such a moment.

Jean Michel took his usual place in the first row behind the orchestra. He leaned on the balustrade, and began a long conversation with the contra-bass. He was at home there; there he was listened to because of his authority as a musician, and he made the most of it; it might almost be said that he abused it. Jean-Christophe could hear nothing. He was overwhelmed by his expectation of the play, by the appearance of the theater, which seemed magnificent to him, by the splendor of the audience, who frightened him terribly. He dared not turn his head, for he thought that all eyes were fixed on him. He hugged his little cap between his knees, and he stared at the magic curtain with round eyes.

At last three blows were struck. His grandfather blew his nose, and drew the *libretto* from his pocket. He always followed it scrupulously, so much so that sometimes he neglected what was happening on the stage. The orchestra began to play. With the opening chords Jean-Christophe felt more at ease. He was at home in this world of sound, and from that moment, however extravagant the play might be, it seemed natural to him.

The curtain was raised, to reveal pasteboard trees and creatures who were not much more real. The boy looked at it all, gaping with admiration, but he was not surprised. The piece was set in a fantastic East, of which he could have had no idea. The poem was a web of ineptitudes, in which no human quality was perceptible. Jean-Christophe hardly grasped it at all; he made extraordinary mistakes, took one character for another, and pulled at his grandfather's sleeve to ask him absurd questions, which showed that he had understood nothing. He was not bored: passionately interested, on the contrary. Round the idiotic *libretto* he built a romance of his own invention, which had no sort of relation to the one that was represented on the stage. Every moment some incident upset his romance, and he had to repair it, but that did not worry him. He had made his choice of the people who moved upon the stage, making all sorts of different sounds, and breathlessly he followed the fate of those upon whom he had fastened his sympathy. He was especially concerned with a fair lady, of uncertain age, who had long, brilliantly fair hair, eyes of an unnatural size, and bare feet. The monstrous improbabilities of the setting did not shock him. His keen, childish eyes did not perceive the grotesque ugliness of the actors, large and fleshy, and the deformed chorus of all sizes in two lines, nor the pointlessness of their gestures, nor their faces bloated by their shrieks, nor the full wigs, nor the high heels of the tenor, nor the make-up of his lady-love, whose face was streaked with variegated penciling. He was in the condition of a lover, whose passion blinds him to the actual aspect of the beloved object. The marvelous power of illusion, natural to children, stopped all unpleasant sensations on the way, and transformed them.

The music especially worked wonders. It bathed the whole scene in a misty atmosphere, in which everything became beautiful, noble, and desirable. It bred in the soul a desperate need of love, and at the same time showed phantoms of love on all sides, to fill the void that itself had created. Little Jean-Christophe was overwhelmed by his emotion. There were

words, gestures, musical phrases which disturbed him; he dared not then raise his eyes; he knew not whether it were well or ill; he blushed and grew pale by turns; sometimes there came drops of sweat upon his brow, and he was fearful lest all the people there should see his distress. When the catastrophe came about which inevitably breaks upon lovers in the fourth act of an opera so as to provide the tenor and the *prima donna* with an opportunity for showing off their shrillest screams, the child thought he must choke; his throat hurt him as though he had caught cold; he clutched at his neck with his hands, and could not swallow his saliva; tears welled up in him; his hands and feet were frozen. Fortunately, his grandfather was not much less moved. He enjoyed the theater with a childish simplicity. During the dramatic passages he coughed carelessly to hide his distress, but Jean-Christophe saw it, and it delighted him. It was horribly hot; Jean-Christophe was dropping with sleep, and he was very uncomfortable. But he thought only: "Is there much longer? It cannot be finished!" Then suddenly it was finished, without his knowing why. The curtain fell; the audience rose; the enchantment was broken.

They went home through the night, the two children—the old man and the little boy. What a fine night! What a serene moonlight! They said nothing; they were turning over their memories. At last the old man said:

"Did you like it, boy?"

Jean-Christophe could not reply; he was still fearful from emotion, and he would not speak, so as not to break the spell; he had to make an effort to whisper, with a sigh:

"Oh yes."

The old man smiled. After a time he went on:

"It's a fine thing—a musician's trade! To create things like that, such marvelous spectacles—is there anything more glorious? It is to be God on earth!"

The boy's mind leaped to that. What! a man had made all that! That had not occurred to him. It had seemed that it must have made itself, must be the work of Nature. A man, a musician, such as he would be some day! Oh, to be that for one day, only one day! And then afterwards . . . afterwards, whatever you like! Die, if necessary! He asked:

"What man made that, grandfather?"

The old man told him of François Marie Hassler, a young German artist who lived at Berlin. He had known him once. Jean-Christophe listened, all ears. Suddenly he said:

"And you, grandfather?"

The old man trembled.

"What?" he asked.

"Did you do things like that—you too?"

"Certainly," said the old man a little crossly.

He was silent, and after they had walked a little he sighed heavily. It was one of the sorrows of his life. He had always longed to write for the theater, and inspiration had always betrayed him. He had in his desk one or two acts written, but he had so little illusion as to their worth that he had never dared to submit them to an outside judgment.

They said no more until they reached home. Neither slept. The old man was troubled. He took his Bible for consolation. In bed Jean-Christophe turned over and over the events of the evening; he recollected the smallest details, and the girl with the bare feet reappeared before him. As he dozed off a musical phrase rang in his ears as distinctly as if the orchestra were there. All his body leaped; he sat up on his pillow, his head buzzing with music, and he thought: "Some day I also shall write. Oh, can I ever do it?"

From that moment he had only one desire, to go to the theater again, and he set himself to work more keenly, because they made a visit to the theater his reward. He thought of nothing but that; half the week he thought of the last performance, and the other half he thought of the next. He was fearful of being ill on a theater day, and this fear made him often find in himself the symptoms of three or four illnesses. When the day came he did not eat; he fidgeted like a soul in agony; he looked at the clock fifty times, and thought that the evening would never come; finally, unable to contain himself, he would go out an hour before the office opened, for fear of not being able to procure a seat, and, as he was the first in the empty theater, he used to grow uneasy. His grandfather had told him that once or twice the audience had not been large enough, and so the players had preferred not to perform, and to give back the money. He watched the arrivals and counted them, thinking: "Twenty-three, twenty-four, twenty-five. . . . Oh, it is not enough . . . there will never be enough!" And when he saw some important person enter the circle or the stalls, his heart was lighter, and he said to himself: "They will never dare to send him away. Surely they will play for him." But he was not convinced; he would not be reassured until the musicians took their places. And even then he would be afraid that the curtain would rise, and they would announce, as they had done one evening, a change of program. With lynx eyes he watched the stand of the contra-bass to see if the title written on his music was that of the piece announced. And when he had seen it there, two minutes later he would look again to make quite sure that he had not been wrong. The conductor was not there. He must be ill. There was a stirring behind the curtain, and a sound of voices and hurried footsteps. Was there an accident, some untoward misfortune? Silence again. The conductor was at his post.

Everything seemed ready at last. . . . They did not begin! What was happening? He boiled over with impatience. Then the bell rang. His heart thumped away. The orchestra began the overture, and for a few hours Jean-Christophe would swim in happiness, troubled only by the idea that it must soon come to an end.

Some time after that a musical event brought even more excitement into Jean-Christophe's thoughts. François Marie Hassler, the author of the first opera which had so bowled him over, was to visit the town. He was to conduct a concert consisting of his compositions. The town was excited. The young musician was the subject of violent discussion in Germany, and for a fortnight he was the only topic of conversation. It was a different matter when he arrived. The friends of Melchior and old Jean Michel continually came for news, and they went away with the most extravagant notions of the musician's habits and eccentricities. The child followed these narratives with eager attention. The idea that the great man was there in the town, breathing the same air as himself, treading the same stones, threw him into a state of dumb exaltation. He lived only in the hope of seeing him.

Hassler was staying at the Palace as the guest of the Grand Duke. He hardly went out, except to the theater for rehearsals, to which Jean-Christophe was not admitted, and as he was very lazy, he went to and fro in the Prince's carriage. Therefore, Jean-Christophe did not have many opportunities of seeing him, and he only succeeded once in catching sight of him as he drove in the carriage. He saw his fur coat, and wasted hours in waiting in the street, thrusting and jostling his way to right and left, and before and behind, to win and keep his place in front of the loungers. He consoled himself with spending half his days watching the windows of the Palace which had been pointed out as those of the master. Most often he only saw the shutters, for Hassler got up late, and the windows were closed almost all morning. This habit had made well-informed persons say that Hassler could not bear the light of day, and lived in eternal night.

At length Jean-Christophe was able to approach his hero. It was the day of the concert. All the town was there. The Grand Duke and his Court occupied the great royal box, surmounted with a crown supported by two chubby cherubims. The theater was in gala array. The stage was decorated with branches of oak and flowering laurel. All the musicians of any account made it a point of honor to take their places in the orchestra. Melchior was at his post, and Jean Michel was conducting the chorus.

When Hassler appeared there was loud applause from every part of the house, and the ladies rose to see him better. Jean-Christophe devoured him with his eyes. Hassler had a young, sensitive face, though it was already rather puffy and tired-looking; his temples were bald, and his hair was thin on the crown of his head; for the rest, fair, curly hair. His blue eyes looked vague. He had a little fair mustache and an expressive mouth, which was rarely still, but twitched with a thousand imperceptible movements. He was tall, and held himself badly—not from awkwardness, but from weariness or boredom. He conducted capriciously and lithely, with his whole awkward body swaying, like his music, with gestures, now caressing, now sharp and jerky. It was easy to see that he was very nervous, and his music was the exact reflection of himself. The quivering and jerky life of it broke through the usual apathy of the orchestra. Jean-Christophe breathed heavily; in spite of his fear of drawing attention to himself, he could not stand still in his place; he fidgeted, got up, and the music gave him such violent and unexpected shocks that he had to move his head, arms, and legs, to the great discomfort of his neighbors, who warded off his kicks as best they could. The whole audience was enthusiastic, fascinated by the success, rather than by the compositions. At the end there was a storm of applause and cries, in which the trumpets in the orchestra joined, German fashion, with their triumphant blare in salute of the conqueror. Jean-Christophe trembled with pride, as though these honors were for himself. He enjoyed seeing Hassler's face light up with childish pleasure. The ladies threw flowers, the men waved their hats, and the audience rushed for the platform. Every one wanted to shake the master's hand. Jean-Christophe saw one enthusiast raise the master's hand to his lips, another steal a handkerchief that Hassler had left on the corner of his desk. He wanted to reach the platform also, although he did not know why, for if at that moment he had found himself near Hassler, he would have fled at once in terror and emotion. But he butted with all his force, like a ram, among the skirts and legs that divided him from Hassler. He was too small; he could not break through.

Fortunately, when the concert was over, his grandfather came and took him to join in a party to serenade Hassler. It was night, and torches were lighted. All the musicians of the orchestra were there. They talked only of the marvelous compositions they had heard. They arrived outside the Palace, and took up their places without a sound under the master's windows. They took on an air of secrecy, although everybody, including Hassler, knew what was to come. In the silence of the night they began to play certain famous fragments of Hassler's compositions. He appeared at the window with the Prince, and they roared in their honor. Both bowed. A servant came from the Prince to invite the musicians to enter the Palace. They passed through great rooms, with frescoes representing naked men with helmets; they were of a reddish color, and were making gestures of defiance. The sky was covered with great clouds like sponges. There were also men and women of marble clad in waist-cloths made of iron. The guests walked on carpets so thick that their tread was inaudible, and they came at length to a room which was as light as day, and there were tables laden with drinks and good things.

The Grand Duke was there, but Jean-Christophe did not see him; he had eyes only for Hassler. Hassler came towards them; he thanked them. He picked his words carefully, stopped awkwardly in the middle of a sentence, and extricated himself with a quip which made everybody laugh. They began to eat. Hassler took four or five musicians aside. He singled out Jean-Christophe's grandfather, and addressed very flattering words to him: he recollected that Jean Michel had been one of the first to perform his works, and he said that he had often heard tell of his excellence from a friend of his who had been a pupil of the old man's. Jean-Christophe's grandfather expressed his gratitude profusely; he replied with such extraordinary eulogy that, in spite of his adoration of Hassler, the boy was ashamed. But to Hassler it seemed to be pleasant and in the rational order. Finally, the old man, who had lost himself in his rigmarole, took Jean-Christophe by the hand, and presented him to Hassler. Hassler smiled at Jean-Christophe, and carelessly patted his head, and when he learned that the boy liked his music, and had not slept for several nights in anticipation of seeing him, he took him in his arms and plied him with questions. Jean-Christophe, struck dumb and blushing with pleasure, dared not look at him. Hassler took him by the chin and lifted his face up. Jean-Christophe ventured to look. Hassler's eyes were kind and smiling; he began to smile too. Then he felt so happy, so wonderfully happy in the great man's arms, that he burst into tears. Hassler was touched by this simple affection, and was more kind than ever. He kissed the boy and talked to him tenderly. At the same time he said funny things and tickled him to make him laugh; and Jean-Christophe could not help laughing through his tears. Soon he became at ease, and answered Hassler readily, and of his own accord he began to whisper in his ear all his small ambitions, as though he and Hassler were old friends; he told him how he wanted to be a musician like Hassler, and, like Hassler, to make beautiful things, and to be a great man. He, who was always ashamed, talked confidently; he did not know what he was saying; he was in a sort of ecstasy. Hassler smiled at his prattling and said:

"When you are a man, and have become a good musician, you shall come and see me in Berlin. I shall make something of you."

Jean-Christophe was too delighted to reply.

Hassler teased him.

"You don't want to?"

Jean-Christophe nodded his head violently five or six times, meaning "Yes."

"It is a bargain, then?"

Jean-Christophe nodded again.

"Kiss me, then."

Jean-Christophe threw his arms round Hassler's neck and hugged him with all his strength.

"Oh, you are wetting me! Let go! Your nose wants wiping!"

Hassler laughed, and wiped the boy's nose himself, a little self-consciously, though he was quite jolly. He put him down, then took him by the hand and led

him to a table, where he filled his pockets with cake, and left him, saying:

"Good-bye! Remember your promise."

Jean-Christophe swam in happiness. The rest of the world had ceased to exist for him. He could remember nothing of what had happened earlier in the evening; he followed lovingly Hassler's every expression and gesture. One thing that he said struck him. Hassler was holding a glass in his hand; he was talking, and his face suddenly hardened, and he said:

"The joy of such a day must not make us forget our enemies. We must never forget our enemies. It is not their fault that we are not crushed out of existence. It will not be our fault if that does not happen to them. That is why the toast I propose is that there are people whose health . . . we will not drink!"

Everybody applauded and laughed at this original toast. Hassler had laughed with the others and his good-humored expression had returned. But Jean-Christophe was put out by it. Although he did not permit himself to criticize any action of his hero, it hurt him that he had thought ugly things, when on such a night there ought to be nothing but brilliant thoughts and fancies. But he did not examine what he felt, and the impression that it made was soon driven out by his great joy and the drop of champagne which he drank out of his grandfather's glass.

On the way back the old man never stopped talking; he was delighted with the praise that Hassler had given him; he cried out that Hassler was a genius such as had not been known for a century. Jean-Christophe said nothing, locking up in his heart his intoxication of love. *He* had kissed him. *He* had held him in his arms! How good *he* was! How great!

"Ah," he thought in bed, as he kissed his pillow passionately, "I would die for him—die for him!"

The brilliant meteor which had flashed

across the sky of the little town that night had a decisive influence on Jean-Christophe's mind. All his childhood Hassler was the model on which his eyes were fixed, and to follow his example the little man of six decided that he also would write music. To tell the truth, he had been doing so for long enough without knowing it, and he had not waited to be conscious of composing before he composed.

Everything is music for the born musician. Everything that throbs, or moves, or stirs, or palpitates—sunlit summer days, nights when the wind howls, flickering light, the twinkling of the stars, storms, the song of birds, the buzzing of insects, the murmuring of trees, voices, loved or loathed, familiar fireside sounds, a creaking door, blood moving in the veins in the silence of the night—everything that is is music; all that is needed is that it should be heard. All the music of creation found its echo in Jean-Christophe. Everything that he saw, everything that he felt, was translated into music without his being conscious of it. He was like a buzzing hive of bees. But no one noticed it, himself least of all.

Like all children, he hummed perpetually at every hour of the day. Whatever he was doing—whether he was walking in the street, hopping on one foot, or lying on the floor at his grandfather's, with his head in his hands, absorbed in the pictures of a book, or sitting in his little chair in the darkest corner of the kitchen, dreaming aimlessly in the twilight—always the monotonous murmuring of his little trumpet was to be heard, played with lips closed and cheeks blown out. His mother seldom paid any heed to it, but, once in a while, she would protest.

When he was tired of this state of half-sleep he would have to move and make a noise. Then he made music, singing it at the top of his voice. He had made tunes for every occasion. He had a tune for splashing in his wash-basin in the morning, like a little duck. He had a tune for sitting on the piano-stool in front of the detested instrument, and another for getting off it, and this was a more brilliant affair than the other. He had one for his mother putting the soup on the table; he used to go before her then blowing a blare of trumpets. He played triumphal marches by which to go solemnly from the dining-room to the bedroom. Sometimes he would organize little processions with his two small brothers; all then would file out gravely, one after another, and each had a tune to march to. But, as was right and proper, Jean-Christophe kept the best for himself. Every one of his tunes was strictly appropriated to its special occasion, and Jean-Christophe never by any chance confused them. Anybody else would have made mistakes, but he knew the shades of difference between them exactly.

One day at his grandfather's house he was going round the room clicking his heels, head up and chest out; he went round and round and round, so that it was a wonder he did not turn sick, and played one of his compositions. The old man, who was shaving, stopped in the middle of it, and, with his face covered with lather, came to look at him, and said:

"What are you singing, boy?"

Jean-Christophe said he did not know.

"Sing it again!" said Jean Michel.

Jean-Christophe tried; he could not remember the tune. Proud of having attracted his grandfather's attention, he tried to make him admire his voice, and sang after his own fashion an air from some opera, but that was not what the old man wanted. Jean Michel said nothing, and seemed not to notice him any more. But he left the door of his room ajar while the boy was playing alone in the next room.

A few days later Jean-Christophe, with the chairs arranged about him, was playing a comedy in music, which he had made up of scraps that he remembered from the theater, and he was making steps and bows, as he had seen them done in a minuet, and addressing himself to the portrait of Beethoven which hung above the table. As he turned with a pirouette he saw his grandfather watching him through the half-open door. He thought the old man was laughing at him; he was abashed, and stopped dead; he ran to the window, and pressed his face against the panes, pretending that he had been watching something of the greatest interest. But the old man said nothing; he came to him and kissed him, and Jean-Christophe saw that he was pleased. His vanity made the most of these signs; he was clever enough to see that he had been appreciated; but he did not know exactly which his grandfather had admired most—his talent as a dramatic author, or as a musician, or as a singer, or as a dancer. He inclined to the latter, for he prided himself on this.

A week later, when he had forgotten the whole affair, his grandfather said mysteriously that he had something to show him. He opened his desk, took out a music-book, and put it on the rack of the piano, and told the boy to play. Jean-Christophe was very much interested, and deciphered it fairly well. The notes were written by hand in the old man's large handwriting, and he had taken special pains with it. The headings were adorned with scrolls and flourishes. After some moments the old man, who was sitting beside Jean-Christophe turning the pages for him, asked him what the music was. Jean-Christophe had been too much absorbed in his playing to notice what he

had played, and said that he did not know it.

"Listen! . . . You don't know it?"

Yes; he thought he knew it, but he did not know where he had heard it. The old man laughed.

"Think."

Jean-Christophe shook his head.

"I don't know."

A light was fast dawning in his mind; it seemed to him that the air . . . But, no! He dared not. . . . He would not recognize it.

"I don't know, grandfather."

He blushed.

"What, you little fool, don't you see that it is your own?"

He was sure of it, but to hear it said made his heart thump.

"Oh! grandfather! . . ."

Beaming, the old man showed him the book.

"See: *Aria*. It is what you were singing on Tuesday when you were lying on the floor. *March*. That is what I asked you to sing again last week, and you could not remember it. *Minuet*. That is what you were dancing by the armchair. Look!"

On the cover was written in wonderful Gothic letters:

"The Pleasures of Childhood: Aria, Minuetto, Valse, and Marcia, Op. 1, by Jean-Christophe Krafft."

Jean-Christophe was dazzled by it. To see his name, and that fine title, and that large book—his work! . . . He went on murmuring:

"Oh! grandfather! grandfather! . . ."

The old man drew him to him. Jean-Christophe threw himself on his knees, and hid his head in Jean Michel's bosom. He was covered with blushes from his happiness. The old man was even happier, and went on, in a voice which he tried to make indifferent, for he felt that he was on the point of breaking down:

"Of course, I added the accompaniment and the harmony to fit the song. And then"—he coughed—"and then, I added a *trio* to the minuet, because . . . because it is usual . . . and then . . . I think it is not at all bad."

He played it. Jean-Christophe was very proud of collaborating with his grandfather.

"But, grandfather, you must put your name to it too."

"It is not worth while. It is not worth while others besides yourself knowing it. Only"—here his voice trembled—"only, later on, when I am no more, it will remind you of your old grandfather . . . eh? You won't forget him?"

The poor old man did not say that he had been unable to resist the quite innocent pleasure of introducing one of his own unfortunate airs into his grandson's work, which he felt was destined to survive him; but his desire to share in this imaginary glory was very humble and very touching, since it was enough for him anonymously to transmit to posterity a scrap of his own thought, so as not altogether to perish. Jean-Christophe was touched by it, and covered his face with kisses, and the old man, growing more and more tender, kissed his hair.

"You will remember me? Later on, when you are a good musician, a great artist, who will bring honor to his family, to his art, and to his country, when you are famous, you will remember that it was your old grandfather who first perceived it, and foretold what you would be?"

There were tears in his eyes as he listened to his own words. He was reluctant to let such signs of weakness be seen. He had an attack of coughing, became moody, and sent the boy away hugging the precious manuscript.

Jean-Christophe went home bewildered by his happiness. The stones danced about him. The reception he had

from his family sobered him a little. When he blurted out the splendor of his musical exploit they cried out upon him. His mother laughed at him. Melchior declared that the old man was mad, and that he would do better to take care of himself than to set about turning the boy's head. As for Jean-Christophe, he would oblige by putting such follies from his mind, and sitting down *illico* at the piano and playing exercises for four hours. He must first learn to play properly; and as for composing, there was plenty of time for that later on when he had nothing better to do.

Melchior was not, as these words of wisdom might indicate, trying to keep the boy from the dangerous exaltation of a too early pride. On the contrary, he proved immediately that this was not so. But never having himself had any idea to express in music, and never having had the least need to express an idea, he had come, as a *virtuoso*, to consider composing a secondary matter, which was only given value by the art of the executant. He was not insensible of the tremendous enthusiasm roused by great composers like Hassler. For such ovations he had the respect which he always paid to success—mingled, perhaps, with a little secret jealousy—for it seemed to him that such applause was stolen from him. But he knew by experience that the successes of the great *virtuosi* are no less remarkable, and are more personal in character, and therefore more fruitful of agreeable and flattering consequences. He affected to pay profound homage to the genius of the master musicians; but he took a great delight in telling absurd anecdotes of them, presenting their intelligence and morals in a lamentable light. He placed the *virtuoso* at the top of the artistic ladder, for, he said, it is well known that the tongue is the noblest member of the body, and what would thought be without words? What would music be without the executant? But whatever may have been the reason for the scolding that he gave Jean-Christophe, it was not without its uses in restoring some common sense to the boy, who was almost beside himself with his grandfather's praises. It was not quite enough. Jean-Christophe, of course, decided that his grandfather was much cleverer than his father, and though he sat down at the piano without sulking, he did so not so much for the sake of obedience as to be able to dream in peace, as he always did while his fingers ran mechanically over the keyboard. While he played his interminable exercises he heard a proud voice inside himself saying over and over again: "I am a composer—a great composer."

From that day on, since he was a composer, he set himself to composing. Before he had even learned to write, he continued to cipher crotchets and quavers on scraps of paper, which he tore from the household account-books. But in the effort to find out what he was thinking, and to set it down in black and white, he arrived at thinking nothing, except when he wanted to think something. But he did not for that give up making musical phrases, and as he was a born musician he made them somehow, even if they meant nothing at all. Then he would take them in triumph to his grandfather, who wept with joy over them—he wept easily now that he was growing old—and vowed that they were wonderful.

All this was like to spoil him altogether. Fortunately, his own good sense saved him, helped by the influence of a man who made no pretension of having any influence over anybody, and set nothing before the eyes of the world but a common-sense point of view. This man was Louisa's brother.

Like her, he was small, thin, puny, and rather round-shouldered. No one knew exactly how old he was; he could not be more than forty, but he looked more than fifty. He had a little wrinkled face, with a pink complexion, and kind pale blue eyes, like faded forget-me-nots. When he took off his cap, which he used fussily to wear everywhere from his fear of draughts, he exposed a little pink bald head, conical in shape, which was the great delight of Jean-Christophe and his brothers. They never left off teasing him about it, asking him what he had done with his hair, and, encouraged by Melchior's pleasantries, threatening to smack it. He was the first to laugh at them, and put up with their treatment of him patiently. He was a peddler; he used to go from village to village with a pack on his back, containing everything—groceries, stationery, confectionery, handkerchiefs, scarves, shoes, pickles, almanacs, songs, and drugs. Several attempts had been made to make him settle down, and to buy him a little business—a store or a drapery shop. But he could not do it. One night he would get up, push the key under the door, and set off again with his pack. Weeks and months went by before he was seen again. Then he would reappear. Some evening they would hear him fumbling at the door; it would half open, and the little bald head, politely uncovered, would appear with its kind eyes and timid smile. He would say, "Good-evening, everybody," carefully wipe his shoes before entering, salute everybody, beginning with the eldest, and go and sit in the most remote corner of the room. There he would light his pipe, and sit huddled up, waiting quietly until the usual storm of questions was over. The two Kraffts, Jean-Christophe's father and grandfather, had a jeering contempt for him. The little freak seemed ridiculous to them, and their pride was touched by the low degree of the peddler. They made him feel it, but he seemed to take no notice of it, and showed them a profound respect which disarmed them, especially the old man, who was very sensitive to what people thought of him. They used to crush him with heavy pleasantries, which often brought the blush to Louisa's cheeks. Accustomed to bow without dispute to the intellectual superiority of the Kraffts, she had no doubt that her husband and father-in-law were right; but she loved her brother, and her brother had for her a dumb adoration. They were the only members of their family, and they were both humble, crushed, and thrust aside by life; they were united in sadness and tenderness by a bond of mutual pity and common suffering, borne in secret. With the Kraffts—robust, noisy, brutal, solidly built for living, and living joyously— these two weak, kindly creatures, out of their setting, so to speak, outside life, understood and pitied each other without ever saying anything about it.

Jean-Christophe, with the cruel carelessness of childhood, shared the contempt of his father and grandfather for the little peddler. He made fun of him, and treated him as a comic figure; he worried him with stupid teasing, which his uncle bore with his unshakable phlegm. But Jean-Christophe loved him, without quite knowing why. He loved him first of all as a plaything with which he did what he liked. He loved him also because he always gave him something nice—a dainty, a picture, an amusing toy. The little man's return was a joy for the children, for he always had some surprise for them. Poor as he was, he always contrived to bring them each a present, and he never forgot the birthday of any one of the family. He always turned up on these august days, and brought out of his pocket some jolly present, lovingly chosen. They were so used to it that they hardly thought of thanking him; it seemed natural, and he

appeared to be sufficiently repaid by the pleasure he had given. But Jean-Christophe, who did not sleep very well, and during the night used to turn over in his mind the events of the day, used sometimes to think that his uncle was very kind, and he used to be filled with floods of gratitude to the poor man. He never showed it when the day came, because he thought that the others would laugh at him. Besides, he was too little to see in kindness all the rare value that it has. In the language of children, kind and stupid are almost synonymous, and Uncle Gottfried seemed to be the living proof of it.

One evening when Melchior was dining out, Gottfried was left alone in the living-room, while Louisa put the children to bed. He went out, and sat by the river a few yards away from the house. Jean-Christophe, having nothing better to do, followed him, and, as usual, tormented him with his puppy tricks until he was out of breath, and dropped down on the grass at his feet. Lying on his belly, he buried his nose in the turf. When he had recovered his breath, he cast about for some new crazy thing to say. When he found it he shouted it out, and rolled about with laughing, with his face still buried in the earth. He received no answer. Surprised by the silence, he raised his head, and began to repeat his joke. He saw Gottfried's face lit up by the last beams of the setting sun cast through golden mists. He swallowed down his words. Gottfried smiled with his eyes half closed and his mouth half open, and in his sorrowful face was an expression of sadness and unutterable melancholy. Jean-Christophe, with his face in his hands, watched him. The night came; little by little Gottfried's face disappeared. Silence reigned. Jean-Christophe in his turn was filled with the mysterious impressions which had been reflected on Gottfried's face. He fell into a vague stupor. The earth was in darkness, the sky was bright; the stars peeped out. The little waves of the river chattered against the bank. The boy grew sleepy. Without seeing them, he bit off little blades of grass. A grasshopper chirped near him. It seemed to him that he was going to sleep.

Suddenly, in the dark, Gottfried began to sing. He sang in a weak, husky voice, as though to himself; he could not have been heard twenty yards away. But there was sincerity and emotion in his voice; it was as though he were thinking aloud, and that through the song, as through clear water, the very inmost heart of him was to be seen. Never had Jean-Christophe heard such singing, and never had he heard such a song. Slow, simple, childish, it moved gravely, sadly, a little monotonously, never hurrying—with long pauses—then setting out again on its way, careless where it arrived, and losing itself in the night. It seemed to cóme from far away, and it went no man knows whither. Its serenity was full of sorrow, and beneath its seeming peace there dwelt an agony of the ages. Jean-Christophe held his breath; he dared not move; he was cold with emotion. When it was done he crawled towards Gottfried, and in a choking voice said:

"Uncle!"

Gottfried did not reply.

"Uncle!" repeated the boy, placing his hands and chin on Gottfried's knees.

Gottfried said kindly:

"Well, boy . . ."

"What is it, uncle? Tell me! What were you singing?"

"I don't know."

"Tell me what it is!"

"I don't know. Just a song."

"A song that you made?"

"No, not I! What an idea! . . . It is an old song."

"Who made it?"

"No one knows. . . ."

"When?"

"No one knows. . . ."

"When you were little?"

"Before I was born, before my father was born, and before his father, and before his father's father. . . . It has always been."

"How strange! No one has ever told me about it."

He thought for a moment.

"Uncle, do you know any other?"

"Yes."

"Sing another, please."

"Why should I sing another? One is enough. One sings when one wants to sing, when one has to sing. One must not sing for the fun of it."

"But what about when one makes music?"

"That is not music."

The boy was lost in thought. He did not quite understand. But he asked for no explanation. It was true, it was not music, not like all the rest. He went on:

"Uncle, have you ever made them?"

"Made what?"

"Songs!"

"Songs? Oh! How should I make them? They can't be made."

With his usual logic the boy insisted:

"But, uncle, it must have been made once. . . ."

Gottfried shook his head obstinately.

"It has always been."

The boy returned to the attack:

"But, uncle, isn't it possible to make other songs, new songs?"

"Why make them? There are enough for everything. There are songs for when you are sad, and for when you are gay; for when you are weary, and for when you are thinking of home; for when you despise yourself, because you have been a vile sinner, a worm upon the earth; for when you want to weep, because people have not been kind to you; and for when your heart is glad because the world is beautiful, and you see God's heaven, which, like Him, is always kind, and seems to laugh at you. . . . There are songs for everything, everything. Why should I make them?"

"To be a great man!" said the boy, full of his grandfather's teaching and his simple dreams.

Gottfried laughed softly. Jean-Christophe, a little hurt, asked him:

"Why are you laughing?"

Gottfried said:

"Oh! I? . . . I am nobody."

He kissed the boy's head, and said:

"You want to be a great man?"

"Yes," said Jean-Christophe proudly. He thought Gottfried would admire him. But Gottfried replied:

"What for?"

Jean-Christophe was taken aback. He thought for a moment, and said:

"To make beautiful songs!"

Gottfried laughed again, and said:

"You want to make beautiful songs, so as to be a great man; and you want to be a great man, so as to make beautiful songs. You are like a dog chasing its own tail."

Jean-Christophe was dashed. At any other time he would not have borne his uncle laughing at him, he at whom he was used to laughing. And, at the same time, he would never have thought Gottfried clever enough to stump him with an argument. He cast about for some answer or some impertinence to throw at him, but could find none. Gottfried went on:

"When you are as great as from here to Coblentz, you will never make a single song."

Jean-Christophe revolted on that.

"And if I will! . . ."

"The more you want to, the less you can. To make songs, you have to be like those creatures. Listen. . . ."

The moon had risen, round and gleaming, behind the fields. A silvery mist hovered above the ground and the shim-

mering waters. The frogs croaked, and in the meadows the melodious fluting of the toads arose. The shrill tremolo of the grasshoppers seemed to answer the twinkling of the stars. The wind rustled softly in the branches of the alders. From the hills above the river there came down the sweet light song of a nightingale.

"What need is there to sing?" sighed Gottfried, after a long silence. (It was not clear whether he were talking to himself or to Jean-Christophe.) "Don't they sing sweeter than anything that you could make?"

Jean-Christophe had often heard these sounds of the night, and he loved them. But never had he heard them as he heard them now. It was true: what need was there to sing? . . . His heart was full of tenderness and sorrow. He was fain to embrace the meadows, the river, the sky, the clear stars. He was filled with love for his uncle Gottfried, who seemed to him now the best, the cleverest, the most beautiful of men. He thought how he had misjudged him, and he thought that his uncle was sad because he, Jean-Christophe, had misjudged him. He was remorseful. He wanted to cry out: "Uncle, do not be sad! I will not be naughty again. Forgive me, I love you!" But he dared not. And suddenly he threw himself into Gottfried's arms, but the words would not come, only he repeated, "I love you!" and kissed him passionately. Gottfried was surprised and touched, and went on saying, "What? What?" and kissed him. Then he got up, took him by the hand, and said: "We must go in." Jean-Christophe was sad because his uncle had not understood him. But as they came to the house, Gottfried said: "If you like we'll go again to hear God's music, and I will sing you some more songs." And when Jean-Christophe kissed him gratefully as they said goodnight, he saw that his uncle had understood.

Thereafter they often went for walks together in the evening, and they walked without a word along by the river, or through the fields. Gottfried slowly smoked his pipe, and Jean-Christophe, a little frightened by the darkness, would give him his hand. They would sit down on the grass, and after a few moments of silence Gottfried would talk to him about the stars and the clouds; he taught him to distinguish the breathing of the earth, air, and water, the songs, cries, and sounds of the little worlds of flying, creeping, hopping, and swimming things swarming in the darkness, and the signs of rain and fine weather, and the countless instruments of the symphony of the night. Sometimes Gottfried would sing tunes, sad or gay, but always of the same kind, and always in the end Jean-Christophe would be brought to the same sorrow. But he would never sing more than one song in an evening, and Jean-Christophe noticed that he did not sing gladly when he was asked to do so; it had to come of itself, just when he wanted to. Sometimes they had to wait for a long time without speaking, and just when Jean-Christophe was beginning to think, "He is not going to sing this evening," Gottfried would make up his mind.

One evening, when nothing would induce Gottfried to sing, Jean-Christophe thought of submitting to him one of his own small compositions, in the making of which he found so much trouble and pride. He wanted to show what an artist he was. Gottfried listened very quietly, and then said:

"That is very ugly, my poor dear Jean-Christophe!"

Jean-Christophe was so hurt that he could find nothing to say. Gottfried went on pityingly:

"Why did you do it? It is so ugly! No one forced you to do it."

Hot with anger, Jean-Christophe protested:

"My grandfather thinks my music fine."

"Ah!" said Gottfried, not turning a hair. "No doubt he is right. He is a learned man. He knows all about music. I know nothing about it. . . ."

And after a moment:

"But I think that is very ugly."

He looked quietly at Jean-Christophe, and saw his angry face, and smiled, and said:

"Have you composed any others? Perhaps I shall like the others better than that."

Jean-Christophe thought that his other compositions might wipe out the impression of the first, and he sang them all. Gottfried said nothing; he waited until they were finished. Then he shook his head, and with profound conviction said:

"They are even more ugly."

Jean-Christophe shut his lips, and his chin trembled; he wanted to cry. Gottfried went on as though he himself were upset.

"How ugly they are!"

Jean-Christophe, with tears in his voice, cried out:

"But why do you say they are ugly?"

Gottfried looked at him with his frank eyes.

"Why? . . . I don't know. . . . Wait. . . . They are ugly . . . first, because they are stupid. . . . Yes, that's it. . . . They are stupid, they don't mean anything. . . . You see? When you wrote, you had nothing to say. Why did you write them?"

"I don't know," said Jean-Christophe, in a piteous voice. "I wanted to write something pretty."

"There you are! You wrote for the sake of writing. You wrote because you wanted to be a great musician, and to be admired. You have been proud; you have been a liar; you have been punished. . . . You see! A man is always punished when he is proud and a liar in music.

Music must be modest and sincere—or else, what is it? Impious, a blasphemy of the Lord, who has given us song to tell the honest truth."

He saw the boy's distress, and tried to kiss him. But Jean-Christophe turned angrily away, and for several days he sulked. He hated Gottfried. But it was in vain that he said over and over to himself: "He is an ass! He knows nothing—nothing! My grandfather, who is much cleverer, likes my music." In his heart he knew that his uncle was right, and Gottfried's words were graven on his innermost soul; he was ashamed to have been a liar.

And, in spite of his resentment, he always thought of it when he was writing music, and often he tore up what he had written, being ashamed already of what Gottfried would have thought of it. When he got over it, and wrote a melody which he knew to be not quite sincere, he hid it carefully from his uncle; he was fearful of his judgment, and was quite happy when Gottfried just said of one of his pieces: "That is not so very ugly. . . . I like it. . . ."

Sometimes, by way of revenge, he used to trick him by giving him as his own melodies from the great musicians, and he was delighted when it happened that Gottfried disliked them heartily. But that did not trouble Gottfried. He would laugh loudly when he saw Jean-Christophe clap his hands and dance about him delightedly, and he always returned to his usual argument: "It is well enough written, but it says nothing." He always refused to be present at one of the little concerts given in Melchior's house. However beautiful the music might be, he would begin to yawn and look sleepy with boredom. Very soon he would be unable to bear it any longer, and would steal away quietly. He used to say:

"You see, my boy, everything that you write in the house is not music. Music in a house is like sunshine in a room. Music is to be found outside where you breathe God's dear fresh air."

He was always talking of God, for he was very pious, unlike the two Kraffts, father and son, who were free-thinkers, and took care to eat meat on Fridays.

Suddenly, for no apparent reason, Melchior changed his opinion. Not only did he approve of his father having put together Jean-Christophe's inspirations, but, to the boy's great surprise, he spent several evenings in making two or three copies of his manuscript. To every question put to him on the subject, he replied impressively, "We shall see; . . ." or he would rub his hands and laugh, smack the boy's head by way of a joke, or turn him up and blithely spank him. Jean-Christophe loathed these familiarities, but he saw that his father was pleased, and did not know why.

Then there were mysterious confabulations between Melchior and his father. And one evening Jean-Christophe, to his astonishment, learned that he, Jean-Christophe, had dedicated to H.S.H. the Grand Duke Leopold the *Pleasures of Childhood*. Melchior had sounded the disposition of the Prince, who had shown himself graciously inclined to accept the homage. Thereupon Melchior declared that without losing a moment they must, *primo*, draw up the official request to the Prince; *secondo*, publish the work; *tertio*, organize a concert to give it a hearing.

There were further long conferences between Melchior and Jean Michel. They argued heatedly for two or three evenings. It was forbidden to interrupt them. Melchior wrote, erased; erased, wrote. The old man talked loudly, as though he were reciting verses. Sometimes they squabbled or thumped on the table because they could not find a word.

Then Jean-Christophe was called,

made to sit at the table with a pen in his hand, his father on his right, his grandfather on his left, and the old man began to dictate words which he did not understand, because he found it difficult to write every word in his enormous letters, because Melchior was shouting in his ear, and because the old man declaimed with such emphasis that Jean-Christophe, put out by the sound of the words, could not bother to listen to their meaning. The old man was no less in a state of emotion. He could not sit still, and he walked up and down the room, involuntarily illustrating the text of what he read with gestures, but he came every minute to look over what the boy had written, and Jean-Christophe, frightened by the two large faces looking over his shoulder, put out his tongue, and held his pen clumsily. A mist floated before his eyes; he made too many strokes, or smudged what he had written; and Melchior roared, and Jean Michel stormed; and he had to begin again, and then again, and when he thought that they had at last come to an end, a great blot fell on the immaculate page. Then they pulled his ears, and he burst into tears; but they forbade him to weep, because he was spoiling the paper, and they began to dictate, beginning all over again, and he thought it would go on like that to the end of his life.

At last it was finished, and Jean Michel leaned against the mantelpiece, and read over their handiwork in a voice trembling with pleasure, while Melchior sat straddled across a chair, and looked at the ceiling and wagged his chair and, as a connoisseur, rolled round his tongue the style of the following epistle:

"Most Noble and Sublime Highness!
Most Gracious Lord!

"From my fourth year Music has been the first occupation of my childish days. So soon as I allied myself to the noble Muse, who roused my soul to pure harmony, I loved her, and, as it seemed to me, she returned my love. Now I am in my sixth year, and for some time my Muse in hours of inspiration has whispered in my ears: 'Be bold! Be bold! Write down the harmonies of thy soul!' 'Six years old,' thought I, 'and how should I be bold? What would the learned in the art say of me?' I hesitated. I trembled. But my Muse insisted. I obeyed. I wrote.

"And now shall I,

O Most Sublime Highness!

—shall I have the temerity and audacity to place upon the steps of Thy Throne the first-fruits of my youthful labors? . . . Shall I make so bold as to hope that Thou wilt let fall upon them the august approbation of Thy paternal regard? . . .

"Oh, yes! For Science and the Arts have ever found in Thee their sage Mæcenas, their generous champion, and talent puts forth its flowers under the ægis of Thy holy protection.

"In this profound and certain faith I dare, then, approach Thee with these youthful efforts. Receive them as a pure offering of my childish veneration, and of Thy goodness deign,

O Most Sublime Highness!

to glance at them, and at their young author, who bows at Thy feet deeply and in humility!

"From the most submissive, faithful, and obedient servant of His Most Noble and Most Sublime Highness,
      "JEAN-CHRISTOPHE KRAFFT."

Jean-Christophe heard nothing. He was very happy to have finished, and, fearing that he would be made to begin again, he ran away to the fields. He had no idea of what he had written, and he cared not at all. But when the old man had finished his reading he began again to taste the full flavor of it, and when the second reading came to an end Melchior and he declared that it was a little masterpiece. That was also the opinion of the Grand Duke, to whom the letter was presented, with a copy of the musical work. He was kind enough to send word that he found both quite charming. He granted permission for the concert, and ordered that the hall of his Academy of Music should be put at Melchior's disposal, and deigned to promise that he would have the young artist presented to himself on the day of the performance.

Melchior set about organizing the concert as quickly as possible. He engaged the support of the *Hof Musik Verein,* and as the success of his first ventures had blown out his sense of proportion, he undertook at the same time to publish a magnificent edition of the *Pleasures of Childhood.* He wanted to have printed on the cover of it a portrait of Jean-Christophe at the piano, with himself, Melchior, standing by his side, violin in hand. He had to abandon that, not on account of the cost—Melchior did not stop at any expense—but because there was not time enough. He fell back on an allegorical design representing a cradle, a trumpet, a drum, a wooden horse, grouped round a lyre which put forth rays like the sun. The title-page bore, together with a long dedication, in which the name of the Prince stood out in enormous letters, a notice to the effect that "Herr Jean-Christophe Krafft was six years old." He was, in fact, seven and a half. The printing of the design was very expensive. To meet the bill for it, Jean Michel had to sell an old eighteenth-century chest, carved with faces, which he had never consented to sell, in spite of the repeated offers of Wormser, the furniture-dealer. But Melchior had no doubt

but the subscriptions would cover the cost, and beyond that the expenses of printing the composition.

One other question occupied his mind: how to dress Jean-Christophe on the day of the concert. There was a family council to decide the matter. Melchior would have liked the boy to appear in a short frock and bare legs, like a child of four. But Jean-Christophe was very large for his age, and everybody knew him. They could not hope to deceive any one. Melchior had a great idea. He decided that the boy should wear a dress-coat and white tie. In vain did Louisa protest that they would make her poor boy ridiculous. Melchior anticipated exactly the success and merriment that would be produced by such an unexpected appearance. It was decided on, and the tailor came and measured Jean-Christophe for his little coat. He had also to have fine linen and patent-leather pumps, and all that swallowed up their last penny. Jean-Christophe was very uncomfortable in his new clothes. To make him used to them they made him try on his various garments. For a whole month he hardly left the piano-stool. They taught him to bow. He had never a moment of liberty. He raged against it, but dared not rebel, for he thought that he was going to accomplish something startling. He was both proud and afraid of it. They pampered him; they were afraid he would catch cold; they swathed his neck in scarves; they warmed his boots in case they were wet; and at table he had the best of everything.

At last the great day arrived. The barber came to preside over his toilet and curl Jean-Christophe's rebellious hair. He did not leave it until he had made it look like a sheep-skin. All the family walked round Jean-Christophe and declared that he was superb. Melchior, after looking him up and down, and turning him about and about, was seized with an idea, and went off to fetch a large flower, which he put in his buttonhole. But when Louisa saw him she raised her hands, and cried out distressfully that he looked like a monkey. That hurt him cruelly. He did not know whether to be ashamed or proud of his garb. Instinctively he felt humiliated, and he was more so at the concert. Humiliation was to be for him the outstanding emotion of that memorable day.

The concert was about to begin. The hall was half empty; the Grand Duke had not arrived. One of those kindly and well-informed friends who always appear on these occasions came and told them that there was a Council being held at the Palace, and that the Grand Duke would not come. He had it on good authority. Melchior was in despair. He fidgeted, paced up and down, and looked repeatedly out of the window. Old Jean Michel was also in torment, but he was concerned for his grandson. He bombarded him with instructions. Jean-Christophe was infected by the nervousness of his family. He was not in the least anxious about his compositions, but he was troubled by the thought of the bows that he had to make to the audience, and thinking of them brought him to agony.

However, he had to begin; the audience was growing impatient. The orchestra of the *Hof Musik Verein* began the *Coriolan Overture*. The boy knew neither Coriolan nor Beethoven, for though he had often heard Beethoven's music, he had not known it. He never bothered about the names of the works he heard. He gave them names of his own invention, while he created little stories or pictures for them. He classified them usually in three categories: fire, water, and earth, with a thousand degrees between each. Mozart belonged almost always to water. He was a meadow by the side of a river, a transparent mist floating over the water, a spring shower, or a rainbow. Beethoven was fire—now a furnace with gigantic flames and vast columns of smoke; now a burning forest, a heavy and terrible cloud, flashing lightning; now a wide sky full of quivering stars, one of which breaks free, swoops, and dies on a fine September night setting the heart beating. Now the imperious ardor of that heroic soul burned him like fire. Everything else disappeared. What was it all to him?—Melchior in despair, Jean Michel agitated, all the busy world, the audience, the Grand Duke, little Jean-Christophe. What had he to do with all these? What lay between them and him? Was that he—he, himself? . . . He was given up to the furious will that carried him headlong. He followed it breathlessly, with tears in his eyes, and his legs numb, thrilling from the palms of his hands to the soles of his feet. His blood drummed "Charge!" and he trembled in every limb. And as he listened so intensely, hiding behind a curtain, his heart suddenly leaped violently. The orchestra had stopped short in the middle of a bar, and after a moment's silence, it broke into a crashing of brass and cymbals with a military march, officially strident. The transition from one sort of music to another was so brutal, so unexpected, that Jean-Christophe ground his teeth and stamped his foot with rage, and shook his fist at the wall. But Melchior rejoiced. The Grand Duke had come in, and the orchestra was saluting him with the National Anthem. And in a trembling voice Jean Michel gave his last instructions to his grandson.

The overture began again, and this time was finished. It was now Jean-Christophe's turn. Melchior had arranged the program to show off at the same time the skill of both father and son. They were to play together a sonata of Mozart for violin and piano. For the sake of effect he had decided that Jean-Christophe should enter alone. He was led to the entrance of the stage and showed the piano at the front, and for the last time it was explained what he had to do, and then he was pushed on from the wings.

He was not much afraid, for he was used to the theater; but when he found himself alone on the platform, with hundreds of eyes staring at him, he became suddenly so frightened that instinctively he moved backwards and turned towards the wings to go back again. He saw his father there gesticulating and with his eyes blazing. He had to go on. Besides, the audience had seen him. As he advanced there arose a twittering of curiosity, followed soon by laughter, which grew louder and louder. Melchior had not been wrong, and the boy's garb had all the effect anticipated. The audience rocked with laughter at the sight of the child with his long hair and gipsy complexion timidly trotting across the platform in the evening dress of a man of the world. They got up to see him better. Soon the hilarity was general. There was nothing unkindly in it, but it would have made the most hardened musician lose his head. Jean-Christophe, terrified by the noise, and the eyes watching, and the glasses turned upon him, had only one idea: to reach the piano as quickly as possible, for it seemed to him a refuge, an island in the midst of the sea. With head down, looking neither to right nor left, he ran quickly across the platform, and when he reached the middle of it, instead of bowing to the audience, as had been arranged, he turned his back on it, and plunged straight for the piano. The chair was too high for him to sit down without his father's help, and in his distress, instead of waiting, he climbed up on to it on his knees. That increased the merriment of the audience, but now Jean-Christophe was safe. Sitting at his instrument, he was afraid of no one.

Melchior came at last. He gained by the good-humor of the audience, who welcomed him with warm applause. The sonata began. The boy played it with imperturbable certainty, with his lips pressed tight in concentration, his eyes fixed on the keys, his little legs hanging down from the chair. He became more at ease as the notes rolled out; he was among friends that he knew. A murmur of approbation reached him, and waves of pride and satisfaction surged through him as he thought that all these people were silent to listen to him and to admire him. But hardly had he finished when fear overcame him again, and the applause which greeted him gave him more shame than pleasure. His shame increased when Melchior took him by the hand, and advanced with him to the edge of the platform, and made him bow to the public. He obeyed, and bowed very low, with a funny awkwardness; but he was humiliated, and blushed for what he had done, as though it were a thing ridiculous and ugly.

He had to sit at the piano again, and he played the *Pleasures of Childhood*. Then the audience was enraptured. After each piece they shouted enthusiastically. They wanted him to begin again, and he was proud of his success and at the same time almost hurt by such applause, which was also a command. At the end the whole audience rose to acclaim him; the Grand Duke led the applause. But as Jean-Christophe was now alone on the platform he dared not budge from his seat. The applause redoubled. He bent his head lower and lower, blushing and hang-dog in expression, and he looked steadily away from the audience. Melchior came. He took him in his arms, and told him to blow kisses. He pointed out to him the Grand Duke's box. Jean-Christophe turned a deaf ear. Melchior took his arm, and threatened him in a low voice. Then he did as he was told passively, but he did not look at anybody, he did not raise his eyes, but went on turning his head away, and he was unhappy. He was suffering; how, he did not know. His vanity was suffering. He did not like the people who were there at all. It was no use their applauding; he could not forgive them for having laughed and for being amused by his humiliation; he could not forgive them for having seen him in such a ridiculous position—held in mid-air to blow kisses. He disliked them even for applauding, and when Melchior did at last put him down, he ran away to the wings. A lady threw a bunch of violets up at him as he went. It brushed his face. He was panic-stricken and ran as fast as he could, turning over a chair that was in his way. The faster he ran the more they laughed, and the more they laughed the faster he ran.

At last he reached the exit, which was filled with people looking at him. He forced his way through, butting, and ran and hid himself at the back of the ante-room. His grandfather was in high feather, and covered him with blessings. The musicians of the orchestra shouted with laughter, and congratulated the boy, who refused to look at them or to shake hands with them. Melchior listened intently, gauging the applause, which had not yet ceased, and wanted to take Jean-Christophe on to the stage again. But the boy refused angrily, clung to his grandfather's coat-tails, and kicked at everybody who came near him. At last he burst into tears, and they had to let him be.

Just at this moment an officer came to say that the Grand Duke wished the artists to go to his box. How could the child be presented in such a state? Melchior swore angrily, and his wrath only had the effect of making Jean-Christophe's tears flow faster. To stop them, his grandfather promised him a pound of chocolates if he would not cry any more, and Jean-Christophe, who was greedy, stopped dead, swallowed down his tears, and let them carry him off; but they had to swear at first most solemnly that they would not take him on to the platform again.

In the anteroom of the Grand Ducal box he was presented to a gentleman in a dress-coat, with a face like a pug-dog, bristling mustaches, and a short, pointed beard—a little red-faced man, inclined to stoutness, who addressed him with bantering familiarity, and called him "Mozart *redivivus!*" This was the Grand Duke. Then he was presented in turn to the Grand Duchess and her daughter, and their suite. But as he did not dare raise his eyes, the only thing he could remember of this brilliant company was a series of gowns and uniforms from the waist down to the feet. He sat on the lap of the young Princess, and dared not move or breathe. She asked him questions, which Melchior answered in an obsequious voice with formal replies, respectful and servile; but she did not listen to Melchior, and went on teasing the child. He grew redder and redder, and, thinking that everybody must have noticed it, he thought he must explain it away and said with a long sigh:

"My face is red. I am hot."

That made the girl shout with laughter. But Jean-Christophe did not mind it in her, as he had in his audience just before, for her laughter was pleasant, and she kissed him, and he did not dislike that.

Then he saw his grandfather in the passage at the door of the box, beaming and bashful. The old man was fain to show himself, and also to say a few words, but he dared not, because no one had spoken to him. He was enjoying his grandson's glory at a distance. Jean-Christophe became tender, and felt an irresistible impulse to procure justice also for the old man, so that they should know his worth. His tongue was loosed, and he reached up to the ear of his new friend and whispered to her:

"I will tell you a secret."

She laughed, and said:

"What?"

"You know," he went on—"you know the pretty *trio* in my *minuetto,* the *minuetto* I played? . . . You know it? . . ." (He hummed it gently.) ". . . Well, grandfather wrote it, not I. All the other airs are mine. But that is the best. Grandfather wrote it. Grandfather did not want me to say anything. You won't tell anybody? . . ." (He pointed out the old man.) "That is my grandfather. I love him; he is very kind to me."

At that the young Princess laughed again, said that he was a darling, covered him with kisses, and, to the consternation of Jean-Christophe and his grandfather, told everybody. Everybody laughed then, and the Grand Duke congratulated the old man, who was covered with confusion, tried in vain to explain himself, and stammered like a guilty criminal. But Jean-Christophe said not another word to the girl, and in spite of her wheedling he remained dumb and stiff. He despised her for having broken her promise. His idea of princes suffered considerably from this disloyalty. He was so angry about it that he did not hear anything that was said, or that the Prince had appointed him laughingly his pianist in ordinary, his *Hof Musicus.*

He went out with his relatives, and found himself surrounded in the corridors of the theater, and even in the street, with people congratulating him or kissing him. That displeased him greatly, for he did not like being kissed, and did not like people meddling with him without asking his permission.

At last they reached home, and then hardly was the door closed than Melchior began to call him a "little idiot" because he had said that the *trio* was not his own. As the boy was under the impression that he had done a fine thing, which deserved praise, and not blame, he rebelled, and was impertinent. Melchior lost his temper, and said that he would box his ears, although he had played his music well enough, because with his idiocy he had spoiled the whole effect of the concert. Jean-Christophe had a profound sense of justice. He went and sulked in a corner; he visited his contempt upon his father, the Princess, and the whole world. He was hurt also because the neighbors came and congratulated his parents and laughed with them, as if it were they who had played, and as if it were their affair.

At this moment a servant of the Court came with a beautiful gold watch from the Grand Duke and a box of lovely sweets from the young Princess. Both presents gave great pleasure to Jean-Christophe, and he did not know which gave him the more: but he was in such a bad temper that he would not admit it to himself, and he went on sulking, scowling at the sweets, and wondering whether he could properly accept a gift from a person who had betrayed his confidence. As he was on the point of giving in his father wanted to set him down at once at the table, and make him write at his dictation a letter of thanks. This was too much. Either from the nervous strain of the day, or from instinctive shame at beginning the letter, as Melchior wanted him to, with the words, "The little servant and musician—*Knecht und Musicus* —of Your Highness . . ." he burst into tears, and was inconsolable. The servant waited and scoffed. Melchior had to write the letter. That did not make him exactly kindly disposed towards Jean-Christophe. As a crowning misfortune, the boy let his watch fall and broke it. A storm of reproaches broke upon him. Melchior shouted that he would have to go without dessert. Jean-Christophe said angrily that

that was what he wanted. To punish him, Louisa said that she would begin by confiscating his sweets. Jean-Christophe was up in arms at that, and said that the box was his, and no one else's, and that no one should take it away from him! He was smacked, and in a fit of anger snatched the box from his mother's hands, hurled it on the floor, and stamped on it. He was whipped, taken to his room, undressed, and put to bed.

In the evening he heard his parents dining with friends—a magnificent repast, prepared a week before in honor of the concert. He was like to die with wrath at such injustice. They laughed loudly, and touched glasses. They had told the guests that the boy was tired, and no one bothered about him. Only after dinner, when the party was breaking up, he heard a slow, shuffling step come into his room, and old Jean Michel bent over his bed and kissed him, and said: "Dear little Jean-Christophe! . . ." Then, as if he were ashamed, he went away without another word. He had slipped into his hand some sweetmeats which he had hidden in his pocket.

That softened Jean-Christophe; but he was so tired with all the day's emotions that he had not the strength to think about what his grandfather had done. He had not even the strength to reach out to the good things the old man had given him. He was worn out, and went to sleep almost at once.

His sleep was light. He had acute nervous attacks, like electric shocks, which shook his whole body. In his dreams he was haunted by wild music. He awoke in the night. The Beethoven overture that he had heard at the concert was roaring in his ears. It filled the room with its mighty beat. He sat up in his bed, rubbed his eyes and ears, and asked himself if he were asleep. No; he was not asleep. He recognized the sound, he recognized those roars of anger, those savage cries;

he heard the throbbing of that passionate heart leaping in his bosom, that tumult of the blood; he felt on his face the frantic beating of the wind, lashing and destroying, then stopping suddenly, cut off by an Herculean will. That Titanic soul entered his body, blew out his limbs and his soul, and seemed to give them colossal proportions. He strode over all the world. He was like a mountain, and storms raged within him—storms of wrath, storms of sorrow! . . . Ah, what sorrow! . . . But they were nothing! He felt so strong! . . . To suffer—still to suffer! . . . Ah, how good it is to be strong! How good it is to suffer when a man is strong! . . .

He laughed. His laughter rang out in the silence of the night. His father woke up and cried:

"Who is there?"

His mother whispered:

"Ssh! the boy is dreaming!"

All then were silent; round them all was silence. The music died away, and nothing sounded but the regular breathing of the human creatures asleep in the room, comrades in misery, thrown together by Fate in the same frail barque, bound onwards by a wild whirling force through the night.

(Jean-Christophe's letter to the Grand Duke Leopold is inspired by Beethoven's letter to the Prince Elector of Bonn, written when he was eleven.)

YOUTH

Christofori faciem die quacunque tueris,
Illa nempe die non morte mala morieris.

I

THE HOUSE OF EULER

The house was plunged in silence. Since Melchior's death everything seemed dead. Now that his loud voice was stilled, from morning to night nothing was heard but the wearisome murmuring of the river.

Christophe hurled himself into his work. He took a fiercely angry pleasure in self-castigation for having wished to be happy. To expressions of sympathy and kind words he made no reply, but was proud and stiff. Without a word he went about his daily task, and gave his lessons with icy politeness. His pupils who knew of his misfortune were shocked by his insensibility. But those who were older and had some experience of sorrow knew that this apparent coldness might, in a child, be used only to conceal suffering: and they pitied him. He was not grateful for their sympathy. Even music could bring him no comfort. He played without pleasure, and as a duty. It was as though he found a cruel joy in no longer taking pleasure in anything, or in persuading himself that he did not: in depriving himself of every reason for living, and yet going on.

His two brothers, terrified by the silence of the house of death, ran away from it as quickly as possible. Rodolphe went into the office of his uncle Theodore, and lived with him, and Ernest, after trying two or three trades, found work on one of the Rhine steamers plying between Mainz and Cologne, and he used to come back only when he wanted money. Christophe was left alone with his mother in the house, which was too large for them; and the meagerness of their resources, and the payment of certain debts which had been discovered after his father's death, forced them, whatever pain it might cost, to seek another more lowly and less expensive dwelling.

They found a little flat,—two or three rooms on the second floor of a house in the Market Street. It was a noisy district in the middle of the town, far from the river, far from the trees, far from the country and all the familiar places. But they had to consult reason, not sentiment, and Christophe found in it a fine opportunity for gratifying his bitter creed of self-mortification. Besides, the owner of the house, old registrar Euler, was a friend of his grandfather, and knew the family: that was enough for Louisa, who was lost in her empty house, and was irresistibly drawn towards those who had known the creatures whom she had loved.

They got ready to leave. They took long draughts of the bitter melancholy of the last days passed by the sad, beloved fireside that was to be left forever. They dared hardly tell their sorrow: they were ashamed of it, or afraid. Each thought that they ought not to show their weakness to the other. At table, sitting alone in a dark room with half-closed shutters, they dared not raise their voices: they ate hurriedly and did not look at each other for fear of not being able to conceal their trouble. They parted as soon as they had finished. Christophe went back to his work; but as soon as he was free for a moment, he would come back, go stealthily home, and creep on tiptoe to his room or to the attic. Then he would shut the door, sit down in a corner on an old trunk or on the window-ledge, or stay there without thinking, letting the indefinable buzzing and humming of the old house, which trembled with the lightest tread, thrill through him. His heart would tremble with it. He would listen anxiously for the faintest breath in or out of doors, for the creaking of floors, for all the imperceptible familiar noises: he knew them all. He would lose consciousness, his thoughts would be filled with the images of the past, and he would issue from his stupor only at the sound of St. Martin's clock, reminding him that it was time to go.

In the room below him he could hear Louisa's footsteps passing softly to and fro, then for hours she could not be heard; she made no noise. Christophe would listen intently. He would go down, a little uneasy, as one is for a long time after a great misfortune. He would push the door ajar; Louisa would turn her back on him; she would be sitting in front of a cupboard in the midst of a heap of things—rags, old belongings, odd garments, treasures, which she had brought out intending to sort them. But she had no strength for it; everything reminded her of something; she would turn and turn it in her hands and begin to dream; it would drop from her hands; she would stay for hours together with her arms hanging down, lying back exhausted in a chair, given up to a stupor of sorrow.

Poor Louisa was now spending most of her life in the past—that sad past, which had been very niggardly of joy for her; but she was so used to suffering that she was still grateful for the least tenderness shown to her, and the pale lights which had shone here and there in the drab days of her life, were still enough to make them bright. All the evil that Melchior had done her was forgotten; she remembered only the good. Her marriage had been the great romance of her life. If Melchior had been drawn into it by a caprice, of which he had quickly repented, she had given herself with her whole heart; she thought that she was loved as much as she had loved; and to Melchior she was ever most tenderly grateful. She did not try to understand what he had become in the sequel. Incapable of seeing reality as it is, she only knew how to bear it as it is, humbly and honestly, as a woman who has no need of understanding life in order to be able to live. What she could not explain, she left to God for explanation. In her singular piety, she put upon God the responsibility for all the injustice that she had suffered at the hands of Melchior and the others, and only visited them with the

good that they had given her. And so her life of misery had left her with no bitter memory. She only felt worn out—weak as she was—by those years of privation and fatigue. And now that Melchior was no longer there, now that two of her sons were gone from their home, and the third seemed to be able to do without her, she had lost all heart for action; she was tired, sleepy; her will was stupefied. She was going through one of those crises of neurasthenia which often come upon active and industrious people in the decline of life, when some unforeseen event deprives them of every reason for living. She had not the heart even to finish the stocking she was knitting, to tidy the drawer in which she was looking, to get up to shut the window; she would sit there, without a thought, without strength—save for recollection. She was conscious of her collapse, and was ashamed of it or blushed for it; she tried to hide it from her son; and Christophe, wrapped up in the egoism of his own grief, never noticed it. No doubt he was often secretly impatient with his mother's slowness in speaking, and acting, and doing the smallest thing; but different though her ways were from her usual activity, he never gave a thought to the matter until then.

Suddenly on that day it came home to him for the first time when he surprised her in the midst of her rags, turned out on the floor, heaped up at her feet, in her arms, and in her lap. Her neck was drawn out, her head was bowed, her face was stiff and rigid. When she heard him come in she started; her white cheeks were suffused with red; with an instinctive movement she tried to hide the things she was holding, and muttered with an awkward smile:

"You see, I was sorting . . ."

The sight of the poor soul stranded among the relics of the past cut to his heart, and he was filled with pity. But he spoke with a bitter asperity and seemed to scold, to drag her from her apathy:

"Come, come, mother; you must not stay there, in the middle of all that dust, with the room all shut up! It is not good for you. You must pull yourself together, and have done with all this."

"Yes," said she meekly.

She tried to get up to put the things back in the drawer. But she sat down again at once and listlessly let them fall from her hands.

"Oh! I can't . . . I can't," she moaned. "I shall never finish!"

He was frightened. He leaned over her. He caressed her forehead with his hands.

"Come, mother, what is it?" he said. "Shall I help you? Are you ill?"

She did not answer. She gave a sort of stifled sob. He took her hands, and knelt down by her side, the better to see her in the dusky room.

"Mother!" he said anxiously.

Louisa laid her head on his shoulder and burst into tears.

"My boy, my boy," she cried, holding close to him. "My boy! . . . You will not leave me? Promise me that you will not leave me?"

His heart was torn with pity.

"No, mother, no. I will not leave you. What made you think of such a thing?"

"I am so unhappy! They have all left me, all. . . ."

She pointed to the things all about her, and he did not know whether she was speaking of them or of her sons and the dead.

"You will stay with me? You will not leave me? . . . What should I do, if you went too?"

"I will not go, I tell you; we will stay together. Don't cry. I promise."

She went on weeping. She could not stop herself. He dried her eyes with his handkerchief.

"What is it, mother dear? Are you in pain?"

"I don't know; I don't know what it is." She tried to calm herself and to smile.

"I do try to be sensible. I do. But just nothing at all makes me cry. . . . You see, I'm doing it again. . . . Forgive me. I am so stupid. I am old. I have no strength left. I have no taste for anything any more. I am no good for anything. I wish I were buried with all the rest. . . ."

He held her to him, close, like a child.

"Don't worry, mother; be calm; don't think about it. . . ."

Gradually she grew quiet.

"It is foolish. I am ashamed. . . . But what is it? What is it?"

She who had always worked so hard could not understand why her strength had suddenly snapped, and she was humiliated to the very depths of her being. He pretended not to see it.

"A little weariness, mother," he said, trying to speak carelessly. "It is nothing; you will see; it is nothing."

But he too was anxious. From his childhood he had been accustomed to see her brave, resigned, in silence withstanding every test. And he was astonished to see her suddenly broken: he was afraid.

He helped her to sort the things scattered on the floor. Every now and then she would linger over something, but he would gently take it from her hands, and she suffered him.

From that time on he took pains to be more with her. As soon as he had finished his work, instead of shutting himself up in his room, as he loved to do, he would return to her. He felt her loneliness and that she was not strong enough to be left alone: there was danger in leaving her alone.

He would sit by her side in the evening near the open window looking on to the road. The view would slowly disappear. The people were returning home. Little lights appeared in the houses far off.

They had seen it all a thousand times. But soon they would see it no more. They would talk disjointedly. They would point out to each other the smallest of the familiar incidents and expectations of the evening, always with fresh interest. They would have long intimate silences, or Louisa, for no apparent reason, would tell some reminiscence, some disconnected story that passed through her mind. Her tongue was loosed a little now that she felt that she was with one who loved her. She tried hard to talk. It was difficult for her, for she had grown used to living apart from her family; she looked upon her sons and her husband as too clever to talk to her, and she had never dared to join in their conversation. Christophe's tender care was a new thing to her and infinitely sweet, though it made her afraid. She deliberated over her words; she found it difficult to express herself; her sentences were left unfinished and obscure. Sometimes she was ashamed of what she was saying; she would look at her son, and stop in the middle of her narrative. But he would press her hand, and she would be reassured. He was filled with love and pity for the childish, motherly creature, to whom he had turned when he was a child, and now she turned to him for support. And he took a melancholy pleasure in her prattle, that had no interest for anybody but himself, in her trivial memories of a life that had always been joyless and mediocre, though it seemed to Louisa to be of infinite worth. Sometimes he would try to interrupt her; he was afraid that her memories would make her sadder than ever, and he would urge her to sleep. She would understand what he was at, and would say with gratitude in her eyes:

"No. I assure you, it does one good; let us stay a little longer."

They would stay until the night was far gone and the neighbors were abed.

Then they would say good-night, she a little comforted by being rid of some of her trouble, he with a heavy heart under this new burden added to that which already he had to bear.

The day came for their departure. On the night before they stayed longer than usual in the unlighted room. They did not speak. Every now and then Louisa moaned: "Fear God! Fear God!" Christophe tried to keep her attention fixed on the thousand details of the morrow's removal. She would not go to bed until he gently compelled her. But he went up to his room and did not go to bed for a long time. When leaning out of the window he tried to gaze through the darkness to see for the last time the moving shadows of the river beneath the house. He heard the wind in the tall trees in Minna's garden. The sky was black. There was no one in the street. A cold rain was just falling. The weathercocks creaked. In a house nearby a child was crying. The night weighed with an overwhelming heaviness upon the earth and upon his soul. The dull chiming of the hours, the cracked note of the halves and quarters, dropped one after another into the grim silence, broken only by the sound of the rain on the roofs and the cobbles.

When Christophe at last made up his mind to go to bed, chilled in body and soul, he heard the window below him shut. And, as he lay, he thought sadly that it is cruel for the poor to dwell on the past, for they have no right to have a past, like the rich: they have no home, no corner of the earth wherein to house their memories: their joys, their sorrows, all their days, are scattered in the wind.

Next day in beating rain they moved their scanty furniture to their new dwelling. Fischer, the old furniture dealer, lent them a cart and a pony; he came and helped them himself. But they could not take everything, for the rooms to which they were going were much smaller than the old. Christophe had to make his mother leave the oldest and most useless of their belongings. It was not altogether easy; the least thing had its worth for her: a shaky table, a broken chair, she wished to leave nothing behind. Fischer, fortified by the authority of his old friendship with Jean Michel, had to join Christophe in complaining, and, good-fellow that he was and understanding her grief, had even to promise to keep some of her precious rubbish for her against the day when she should want it again. Then she agreed to tear herself away.

The two brothers had been told of the removal, but Ernest came on the night before to say that he could not be there, and Rodolphe appeared for a moment about noon; he watched them load the furniture, gave some advice, and went away again looking mightily busy.

The procession set out through the muddy streets. Christophe led the horse, which slipped on the greasy cobbles. Louisa walked by her son's side, and tried to shelter him from the rain. And so they had a melancholy homecoming in the damp rooms, that were made darker than ever by the dull light coming from the lowering sky. They could not have fought against the depression that was upon them had it not been for the attentions of their landlord and his family. But, when the cart had driven away, as night fell, leaving the furniture heaped up in the room; and Christophe and Louisa were sitting, worn out, one on a box, the other on a sack; they heard a little dry cough on the staircase; there was a knock at the door. Old Euler came in. He begged pardon elaborately for disturbing his guests, and said that by way of celebrating their first evening he hoped that they would be kind enough to sup with himself and his family. Louisa, stunned by her sorrow, wished to refuse. Christophe was not much more tempted than

she by this friendly gathering, but the old man insisted and Christophe, thinking that it would be better for his mother not to spend their first evening in their new home alone with her thoughts, made her accept.

They went down to the floor below, where they found the whole family collected: the old man, his daughter, his son-in-law, Vogel, and his grandchildren, a boy and a girl, both a little younger than Christophe. They clustered around their guests, bade them welcome, asked if they were tired, if they were pleased with their rooms, if they needed anything; putting so many questions that Christophe in bewilderment could make nothing of them, for everybody spoke at once. The soup was placed on the table; they sat down. But the noise went on. Amalia, Euler's daughter, had set herself at once to acquaint Louisa with local details: with the topography of the district, the habits and advantages of the house, the time when the milkman called, the time when she got up, the various trades-people and the prices that she paid. She did not stop until she had explained everything. Louisa, half-asleep, tried hard to take an interest in the information, but the remarks which she ventured showed that she had understood not a word, and provoked Amalia to indignant exclamations and repetition of every detail. Old Euler, a clerk, tried to explain to Christophe the difficulties of a musical career. Christophe's other neighbor, Rosa, Amalia's daughter, never stopped talking from the moment when they sat down,— so volubly that she had no time to breathe; she lost her breath in the middle of a sentence, but at once she was off again. Vogel was gloomy and complained of the food, and there were embittered arguments on the subject. Amalia, Euler, the girl, left off talking to take part in the discussion; and there were endless controversies as to whether there was too much salt in the stew or not enough; they called each other to witness, and, naturally, no two opinions were the same. Each despised his neighbor's taste, and thought only his own healthy and reasonable. They might have gone on arguing until the Last Judgment.

But, in the end, they all joined in crying out upon the bad weather. They all commiserated Louisa and Christophe upon their troubles, and in terms which moved him greatly they praised him for his courageous conduct. They took great pleasure in recalling not only the misfortunes of their guests, but also their own, and those of their friends and all their acquaintance, and they all agreed that the good are always unhappy, and that there is joy only for the selfish and dishonest. They decided that life is sad, that it is quite useless, and that they were all better dead, were it not the indubitable will of God that they should go on living so as to suffer. As these ideas came very near to Christophe's actual pessimism, he thought the better of his landlord, and closed his eyes to their little oddities.

When he went upstairs again with his mother to the disordered rooms, they were weary and sad, but they felt a little less lonely; and while Christophe lay awake through the night, for he could not sleep because of his weariness and the noise of the neighborhood, and listened to the heavy carts shaking the walls, and the breathing of the family sleeping below, he tried to persuade himself that he would be, if not happy, at least less unhappy here, with these good people—a little tiresome, if the truth be told—who suffered from like misfortunes, who seemed to understand him, and whom, he thought, he understood.

But when at last he did fall asleep, he was roused unpleasantly at dawn by the voices of his neighbors arguing, and the creaking of a pump worked furiously by some one who was in a hurry to swill the yard and the stairs.

Justus Euler was a little bent old man, with uneasy, gloomy eyes, a red face, all lines and pimples, gap-toothed, with an unkempt beard, with which he was forever fidgeting with his hands. Very honest, quite able, profoundly moral, he had been on quite good terms with Christophe's grandfather. He was said to be like him. And, in truth, he was of the same generation and brought up with the same principles; but he lacked Jean Michel's strong physique, that is, while he was of the same opinion on many points, fundamentally he was hardly at all like him, for it is temperament far more than ideas that makes a man, and whatever the divisions, fictitious or real, marked between men by intellect, the great divisions between men and men are into those who are healthy and those who are not. Old Euler was not a healthy man. He talked morality, like Jean Michel, but his morals were not the same as Jean Michel's; he had not his sound stomach, his lungs, or his jovial strength. Everything in Euler and his family was built on a more parsimonious and niggardly plan. He had been an official for forty years, was now retired, and suffered from that melancholy that comes from inactivity and weighs so heavily upon old men, who have not made provision in their inner life for their last years. All his habits, natural and acquired, all the habits of his trade had given him a meticulous and peevish quality, which was reproduced to a certain extent in each of his children.

His son-in-law, Vogel, a clerk at the Chancery Court, was fifty years old. Tall, strong, almost bald, with gold spectacles, fairly good-looking, he considered himself ill, and no doubt was so, although obviously he did not have the diseases which he thought he had, but only a mind soured by the stupidity of his calling and a body ruined to a certain extent by his sedentary life. Very industrious, not without merit, even cultured up to a point, he was a victim of our ridiculous modern life, or like so many clerks, locked up in their offices, he had succumbed to the demon of hypochondria. One of those unfortunates whom Goethe called *"ein trauriger, ungriechischer Hypochondrist"*—"a gloomy and un-Greek hypochondriac,"—and pitied, though he took good care to avoid them.

Amalia was neither the one nor the other. Strong, loud, and active, she wasted no sympathy on her husband's jeremiads; she used to shake him roughly. But no human strength can bear up against living together, and when in a household one or other is neurasthenic, the chances are that in time they will both be so. In vain did Amalia cry out upon Vogel, in vain did she go on protesting either from habit or because it was necessary; next moment she herself was lamenting her condition more loudly even than he, and, passing imperceptibly from scolding to lamentation, she did him no good; she increased his ills tenfold by loudly singing chorus to his follies. In the end not only did she crush the unhappy Vogel, terrified by the proportions assumed by his own outcries sent sounding back by this echo, but she crushed everybody, even herself. In her turn she caught the trick of unwarrantably bemoaning her health, and her father's, and her daughter's, and her son's. It became a mania; by constant repetition she came to believe what she said. She took the least chill tragically; she was uneasy and worried about everybody. More than that, when they were well, she still worried, because of the sickness that was bound to come. So life was passed in perpetual fear. Outside that

they were all in fairly good health, and it seemed as though their state of continual moaning and groaning did serve to keep them well. They all ate and slept and worked as usual, and the life of this household was not relaxed for it all. Amalia's activity was not satisfied with working from morning to night up and down the house; they all had to toil with her, and there was forever a moving of furniture, a washing of floors, a polishing of wood, a sound of voices, footsteps, quivering, movement.

The two children, crushed by such loud authority, leaving nobody alone, seemed to find it natural enough to submit to it. The boy, Leonard, was good looking, though insignificant of feature, and stiff in manner. The girl, Rosa, fair-haired, with pretty blue eyes, gentle and affectionate, would have been pleasing especially with the freshness of her delicate complexion, and her kind manner, had her nose not been quite so large or so awkwardly placed; it made her face heavy and gave her a foolish expression. She was like a girl of Holbein, in the gallery at Basle—the daughter of burgomaster Meier—sitting, with eyes cast down, her hands on her knees, her fair hair falling down to her shoulders, looking embarrassed and ashamed of her uncomely nose. But so far Rosa had not been troubled by it, and it never had broken in upon her inexhaustible chatter. Always her shrill voice was heard in the house telling stories, always breathless, as though she had no time to say everything, always excited and animated, in spite of the protests which she drew from her mother, her father, and even her grandfather, exasperated, not so much because she was forever talking as because she prevented them talking themselves. For these good people, kind, loyal, devoted—the very cream of good people —had almost all the virtues, but they lacked one virtue which is capital, and is the charm of life: the virtue of silence.

Christophe was in tolerant mood. His sorrow had softened his intolerant and emphatic temper. His experience of the cruel indifference of the elegant made him more conscious of the worth of these honest folk, graceless and devilish tiresome, who had yet an austere conception of life, and because they lived joylessly, seemed to him to live without weakness. Having decided that they were excellent, and that he ought to like them, like the German that he was, he tried to persuade himself that he did in fact like them. But he did not succeed; he lacked that easy Germanic idealism, which does not wish to see, and does not see, what would be displeasing to its sight, for fear of disturbing the very proper tranquillity of its judgment and the pleasantness of its existence. On the contrary, he never was so conscious of the defects of these people as when he loved them, when he wanted to love them absolutely without reservation; it was a sort of unconscious loyalty, and an inexorable demand for truth, which, in spite of himself, made him more clear-sighted, and more exacting, with what was dearest to him. And it was not long before he began to be irritated by the oddities of the family. They made no attempt to conceal them. Contrary to the usual habit they displayed every intolerable quality they possessed, and all the good in them was hidden. So Christophe told himself, for he judged himself to have been unjust, and tried to surmount his first impressions, and to discover in them the excellent qualities which they so carefully concealed.

He tried to converse with old Justus Euler, who asked nothing better. He had a secret sympathy with him, remembering that his grandfather had liked to praise him. But good old Jean Michel had more of the pleasant faculty of deceiving himself about his friends than

Christophe, and Christophe soon saw that. In vain did he try to accept Euler's memories of his grandfather. He could only get from him a discolored caricature of Jean Michel, and scraps of talk that were utterly uninteresting. Euler's stories used invariably to begin with:

"As I used to say to your poor grandfather . . ." He could remember nothing else. He had heard only what he had said himself.

Perhaps Jean Michel used only to listen in the same way. Most friendships are little more than arrangements for mutual satisfaction, so that each party may talk about himself to the other. But at least Jean Michel, however naïvely he used to give himself up to the delight of talking, had sympathy which he was always ready to lavish on all sides. He was interested in everything; he always regretted that he was no longer fifteen, so as to be able to see the marvelous inventions of the new generations, and to share their thoughts. He had the quality perhaps the most precious in life, a curiosity always fresh, never changing with the years, born anew every morning. He had not the talent to turn this gift to account; but how many men of talent might envy him! Most men die at twenty or thirty; thereafter they are only reflections of themselves: for the rest of their lives they are aping themselves, repeating from day to day more and more mechanically and affectedly what they said and did and thought and loved when they were alive.

It was so long since old Euler had been alive, and he had been such a small thing then, that what was left of him now was very poor and rather ridiculous. Outside his former trade and his family life he knew nothing, and wished to know nothing. On every subject he had ideas ready-made, dating from his youth. He pretended to some knowledge of the arts, but he clung to certain hallowed names of men, about whom he was forever reiterating his emphatic formulæ: everything else was naught and had never been. When modern interests were mentioned he would not listen, and talked of something else. He declared that he loved music passionately, and he would ask Christophe to play. But as soon as Christophe, who had been caught once or twice, began to play, the old fellow would begin to talk loudly to his daughter, as though the music only increased his interest in everything but music. Christophe would get up exasperated in the middle of his piece, so one would notice it. There were only a few old airs—three or four—some very beautiful, others very ugly, but all equally sacred, which were privileged to gain comparative silence and absolute approval. With the very first notes the old man would go into ecstasies, tears would come to his eyes, not so much for the pleasure he was enjoying as for the pleasure which once he had enjoyed. In the end Christophe had a horror of these airs, though some of them, like the *Adelaide* of Beethoven, were very dear to him; the old man was always humming the first bars of them, and never failed to declare, "There, that is music," contemptuously comparing it with "all the blessed modern music, in which there is no melody." Truth to tell, he knew nothing whatever about it.

His son-in-law was better educated and kept in touch with artistic movements: but that was even worse, for in his judgment there was always a disparaging tinge. He was lacking neither in taste nor intelligence; but he could not bring himself to admire anything modern. He would have disparaged Mozart and Beethoven, if they had been contemporary, just as he would have acknowledged the merits of Wagner and Richard Strauss had they been dead for a century. His discontented temper refused to allow that there might be great men living during

his own lifetime; the idea was distasteful to him. He was so embittered by his wasted life that he insisted on pretending that every life was wasted, that it could not be otherwise, and that those who thought the opposite, or pretended to think so, were one of two things: fools or humbugs.

And so he never spoke of any new celebrity except in a tone of bitter irony, and as he was not stupid he never failed to discover at the first glance the weak or ridiculous sides of them. Any new name roused him to distrust; before he knew anything about the man he was inclined to criticize him—because he knew nothing about him. If he was sympathetic towards Christophe it was because he thought that the misanthropic boy found life as evil as he did himself, and that he was not a genius. Nothing so unites the small of soul in their suffering and discontent as the statement of their common impotence. Nothing so much restores the desire for health or life to those who are healthy and made for the joy of life as contact with the stupid pessimism of the mediocre and the sick, who, because they are not happy, deny the happiness of others. Christophe felt this. And yet these gloomy thoughts were familiar to him; but he was surprised to find them on Vogel's lips, where they were unrecognizable; more than that, they were repugnant to him; they offended him.

He was even more in revolt against Amalia's ways. The good creature did no more than practice Christophe's theories of duty. The word was upon her lips at every turn. She worked unceasingly, and wanted everybody to work as she did. Her work was never directed towards making herself and others happier; on the contrary. It almost seemed as though it was mainly intended to incommode everybody and to make life as disagreeable as possible so as to sanctify it.

Nothing would induce her for a moment to relinquish her holy duties in the household, that sacro-sanct institution which in so many women takes the place of all other duties, social and moral. She would have thought herself lost had she not on the same day, at the same time, polished the wooden floors, washed the tiles, cleaned the door-handles, beaten the carpets, moved the chairs, the cupboards, the tables. She was ostentatious about it. It was as though it was a point of honor with her. And after all, is it not in much the same spirit that many women conceive and defend their honor? It is a sort of piece of furniture which they have to keep polished, a well waxed floor, cold, hard—and slippery.

The accomplishment of her task did not make Frau Vogel more amiable. She sacrificed herself to the trivialities of the household, as to a duty imposed by God. And she despised those who did not do as she did, those who rested, and were able to enjoy life a little in the intervals of work. She would go and rouse Louisa in her room when from time to time she sat down in the middle of her work to dream. Louisa would sigh, but she submitted to it with a half-shamed smile. Fortunately, Christophe knew nothing about it; Amalia used to wait until he had gone out before she made these irruptions into their rooms, and so far she had not directly attacked him; he would not have put up with it. When he was with her he was conscious of a latent hostility within himself. What he could least forgive her was the noise she made. He was maddened by it. When he was locked in his room—a little low room looking out on the yard—with the window hermetically sealed, in spite of the want of air, so as not to hear the clatter in the house, he could not escape from it. Involuntarily he was forced to listen attentively for the least sound coming up from below, and when the terrible voice

which penetrated all the walls broke out again after a moment of silence he was filled with rage; he would shout, stamp with his foot, and roar insults at her through the wall. In the general uproar, no one ever noticed it; they thought he was composing. He would consign Frau Vogel to the depths of hell. He had no respect for her, nor esteem to check him. At such times it seemed to him that he would have preferred the loosest and most stupid of women, if only she did not talk, to cleverness, honesty, all the virtues, when they make too much noise.

His hatred of noise brought him in touch with Leonard. In the midst of the general excitement the boy was the only one to keep calm, and never to raise his voice more at one moment than another. He always expressed himself correctly and deliberately, choosing his words, and never hurrying. Amalia, simmering, never had patience to wait until he had finished; the whole family cried out upon his slowness. He did not worry about it. Nothing could upset his calm, respectful deference. Christophe was the more attracted to him when he learned that Leonard intended to devote his life to the Church, and his curiosity was roused.

With regard to religion, Christophe was in a queer position; he did not know himself how he stood towards it. He had never had time to think seriously about it. He was not well enough educated, and he was too much absorbed by the difficulties of existence to be able to analyze himself and to set his ideas in order. His violence led him from one extreme to the other, from absolute facts to complete negation, without troubling to find out whether in either case he agreed with himself. When he was happy he hardly thought of God at all, but he was quite ready to believe in Him. When he was unhappy he thought of Him, but did not believe; it seemed to him impossible that a God could authorize unhappiness and injustice. But these difficulties did not greatly exercise him. He was too fundamentally religious to think much about God. He lived in God; he had no need to believe in Him. That is well enough for the weak and worn, for those whose lives are anemic. They aspire to God, as a plant does to the sun. The dying cling to life. But he who bears in his soul the sun and life, what need has he to seek them outside himself?

Christophe would probably never have bothered about these questions had he lived alone. But the obligations of social life forced him to bring his thoughts to bear on these puerile and useless problems, which occupy a place out of all proportion in the world; it is impossible not to take them into account since at every step they are in the way. As if a healthy, generous creature, overflowing with strength and love, had not a thousand more worthy things to do than to worry as to whether God exists or no! . . . If it were only a question of believing in God! But it is needful to believe in *a* God, of whatever shape or size and color and race. So far Christophe never gave a thought to the matter. Jesus hardly occupied his thoughts at all. It was not that he did not love him: he loved him when he thought of him: but he never thought of him. Sometimes he reproached himself for it, was angry with himself, could not understand why he did not take more interest in him. And yet he professed, all his family professed; his grandfather was forever reading the Bible; he went regularly to Mass; he served it in a sort of way, for he was an organist; and he set about his task conscientiously and in an exemplary manner. But when he left the church he would have been hard put to it to say what he had been thinking about. He set himself to read the Holy Books in order to fix his ideas, and he found amusement and even pleasure in them, just as in any beautiful

strange books, not essentially different from other books, which no one ever thinks of calling sacred. In truth, if Jesus appealed to him, Beethoven did no less. And at his organ in Saint Florian's Church, where he accompanied on Sundays, he was more taken up with his organ than with Mass, and he was more religious when he played Bach than when he played Mendelssohn. Some of the ritual brought him to a fervor of exaltation. But did he then love God, or was it only the music, as an impudent priest said to him one day in jest, without thinking of the unhappiness which his quip might cause in him? Anybody else would not have paid any attention to it, and would not have changed his mode of living—(so many people put up with not knowing what they think!) But Christophe was cursed with an awkward need for sincerity, which filled him with scruples at every turn. And when scruples came to him they possessed him forever. He tortured himself; he thought that he had acted with duplicity. Did he believe or did he not? . . . He had no means, material or intellectual—(knowledge and leisure are necessary)—of solving the problem by himself. And yet it had to be solved, or he was either indifferent or a hypocrite. Now, he was incapable of being either one or the other.

He tried timidly to sound those about him. They all seemed to be sure of themselves. Christophe burned to know their reasons. He could not discover them. Hardly did he receive a definite answer; they always talked obliquely. Some thought him arrogant, and said that there is no arguing these things, that thousands of men cleverer and better than himself had believed without argument, and that he needed only to do as they had done. There were some who were a little hurt, as though it were a personal affront to ask them such a question, and yet they were of all perhaps the least certain of their facts. Others shrugged their shoulders and said with a smile: "Bah! it can't do any harm." And their smile said: "And it is so useful! . . ." Christophe despised them with all his heart.

He had tried to lay his uncertainties before a priest, but he was discouraged by the experiment. He could not discuss the matter seriously with him. Though his interlocution was quite pleasant, he made Christophe feel, quite politely, that there was no real equality between them; he seemed to assume in advance that his superiority was beyond dispute, and that the discussion could not exceed the limits which he laid down for it, without a kind of impropriety; it was just a fencing bout, and was quite inoffensive. When Christophe wished to exceed the limits and to ask questions, which the worthy man was pleased not to answer, he stepped back with a patronizing smile, and a few Latin quotations, and a fatherly objurgation to pray, pray that God would enlighten him. Christophe issued from the interview humiliated and wounded by his love of polite superiority. Wrong or right, he would never again for anything in the world have recourse to a priest. He admitted that these men were his superiors in intelligence or by reason of their sacred calling; but in argument there is neither superiority, nor inferiority, nor title, nor age, nor name; nothing is of worth but truth, before which all men are equal.

So he was glad to find a boy of his own age who believed. He asked no more than belief, and he hoped that Leonard would give him good reason for believing. He made advances to him. Leonard replied with his usual gentleness, but without eagerness; he was never eager about anything. As they could not carry on a long conversation in the house without being interrupted every moment by Amalia or the old man, Christophe proposed that they should go for a walk one evening after dinner. Leonard was too polite to refuse, although he would gladly have got out of it, for his indolent nature disliked walking, talking, and anything that cost him an effort.

Christophe had some difficulty in opening up the conversation. After two or three awkward sentences about trivialities he plunged with a brusqueness that was almost brutal. He asked Leonard if he were really going to be a priest, and if he liked the idea. Leonard was nonplussed, and looked at him uneasily, but when he saw that Christophe was not hostilely disposed he was reassured.

"Yes," he replied. "How could it be otherwise?"

"Ah!" said Christophe. "You are very happy." Leonard was conscious of a shade of envy in Christophe's voice and was agreeably flattered by it. He altered his manner, became expansive, his face brightened.

"Yes," he said, "I am happy." He beamed.

"What do you do to be so?" asked Christophe.

Before replying Leonard proposed that they should sit down on a quiet seat in the cloisters of St. Martin's. From there they could see a corner of the little square, planted with acacias, and beyond it the town, the country, bathed in the evening mists. The Rhine flowed at the foot of the hill. An old deserted cemetery, with graves lost under the rich grass, lay in slumber beside them behind the closed gates.

Leonard began to talk. He said, with his eyes shining with contentment, how happy he was to escape from life, to have found a refuge, where a man is, and forever will be, in shelter. Christophe, still sore from his wounds, felt passionately the desire for rest and forgetfulness; but it was mingled with regret. He asked with a sigh:

"And yet, does it cost you nothing to renounce life altogether?"

"Oh!" said Leonard quietly. "What is there to regret? Isn't life sad and ugly?"

"There are lovely things too," said Christophe, looking at the beautiful evening.

"There are some beautiful things, but very few."

"The few that there are are yet many to me."

"Oh, well! it is simply a matter of common sense. On the one hand a little good and much evil; on the other neither good nor evil on earth, and after, infinite happiness—how can one hesitate?"

Christophe was not very pleased with this sort of arithmetic. So economic a life seemed to him very poor. But he tried to persuade himself that it was wisdom.

"So," he asked a little ironically, "there is no risk of your being seduced by an hour's pleasure?"

"How foolish! When you know that it is only an hour, and that after it there is all eternity!"

"You are quite certain of eternity?"

"Of course."

Christophe questioned him. He was thrilled with hope and desire. Perhaps Leonard would at last give him impregnable reasons for believing. With what a passion he would himself renounce all the world to follow him to God.

At first Leonard, proud of his rôle of apostle, and convinced that Christophe's doubts were only a matter of form, and that they would of course give way before his first arguments, relied upon the Holy Books, the authority of the Gospel, the miracles, and traditions. But he began to grow gloomy when, after Christophe had listened for a few minutes, he stopped him and said that he was answering questions with questions, and that he had not asked him to tell exactly what it was that he was doubting, but to give some means of resolving his doubts.

Leonard then had to realize that Christophe was much more ill than he seemed, and that he would only allow himself to be convinced by the light of reason. But he still thought that Christophe was playing the free thinker—(it never occurred to him that he might be so sincerely).— He was not discouraged, and, strong in his recently acquired knowledge, he turned back to his school learning: he unfolded, higgledy piggledy, with more authority than order, his metaphysical proofs of the existence of God and the immortality of the soul. Christophe, with his mind at stretch, and his brow knit in the effort, labored in silence, and made him say it all over again; tried hard to gather the meaning, and to take it to himself, and to follow the reasoning. Then suddenly he burst out, vowed that Leonard was laughing at him, that it was all tricks, jests of the fine talkers who forged words and then amused themselves with pretending that these words were things. Leonard was nettled, and guaranteed the good faith of his authors. Christophe shrugged his shoulders, and said with an oath that they were only humbugs, infernal writers; and he demanded fresh proof.

Leonard perceived to his horror that Christophe was incurably attainted, and took no more interest in him. He remembered that he had been told not to waste his time in arguing with skeptics,—at least when they stubbornly refuse to believe. There was the risk of being shaken himself, without profiting the other. It was better to leave the unfortunate fellow to the will of God, who, if He so designs, would see to it that the skeptic was enlightened: or if not, who would dare to go against the will of God? Leonard did not insist then on carrying on the discussion. He only said gently that for the time being there was nothing to be done, that no reasoning could show the way to a man who was determined not to see it, and that Jean-Christophe must pray and appeal to grace: nothing is possible without that: he must desire grace, and the will to believe.

"The will," thought Christophe bitterly. "So then, God will exist because I will Him to exist? So then, death will not exist, because it pleases me to deny it! . . . Alas! How easy life is to those who have no need to see the truth, to those who can see what they wish to see, and are forever forging pleasant dreams in which softly to sleep!" In such a bed, Christophe knew well that he would never sleep. . . .

Leonard went on talking. He had fallen back on his favorite subject, the sweets of the contemplative life, and once on this neutral ground, he was inexhaustible. In his monotonous voice, that shook with the pleasure in him, he told of the joys of the life in God, outside, above the world, far from noise, of which he spoke in a sudden tone of hatred (he detested it almost as much as Christophe), far from violence, far from frivolity, far from the little miseries that one has to suffer every day, in the warm, secure nest of faith, from which you can contemplate in peace the wretchedness of a strange and distant world. And as Christophe listened, he perceived the egoism of that faith. Leonard saw that. He hurriedly explained: the contemplative life was not a lazy life. On the contrary, a man is more active in prayer than in action. What would the world be without prayer? You expiate the sins of others, you bear the burden of their misdeeds, you offer up your talents, you intercede between the world and God.

Christophe listened in silence with increasing hostility. He was conscious of the hypocrisy of such renunciation in Leonard. He was not unjust enough to assume hypocrisy in all those who believe. He knew well that with a few, such abdication of life comes from the impossibility of living, from a bitter despair, an appeal to death,—that with still fewer, it is an ecstasy of passion. . . . (How long does it last?) . . . But with the majority of men is it not too often the cold reasoning of souls more busied with their own ease and peace than with the happiness of others, or with truth? And if sincere men are conscious of it, how much they must suffer by such profanation of their ideal! . . .

Leonard was quite happy, and now set forth the beauty and harmony of the world, seen from the loftiness of the divine roost: below all was dark, unjust, sorrowful; seen from on high, it all became clear, luminous, ordered: the world was like the works of a clock, perfectly ordered. . . .

Now Christophe only listened absently. He was asking himself: "Does he believe, or does he believe that he believes?" And yet his own faith, his own passionate desire for faith was not shaken. Not the mediocrity of soul, and the poverty of argument of a fool like Leonard could touch that. . . .

Night came down over the town. The seat on which they were sitting was in darkness: the stars shone out, a white mist came up from the river, the crickets chirped under the trees in the cemetery. The bells began to ring: first the highest of them, alone, like a plaintive bird, challenging the sky: then the second, a third lower, joined in its plaint: at last came the deepest, on the fifth, and seemed to answer them. The three voices were merged in each other. At the bottom of the towers there was a buzzing, as of a gigantic hive of bees. The air and the boy's heart quivered. Christophe held his breath, and thought how poor was the music of musicians compared with such an ocean of music, with all the sounds of thousands of creatures: the former, the free world of sounds, compared with the world tamed, catalogued, coldly labeled

by human intelligence. He sank and sank into that sonorous and immense world without continents or bounds. . . .

And when the great murmuring had died away, when the air had ceased at last to quiver, Christophe woke up. He looked about him startled. . . . He knew nothing. Around him and in him everything was changed. There was no God. . . .

As with faith, so the loss of faith is often equally a flood of grace, a sudden light. Reason counts for nothing: the smallest thing is enough—a word, silence, the sound of bells. A man walks, dreams, expects nothing. Suddenly the world crumbles away. All about him is in ruins. He is alone. He no longer believes.

Christophe was terrified, and could not understand how it had come about. It was like the flooding of a river in the spring. . . .

Leonard's voice was still sounding, more monotonous than the voice of a cricket. Christophe did not hear it: he heard nothing. Night was fully come. Leonard stopped. Surprised to find Christophe motionless, uneasy because of the lateness of the hour, he suggested that they should go home. Christophe did not reply. Leonard took his arm. Christophe trembled, and looked at Leonard with wild eyes.

"Christophe, we must go home," said Leonard.

"Go to hell!" cried Christophe furiously.

"Oh! Christophe! What have I done?" asked Leonard tremulously. He was dumfounded.

Christophe came to himself.

"Yes. You are right," he said more gently. "I do not know what I'm saying. Go to God! Go to God!"

He was alone. He was in bitter distress.

"Ah! my God! my God!" he cried, wringing his hands, passionately raising his face to the dark sky. "Why do I no

longer believe? Why can I believe no more? What has happened to me? . . ."

The disproportion between the wreck of his faith and the conversation that he had just had with Leonard was too great: it was obvious that the conversation had no more brought it about than that the boisterousness of Amalia's gabble and the pettiness of the people with whom he lived were not the cause of the upheaval which for some days had been taking place in his moral resolutions. These were only pretexts. The uneasiness had not come from without. It was within himself. He felt stirring in his heart monstrous and unknown things, and he dared not rely on his thoughts to face the evil. The evil? Was it evil? A languor, an intoxication, a voluptuous agony filled all his being. He was no longer master of himself. In vain he sought to fortify himself with his former stoicism. His whole being crashed down. He had a sudden consciousness of the vast world, burning, wild, a world immeasurable. . . . How it swallows up God!

Only for a moment. But the whole balance of his old life was in that moment destroyed.

There was only one person in the family to whom Christophe paid no attention: this was little Rosa. She was not beautiful: and Christophe, who was far from beautiful himself, was very exacting of beauty in others. He had that calm cruelty of youth, for which a woman does not exist if she be ugly,—unless she has passed the age for inspiring tenderness, and there is then no need to feel for her anything but grave, peaceful, and quasi-religious sentiments. Rosa also was not distinguished by any especial gift, although she was not without intelligence: and she was cursed with a chattering tongue which drove Christophe from her. And he had never taken the trouble to know her, thinking that there was in her nothing to know; and the most he ever did was to glance at her.

But she was of better stuff than most girls: she was certainly better than Minna, whom he had so loved. She was a good girl, no coquette, not at all vain, and until Christophe came it had never occurred to her that she was plain, or if it had it had not worried her: for none of her family bothered about it. Whenever her grandfather or her mother told her so out of a desire to grumble, she only laughed: she did not believe it, or she attached no importance to it: nor did they. So many others, just as plain, and more, had found some one to love them! The Germans are very mildly indulgent to physical imperfections: they cannot see them: they are even able to embellish them, by virtue of an easy imagination which finds unexpected qualities in the face of their desire to make them like the most illustrious examples of human beauty. Old Euler would not have needed much urging to make him declare that his granddaughter had the nose of the Juno Ludovisi. Happily he was too grumpy to pay compliments: and Rosa, unconcerned about the shape of her nose, had no vanity except in the accomplishment, with all the ritual, of the famous household duties. She had accepted as Gospel all that she had been taught. She hardly ever went out, and she had very little standard of comparison; she admired her family naïvely, and believed what they said. She was of an expansive and confiding nature, easily satisfied, and tried to fall in with the mournfulness of her home, and docilely used to repeat the pessimistic ideas which she heard. She was a creature of devotion—always thinking of others, trying to please, sharing anxieties, guessing at what others wanted; she had a great need of loving without demanding anything in return. Naturally her family took advantage of her, although they were kind and

loved her: but there is always a temptation to take advantage of the love of those who are absolutely delivered into your hands. Her family were so sure of her attentions that they were not at all grateful for them: whatever she did, they expected more. And then, she was clumsy; she was awkward and hasty; her movements were jerky and boyish; she had outbursts of tenderness which used to end in disaster: a broken glass, a jug upset, a door slammed to: things which let loose upon her the wrath of everybody in the house. She was always being snubbed and would go and weep in a corner. Her tears did not last long. She would soon smile again, and begin to chatter without a suspicion of rancor against anybody.

Christophe's advent was an important event in her life. She had often heard of him. Christophe had some place in the gossip of the town: he was a sort of little local celebrity: his name used often to recur in the family conversation, especially when old Jean Michel was alive, who, proud of his grandson, used to sing his praises to all of his acquaintance. Rosa had seen the young musician once or twice at concerts. When she heard that he was coming to live with them, she clapped her hands. She was sternly rebuked for her breach of manners and became confused. She saw no harm in it. In a life so monotonous as hers, a new lodger was a great distraction. She spent the last few days before his arrival in a fever of expectancy. She was fearful lest he should not like the house, and she tried hard to make every room as attractive as possible. On the morning of his arrival, she even put a little bunch of flowers on the mantelpiece to bid him welcome. As to herself, she took no care at all to look her best; and one glance was enough to make Christophe decide that she was plain, and slovenly dressed. She did not think the same of him, though she had good reason to do so: for Christophe, busy, exhausted, ill-kempt, was even more ugly than usual. But Rosa, who was incapable of thinking the least ill of anybody, Rosa, who thought her grandfather, her father, and her mother, all perfectly beautiful, saw Christophe exactly as she had expected to see him, and admired him with all her heart. She was frightened at sitting next to him at table; and unfortunately her shyness took the shape of a flood of words, which at once alienated Christophe's sympathies. She did not see this, and that first evening remained a shining memory in her life. When she was alone in her room, after they had all gone upstairs, she heard the tread of the new lodgers as they walked over her head; and the sound of it ran joyously through her; the house seemed to her to have taken new life.

The next morning for the first time in her life she looked at herself in the mirror carefully and uneasily, and without exactly knowing the extent of her misfortune she began to be conscious of it. She tried to decide about her features, one by one; but she could not. She was filled with sadness and apprehension. She sighed deeply, and thought of introducing certain changes in her toilet, but she only made herself look still more plain. She conceived the unlucky idea of overwhelming Christophe with her kindness. In her naïve desire to be always seeing her new friends, and doing them service, she was forever going up and down the stairs, bringing them some utterly useless thing, insisting on helping them, and always laughing and talking and shouting. Her zeal and her stream of talk could only be interrupted by her mother's impatient voice calling her. Christophe looked grim; but for his good resolutions he must have lost his temper quite twenty times. He restrained himself for two days; on the third, he locked his door.

Rosa knocked, called, understood, went downstairs in dismay, and did not try again. When he saw her he explained that he was very busy and could not be disturbed. She humbly begged his pardon. She could not deceive herself as to the failure of her innocent advances: they had accomplished the opposite of her intention: they had alienated Christophe. He no longer took the trouble to conceal his ill-humor; he did not listen when she talked, and did not disguise his impatience. She felt that her chatter irritated him, and by force of will she succeeded in keeping silent for a part of the evening: but the thing was stronger than herself: suddenly she would break out again and her words would tumble over each other more tumultuously than ever. Christophe would leave her in the middle of a sentence. She was not angry with him. She was angry with herself. She thought herself stupid, tiresome, ridiculous: all her faults assumed enormous proportions and she tried to wrestle with them: but she was discouraged by the check upon her first attempts, and said to herself that she could not do it, that she was not strong enough. But she would try again.

But there were other faults against which she was powerless: what could she do against her plainness? There was no doubt about it. The certainty of her misfortune had suddenly been revealed to her one day when she was looking at herself in the mirror; it came like a thunderclap. Of course she exaggerated the evil, and saw her nose as ten times larger than it was; it seemed to her to fill all her face; she dared not show herself; she wished to die. But there is in youth such a power of hope that these fits of discouragement never lasted long: she would end by pretending that she had been mistaken; she would try to believe it, and for a moment or two would actually succeed in thinking her nose quite ordinary and almost shapely. Her instinct made her attempt, though very clumsily, certain childish tricks, a way of doing her hair so as not so much to show her forehead and so accentuate the disproportion of her face. And yet, there was no coquetry in her; no thought of love had crossed her mind, or she was unconscious of it. She asked little: nothing but a little friendship: but Christophe did not show any inclination to give her that little. It seemed to Rosa that she would have been perfectly happy had he only condescended to say good-day when they met. A friendly good-evening with a little kindness. But Christophe usually looked so hard and so cold! It chilled her. He never said anything disagreeable to her, but she would rather have had cruel reproaches than such cruel silence.

One evening Christophe was playing his piano. He had taken up his quarters in a little attic at the top of the house so as not to be so much disturbed by the noise. Downstairs Rosa was listening to him, deeply moved. She loved music though her taste was bad and unformed. While her mother was there, she stayed in a corner of the room and bent over her sewing, apparently absorbed in her work; but her heart was with the sounds coming from upstairs, and she wished to miss nothing. As soon as Amalia went out for a walk in the neighborhood, Rosa leaped to her feet, threw down her sewing, and went upstairs with her heart beating until she came to the attic door. She held her breath and laid her ear against the door. She stayed like that until Amalia returned. She went on tiptoe, taking care to make no noise, but as she was not very sure-footed, and was always in a hurry, she was always tripping upon the stairs; and once while she was listening, leaning forward with her cheek glued to the keyhole, she lost her balance, and banged her forehead against the door. She was so alarmed that she

lost her breath. The piano stopped dead: she could not escape. She was getting up when the door opened. Christophe saw her, glared at her furiously, and then without a word, brushed her aside, walked angrily downstairs, and went out. He did not return until dinner time, paid no heed to the despairing looks with which she asked his pardon, ignored her existence, and for several weeks he never played at all. Rosa secretly shed many tears; no one noticed it, no one paid any attention to her. Ardently she prayed to God . . . for what? She did not know. She had to confide her grief in some one. She was sure that Christophe detested her.

And, in spite of all, she hoped. It was enough for her if Christophe seemed to show any sign of interest in her, if he appeared to listen to what she said, if he pressed her hand with a little more friendliness than usual. . . .

A few imprudent words from her relations set her imagination off upon a false road.

The whole family was filled with sympathy for Christophe. The big boy of sixteen, serious and solitary, who had such lofty ideas of his duty, inspired a sort of respect in them all. His fits of ill-temper, his obstinate silences, his gloomy air, his brusque manner, were not surprising in such a house as that. Frau Vogel, herself, who regarded every artist as a loafer, dared not reproach him aggressively, as she would have liked to do, with the hours that he spent in stargazing in the evening, leaning, motionless, out of the attic window overlooking the yard, until night fell; for she knew that during the rest of the day he was hard at work with his lessons; and she humored him—like the rest—for an ulterior motive which no one expressed though everybody knew it.

Rosa had seen her parents exchanging

looks and mysterious whisperings when she was talking to Christophe. At first she took no notice of it. Then she was puzzled and roused by it; she longed to know what they were saying, but dared not ask.

One evening when she had climbed on to a garden seat to untie the clothes-line hung between two trees, she leaned on Christophe's shoulder to jump down. Just at that moment her eyes met her grandfather's and her father's; they were sitting smoking their pipes, and leaning against the wall of the house. The two men winked at each other, and Justus Euler said to Vogel:

"They will make a fine couple."

Vogel nudged him, seeing that the girl was listening, and he covered his remark very cleverly—(or so he thought)—with a loud "Hm! hm!" that could have been heard twenty yards away. Christophe, whose back was turned, saw nothing, but Rosa was so bowled over by it that she forgot that she was jumping down, and sprained her foot. She would have fallen had not Christophe caught her, muttering curses on her clumsiness. She had hurt herself badly, but she did not show it; she hardly thought of it; she thought only of what she had just heard. She walked to her room; every step was agony to her; she stiffened herself against it so as not to let it be seen. A delicious, vague uneasiness surged through her. She fell into a chair at the foot of her bed and hid her face in the coverlet. Her cheeks were burning; there were tears in her eyes, and she laughed. She was ashamed, she wished to sink into the depths of the earth, she could not fix her ideas; her blood beat in her temples, there were sharp pains in her ankle; she was in a feverish stupor. Vaguely she heard sounds outside, children crying and playing in the street, and her grandfather's words were ringing in her ears; she was thrilled, she laughed softly, she blushed,

with her face buried in the eiderdown: she prayed, gave thanks, desired, feared—she loved.

Her mother called her. She tried to get up. At the first step she felt a pain so unbearable that she almost fainted; her head swam. She thought she was going to die, she wished to die, and at the same time she wished to live with all the forces of her being, to live for the promised happiness. Her mother came at last, and the whole household was soon excited. She was scolded as usual, her ankle was dressed, she was put to bed, and sank into the sweet bewilderment of her physical pain and her inward joy. The night was sweet. . . . The smallest memory of that dear evening was hallowed for her. She did not think of Christophe, she knew not what she thought. She was happy.

The next day, Christophe, who thought himself in some measure responsible for the accident, came to make inquiries, and for the first time he made some show of affection for her. She was filled with gratitude, and blessed her sprained ankle. She would gladly have suffered all her life, if, all her life, she might have such joy.—She had to lie down for several days and never move; she spent them in turning over and over her grandfather's words, and considering them. Had he said:

"They will . . ."

Or:

"They would . . . ?"

But it was possible that he had never said anything of this kind?—Yes. He had said it; she was certain of it. . . . What! Did they not see that she was ugly, and that Christophe could not bear her? . . . But it was so good to hope! She came to believe that perhaps she had been wrong, that she was not as ugly as she thought; she would sit up on her sofa to try and see herself in the mirror on the wall opposite, above the mantelpiece; she did

[175]

not know what to think. After all, her father and her grandfather were better judges than herself; people cannot tell about themselves. . . . Oh! Heaven, if it were possible! . . . If it could be . . . if, she never dared think it, if . . . if she were pretty! . . . Perhaps, also, she had exaggerated Christophe's antipathy. No doubt he was indifferent, and after the interest he had shown in her the day after the accident did not bother about her any more; he forgot to inquire; but Rosa made excuses for him, he was so busy! How should he think of her? An artist cannot be judged like other men. . . .

And yet, resigned though she was, she could not help expecting with beating heart a word of sympathy from him when he came near her. A word only, a look . . . her imagination did the rest. In the beginning love needs so little food! It is enough to see, to touch as you pass; such a power of dreams flows from the soul in such moments, that almost of itself it can create its love: a trifle can plunge it into ecstasy that later, when it is more satisfied, and in proportion more exacting, it will hardly find again when at last it does possess the object of its desire.—Rosa lived absolutely, though no one knew it, in a romance of her own fashioning, pieced together by herself: Christophe loved her secretly, and was too shy to confess his love, or there was some stupid reason, fantastic or romantic, delightful to the imagination of the sentimental little ninny. She fashioned endless stories, and all perfectly absurd; she knew it herself, but tried not to know it; she lied to herself voluptuously for days and days as she bent over her sewing. It made her forget to talk: her flood of words was turned inward, like a river which suddenly disappears underground. But then the river took its revenge. What a debauch of speeches, of unuttered conversations which no one heard but herself! Sometimes her lips would move as they do with people who have to spell out the syllables to themselves as they read so as to understand them.

When her dreams left her she was happy and sad. She knew that things were not as she had just told herself: but she was left with a reflected happiness, and had greater confidence for her life. She did not despair of winning Christophe.

She did not admit it to herself, but she set about doing it. With the sureness of instinct that great affection brings, the awkward, ignorant girl contrived immediately to find the road by which she might reach her beloved's heart. She did not turn directly to him. But as soon as she was better and could once more walk about the house she approached Louisa. The smallest excuse served. She found a thousand little services to render her. When she went out she never failed to undertake various errands: she spared her going to the market, arguments with tradespeople, she would fetch water for her from the pump in the yard; she cleaned the windows and polished the floors in spite of Louisa's protestations, who was confused when she did not do her work alone; but she was so weary that she had not the strength to oppose anybody who came to help her. Christophe was out all day. Louisa felt that she was deserted, and the companionship of the affectionate, chattering girl was pleasant to her. Rosa took up her quarters in her room. She brought her sewing, and talked all the time. By clumsy devices she tried to bring conversation round to Christophe. Just to hear of him, even to hear his name, made her happy; her hands would tremble; she would sit with downcast eyes. Louisa was delighted to talk of her beloved Christophe, and would tell little tales of his childhood, trivial and just a little ridiculous; but there was no fear of Rosa thinking them so: she took a great joy, and there was a dear emotion for her in imagining Christophe as a child, and doing all the tricks and having all the darling ways of children: in her the motherly tenderness which lies in the hearts of all women was mingled deliciously with that other tenderness: she would laugh heartily and tears would come to her eyes. Louisa was touched by the interest that Rosa took in her. She guessed dimly what was in the girl's heart, but she never let it appear that she did so; but she was glad of it; for of all in the house she only knew the worth of the girl's heart. Sometimes she would stop talking to look at her. Rosa, surprised by her silence, would raise her eyes from her work. Louisa would smile at her. Rosa would throw herself into her arms, suddenly, passionately, and would hide her face in Louisa's bosom. Then they would go on working and talking, as if nothing had happened.

In the evening when Christophe came home, Louisa, grateful for Rosa's attentions, and in pursuance of the little plan she had made, always praised the girl to the skies. Christophe was touched by Rosa's kindness. He saw how much good she was doing his mother, in whose face there was more serenity: and he would thank her effusively. Rosa would murmur, and escape to conceal her embarrassment: so she appeared a thousand times more intelligent and sympathetic to Christophe than if she had spoken. He looked at her less with a prejudiced eye, and did not conceal his surprise at finding unsuspected qualities in her. Rosa saw that; she marked the progress that she made in his sympathy and thought that his sympathy would lead to love. She gave herself up more than ever to her dreams. She came near to believing with the beautiful presumption of youth that what you desire with all your being is always accomplished in the end. Besides,

how was her desire unreasonable? Should not Christophe have been more sensible than any other of her goodness and her affectionate need of self-devotion?

But Christophe gave no thought to her. He esteemed her; but she filled no room in his thoughts. He was busied with far other things at the moment. Christophe was no longer Christophe. He did not know himself. He was in a mighty travail that was like to sweep everything away, a complete upheaval.

Christophe was conscious of extreme weariness and great uneasiness. He was for no reason worn out; his head was heavy, his eyes, his ears, all his senses were dumb and throbbing. He could not give his attention to anything. His mind leaped from one subject to another, and was in a fever that sucked him dry. The perpetual fluttering of images in his mind made him giddy. At first he attributed it to fatigue and the enervation of the first days of spring. But spring passed and his sickness only grew worse.

It was what the poets who only touch lightly on things call the unease of adolescence, the trouble of the cherubim, the waking of the desire of love in the young body and soul. As if the fearful crisis of all a man's being, breaking up, dying, and coming to full rebirth, as if the cataclysm in which everything, faith, thought, action, all life, seems like to be blotted out, and then to be new-forged in the convulsions of sorrow and joy, can be reduced to terms of a child's folly!

All his body and soul were in a ferment. He watched them, having no strength to struggle, with a mixture of curiosity and disgust. He did not understand what was happening in himself. His whole being was disintegrated. He spent days together in absolute torpor. Work was torture to him. At night he slept heavily and in snatches, dreaming monstrously, with gusts of desire; the soul of a beast was racing madly in him. Burning, bathed in sweat, he watched himself in horror; he tried to break free of the crazy and unclean thoughts that possessed him, and he wondered if he were going mad.

The day gave him no shelter from his brutish thoughts. In the depths of his soul he felt that he was slipping down and down; there was no stay to clutch at; no barrier to keep back chaos. All his defenses, all his citadels, with the quadruple rampart that hemmed him in so proudly—his God, his art, his pride, his moral faith, all was crumbling away, falling piece by piece from him. He saw himself naked, bound, lying unable to move, like a corpse on which vermin swarm. He had spasms of revolt: where was his will, of which he was so proud? He called to it in vain: it was like the efforts that one makes in sleep, knowing that one is dreaming, and trying to awake. Then one succeeds only in falling from one dream to another like a lump of lead, and in being more and more choked by the suffocation of the soul in bondage. At last he found that it was less painful not to struggle. He decided not to do so, with fatalistic apathy and despair.

The even tenor of his life seemed to be broken up. Now he slipped down a subterranean crevasse and was like to disappear; now he bounded up again with a violent jerk. The chain of his days was snapped. In the midst of the even plain of the hours great gaping holes would open to engulf his soul. Christophe looked on at the spectacle as though it did not concern him. Everything, everybody,—and himself—were strange to him. He went about his business, did his work, automatically: it seemed to him that the machinery of his life might stop at any moment: the wheels were out of gear. At dinner with his mother and the others, in the orchestra with the musicians and the audience, suddenly there

would be a void and emptiness in his brain: he would look stupidly at the grinning faces about him: and he could not understand. He would ask himself:

"What is there between these creatures and . . . ?"

He dared not even say:

". . . and me."

For he knew not whether he existed. He would speak and his voice would seem to issue from another body. He would move, and he saw his movements from afar, from above—from the top of a tower. He would pass his hand over his face, and his eyes would wander. He was often near doing crazy things.

It was especially when he was most in public that he had to keep guard on himself. For example, on the evenings when he went to the Palace or was playing in public. Then he would suddenly be seized by a terrific desire to make a face, or say something outrageous, to pull the Grand Duke's nose, or to take a running kick at one of the ladies. One whole evening while he was conducting the orchestra, he struggled against an insensate desire to undress himself in public: and he was haunted by the idea from the moment when he tried to check it: he had to exert all his strength not to give way to it. When he issued from the brute struggle he was dripping with sweat and his mind was blank. He was really mad. It was enough for him to think that he must not do a thing for it to fasten on him with the maddening tenacity of a fixed idea.

So his life was spent in a series of unbridled outbreaks and of endless falls into emptiness. A furious wind in the desert. Whence came this wind? From what abyss came these desires that wrenched his body and mind? He was like a bow stretched to breaking point by a strong hand,—to what end unknown? —which then springs back like a piece of dead wood. Of what force was he the prey? He dared not probe for it. He felt that he was beaten, humiliated, and he would not face his defeat. He was weary and broken in spirit. He understood now the people whom formerly he had despised: those who will not seek awkward truth. In the empty hours, when he remembered that time was passing, his work neglected, the future lost, he was frozen with terror. But there was no reaction: and his cowardice found excuses in desperate affirmation of the void in which he lived: he took a bitter delight in abandoning himself to it like a wreck on the waters. What was the good of fighting? There was nothing beautiful, nor good; neither God, nor life, nor being of any sort. In the street as he walked, suddenly the earth would sink away from him: there was neither ground, nor air, nor light, nor himself: there was nothing. He would fall, his head would drag him down, face forwards: he could hardly hold himself up; he was on the point of collapse. He thought he was going to die, suddenly, struck down. He thought he was dead. . . .

Christophe was growing a new skin. Christophe was growing a new soul. And seeing the worn out and rotten soul of his childhood falling away he never dreamed that he was taking on a new one, young and stronger. As through life we change our bodies, so also do we change our souls: and the metamorphosis does not always take place slowly over many days; there are times of crisis when the whole is suddenly renewed. The adult changes his soul. The old soul that is cast off dies. In those hours of anguish we think that all is at an end. And the whole thing begins again. A life dies. Another life has already come into being.

One night he was alone in his room, with his elbow on his desk under the light of a candle. His back was turned to the window. He was not working. He had not been able to work for weeks. Every-

thing was twisting and turning in his head. He had brought everything under scrutiny at once: religion, morals, art, the whole of life. And in the general dissolution of his thoughts was no method, no order: he had plunged into the reading of books taken haphazard from his grandfather's heterogeneous library or from Vogel's collection of books: books of theology, science, philosophy, an odd lot, of which he understood nothing, having everything to learn: he could not finish any of them, and in the middle of them went off on divagations, endless whimsies, which left him weary, empty, and in mortal sorrow.

So, that evening, he was sunk in an exhausted torpor. The whole house was asleep. His window was open. Not a breath came up from the yard. Thick clouds filled the sky. Christophe mechanically watched the candle burn away at the bottom of the candlestick. He could not go to bed. He had no thought of anything. He felt the void growing, growing from moment to moment. He tried not to see the abyss that drew him to its brink: and in spite of himself he leaned over and his eyes gazed into the depths of the night. In the void, chaos was stirring, and faint sounds came from the darkness. Agony filled him: a shiver ran down his spine: his skin tingled: he clutched the table so as not to fall. Convulsively he awaited nameless things, a miracle, a God. . . .

Suddenly, like an opened sluice, in the yard behind him, a deluge of water, a heavy rain, large drops, down pouring, fell. The still air quivered. The dry, hard soil rang out like a bell. And the vast scent of the earth, burning, warm as that of an animal, the smell of the flowers, fruit, and amorous flesh rose in a spasm of fury and pleasure. Christophe, under illusion, at fullest stretch, shook. He trembled. . . . The veil was rent. He was blinded. By a flash of lightning, he

saw, in the depths of the night, he saw—
he was God. God was in himself; He
burst the ceiling of the room, the walls of
the house; He cracked the very bounds of
existence. He filled the sky, the universe,
space. The world coursed through Him,
like a cataract. In the horror and ecstasy
of that cataclysm, Christophe fell too,
swept along by the whirlwind which
brushed away and crushed like straws the
laws of nature. He was breathless: he
was drunk with the swift hurtling down
into God . . . God-abyss! God-gulf!
Fire of Being! Hurricane of life! Madness
of living,—aimless, uncontrolled, beyond
reason,—for the fury of living!

When the crisis was over, he fell into a
deep sleep and slept as he had not done
for long enough. Next day when he
awoke his head swam: he was as broken
as though he had been drunk. But in his
inmost heart he had still a beam of that
somber and great light that had struck
him down the night before. He tried to
relight it. In vain. The more he pursued
it, the more it eluded him. From that
time on, all his energy was directed towards recalling the vision of a moment.
The endeavor was futile. Ecstasy does
not answer the bidding of the will.

But that mystic exaltation was not the
only experience that he had of it: it recurred several times, but never with the
intensity of the first. It came always at
moments when Christophe was least expecting it, for a second only, a time so
short, so sudden,—no longer than a wink
of an eye or a raising of a hand—that the
vision was gone before he could discover
what it was: and then he would wonder
whether he had not dreamed it. After
that fiery bolt that had set the night
aflame, it was a gleaming dust, shedding
fleeting sparks, which the eye could
hardly see as they sped by. But they
reappeared more and more often: and in

the end they surrounded Christophe with
a halo of perpetual misty dreams, in
which his spirit melted. Everything that
distracted him in his state of semi-hallu-
cination was an irritation to him. It was
impossible to work; he gave up thinking
about it. Society was odious to him; and
more than any, that of his intimates,
even that of his mother, because they
arrogated to themselves more rights over
his soul.

He left the house: he took to spending
his days abroad, and never returned until
nightfall. He sought the solitude of the
fields, and delivered himself up to it,
drank his fill of it, like a maniac who
wishes not to be disturbed by anything in
the obsession of his fixed ideas.—But in
the great sweet air, in contact with the
earth, his obsession relaxed, his ideas
ceased to appear like specters. His exaltation was no less: rather it was heightened, but it was no longer a dangerous
delirium of the mind but a healthy intoxication of his whole being: body and
soul crazy in their strength.

He rediscovered the world, as though
he had never seen it. It was a new childhood. It was as though a magic word had
been uttered. An "Open Sesame!"—Nature flamed with gladness. The sun
boiled. The liquid sky ran like a clear
river. The earth steamed and cried aloud
in delight. The plants, the trees, the insects, all the innumerable creatures were
like dazzling tongues of flame in the fire
of life writhing upwards. Everything sang
aloud in joy.

And that joy was his own. That
strength was his own. He was no longer
cut off from the rest of the world. Till
then, even in the happy days of childhood, when he saw nature with ardent
and delightful curiosity, all creatures had
seemed to him to be little worlds shut up,
terrifying and grotesque, unrelated to
himself, and incomprehensible. He was

not even sure that they had feeling and life. They were strange machines. And sometimes Christophe had even, with the unconscious cruelty of a child, dismembered wretched insects without dreaming that they might suffer—for the pleasure of watching their queer contortions. His uncle Gottfried, usually so calm, had one day indignantly to snatch from his hands an unhappy fly that he was torturing. The boy had tried to laugh at first: then he had burst into tears, moved by his uncle's emotion: he began to understand that his victim did really exist, as well as himself, and that he had committed a crime. But if thereafter nothing would have induced him to do harm to the beasts, he never felt any sympathy for them: he used to pass them by without ever trying to feel what it was that worked their machinery: rather he was afraid to think of it: it was something like a bad dream.—And now everything was made plain. These humble, obscure creatures became in their turn centers of light.

Lying on his belly in the grass where creatures swarmed, in the shade of the trees that buzzed with insects, Christophe would watch the fevered movements of the ants, the long-legged spiders, that seemed to dance as they walked, the bounding grasshoppers, that leap aside, the heavy, bustling beetles, and the naked worms, pink and glabrous, mottled with white, or with his hands under his head and his eyes closed he would listen to the invisible orchestra, the roundelay of the frenzied insects circling in a sunbeam about the scented pines, the trumpeting of the mosquitoes, the organ notes of the wasps, the brass of the wild bees humming like bells in the tops of the trees, and the godlike whispering of the swaying trees, the sweet moaning of the wind in the branches, the soft whispering of the waving grass, like a breath of wind

rippling the limpid surface of a lake, like the rustling of a light dress and lovers' footsteps coming near, and passing, then lost upon the air.

He heard all these sounds and cries within himself. Through all these creatures from the smallest to the greatest flowed the same river of life: and in it he too swam. So, he was one of them, he was of their blood, and, brotherly, he heard the echo of their sorrows and their joys: their strength was merged in his like a river fed with thousands of streams. He sank into them. His lungs were like to burst with the wind, too freely blowing, too strong, that burst the windows and forced its way into the closed house of his suffocating heart. The change was too abrupt: after finding everywhere a void, when he had been buried only in his own existence, and had felt it slipping from him and dissolving like rain, now everywhere he found infinite and unmeasured Being, now that he longed to forget himself, to find rebirth in the universe. He seemed to have issued from the grave. He swam voluptuously in life flowing free and full: and borne on by its current he thought that he was free. He did not know that he was less free than ever, that no creature is ever free, that even the law that governs the universe is not free, that only death—perhaps—can bring deliverance.

But the chrysalis issuing from its stifling sheath, joyously stretched its limbs in its new shape, and had no time as yet to mark the bounds of its new prison.

There began a new cycle of days. Days of gold and fever, mysterious, enchanted, like those of his childhood, when one by one he discovered things for the first time. From dawn to set of sun he lived in one long mirage. He deserted all his business. The conscientious boy, who for years had never missed a lesson, or an orchestra rehearsal, even when he was ill, was forever finding paltry excuses for neglecting his work. He was not afraid to lie. He had no remorse about it. The stoic principles of life, to which he had hitherto delighted to bend his will, morality, duty, now seemed to him to have no truth, nor reason. Their jealous despotism was smashed against Nature. Human nature, healthy, strong, free, that alone was virtue: to hell with all the rest! It provoked pitying laughter to see the little peddling rules of prudence and policy which the world adorns with the name of morality, while it pretends to inclose all life within them. A preposterous mole-hill, an ant-like people! Life sees to it that they are brought to reason. Life does but pass, and all is swept away. . . .

Bursting with energy Christophe had moments when he was consumed with a desire to destroy, to burn, to smash, to glut with actions blind and uncontrolled the force which choked him. These outbursts usually ended in a sharp reaction: he would weep, and fling himself down on the ground, and kiss the earth, and try to dig into it with his teeth and hands, to feed himself with it, to merge into it: he trembled then with fever and desire.

One evening he was walking in the outskirts of a wood. His eyes were swimming with the light, his head was whirling: he was in that state of exaltation when all creatures and things were transfigured. To that was added the magic of the soft warm light of evening. Rays of purple and gold hovered in the trees. From the meadows seemed to come a phosphorescent glimmer. In a field nearby a girl was making hay. In her blouse and short skirt, with her arms and neck bare, she was raking the hay and heaping it up. She had a short nose, wide cheeks, a round face, a handkerchief thrown over her hair. The setting sun touched with red her sunburned skin, which, like a piece of pottery, seemed to absorb the last beams of the day.

She fascinated Christophe. Leaning against a beech-tree he watched her come towards the verge of the woods, eagerly, passionately. Everything else had disappeared. She took no notice of him. For a moment she looked at him cautiously: he saw her eyes blue and hard in her brown face. She passed so near to him that, when she leaned down to gather up the hay, through her open blouse he saw a soft down on her shoulders and back. Suddenly the vague desire which was in him leaped forth. He hurled himself at her from behind, seized her neck and waist, threw back her head and fastened his lips upon hers. He kissed her dry, cracked lips until he came against her teeth that bit him angrily. His hands ran over her rough arms, over her blouse wet with her sweat. She struggled. He held her tighter, he wished to strangle her. She broke loose, cried out, spat, wiped her lips with her hand, and hurled insults at him. He let her go and fled across the fields. She threw stones at him and went on discharging after him a litany of filthy epithets. He blushed, less for anything that she might say or think, but for what he was thinking himself. The sudden unconscious act filled him with terror. What had he done? What should he do? What he was able to understand of it all only filled him with disgust. And he was tempted by his disgust. He fought against himself and knew not on which side was the real Christophe. A blind force beset him: in vain did he fly from it: it was only to fly from himself. What would she do about him? What should he do tomorrow . . . in an hour . . . the time it took to cross the plowed field to reach the road? . . . Would he ever reach it? Should he not stop, and go back, and run back to the girl? And then? . . . He remembered that delirious moment when he had held her by the throat. Everything was possible. All things were worth while. A crime even. . . . Yes, even a crime. . . . The turmoil in his heart made him breathless. When he reached the road he stopped to breathe. Over there the girl was talking to another girl who had been attracted by her cries: and with arms akimbo, they were looking at each other and shouting with laughter.

II

SABINE

He went home. He shut himself up in his room and never stirred for several days. He only went out even into the town when he was compelled. He was fearful of ever going out beyond the gates and venturing forth into the fields: he was afraid of once more falling in with the soft, maddening breath that had blown upon him like a rushing wind during a calm in a storm. He thought that the walls of the town might preserve him from it. He never dreamed that for the enemy to slip within there needed be only the smallest crack in the closed shutters, no more than is needed for a peep out.

In a wing of the house, on the other side of the yard, there lodged on the ground floor a young woman of twenty, some months a widow, with a little girl. Frau Sabine Froehlich was also a tenant of old Euler's. She occupied the shop which opened on to the street, and she had as well two rooms looking on to the yard, together with a little patch of garden, marked off from the Eulers' by a wire fence up which ivy climbed. They did not often see her: the child used to play down in the garden from morning to night making mud pies: and the garden was left to itself, to the great distress of old Justus, who loved tidy paths and

neatness in the beds. He had tried to bring the matter to the attention of his tenant: but that was probably why she did not appear: and the garden was not improved by it.

Frau Froehlich kept a little draper's shop which might have had customers enough, thanks to its position in a street of shops in the center of the town: but she did not bother about it any more than about her garden. Instead of doing her housework herself, as, according to Frau Vogel, every self-respecting woman ought to do—especially when she is in circumstances which do not permit much less excuse idleness—she had hired a little servant, a girl of fifteen, who came in for a few hours in the morning to clean the rooms and look after the shop, while the young woman lay in bed or dawdled over her toilet.

Christophe used to see her sometimes, through his windows, walking about her room, with bare feet, in her long nightgown, or sitting for hours together before her mirror: for she was so careless that she used to forget to draw her curtains: and when she saw him, she was so lazy that she could not take the trouble to go and lower them. Christophe, more modest than she, would leave the window so as not to incommode her: but the temptation was great. He would blush a little and steal a glance at her bare arms, which were rather thin, as she drew them languidly around her flowing hair, and with her hands clasped behind her head, lost herself in a dream, until they were numbed, and then she would let them fall. Christophe would pretend that he only saw these pleasant sights inadvertently as he happened to pass the window, and that they did not disturb him in his musical thoughts: but he liked it, and in the end he wasted as much time in watching Frau Sabine, as she did over her toilet. Not that she was a coquette: she was rather careless, generally, and did not take anything like the meticulous care with her appearance that Amalia or Rosa did. If she dawdled in front of her dressing table it was from pure laziness: every time she put in a pin she had to rest from the effort of it, while she made little piteous faces at herself in the mirrors. She was never quite properly dressed at the end of the day.

Often her servant used to go before Sabine was ready: and a customer would ring the shop-bell. She would let him ring and call once or twice before she could make up her mind to get up from her chair. She would go down, smiling, and never hurrying,—never hurrying would look for the article required,—and if she could not find it after looking for some time, or even (as happened sometimes) if she had to take too much trouble to reach it, as for instance, taking the ladder from one end of the shop to the other,— she would say calmly that she did not have it in stock: and as she never bothered to put her stock in order, or to order more of the articles of which she had run out, her customers used to lose patience and go elsewhere. But she never minded. How could you be angry with such a pleasant creature who spoke so sweetly, and was never excited about anything! She did not mind what anybody said to her: and she made this so plain that those who began to complain never had the courage to go on: they used to go, answering her charming smile with a smile: but they never came back. She never bothered about it. She went on smiling.

She was like a little Florentine figure. Her well marked eyebrows were arched: her gray eyes were half open behind the curtain of her lashes. The lower eyelid was a little swollen, with a little crease below it. Her little, finely drawn nose turned up slightly at the end. Another little curve lay between it and her upper lip, which curled up above her half-open mouth, pouting in a weary smile. Her lower lip was a little thick: the lower part of her face was rounded, and had the serious expression of the little virgins of Filippo Lippi. Her complexion was a little muddy, her hair was light brown, always untidy, and done up in a slovenly chignon. She was slight of figure, small-boned. And her movements were lazy. Dressed carelessly—a gaping bodice, buttons missing, ugly, worn shoes, always looking a little slovenly—she charmed by her grace and youth, her gentleness, her instinctively coaxing ways. When she appeared to take the air at the door of her shop, the young men who passed used to look at her with pleasure: and although she did not bother about them, she noticed it none the less. Always then she wore that grateful and glad expression which is in the eyes of all women when they know that they have been seen with sympathetic eyes. It seemed to say:

"Thank you! . . . Again! Look at me again!" But though it gave her pleasure to please, her indifference would never let her make the smallest effort to please.

She was an object of scandal to the Euler-Vogels. Everything about her offended them: her indolence, the untidiness of her house, the carelessness of her dress, her polite indifference to their remarks, her perpetual smile, the impertinent serenity with which she had accepted her husband's death, her child's illnesses, her straitened circumstances, the great and small annoyances of her daily life, while nothing could change one jot of her favorite habits, or her eternal longing,—everything about her offended them: and the worst of all was that, as she was, she did give pleasure. Frau Vogel could not forgive her that. It was almost as though Sabine did it on purpose, on purpose, ironically, to set at naught by her conduct the great traditions, the true principles, the savorless duty, the pleasureless labor, the restlessness, the noise, the quarrels, the mooning ways, the healthy pessimism which was the motive power of the Euler family, as it is that of all respectable persons, and made their life a foretaste of purgatory. That a woman who did nothing but dawdle about all the blessed day should take upon herself to defy them with her calm insolence, while they bore their suffering in silence like galley-slaves,— and that people should approve of her into the bargain—that was beyond the limit, that was enough to turn you against respectability! . . . Fortunately, thank God, there were still a few sensible people left in the world. Frau Vogel consoled herself with them. They exchanged remarks about the little widow, and spied on her through her shutters. Such gossip was the joy of the family when they met at supper. Christophe would listen absently. He was so used to hearing the Vogels set themselves up as censors of their neighbors that he never took any notice of it. Besides he knew nothing of Frau Sabine except her bare neck and arms, and though they were pleasing enough, they did not justify his coming to a definite opinion about her. However, he was conscious of a kindly feeling towards her: and in a contradictory spirit he was especially grateful to her for displeasing Frau Vogel.

After dinner in the evening when it was very hot it was impossible to stay in the stifling yard, where the sun shone the whole afternoon. The only place in the house where it was possible to breathe was the rooms looking into the street. Euler and his son-in-law used sometimes to go and sit on the doorstep with Louisa. Frau Vogel and Rosa would only appear for a moment: they were kept by their housework: Frau Vogel took a pride in showing that she had no time for dawdling: and she used to say, loudly enough to be overheard, that all the people sitting there and yawning on their doorsteps, without doing a stitch of work, got on her nerves. As she could not—(to her sorrow)—compel them to work, she would pretend not to see them, and would go in and work furiously. Rosa thought she must do likewise. Euler and Vogel would discover draughts everywhere, and fearful of catching cold, would go up to their rooms: they used to go to bed early, and would have thought themselves ruined had they changed the least of their habits. After nine o'clock only Louisa and Christophe would be left. Louisa spent the day in her room: and, in the evening, Christophe used to take pains to be with her, whenever he could, to make her take the air. If she were left alone she would never go out: the noise of the street frightened her. Children were always chasing each other with shrill cries. All the dogs of the neighborhood took it up and barked. The sound of a piano came up, a little farther off a clarinet, and in the next street a cornet à piston. Voices chattered. People came and went and stood in groups in front of their houses. Louisa would have lost her head if she had been left alone in all the uproar. But when her son was with her it gave her pleasure. The noise would gradually die down. The children and the dogs would go to bed first. The groups of people would break up. The air would become more pure. Silence would descend upon the street. Louisa would tell in her thin voice the little scraps of news that she had heard from Amalia or Rosa. She was not greatly interested in them. But she never knew what to talk about to her son, and she felt the need of keeping in touch with him, of saying something to him. And Christophe, who felt her need, would pretend to be interested in everything she said: but he did not listen. He was off in vague dreams, turning over in his mind the doings of the day.

One evening when they were sitting there—while his mother was talking he saw the door of the draper's shop open. A woman came out silently and sat in the street. Her chair was only a few yards from Louisa. She was sitting in the darkest shadow. Christophe could not see her face: but he recognized her. His dreams vanished. The air seemed sweeter to him. Louisa had not noticed Sabine's presence, and went on with her chatter in a low voice. Christophe paid more attention to her, and he felt impelled to throw out a remark here and there, to talk, perhaps to be heard. The slight figure sat there without stirring, a little limp, with her legs lightly crossed and her hands lying crossed in her lap. She was looking straight in front of her, and seemed to hear nothing. Louisa was overcome with drowsiness. She went in. Christophe said he would stay a little longer.

It was nearly ten. The street was empty. The people were going indoors. The sound of the shops being shut was heard. The lighted windows winked and then were dark again. One or two were still lit: then they were blotted out. Silence. . . . They were alone, they did not look at each other, they held their breath, they seemed not to be aware of each other. From the distant fields came the smell of the new-mown hay, and from a balcony in a house nearby the scent of a pot of cloves. No wind stirred. Above their heads was the Milky Way. To their right red Juniper. Above a chimney Charles' Wain bent its axles: in the pale green sky its stars flowered like daisies. From the bells of the parish church eleven o'clock rang out and was caught up by all the other churches, with their voices clear or muffled, and, from the houses, by the dim chiming of the clock or husky cuckoos.

They awoke suddenly from their dreams, and got up at the same moment. And just as they were going indoors they both bowed without speaking. Christophe went up to his room. He lighted his candle, and sat down by his desk with his head in his hands, and stayed so for a long time without a thought. Then he sighed and went to bed.

Next day when he got up, mechanically he went to his window to look down into Sabine's room. But the curtains were drawn. They were drawn the whole morning. They were drawn ever after.

Next evening Christophe proposed to his mother that they should go again to sit by the door. He did so regularly. Louisa was glad of it: she did not like his shutting himself up in his room immediately after dinner with the window and shutters closed.—The little silent shadow never failed to come and sit in its usual place. They gave each other a quick nod, which Louisa never noticed. Christophe would talk to his mother. Sabine would smile at her little girl, playing in the street: about nine she would go and put her to bed and would then return noiselessly. If she stayed a little Christophe would begin to be afraid that she would not come back. He would listen for sounds in the house, the laughter of the little girl who would not go to sleep: he would hear the rustling of Sabine's dress before she appeared on the threshold of the shop. Then he would look away and talk to his mother more eagerly. Sometimes he would feel that Sabine was looking at him. In turn he would furtively look at her. But their eyes would never meet.

The child was a bond between them. She would run about in the street with other children. They would find amusement in teasing a good-tempered dog sleeping there with his nose in his paws: he would cock a red eye and at last would emit a growl of boredom: then they would fly this way and that screaming in terror and happiness. The little girl would give piercing shrieks, and look behind her as though she were being pursued: she would throw herself into Louisa's lap, and Louisa would smile fondly. She would keep the child and question her: and so she would enter into conversation with Sabine. Christophe never joined in. He never spoke to Sabine. Sabine never spoke to him. By tacit agreement they pretended to ignore each other. But he never lost a word of what they said as they talked over him. His silence seemed unfriendly to Louisa. Sabine never thought it so: but it would make her shy, and she would grow confused in her remarks. Then she would find some excuse for going in.

For a whole week Louisa kept indoors for a cold. Christophe and Sabine were left alone. The first time they were frightened by it. Sabine, to seem at her ease, took her little girl on her knees and loaded her with caresses. Christophe was embarrassed and did not know whether he ought to go on ignoring what was happening at his side. It became difficult: although they had not spoken a single word to each other, they did know each other, thanks to Louisa. He tried to begin several times: but the words stuck in his throat. Once more the little girl extricated them from their difficulty. She played hide-and-seek, and went round Christophe's chair. He caught her as she passed and kissed her. He was not very fond of children: but it was curiously pleasant to him to kiss the little girl. She struggled to be free, for she was busy with her game. He teased her, she bit his hands: he let her fall. Sabine laughed. They looked at the child and exchanged a few trivial words. Then Christophe tried—(he thought he must)—to enter into conversation: but he had nothing very much to go upon: and Sabine did not make his task any the easier: she only repeated what he said:

"It is a fine evening."

"Yes. It is a very fine evening."

"Impossible to breathe in the yard."

"Yes. The yard was stifling."

Conversation became very difficult. Sabine discovered that it was time to take the little girl in, and went in herself: and she did not appear again.

Christophe was afraid she would do the same on the evenings that followed and that she would avoid being left alone with him, as long as Louisa was not there. But on the contrary, the next evening Sabine tried to resume their conversation. She did so deliberately rather than for pleasure: she was obviously taking a great deal of trouble to find subjects of conversation, and bored with the questions she put: questions and answers came between heartbreaking silences. Christophe remembered his first interviews with Otto: but with Sabine their subjects were even more limited than then, and she had not Otto's patience. When she saw the small success of her endeavors she did not try any more: she had to give herself too much trouble, and she lost interest in it. She said no more, and he followed her lead.

And then there was sweet peace again. The night was calm once more, and they returned to their inward thoughts. Sabine rocked slowly in her chair, dreaming. Christophe also was dreaming. They said nothing. After half an hour Christophe began to talk to himself, and in a low voice cried out with pleasure in the delicious scent brought by the soft wind that came from a cart of strawberries. Sabine said a word or two in reply. Again they were silent. They were enjoying the charm of these indefinite silences, and trivial words. Their dreams were the same, they had but one thought: they did not know what it was: they did not admit it to themselves. At eleven they smiled and parted.

Next day they did not even try to talk:

they resumed their sweet silence. At long intervals a word or two let them know that they were thinking of the same things.

Sabine began to laugh.

"How much better it is," she said, "not to try to talk! One thinks one must, and it is so tiresome!"

"Ah!" said Christophe with conviction, "if only everybody thought the same."

They both laughed. They were thinking of Frau Vogel.

"Poor woman!" said Sabine; "how exhausting she is!"

"She is never exhausted," replied Christophe gloomily.

She was tickled by his manner and his jest.

"You think it amusing?" he asked. "That is easy for you. You are sheltered."

"So I am," said Sabine. "I lock myself in." She had a little soft laugh that hardly sounded. Christophe heard it with delight in the calm of the evening. He snuffed the fresh air luxuriously.

"Ah! It is good to be silent!" he said, stretching his limbs.

"And talking is no use!" said she.

"Yes," returned Christophe, "We understand each other so well!"

They relapsed into silence. In the darkness they could not see each other. They were both smiling.

And yet, though they felt the same, when they were together—or imagined that they did—in reality they knew nothing of each other. Sabine did not bother about it. Christophe was more curious. One evening he asked her:

"Do you like music?"

"No," she said simply. "It bores me. I don't understand it."

Her frankness charmed him. He was sick of the lies of people who said that they were mad about music, and were bored to death when they heard it: and it seemed to him almost a virtue not to like it and to say so. He asked if Sabine read.

"No. She had no books."

He offered to lend her his.

"Serious books?" she asked uneasily.

"Not serious books if she did not want them. Poetry."

"But those are serious books."

"Novels, then."

She pouted.

"They don't interest you?"

"Yes. She was interested in them: but they were always too long: she never had the patience to finish them. She forgot the beginning: skipped chapters and then lost the thread. And then she threw the book away."

"Fine interest you take!"

"Bah! Enough for a story that is not true. She kept her interest for better things than books."

"For the theater, then?"

"No. . . . No."

"Didn't she go to the theater?"

"No. It was too hot. There were too many people. So much better at home. The lights tired her eyes. And the actors were so ugly!"

He agreed with her in that. But there were other things in the theater: the play, for instance.

"Yes," she said absently. "But I have no time."

"What do you do all day?"

She smiled.

"There is so much to do."

"True," said he. "There is your shop."

"Oh!" she said calmly. "That does not take much time."

"Your little girl takes up your time then?"

"Oh! no, poor child! She is very good and plays by herself."

"Then?"

He begged pardon for his indiscretion. But she was amused by it.

"There are so many things."

"What things?"

"She could not say. All sorts of things. Getting up, dressing, thinking of dinner, cooking dinner, eating dinner, thinking of supper, cleaning her room. . . . And then the day was over. . . . And besides you must have a little time for doing nothing!"

"And you are not bored?"

"Never."

"Even when you are doing nothing?"

"Especially when I am doing nothing. It is much worse doing something: that bores me."

They looked at each other and laughed.

"You are very happy!" said Christophe. "I can't do nothing."

"It seems to me that you know how."

"I have been learning lately."

"Ah! well, you'll learn."

When he left off talking to her he was at his ease and comfortable. It was enough for him to see her. He was rid of his anxieties, and irritations, and the nervous trouble that made him sick at heart. When he was talking to her he was beyond care: and so when he thought of her. He dared not admit it to himself: but as soon as he was in her presence, he was filled with a delicious soft emotion that brought him almost to unconsciousness. At night he slept as he had never done.

When he came back from his work he would look into this shop. It was not often that he did not see Sabine. They bowed and smiled. Sometimes she was at the door and then they would exchange a few words: and he would open the door and call the little girl and hand her a packet of sweets.

One day he decided to go in. He pretended that he wanted some waistcoat buttons. She began to look for them: but she could not find them. All the buttons were mixed up: it was impossible to pick them out. She was a little put out that he should see her untidiness. He laughed at it and bent over the better to see it.

"No," she said, trying to hide the drawers with her hands. "Don't look! It is a dreadful muddle. . . ."

She went on looking. But Christophe embarrassed her. She was cross, and as she pushed the drawer back she said:

"I can't find any. Go to Lisi, in the next street. She is sure to have them. She has everything that people want."

He laughed at her way of doing business.

"Do you send all your customers away like that?"

"Well. You are not the first," said Sabine warmly.

And yet she was a little ashamed.

"It is too much trouble to tidy up," she said. "I put off doing it from day to day. . . . But I shall certainly do it to-morrow."

"Shall I help you?" asked Christophe.

She refused. She would gladly have accepted: but she dared not, for fear of gossip. And besides it humiliated her.

They went on talking.

"And your buttons?" she said to Christophe a moment later. "Aren't you going to Lisi?"

"Never," said Christophe. "I shall wait until you have tidied up."

"Oh!" said Sabine, who had already forgotten what she had just said, "don't wait all that time!"

Her frankness delighted them both.

Christophe went to the drawer that she had shut.

"Let me look."

She ran to prevent his doing so.

"No, now please. I am sure I haven't any."

"I bet you have."

At once he found the button he wanted, and was triumphant. He wanted others. He wanted to go on rummaging: but she snatched the box from his hands, and, hurt in her vanity, she began to look herself.

The light was fading. She went to the

window. Christophe sat a little away from her: the little girl clambered on to his knees. He pretended to listen to her chatter and answered her absently. He was looking at Sabine and she knew that he was looking at her. She bent over the box. He could see her neck and a little of her cheek.—And as he looked he saw that she was blushing. And he blushed too.

The child went on talking. No one answered her. Sabine did not move. Christophe could not see what she was doing: he was sure she was doing nothing: she was not even looking at the box in her hands. The silence went on and on. The little girl grew uneasy and slipped down from Christophe's knees.

"Why don't you say anything?"

Sabine turned sharply and took her in her arms. The box was spilled on the floor: the little girl shouted with glee and ran on hands and knees after the buttons rolling under the furniture. Sabine went to the window again and laid her cheek against the pane. She seemed to be absorbed in what she saw outside.

"Good-night!" said Christophe, ill at ease. She did not turn her head, and said in a low voice:

"Good-night."

On Sundays the house was empty during the afternoon. The whole family went to church for Vespers. Sabine did not go. Christophe jokingly reproached her with it once when he saw her sitting at her door in the little garden, while the lovely bells were bawling themselves hoarse summoning her. She replied in the same tone that only Mass was compulsory: not Vespers: it was then no use, and perhaps a little indiscreet to be too zealous: and she liked to think that God would be rather pleased than angry with her.

"You have made God in your own image," said Christophe.

"I should be so bored if I were in His place," replied she with conviction.

"You would not bother much about the world if you were in His place."

"All that I should ask of it would be that it should not bother itself about me."

"Perhaps it would be none the worse for that," said Christophe.

"Tssh!" cried Sabine, "we are being irreligious."

"I don't see anything irreligious in saying that God is like you. I am sure He is flattered."

"Will you be silent!" said Sabine, half laughing, half angry. She was beginning to be afraid that God would be scandalized. She quickly turned the conversation.

"Besides," she said, "it is the only time in the week when one can enjoy the garden in peace."

"Yes," said Christophe. "They are gone." They looked at each other.

"How silent it is," muttered Sabine. "We are not used to it. One hardly knows where one is. . . ."

"Oh!" cried Christophe suddenly and angrily.

"There are days when I would like to strangle her!" There was no need to ask of whom he was speaking.

"And the others?" asked Sabine gaily.

"True," said Christophe, a little abashed. "There is Rosa."

"Poor child!" said Sabine.

They were silent.

"If only it were always as it is now!" sighed Christophe.

She raised her laughing eyes to his, and then dropped them. He saw that she was working.

"What are you doing?" he asked.

(The fence of ivy that separated the two gardens was between them.)

"Look!" she said, lifting a basin that she was holding in her lap. "I am shelling peas."

She sighed.

"But that is not unpleasant," he said, laughing.

"Oh!" she replied, "it is disgusting, always having to think of dinner."

"I bet that if it were possible," he said, "you would go without your dinner rather than have the trouble of cooking it."

"That's true," cried she.

"Wait! I'll come and help you."

He climbed over the fence and came to her.

She was sitting in a chair in the door. He sat on a step at her feet. He dipped into her lap for handfuls of green pods: and he poured the little round peas into the basin that Sabine held between her knees. He looked down. He saw Sabine's black stockings clinging to her ankles and feet—one of her feet was half out of its shoe. He dared not raise his eyes to look at her.

The air was heavy. The sky was dull and clouds hung low: there was no wind. No leaf stirred. The garden was inclosed within high walls: there was no world beyond them.

The child had gone out with one of the neighbors. They were alone. They said nothing. They could say nothing. Without looking he went on taking handfuls of peas from Sabine's lap: his fingers trembled as he touched her: among the fresh smooth pods they met Sabine's fingers, and they trembled too. They could not go on. They sat still, not looking at each other: she leaned back in her chair with her lips half-open and her arms hanging: he sat at her feet leaning against her: along his shoulder and arm he could feel the warmth of Sabine's leg. They were breathless. Christophe laid his hands against the stones to cool them: one of his hands touched Sabine's foot, that she had thrust out of her shoe, and he left it there, could not move it. They

shivered. Almost they lost control. Christophe's hand closed on the slender toes of Sabine's little foot. Sabine turned cold, the sweat broke out on her brow, she leaned towards Christophe. . . .

Familiar voices broke the spell. They trembled. Christophe leaped to his feet and crossed the fence again. Sabine picked up the shells in her lap and went in. In the yard he turned. She was at her door. They looked at each other. Drops of rain were beginning to patter on the leaves of the trees. . . . She closed her door. Frau Vogel and Rosa came in. . . . He went up to his room. . . .

In the yellow light of the waning day drowned in the torrents of rain, he got up from his desk in response to an irresistible impulse: he ran to his window and held out his arms to the opposite window. At the same moment through the opposite window in the half-darkness of the room he saw—he thought he saw—Sabine holding out her arms to him.

He rushed from his room. He went downstairs. He ran to the garden fence. At the risk of being seen he was about to clear it. But when he looked at the window at which she had appeared, he saw that the shutters were closed. The house seemed to be asleep. He stopped. Old Euler, going to his cellar, saw him and called him. He retraced his footsteps. He thought he must have been dreaming.

It was not long before Rosa began to see what was happening. She had no diffidence and she did not yet know what jealousy was. She was ready to give wholly and to ask nothing in return. But if she was sorrowfully resigned to not being loved by Christophe, she had never considered the possibility of Christophe loving another.

One evening, after dinner, she had just finished a piece of embroidery at which she had been working for months. She was happy, and wanted for once in a way to leave her work and go and talk to Christophe. She waited until her mother's back was turned and then slipped from the room. She crept from the house like a truant. She wanted to go and confound Christophe, who had vowed scornfully that she would never finish her work. She thought it would be a good joke to go and take them by surprise in the street. It was no use the poor child knowing how Christophe felt towards her: she was always inclined to measure the pleasure which others should have at seeing her by that which she had herself in meeting them.

She went out. Christophe and Sabine were sitting as usual in front of the house. There was a catch at Rosa's heart. And yet she did not stop for the irrational idea that was in her: and she chaffed Christophe warmly. The sound of her shrill voice in the silence of the night struck on Christophe like a false note. He started in his chair, and frowned angrily. Rosa waved her embroidery in his face triumphantly. Christophe snubbed her impatiently.

"It is finished—finished!" insisted Rosa.

"Oh! well—go and begin another," said Christophe curtly.

Rosa was crestfallen. All her delight vanished. Christophe went on crossly:

"And when you have done thirty, when you are very old, you will at least be able to say to yourself that your life has not been wasted!"

Rosa was near weeping.

"How cross you are, Christophe!" she said.

Christophe was ashamed and spoke kindly to her. She was satisfied with so little that she regained confidence: and she began once more to chatter noisily: she could not speak low, she shouted deafeningly, like everybody in the house. In spite of himself Christophe could not conceal his ill-humor. At first he answered her with a few irritated monosyl-

lables: then he said nothing at all, turned his back on her, fidgeted in his chair, and ground his teeth as she rattled on. Rosa saw that he was losing his temper and knew that she ought to stop: but she went on louder than ever. Sabine, a few yards away, in the dark, said nothing, watched the scene with ironic impassivity. Then she was weary and, feeling that the evening was wasted, she got up and went in. Christophe only noticed her departure after she had gone. He got up at once and without ceremony went away with a curt "Good-evening."

Rosa was left alone in the street, and looked in bewilderment at the door by which he had just gone in. Tears came to her eyes. She rushed in, went up to her room without a sound, so as not to have to talk to her mother, undressed hurriedly, and when she was in her bed, buried under the clothes, sobbed and sobbed. She made no attempt to think over what had passed: she did not ask herself whether Christophe loved Sabine, or whether Christophe and Sabine could not bear her: she knew only that all was lost, that life was useless, that there was nothing left to her but death.

Next morning thought came to her once more with eternal illusive hope. She recalled the events of the evening and told herself that she was wrong to attach so much importance to them. No doubt Christophe did not love her: she was resigned to that, though in her heart she thought, though she did not admit the thought, that in the end she would win his love by her love for him. But what reason had she for thinking that there was anything between Sabine and him? How could he, so clever as he was, love a little creature whose insignificance and mediocrity were patent? She was reassured,—but for that she did not watch Christophe any the less closely. She saw nothing all day, because there was nothing to see: but Christophe seeing her prowling about him all day long without any sort of explanation was peculiarly irritated by it. She set the crown on her efforts in the evening when she appeared again and sat with them in the street. The scene of the previous evening was repeated. Rosa talked alone. But Sabine did not wait so long before she went indoors: and Christophe followed her example. Rosa could no longer pretend that her presence was not unwelcome: but the unhappy girl tried to deceive herself. She did not perceive that she could have done nothing worse than to try so to impose on herself: and with her usual clumsiness she went on through the succeeding days.

Next day with Rosa sitting by his side Christophe waited in vain for Sabine to appear.

The day after Rosa was alone. They had given up the struggle. But she gained nothing by it save resentment from Christophe, who was furious at being robbed of his beloved evenings, his only happiness. He was the less inclined to forgive her, for being absorbed with his own feelings, he had no suspicion of Rosa's.

Sabine had known them for some time: she knew that Rosa was jealous even before she knew that she herself was in love: but she said nothing about it: and, with the natural cruelty of a pretty woman, who is certain of her victory, in quizzical silence she watched the futile efforts of her awkward rival.

Left mistress of the field of battle Rosa gazed piteously upon the results of her tactics. The best thing she could have done would have been not to persist, and to leave Christophe alone, at least for the time being: but that was not what she did: and as the worst thing she could have done was to talk to him about Sabine, that was precisely what she did.

With a fluttering at her heart, by way of sounding him, she said timidly that Sabine was pretty. Christophe replied curtly that she was very pretty. And although Rosa might have foreseen the reply she would provoke, her heart thumped when she heard him. She knew that Sabine was pretty: but she had never particularly remarked it: now she saw her for the first time with the eyes of Christophe: she saw her delicate features, her short nose, her fine mouth, her slender figure, her graceful movements. . . . Ah! how sad! . . . What would not she have given to possess Sabine's body, and live in it! She did not go closely into why it should be preferred to her own! . . . Her own! . . . What had she done to possess such a body? What a burden it was upon her. How ugly it seemed to her! It was odious to her. And to think that nothing but death could ever free her from it! . . . She was at once too proud and too humble to complain that she was not loved: she had no right to do so: and she tried even more to humble herself. But her instinct revolted. . . . No. It was not just! . . . Why should she have such a body, she, and not Sabine? . . . And why should Sabine be loved? What had she done to be loved? . . . Rosa saw her with no kindly eye, lazy, careless, egoistic, indifferent towards everybody, not looking after her house, or her child, or anybody, loving only herself, living only for sleeping, dawdling, and doing nothing. . . . And it was such a woman who pleased . . . who pleased Christophe. . . . Christophe who was so severe, Christophe who was so discerning, Christophe whom she esteemed and admired more than anybody! . . . How could Christophe be blind to it?—She could not help from time to time dropping an unkind remark about Sabine in his hearing. She did not wish to do so: but the impulse was stronger than herself. She was always sorry for it, for she was a kind creature and disliked speaking ill of anybody. But she was the more sorry because she drew down on herself such cruel replies as showed how much Christophe was in love. He did not mince matters. Hurt in his love, he tried to hurt in return: and succeeded. Rosa would make no reply and go out with her head bowed, and her lips tight pressed to keep from crying. She thought that it was her own fault, that she deserved it for having hurt Christophe by attacking the object of his love.

Her mother was less patient. Frau Vogel, who saw everything, and old Euler, also, had not been slow to notice Christophe's interviews with their young neighbor: it was not difficult to guess their romance. Their secret projects of one day marrying Rosa to Christophe were set at naught by it: and that seemed to them a personal affront of Christophe, although he was not supposed to know that they had disposed of him without consulting his wishes. But Amalia's despotism did not admit of ideas contrary to her own: and it seemed scandalous to her that Christophe should have disregarded the contemptuous opinion she had often expressed of Sabine.

She did not hesitate to repeat it for his benefit. Whenever he was present she found some excuse for talking about her neighbor: she cast about for the most injurious things to say of her, things which might sting Christophe most cruelly: and with the crudity of her point of view and language she had no difficulty in finding them. The ferocious instinct of a woman, so superior to that of a man in the art of doing evil, as well as of doing good, made her insist less on Sabine's laziness and moral failings than on her uncleanliness. Her indiscreet and prying eye had watched through the window for proofs of it in the secret processes of Sabine's toilet: and she exposed them with coarse complacency. When from decency she could not say everything she left the more to be understood.

Christophe would go pale with shame and anger: he would go white as a sheet and his lips would quiver. Rosa, foreseeing what must happen, would implore her mother to have done: she would even try to defend Sabine. But she only succeeded in making Amalia more aggressive.

And suddenly Christophe would leap from his chair. He would thump on the table and begin to shout that it was monstrous to speak of a woman, to spy upon her, to expose her misfortunes: only an evil mind could so persecute a creature who was good, charming, quiet, keeping herself to herself, and doing no harm to anybody, and speaking no ill of anybody. But they were making a great mistake if they thought they could do her harm: they only made him more sympathetic and made her kindness shine forth only the more clearly.

Amalia would feel then that she had gone too far: but she was hurt by feeling it: and, shifting her ground, she would say that it was only too easy to talk of kindness: that the word was called in as an excuse for everything. Heavens! It was easy enough to be thought kind when you never bothered about anything or anybody, and never did your duty!

To which Christophe would reply that the first duty of all was to make life pleasant for others, but that there were people for whom duty meant only ugliness, unpleasantness, tiresomeness, and everything that interferes with the liberty of others and annoys and injures their neighbors, their servants, their families, and themselves. God save us from such people, and such a notion of duty, as from the plague! . . .

They would grow venomous. Amalia would be very bitter. Christophe would not budge an inch.—And the result of it all was that henceforth Christophe made a point of being seen continually with Sabine. He would go and knock at her door. He would talk gaily and laugh with her. He would choose moments when Amalia and Rosa could see him. Amalia would avenge herself with angry words. But the innocent Rosa's heart was rent and torn by this refinement of cruelty: she felt that he detested them and wished to avenge himself: and she wept bitterly.

So, Christophe, who had suffered so much from injustice, learned unjustly to inflict suffering.

Some time after that Sabine's brother, a miller at Landegg, a little town a few miles away, was to celebrate the christening of a child. Sabine was to be god-mother. She invited Christophe. He had no liking for these functions: but for the pleasure of annoying the Vogels and of being with Sabine he accepted eagerly.

Sabine gave herself the malicious satisfaction of inviting Amalia and Rosa also, being quite sure that they would refuse. They did. Rosa was longing to accept. She did not dislike Sabine: sometimes even her heart was filled with tenderness for her because Christophe loved her: sometimes she longed to tell her so and to throw her arms about her neck. But there was her mother and her mother's example. She stiffened herself in her pride and refused. Then, when they had gone, and she thought of them together, happy together, driving in the country on the lovely July day, while she was left shut up in her room, with a pile of linen to mend, with her mother grumbling by her side, she thought she must choke: and she cursed her pride. Oh! if there were still time! . . . Alas! if it were all to do again, she would have done the same. . . .

The miller had sent his wagonette to fetch Christophe and Sabine. They took up several guests from the town and the farms on the road. It was fresh dry weather. The bright sun made the red berries of the brown trees by the road

and the wild cherry trees in the fields shine. Sabine was smiling. Her pale face was rosy under the keen wind. Christophe had her little girl on his knees. They did not try to talk to each other: they talked to their neighbors without caring to whom or of what: they were glad to hear each other's voices: they were glad to be driving in the same carriage. They looked at each other in childish glee as they pointed out to each other a house, a tree, a passerby. Sabine loved the country: but she hardly ever went into it: her incurable laziness made excursions impossible: it was almost a year since she had been outside the town: and so she delighted in the smallest things she saw. They were not new to Christophe: but he loved Sabine, and like all lovers he saw everything through her eyes, and felt all her thrills of pleasure, and all and more than the emotion that was in her: for, merging himself with his beloved, he endowed her with all that he was himself.

When they came to the mill they found in the yard all the people of the farm and the other guests, who received them with a deafening noise. The fowls, the ducks, and the dogs joined in. The miller, Bertold, a great fair-haired fellow, square of head and shoulders, as big and tall as Sabine was slight, took his little sister in his arms and put her down gently as though he were afraid of breaking her. It was not long before Christophe saw that the little sister, as usual, did just as she liked with the giant, and that while he made heavy fun of her whims, and her laziness, and her thousand and one failings, he was at her feet, her slave. She was used to it, and thought it natural. She did nothing to win love: it seemed to her right that she should be loved: and if she were not, did not care: that is why everybody loved her.

Christophe made another discovery not so pleasing. For a christening a godfather is necessary as well as a god-mother, and the godfather has certain rights over the godmother, rights which he does not often renounce, especially when she is young and pretty. He learned this suddenly when he saw a farmer, with fair curly hair, and rings in his ears, go up to Sabine laughing and kiss her on both cheeks. Instead of telling himself that he was an ass to have forgotten this privilege, and more than an ass to be huffy about it, he was cross with Sabine, as though she had deliberately drawn him into the snare. His crossness grew worse when he found himself separated from her during the ceremony. Sabine turned round every now and then as the procession wound across the fields and threw him a friendly glance. He pretended not to see it. She felt that he was annoyed, and guessed why: but it did not trouble her: it amused her. If she had had a real squabble with some one she loved, in spite of all the pain it might have caused her, she would never have made the least effort to break down any misunderstanding: it would have been too much trouble. Everything would come right if it were only left alone.

At dinner, sitting between the miller's wife and a fat girl with red cheeks whom he had escorted to the service without ever paying any attention to her, it occurred to Christophe to turn and look at his neighbor: and, finding her comely, out of revenge, he flirted desperately with her with the idea of catching Sabine's attention. He succeeded: but Sabine was not the sort of woman to be jealous of anybody or anything: so long as she was loved, she did not care whether her lover did or did not pay court to others: and instead of being angry, she was delighted to see Christophe amusing himself. From the other end of the table she gave him her most charming smile. Christophe was disgruntled: there was no doubt then that

Sabine was indifferent to him: and he relapsed into his sulky mood from which nothing could draw him, neither the soft eyes of his neighbor, nor the wine that he drank. Finally, when he was half asleep, he asked himself angrily what on earth he was doing at such an interminable orgy, and did not hear the miller propose a trip on the water to take certain of the guests home. Nor did he see Sabine beckoning him to come with her so that they should be in the same boat. When it occurred to him, there was no room for him: and he had to go in another boat. This fresh mishap was not likely to make him more amiable until he discovered that he was to be rid of almost all his companions on the way. Then he relaxed and was pleasant. Besides the pleasant afternoon on the water, the pleasure of rowing, the merriment of these good people, rid him of his ill-humor. As Sabine was no longer there he lost his self-consciousness, and had no scruple about being frankly amused like the others.

They were in their boats. They followed each other closely, and tried to pass each other. They threw laughing insults at each other. When the boats bumped Christophe saw Sabine's smiling face: and he could not help smiling too: they felt that peace was made. He knew that very soon they would return together.

They began to sing part songs. Each voice took up a line in time and the refrain was taken up in chorus. The people in the different boats, some way from each other, now echoed each other. The notes skimmed over the water like birds. From time to time a boat would go in to the bank: a few peasants would climb out: they would stand there and wave to the boats as they went further and further away. Little by little they were disbanded. One by one voices left the chorus. At last they were alone, Christophe, Sabine, and the miller.

They came back in the same boat, floating down the river. Christophe and Bertold held the oars, but they did not row. Sabine sat in the stern facing Christophe, and talked to her brother and looked at Christophe. Talking so, they were able to look at each other undisturbedly. They could never have done so had the words ceased to flow. The deceitful words seemed to say: "It is not you that I see." But their eyes said to each other: "Who are you? Who are you? You that I love! . . . You that I love, whoever you be! . . ."

The sky was clouded, mists rose from the fields, the river steamed, the sun went down behind the clouds. Sabine shivered and wrapped her little black shawl round her head and shoulders. She seemed to be tired. As the boat, hugging the bank, passed under the spreading branches of the willows, she closed her eyes: her thin face was pale: her lips were sorrowful: she did not stir, she seemed to suffer,—to have suffered,—to be dead. Christophe's heart ached. He leaned over to her. She opened her eyes again and saw Christophe's uneasy eyes upon her and she smiled into them. It was like a ray of sunlight to him. He asked in a whisper:

"Are you ill?"

She shook her head and said:

"I am cold."

The two men put their overcoats about her, wrapped up her feet, her legs, her knees, like a child being tucked up in bed. She suffered it and thanked them with her eyes. A fine, cold rain was beginning to fall. They took the oars and went quietly home. Heavy clouds hung in the sky. The river was inky black. Lights showed in the windows of the houses here and there in the fields. When they reached the mill the rain was pouring down and Sabine was numbed.

They lit a large fire in the kitchen and waited until the deluge should be over. But it only grew worse, and the wind rose. They had to drive three miles to get back to the town. The miller declared that he would not let Sabine go in such weather: and he proposed that they should both spend the night in the farmhouse. Christophe was reluctant to accept: he looked at Sabine for counsel: but her eyes were fixed on the fire on the hearth: it was as though they were afraid of influencing Christophe's decision. But when Christophe had said "Yes," she turned to him and she was blushing—(or was it the reflection of the fire?)—and he saw that she was pleased.

A jolly evening. . . . The rain stormed outside. In the black chimney the fire darted jets of golden sparks. They spun round and round. Their fantastic shapes were marked against the wall. The miller showed Sabine's little girl how to make shadows with her hands. The child laughed and was not altogether at her ease. Sabine leaned over the fire and poked it mechanically with a heavy pair of tongs: she was a little weary, and smiled dreamily, while, without listening, she nodded to her sister-in-law's chatter of her domestic affairs. Christophe sat in the shadow by the miller's side and watched Sabine smiling. He knew that she was smiling at him. They never had an opportunity of being alone all evening, or of looking at each other: they sought none.

They parted early. Their rooms were adjoining, and communicated by a door. Christophe examined the door and found that the lock was on Sabine's side. He went to bed and tried to sleep. The rain was pattering against the windows. The wind howled in the chimney. On the floor above him a door was banging. Outside the window a poplar bent and groaned under the tempest. Christophe could not close his eyes. He was thinking that he was under the same roof, near her. A wall only divided them. He heard no sound in Sabine's room. But he thought he could see her. He sat up in his bed and called to her in a low voice through the wall: tender, passionate words he said: he held out his arms to her. And it seemed to him that she was holding out her arms to him. In his heart he heard the beloved voice answering him, repeating his words, calling low to him: and he did not know whether it was he who asked and answered all the questions, or whether it was really she who spoke. The voice came louder, the call to him: he could not resist: he leaped from his bed: he groped his way to the door: he did not wish to open it: he was reassured by the closed door. And when he laid his hand once more on the handle he found that the door was opening. . . .

He stopped dead. He closed it softly: he opened it once more: he closed it again. Was it not closed just now? Yes. He was sure it was. Who had opened it? . . . His heart beat so that he choked. He leaned over his bed, and sat down to breathe again. He was overwhelmed by his passion. It robbed him of the power to see or hear or move: his whole body shook. He was in terror of this unknown joy for which for months he had been craving, which was with him now, near him, so that nothing could keep it from him. Suddenly the violent boy filled with love was afraid of these desires newly realized and revolted from them. He was ashamed of them, ashamed of what he wished to do. He was too much in love to dare to enjoy what he loved: he was afraid: he would have done anything to escape his happiness. Is it only possible to love, to love at the cost of the profanation of the beloved? . . .

He went to the door again: and trembling with love and fear, with his hand on the latch he could not bring himself to open it.

And on the other side of the door, standing barefooted on the tiled floor, shivering with cold, was Sabine.

So they stayed . . . for how long? Minutes? Hours? . . . They did not know that they were there: and yet they did know. They held out their arms to each other,—he was overwhelmed by a love so great that he had not the courage to enter,—she called to him, waited for him, trembled lest he should enter . . . And when at last he made up his mind to enter, she had just made up her mind to turn the lock again.

Then he cursed himself for a fool. He leaned against the door with all his strength. With his lips to the lock he implored her:

"Open."

He called to Sabine in a whisper: she could hear his heated breathing. She stayed motionless near the door: she was frozen: her teeth were chattering: she had no strength either to open the door or to go to bed again. . . .

The storm made the trees crack and the doors in the house bang. . . . They turned away and went to their beds, worn out, sad and sick at heart. The cocks crowed huskily. The first light of dawn crept through the wet windows, a wretched, pale dawn, drowned in the persistent rain. . . .

Christophe got up as soon as he could: he went down to the kitchen and talked to the people there. He was in a hurry to be gone and was afraid of being left alone with Sabine again. He was almost relieved when the miller's wife said that Sabine was unwell, and had caught cold during the drive and would not be going that morning.

His journey home was melancholy. He refused to drive, and walked through the soaking fields, in the yellow mist that covered the earth, the trees, the houses, with a shroud. Like the light, life seemed to be blotted out. Everything loomed like a specter. He was like a specter himself.

At home he found angry faces. They were all scandalized at his having passed the night God knows where with Sabine. He shut himself up in his room and applied himself to his work. Sabine returned the next day and shut herself up also. They avoided meeting each other. The weather was still wet and cold: neither of them went out. They saw each other through their closed windows. Sabine was wrapped up by her fire, dreaming. Christophe was buried in his papers. They bowed to each other a little coldly and reservedly and then pretended to be absorbed again. They did not take stock of what they were feeling: they were angry with each other, with themselves, with things generally. The night at the farmhouse had been thrust aside in their memories: they were ashamed of it, and did not know whether they were more ashamed of their folly or of not having yielded to it. It was painful to them to see each other: for that made them remember things from which they wished to escape: and by joint agreement they retired into the depths of their rooms so as utterly to forget each other. But that was impossible, and they suffered keenly under the secret hostility which they felt was between them. Christophe was haunted by the expression of dumb rancor which he had once seen in Sabine's cold eyes. From such thoughts her suffering was not less: in vain did she struggle against them, and even deny them: she could not rid herself of them. They were augmented by her shame that Christophe should have guessed what was happening within her: and the shame of having offered herself . . . the shame of having offered herself without having given.

Christophe gladly accepted an oppor-
tunity which cropped up to go to Cologne and Düsseldorf for some concerts. He was glad to spend two or three weeks away from home. Preparation for the concerts and the composition of a new work that he wished to play at them took up all his time and he succeeded in forgetting his obstinate memories. They disappeared from Sabine's mind too, and she fell back into the torpor of her usual life. They came to think of each other with indifference. Had they really loved each other? They doubted it. Christophe was on the point of leaving for Cologne without saying good-bye to Sabine.

On the evening before his departure they were brought together again by some imperceptible influence. It was one of the Sunday afternoons when everybody was at church. Christophe had gone out too to make his final preparations for the journey. Sabine was sitting in her tiny garden warming herself in the last rays of the sun. Christophe came home: he was in a hurry and his first inclination when he saw her was to bow and pass on. But something held him back as he was passing: was it Sabine's paleness, or some indefinable feeling: remorse, fear, tenderness? . . . He stopped, turned to Sabine, and, leaning over the fence, he bade her good-evening. Without replying she held out her hand. Her smile was all kindness,—such kindness as he had never seen in her. Her gesture seemed to say: "Peace between us. . . ." He took her hand over the fence, bent over it, and kissed it. She made no attempt to withdraw it. He longed to go down on his knees and say, "I love you." . . . They looked at each other in silence. But they offered no explanation. After a moment she removed her hand and turned her head. He turned too to hide his emotion. Then they looked at each other again with untroubled eyes. The sun was setting. Subtle shades of color, violet, orange, and mauve, chased across the cold clear sky. She shivered and drew her shawl closer about her shoulders with a movement that he knew well. He asked:

"How are you?"

She made a little grimace, as if the question were not worth answering. They went on looking at each other and were happy. It was as though they had lost, and had just found each other again. . . .

At last he broke the silence and said:

"I am going away tomorrow."

There was alarm in Sabine's eyes.

"Going away?" she said.

He added quickly:

"Oh! only for two or three weeks."

"Two or three weeks," she said in dismay.

He explained that he was engaged for the concerts, but that when he came back he would not stir all winter.

"Winter," she said. "That is a long time off. . . ."

"Oh! no. It will soon be here."

She saddened and did not look at him.

"When shall we meet again?" she asked a moment later.

He did not understand the question: he had already answered it.

"As soon as I come back: in a fortnight, or three weeks at most."

She still looked dismayed. He tried to tease her:

"It won't be long for you," he said. "You will sleep."

"Yes," said Sabine.

She looked down, she tried to smile: but her eyes trembled.

"Christophe! . . ." she said suddenly, turning towards him.

There was a note of distress in her voice. She seemed to say:

"Stay! Don't go! . . ."

He took her hand, looked at her, did not understand the importance she attached to his fortnight's absence: but he was only waiting for a word from her to say:

"I will stay. . . ."

And just as she was going to speak, the front door was opened and Rosa appeared. Sabine withdrew her hand from Christophe's and went hurriedly into her house. At the door she turned and looked at him once more—and disappeared.

Christophe thought he should see her again in the evening. But he was watched by the Vogels, and followed everywhere by his mother: as usual, he was behindhand with his preparations for his journey and could not find time to leave the house for a moment.

Next day he left very early. As he passed Sabine's door he longed to go in, to tap at the window: it hurt him to leave her without saying good-bye: for he had been interrupted by Rosa before he had had time to do so. But he thought she must be asleep and would be cross with him if he woke her up. And then, what could he say to her? It was too late now to abandon his journey: and what if she were to ask him to do so? . . . He did not admit to himself that he was not averse to exercising his power over her, —if need be, causing her a little pain. . . . He did not take seriously the grief that his departure brought Sabine: and he thought that his short absence would increase the tenderness which, perhaps, she had for him.

He ran to the station. In spite of everything he was a little remorseful. But as soon as the train had started it was all forgotten. There was youth in his heart. Gaily he saluted the old town with its roofs and towers rosy under the sun: and with the carelessness of those who are departing he said good-bye to those whom he was leaving, and thought no more of them.

The whole time that he was at Düsseldorf and Cologne Sabine never once recurred to his mind. Taken up from morning till night with rehearsals and concerts, dinners and talk, busied with a thousand and one new things and the pride and satisfaction of his success he had no time for recollection. Once only, on the fifth night after he left home, he woke suddenly after a dream and knew that he had been thinking of *her* in his sleep and that the thought of *her* had wakened him up; but he could not remember how he had been thinking of her. He was unhappy and feverish. It was not surprising: he had been playing at a concert that evening, and when he left the hall he had been dragged off to a supper at which he had drunk several glasses of champagne. He could not sleep and got up. He was obsessed by a musical idea. He pretended that it was that which had broken in upon his sleep and he wrote it down. As he read through it he was astonished to see how sad it was. There was no sadness in him when he wrote: at least, so he thought. But he remembered that on other occasions when he had been sad he had only been able to write joyous music, so gay that it offended his mood. He gave no more thought to it. He was used to the surprises of his mind world without ever being able to understand them. He went to sleep at once, and knew no more until the next morning.

He extended his stay by three or four days. It pleased him to prolong it, knowing he could return whenever he liked: he was in no hurry to go home. It was only when he was on the way, in the train, that the thought of Sabine came back to him. He had not written to her. He was even careless enough never to have taken the trouble to ask at the post-office for any letters that might have been written to him. He took a secret delight in his silence: he knew that at home he was expected, that he was loved. . . . Loved? She had never told him so: he

had never told her so. No doubt they knew it and had no need to tell it. And yet there was nothing so precious as the certainty of such an avowal. Why had they waited so long to make it? When they had been on the point of speaking always something—some mischance, shyness, embarrassment,—had hindered them. Why? Why? How much time they had lost! . . . He longed to hear the dear words from the lips of the beloved. He longed to say them to her: he said them aloud in the empty carriage. As he neared the town he was torn with impatience, a sort of agony. . . . Faster! Faster! Oh! To think that in an hour he would see her again! . . .

It was half-past six in the morning when he reached home. Nobody was up yet. Sabine's windows were closed. He went into the yard on tiptoe so that she should not hear him. He chuckled at the thought of taking her by surprise. He went up to his room. His mother was asleep. He washed and brushed his hair without making any noise. He was hungry: but he was afraid of waking Louisa by rummaging in the pantry. He heard footsteps in the yard: he opened his window softly and saw Rosa, first up as usual, beginning to sweep. He called her gently. She started in glad surprise when she saw him: then she looked solemn. He thought she was still offended with him: but for the moment he was in a very good temper. He went down to her.

"Rosa, Rosa," he said gaily, "give me something to eat or I shall eat you! I am dying of hunger!"

Rosa smiled and took him to the kitchen on the ground floor. She poured him out a bowl of milk and then could not refrain from plying him with a string of questions about his travels and his concerts. But although he was quite ready to answer them,—(in the happiness of his return he was almost glad to hear Rosa's chatter once more)—Rosa stopped suddenly in the middle of her cross-examination, her face fell, her eyes turned away, and she became sorrowful. Then her chatter broke out again: but soon it seemed that she thought it out of place and once more she stopped short. And he noticed it then and said:

"What is the matter, Rosa? Are you cross with me?"

She shook her head violently in denial, and turning towards him with her usual suddenness took his arm with both hands:

"Oh! Christophe! . . ." she said.

He was alarmed. He let his piece of bread fall from his hands.

"What! What is the matter?" he stammered.

She said again:

"Oh! Christophe! . . . Such an awful thing has happened!"

He thrust away from the table. He stuttered:

"H—here?"

She pointed to the house on the other side of the yard.

He cried:

"Sabine!"

She wept:

"She is dead."

Christophe saw nothing. He got up: he almost fell: he clung to the table, upset the things on it: he wished to cry out. He suffered fearful agony. He turned sick.

Rosa hastened to his side: she was frightened: she held his head and wept.

As soon as he could speak he said:

"It is not true!"

He knew that it was true. But he wanted to deny it, he wanted to pretend that it could not be. When he saw Rosa's face wet with tears he could doubt no more and he sobbed aloud.

Rosa raised her head:

"Christophe!" she said.

He hid his face in his hands. She leaned towards him.

"Christophe! . . . Mamma is coming! . . ."

Christophe got up.

"No, no," he said. "She must not see me."

She took his hand and led him, stumbling and blinded by his tears, to a little woodshed which opened on to the yard. She closed the door. They were in darkness. He sat on a block of wood used for chopping sticks. She sat on the fagots. Sounds from without were deadened and distant. There he could weep without fear of being heard. He let himself go and sobbed furiously. Rosa had never seen him weep: she had even thought that he could not weep: she knew only her own girlish tears and such despair in a man filled her with terror and pity. She was filled with a passionate love for Christophe. It was an absolutely unselfish love: an immense need of sacrifice, a maternal self-denial, a hunger to suffer for him, to take his sorrow upon herself. She put her arm round his shoulders.

"Dear Christophe," she said, "do not cry!"

Christophe turned from her.

"I wish to die!"

Rosa clasped her hands.

"Don't say that, Christophe!"

"I wish to die. I cannot . . . cannot live now. . . . What is the good of living?"

"Christophe, dear Christophe! You are not alone. You are loved. . . ."

"What is that to me? I love nothing now. It is nothing to me whether everything else live or die. I love nothing: I loved only her. I loved only her!"

He sobbed louder than ever with his face buried in his hands. Rosa could find nothing to say. The egoism of Christophe's passion stabbed her to the heart. Now when she thought herself most near to him, she felt more isolated and more

miserable than ever. Grief instead of bringing them together thrust them only the more widely apart. She wept bitterly.

After some time, Christophe stopped weeping and asked:

"How? . . . How? . . ."

Rosa understood.

"She fell ill of influenza on the evening you left. And she was taken suddenly. . . ."

He groaned.

"Dear God! . . . Why did you not write to me?"

She said:

"I did write. I did not know your address: you did not give us any. I went and asked at the theater. Nobody knew it."

He knew how timid she was, and how much it must have cost her. He asked:

"Did she . . . did she tell you to do that?"

She shook her head:

"No. But I thought . . ."

He thanked her with a look. Rosa's heart melted.

"My poor . . . poor Christophe!" she said.

She flung her arms round his neck and wept. Christophe felt the worth of such pure tenderness. He had so much need of consolation! He kissed her:

"How kind you are," he said. "You loved her too?"

She broke away from him, she threw him a passionate look, did not reply, and began to weep again.

That look was a revelation to him. It meant:

"It was not she whom I loved. . . ."

Christophe saw at last what he had not known—what for months he had not wished to see. He saw that she loved him.

" 'Ssh," she said. "They are calling me." They heard Amalia's voice.

Rosa asked:

"Do you want to go back to your room?"

He said:

"No. I could not yet: I could not bear to talk to my mother. . . . Later on. . . ."

She said:

"Stay here. I will come back soon."

He stayed in the dark woodshed to which only a thread of light penetrated through a small airhole filled with cobwebs. From the street there came up the cry of a hawker, against the wall a horse in a stable next door was snorting and kicking. The revelation that had just come to Christophe gave him no pleasure: but it held his attention for a moment. It made plain many things that he had not understood. A multitude of little things that he had disregarded occurred to him and were explained. He was surprised to find himself thinking of it: he was ashamed to be turned aside even for a moment from his misery. But that misery was so frightful, so irrepressible that the mistrust of self-preservation, stronger than his will, than his courage, than his love, forced him to turn away from it, seized on this new idea, as the suicide drowning seizes in spite of himself on the first object which can help him, not to save himself, but to keep himself for a moment longer above the water. And it was because he was suffering that he was able to feel what another was suffering—suffering through him. He understood the tears that he had brought to her eyes. He was filled with pity for Rosa. He thought how cruel he had been to her—how cruel he must still be. For he did not love her. What good was it for her to love him? Poor girl! . . . In vain did he tell himself that she was good (she had just proved it). What was her goodness to him? What was her life to him? . . .

He thought:

"Why is it not she who is dead, and the other who is alive?"

He thought:

"She is alive: she loves me: she can tell me that today, tomorrow, all my life: and the other, the woman I love, she is dead and never told me that she loved me: I never have told her that I loved her: I shall never hear her say it: she will never know it. . . ."

And suddenly he remembered that last evening: he remembered that they were just going to talk when Rosa came and prevented it. And he hated Rosa. . . .

The door of the woodshed was opened. Rosa called Christophe softly, and groped towards him. She took his hand. He felt an aversion in her near presence: in vain did he reproach himself for it: it was stronger than himself.

Rosa was silent: her great pity had taught her silence. Christophe was grateful to her for not breaking in upon his grief with useless words. And yet he wished to know . . . she was the only creature who could talk to him of *her*. He asked in a whisper:

"When did she . . ."

(He dared not say: die.)

She replied:

"Last Saturday week."

Dimly he remembered. He said:

"At night?"

Rosa looked at him in astonishment and said:

"Yes. At night. Between two and three."

The sorrowful melody came back to him. He asked, trembling:

"Did she suffer much?"

"No, no. God be thanked, dear Christophe: she hardly suffered at all. She was so weak. She did not struggle against it. Suddenly they saw that she was lost. . . ."

"And she . . . did she know it?"

"I don't know. I think . . ."

"Did she say anything?"

"No. Nothing. She was sorry for herself like a child."

"You were there?"

"Yes. For the first two days I was there alone, before her brother came."

He pressed her hand in gratitude.

"Thank you."

She felt the blood rush to her heart.

After a silence he murmured the question which was choking him:

"Did she say anything . . . for me?"

Rosa shook her head sadly. She would have given much to be able to let him have the answer he expected: she was almost sorry that she could not lie about it. She tried to console him:

"She was not conscious."

"But she did speak?"

"One could not make out what she said. It was in a very low voice."

"Where is the child?"

"Her brother took her away with him to the country."

"And *she?*"

"She is there too. She was taken away last Monday week."

They began to weep again.

Frau Vogel's voice called Rosa once more. Christophe, left alone again, lived through those days of death. A week, already a week ago. . . . O God! What had become of her? How it had rained that week! . . . And all that time he was laughing, he was happy!

In his pocket he felt a little parcel wrapped up in soft paper: they were silver buckles that he had brought her for her shoes. He remembered the evening when he had placed his hand on the little stockinged foot. Her little feet: where were they now? How cold they must be! . . . He thought the memory of that warm contact was the only one that he had of the beloved creature. He had never dared to touch her, to take her in his arms, to hold her to his breast. She was gone forever, and he had never known her. He knew nothing of her, neither soul nor body. He had no memory of her body, of her life, of her love. . . . Her love? . . . What proof had he of that? . . . He had not even a letter, a token,—nothing. Where could he seek to hold her, in himself, or outside himself? . . . Oh! Nothing! There was nothing left him but the love he had for her, nothing left him but himself.—And in spite of all, his desperate desire to snatch her from destruction, his need of denying death, made him cling to the last piece of wreckage, in an act of blind faith:

"*. . . he son gia morto: e ben c'albergo cangi resto in te vivo. C'or mi vedi e piangi, se l'un nell' altro amante si trasforma.*"

". . . I am not dead: I have changed my dwelling. I live still in thee who art faithful to me. The soul of the beloved is merged in the soul of the lover."

He had never read these sublime words: but they were in him. Each one of us in turn climbs the Calvary of the age. Each one of us finds anew the agony, each one of us finds anew the desperate hope and folly of the ages. Each one of us follows in the footsteps of those who were, of those before us who struggled with death, denied death—and are dead.

He shut himself up in his room. His shutters were closed all day so as not to see the windows of the house opposite. He avoided the Vogels: they were odious to his sight. He had nothing to reproach them with: they were too honest, and too pious not to have thrust back their feelings in the face of death. They knew Christophe's grief and respected it, whatever they might think of it: they never uttered Sabine's name in his presence. But they had been her enemies when she was alive: that was enough to make him their enemy now that she was dead.

Besides they had not altered their noisy habits: and in spite of the sincere though passing pity that they had felt, it was obvious that at bottom they were untouched by the misfortune—(it was too natural)—perhaps even they were secretly relieved by it. Christophe imagined so at least. Now that the Vogels' intentions with regard to himself were made plain he exaggerated them in his own mind. In reality they attached little importance to him: he set too great store by himself. But he had no doubt that the death of Sabine, by removing the greatest obstacle in the way of his landlords' plans, did seem to them to leave the field clear for Rosa. So he detested her. That they—(the Vogels, Louisa, and even Rosa)—should have tacitly disposed of him, without consulting him, was enough in any case to make him lose all affection for the person whom he was destined to love. He shied whenever he thought an attempt was made upon his umbrageous sense of liberty. But now it was not only a question of himself. The rights which these others had assumed over him did not only infringe upon his own rights but upon those of the dead woman to whom his heart was given. So he defended them doggedly, although no one was for attacking them. He suspected Rosa's goodness. She suffered in seeing him suffer and would often come and knock at his door to console him and talk to him about the other. He did not drive her away: he needed to talk of Sabine with some one who had known her: he wanted to know the smallest of what had happened during her illness. But he was not grateful to Rosa: he attributed ulterior motives to her. Was it not plain that her family, even Amalia, permitted these visits and long colloquies which she would never have allowed if they had not fallen in with her wishes? Was not Rosa in league with her family? He could not believe that her pity was absolutely sincere and free of personal thoughts.

And, no doubt, it was not. Rosa pitied

Christophe with all her heart. She tried hard to see Sabine through Christophe's eyes, and through him to love her: she was angry with herself for all the unkind feelings that she had ever had towards her, and asked her pardon in her prayers at night. But could she forget that she was alive, that she was seeing Christophe every moment of the day, that she loved him, that she was no longer afraid of the other, that the other was gone, that her memory would also fade away in its turn, that she was left alone, that one day perhaps . . . ? In the midst of her sorrow, and the sorrow of her friend more hers than her own, could she repress a glad impulse, an unreasoning hope? For that too she was angry with herself. It was only a flash. It was enough. He saw it. He threw her a glance which froze her heart: she read in it hateful thoughts: he hated her for being alive while the other was dead.

The miller brought his cart for Sabine's little furniture. Coming back from a lesson Christophe saw heaped up before the door in the street the bed, the cupboard, the mattress, the linen, all that she had possessed, all that was left of her. It was a dreadful sight to him. He rushed past it. In the doorway he bumped into Bertold, who stopped him.

"Ah! my dear sir," he said, shaking his hand effusively. "Ah! who would have thought it when we were together? How happy we were! And yet it was because of that day, because of that cursed row on the water, that she fell ill. Oh! well. It is no use complaining! She is dead. It will be our turn next. That is life. . . . And how are you? I'm very well, thank God!"

He was red in the face, sweating, and smelled of wine. The idea that he was her brother, that he had rights in her memory, hurt Christophe. It offended him to hear this man talking of his beloved. The miller on the contrary was glad to find a

friend with whom he could talk of Sabine: he did not understand Christophe's coldness. He had no idea of all the sorrow that his presence, the sudden calling to mind of the day at his farm, the happy memories that he recalled so blunderingly, the poor relics of Sabine, heaped upon the ground, which he kicked as he talked, set stirring in Christophe's soul. He made some excuse for stopping Bertold's tongue. He went up the steps: but the other clung to him, stopped him, and went on with his harangue. At last when the miller took to telling him of Sabine's illness, with that strange pleasure which certain people, and especially the common people, take in talking of illness, with a plethora of painful details, Christophe could bear it no longer—(he took a tight hold of himself so as not to cry out in his sorrow). He cut him short:

"Pardon," he said curtly and icily. "I must leave you."

He left him without another word.

His insensibility revolted the miller. He had guessed the secret affection of his sister and Christophe. And that Christophe should now show such indifference seemed monstrous to him: he thought he had no heart.

Christophe had fled to his room: he was choking. Until the removal was over he never left his room. He vowed that he would never look out of the window, but he could not help doing so: and hiding in a corner behind the curtain he followed the departure of the goods and chattels of the beloved eagerly and with profound sorrow. When he saw them disappearing forever he all but ran down to the street to cry: "No! no! Leave them to me! Do not take them from me!" He longed to beg at least for some little thing, only one little thing, so that she should not be altogether taken from him. But how could he ask such a thing of the miller? It was nothing to him. She herself had not known his love: how dared he then reveal it to another? And besides, if he had tried to say a word he would have burst out crying. . . . No. No. He had to say nothing, to watch all go, without being able—without daring to save one fragment from the wreck. . . .

And when it was all over, when the house was empty, when the yard gate was closed after the miller, when the wheels of his cart moved on, shaking the windows, when they were out of hearing, he threw himself on the floor—not a tear left in him, not a thought of suffering, of struggling, frozen, and like one dead.

There was a knock at the door. He did not move. Another knock. He had forgotten to lock the door. Rosa came in. She cried out on seeing him stretched on the floor and stopped in terror. He raised his head angrily:

"What? What do you want? Leave me!"

She did not go: she stayed, hesitating, leaning against the door, and said again:

"Christophe. . . ."

He got up in silence: he was ashamed of having been seen so. He dusted himself with his hand and asked harshly:

"Well. What do you want?"

Rosa said shyly:

"Forgive me . . . Christophe . . . I came in . . . I was bringing you . . ."

He saw that she had something in her hand.

"See," she said, holding it out to him. "I asked Bertold to give me a little token of her. I thought you would like it. . . ."

It was a little silver mirror, the pocket mirror in which she used to look at herself for hours, not so much from coquetry as from want of occupation. Christophe took it, took also the hand which held it.

"Oh! Rosa! . . ." he said.

He was filled with her kindness and the knowledge of his own injustice. On a passionate impulse he knelt to her and kissed her hand.

"Forgive . . . Forgive . . ." he said.

Rosa did not understand at first: then she understood only too well: she blushed, she trembled, she began to weep. She understood that he meant:

"Forgive me if I am unjust. . . . Forgive me if I do not love you. . . . Forgive me if I cannot . . . if I cannot love you, if I can never love you! . . ."

She did not withdraw her hand from him: she knew that it was not herself that he was kissing. And with his cheek against Rosa's hand, he wept hot tears, knowing that she was reading through him: there was sorrow and bitterness in being unable to love her and making her suffer.

They stayed so, both weeping, in the dim light of the room.

At last she withdrew her hand. He went on murmuring:

"Forgive! . . ."

She laid her hand gently on his hand. He rose to his feet. They kissed in silence: they felt on their lips the bitter savor of their tears.

"We shall always be friends," he said softly. She bowed her head and left him, too sad to speak.

They thought that the world is ill made. The lover is unloved. The beloved does not love. The lover who is loved is sooner or later torn from his love. . . . There is suffering. There is the bringing of suffering. And the most wretched is not always the one who suffers.

Once more Christophe took to avoiding the house. He could not bear it. He could not bear to see the curtainless windows, the empty rooms.

A worse sorrow awaited him. Old Euler lost no time in reletting the ground floor. One day Christophe saw strange faces in Sabine's room. New lives blotted out the traces of the life that was gone.

It became impossible for him to stay in his rooms. He passed whole days outside, not coming back until nightfall, when it was too dark to see anything. Once more he took to making expeditions in the country. Irresistibly he was drawn to Bertold's farm. But he never went in, dared not go near it, wandered about it at a distance. He discovered a place on a hill from which he could see the house, the plain, the river: it was thither that his steps usually turned. From thence he could follow with his eyes the meanderings of the water down to the willow clump under which he had seen the shadow of death pass across Sabine's face. From thence he could pick out the two windows of the rooms in which they had waited, side by side, so near, so far, separated by a door—the door to eternity. From thence he could survey the cemetery. He had never been able to bring himself to enter it: from childhood he had had a horror of those fields of decay and corruption, and refused to think of those whom he loved in connection with them. But from a distance and seen from above, the little graveyard never looked grim, it was calm, it slept with the sun. . . . Sleep! . . . She loved to sleep! Nothing would disturb her there. The crowing cocks answered each other across the plains. From the homestead rose the roaring of the mill, the clucking of the poultry yard, the cries of children playing. He could make out Sabine's little girl, he could see her running, he could mark her laughter. Once he lay in wait for her near the gate of the farmyard, in a turn of the sunk road made by the walls: he seized her as she passed and kissed her. The child was afraid and began to cry. She had almost forgotten him already. He asked her:

"Are you happy here?"

"Yes. It is fun. . . ."

"You don't want to come back?"

"No!"

He let her go. The child's indifference plunged him in sorrow. Poor Sabine! . . . And yet it was she, something of her. . . . So little! The child was hardly at all like her mother: had lived in her, but was not she: in that mysterious passage through her being the child had hardly retained more than the faintest perfume of the creature who was gone: inflections of her voice, a pursing of the lips, a trick of bending the head. The rest of her was another being altogether: and that being mingled with the being of Sabine was repulsive to Christophe though he never admitted it to himself.

It was only in himself that Christophe could find the image of Sabine. It followed him everywhere, hovering above him: but he only felt himself really to be with her when he was alone. Nowhere was she nearer to him than in this refuge, on the hill, far from strange eyes, in the midst of the country that was so full of the memory of her. He would go miles to it, climbing at a run, his heart beating as though he were going to a meeting with her: and so it was indeed. When he reached it he would lie on the ground— the same earth in which *her* body was laid: he would close his eyes: and *she* would come to him. He could not see her face: he could not hear her voice: he had no need: she entered into him, held him, he possessed her utterly. In this state of passionate hallucination he would lose the power of thought, he would be unconscious of what was happening: he was unconscious of everything save that he was with her.

That state of things did not last long.—To tell the truth he was only once altogether sincere. From the day following, his will had its share in the proceedings. And from that time on Christophe tried in vain to bring it back to life. It was only then that he thought of evoking in himself the face and form of Sabine: until then he had never thought of it. He succeeded spasmodically and he was fired by it. But it was only at the cost of hours of waiting and of darkness.

"Poor Sabine!" he would think. "They have all forgotten you. There is only I who love you, who keep your memory alive forever. Oh, my treasure, my precious! I have you, I hold you, I will never let you go! . . ."

He spoke these words because already she was escaping him: she was slipping from his thoughts like water through his fingers. He would return again and again, faithful to the tryst. He wished to think of her and he would close his eyes. But after half an hour, or an hour, or sometimes two hours, he would begin to see that he had been thinking of nothing. The sounds of the valley, the roar of the wind, the little bells of the two goats browsing on the hill, the noise of the wind in the little slender trees under which he lay, were sucked up by his thoughts, soft and porous like a sponge. He was angry with his thoughts: they tried to obey him, and to fix the vanished image to which he was striving to attach his life: but his thoughts fell back weary and chastened and once more with a sigh of comfort abandoned themselves to the listless stream of sensations.

He shook off his torpor. He strode through the country hither and thither seeking Sabine. He sought her in the mirror that once had held her smile. He sought her by the river bank where her hands had dipped in the water. But the mirror and the water gave him only the reflection of himself. The excitement of walking, the fresh air, the beating of his

own healthy blood awoke music in him once more. He wished to find change.

"Oh! Sabine! . . ." he sighed.

He dedicated his songs to her: he strove to call her to life in his music, his love, and his sorrow. . . . In vain: love and sorrow came to life surely: but poor Sabine had no share in them. Love and sorrow looked towards the future, not towards the past. Christophe was powerless against his youth. The sap of life swelled up again in him with new vigor. His grief, his regrets, his chaste and ardent love, his baffled desires, heightened the fever that was in him. In spite of his sorrow, his heart beat in lively, sturdy rhythm: wild songs leaped forth in mad, intoxicated strains: everything in him hymned life and even sadness took on a festival shape. Christophe was too frank to persist in self-deception: and he despised himself. But life swept him headlong: and in his sadness, with death in his heart, and life in all his limbs, he abandoned himself to the forces newborn in him, to the absurd, delicious joy of living, which grief, pity, despair, the aching wound of an irreparable loss, all the torment of death, can only sharpen and kindle into being in the strong, as they rowel their sides with furious spur.

And Christophe knew that, in himself, in the secret hidden depths of his soul, he had an inaccessible and inviolable sanctuary where lay the shadow of Sabine. That the flood of life could not bear away. . . . Each of us bears in his soul as it were a little graveyard of those whom he has loved. They sleep there, through the years, untroubled. But a day cometh,—this we know,—when the graves shall reopen. The dead issue from the tomb and smile with their pale lips—loving, always—on the beloved, and the lover, in whose breast their memory dwells, like the child sleeping in the mother's womb.

III

ADA

After the wet summer the autumn was radiant. In the orchards the trees were weighed down with fruit. The red apples shone like billiard balls. Already some of the trees were taking on their brilliant garb of the falling year: flame color, fruit color, color of ripe melon, of oranges and lemons, of good cooking, and fried dishes. Misty lights glowed through the woods: and from the meadows there rose the little pink flames of the saffron.

He was going down a hill. It was a Sunday afternoon. He was striding, almost running, gaining speed down the slope. He was singing a phrase, the rhythm of which had been obsessing him all through his walk. He was red, disheveled: he was walking, swinging his arms, and rolling his eyes like a madman, when as he turned a bend in the road he came suddenly on a fair girl perched on a wall tugging with all her might at a branch of a tree from which she was greedily plucking and eating purple plums. Their astonishment was mutual. She looked at him, stared, with her mouth full. Then she burst out laughing. So did he. She was good to see, with her round face framed in fair curly hair, which was like a sunlit cloud about her, her full pink cheeks, her wide blue eyes, her rather large nose, impertinently turned up, her little red mouth showing white teeth—the canine little, strong, and projecting—her plump chin, and her full figure, large and plump, well built, solidly put together. He called out:

"Good eating!" And was for going on his road. But she called to him:

"Sir! Sir! Will you be very nice? Help me to get down. I can't . . ."

He returned and asked her how she had climbed up.

"With my hands and feet. . . . It is easy enough to get up. . . ."

"Especially when there are tempting plums hanging above your head. . . ."

"Yes. . . . But when you have eaten your courage goes. You can't find the way to get down."

He looked at her on her perch. He said:

"You are all right there. Stay there quietly. I'll come and see you tomorrow. Good-night!"

But he did not budge, and stood beneath her. She pretended to be afraid, and begged him with little glances not to leave her. They stayed looking at each other and laughing. She showed him the branch to which she was clinging and asked:

"Would you like some?"

Respect for property had not developed in Christophe since the days of his expeditions with Otto: he accepted without hesitation. She amused herself with pelting him with plums. When he had eaten she said:

"Now! . . ."

He took a wicked pleasure in keeping her waiting. She grew impatient on her wall. At last he said:

"Come, then!" and held his hand up to her.

But just as she was about to jump down she thought a moment.

"Wait! We must make provision first!"

She gathered the finest plums within reach and filled the front of her blouse with them.

"Carefully! Don't crush them!"

He felt almost inclined to do so.

She lowered herself from the wall and jumped into his arms. Although he was sturdy he bent under her weight and all but dragged her down. They were of the same height. Their faces came together. He kissed her lips, moist and sweet with the juice of the plums: and she returned his kiss without more ceremony.

"Where are you going?" he asked.

"I don't know."

"Are you out alone?"

"No. I am with friends. But I have lost them. . . . Hi! Hi!" she called suddenly as loudly as she could.

No answer.

She did not bother about it any more. They began to walk, at random, following their noses.

"And you . . . where are you going?" said she.

"I don't know, either."

"Good. We'll go together."

She took some plums from her gaping blouse and began to munch them.

"You'll make yourself sick," he said.

"Not I! I've been eating them all day."

Through the gap in her blouse he saw the white of her chemise.

"They are all warm now," she said.

"Let me see!"

She held him one and laughed. He ate it. She watched him out of the corner of her eye as she sucked at the fruit like a child. He did not know how the adventure would end. It is probable that she at least had some suspicion. She waited.

"Hi! Hi!" Voices in the woods.

"Hi! Hi!" she answered. "Ah! There they are!" she said to Christophe. "Not a bad thing, either!"

But on the contrary she was thinking that it was rather a pity. But speech was not given to woman for her to say what she is thinking. . . . Thank God! for there would be an end to morality on earth. . . .

The voices came near. Her friends were near the road. She leaped the ditch, climbed the hedge, and hid behind the trees. He watched her in amazement. She signed to him imperiously to come to her.

He followed her. She plunged into the depths of the wood.

"Hi! Hi!" she called once more when they had gone some distance. "You see, they must look for me!" she explained to Christophe.

Her friends had stopped on the road and were listening for her voice to mark where it came from. They answered her and in their turn entered the woods. But she did not wait for them. She turned about on right and on left. They bawled loudly after her. She let them, and then went and called in the opposite direction. At last they wearied of it, and, making sure that the best way of making her come was to give up seeking her, they called:

"Good-bye!" and went off singing.

She was furious that they should not have bothered about her any more than that. She had tried to be rid of them: but she had not counted on their going off so easily. Christophe looked rather foolish: this game of hide-and-seek with a girl whom he did not know did not exactly enthrall him: and he had no thought of taking advantage of their solitude. Nor did she think of it: in her annoyance she forgot Christophe.

"Oh! It's too much," she said, thumping her hands together. "They have left me."

"But," said Christophe, "you wanted them to."

"Not at all."

"You ran away."

"If I ran away from them that is my affair, not theirs. They ought to look for me. What if I were lost? . . ."

Already she was beginning to be sorry for herself because of what might have happened if . . . if the opposite of what actually had occurred had come about.

"Oh!" she said. "I'll shake them!" She turned back and strode off.

As she went she remembered Chris-

tophe and looked at him once more.—
But it was too late. She began to laugh.
The little demon which had been in her
the moment before was gone. While she
was waiting for another to come she saw
Christophe with the eyes of indifference.
And then, she was hungry. Her stomach
was reminding her that it was supper-
time: she was in a hurry to rejoin her
friends at the inn. She took Christophe's
arm, leaned on it with all her weight,
groaned, and said that she was exhausted. That did not keep her from
dragging Christophe down a slope, running, and shouting, and laughing like a
mad thing.

They talked. She learned who he was:
she did not know his name, and seemed
not to be greatly impressed by his title of
musician. He learned that she was a shop-
girl from a dressmaker's in the *Kaiser-
strasse* (the most fashionable street in the
town): her name was Adelheid—to
friends, Ada. Her companions on the
excursion were one of her friends, who
worked at the same place as herself, and
two nice young men, a clerk at Weiller's
bank, and a clerk from a big linen-
draper's. They were turning their Sunday
to account: they had decided to dine at
the Brochet inn, from which there is a
fine view over the Rhine, and then to
return by boat.

The others had already established
themselves at the inn when they arrived.
Ada made a scene with her friends: she
complained of their cowardly desertion
and presented Christophe as her savior.
They did not listen to her complaints: but
they knew Christophe, the bank-clerk by
reputation, the clerk from having heard
some of his compositions—(he thought it
a good idea to hum an air from one of
them immediately afterwards)—and the
respect which they showed him made an
impression on Ada, the more so as
Myrrha, the other young woman—(her
real name was Hansi or Johanna)—a

brunette with blinking eyes, bumpy forehead, hair screwed back, Chinese face, a
little too animated, but clever and not
without charm, in spite of her goat-like
head and her oily golden-yellow complexion,—at once began to make advances to
their *Hof Musicus*. They begged him to
be so good as to honor their repast with
his presence.

Never had he been in such high
feather: for he was overwhelmed with
attentions, and the two women, like good
friends as they were, tried each to rob the
other of him. Both courted him: Myrrha
with ceremonious manners, sly looks, as
she rubbed her leg against his under the
table—Ada, openly making play with her
fine eyes, her pretty mouth, and all the
seductive resources at her command.
Such coquetry in its almost coarseness
incommoded and distressed Christophe.
These two bold young women were a
change from the unkindly faces he was
accustomed to at home. Myrrha interested him, he guessed her to be more
intelligent than Ada: but her obsequious
manners and her ambiguous smile were
curiously attractive and repulsive to him
at the same time. She could do nothing
against Ada's radiance of life and pleasure: and she was aware of it. When she
saw that she had lost the bout, she abandoned the effort, turned in upon herself,
went on smiling, and patiently waited for
her day to come. Ada, seeing herself
mistress of the field, did not seek to push
forward the advantage she had gained:
what she had done had been mainly to
despite her friend: she had succeeded,
she was satisfied. But she had been
caught in her own game. She felt as she
looked into Christophe's eyes the passion
that she had kindled in him: and that
same passion began to awake in her. She
was silent: she left her vulgar teasing:
they looked at each other in silence: on
their lips they had the savor of their kiss.
From time to time by fits and starts they

joined vociferously in the jokes of the others: then they relapsed into silence, stealing glances at each other. At last they did not even look at each other, as though they were afraid of betraying themselves. Absorbed in themselves they brooded over their desire.

When the meal was over they got ready to go. They had to go a mile and a half through the woods to reach the pier. Ada got up first: Christophe followed her. They waited on the steps until the others were ready: without speaking, side by side, in the thick mist that was hardly at all lit up by the single lamp hanging by the inn door.—Myrrha was dawdling by the mirror.

Ada took Christophe's hand and led him along the house towards the garden into the darkness. Under a balcony from which hung a curtain of vines they hid. All about them was dense darkness. They could not even see each other. The wind stirred the tops of the pines. He felt Ada's warm fingers entwined in his and the sweet scent of a heliotrope flower that she had at her breast.

Suddenly she dragged him to her: Christophe's lips found Ada's hair, wet with the mist, and kissed her eyes, her eyebrows, her nose, her cheeks, the corners of her mouth, seeking her lips, and finding them, staying pressed to them.

The others had gone. They called:

"Ada! . . ."

They did not stir, they hardly breathed, pressed close to each other, lips and bodies.

They heard Myrrha:

"They have gone on."

The footsteps of their companions died away in the night. They held each other closer, in silence, stifling on their lips a passionate murmuring.

In the distance a village clock rang out. They broke apart. They had to run to the pier. Without a word they set out, arms and hands entwined, keeping step—a little quick, firm step, like hers. The road was deserted: no creature was abroad: they could not see ten yards ahead of them: they went, serene and sure, into the beloved night. They never stumbled over the pebbles on the road. As they were late they took a short cut. The path led for some way down through vines and then began to ascend and wind up the side of the hill. Through the mist they could hear the roar of the river and the heavy paddles of the steamer approaching. They left the road and ran across the fields. At last they found themselves on the bank of the Rhine but still far from the pier. Their serenity was not disturbed. Ada had forgotten her fatigue of the evening. It seemed to them that they could have walked all night like that, on the silent grass, in the hovering mists, that grew wetter and more dense along the river that was wrapped in a whiteness as of the moon. The steamer's siren hooted: the invisible monster plunged heavily away and away. They said, laughing:

"We will take the next."

By the edge of the river soft lapping waves broke at their feet. At the landing stage they were told:

"The last boat has just gone."

Christophe's heart thumped. Ada's hand grasped his arm more tightly.

"But," she said, "there will be another one to-morrow."

A few yards away in a halo of mist was the flickering light of a lamp hung on a post on a terrace by the river. A little farther on were a few lighted windows—a little inn.

They went into the tiny garden. The sand ground under their feet. They groped their way to the steps. When they entered, the lights were being put out. Ada, on Christophe's arm, asked for a room. The room to which they were led opened on to the little garden. Christophe leaned out of the window and saw the phosphorescent flow of the river, and the shade of the lamp on the glass of which were crushed mosquitoes with large wings. The door was closed. Ada was standing by the bed and smiling. He dared not look at her. She did not look at him: but through her lashes she followed Christophe's every movement. The floor creaked with every step. They could hear the least noise in the house. They sat on the bed and embraced in silence.

The flickering light of the garden is dead. All is dead. . . .

Night. . . . The abyss. . . . Neither light nor consciousness. . . . Being. The obscure, devouring forces of Being. Joy all-powerful. Joy rending. Joy which sucks down the human creature as the void a stone. The sprout of desire sucking up thought. The absurd delicious law of the blind intoxicated worlds which roll at night. . . .

. . . A night which is many nights, hours that are centuries, records which are death. . . . Dreams shared, words spoken with eyes closed, tears and laughter, the happiness of loving in the voice, of sharing the nothingness of sleep, the swiftly passing images floating in the brain, the hallucinations of the roaring night. . . . The Rhine laps in a little creek by the house: in the distance his waters over the dams and breakwaters make a sound as of a gentle rain falling on sand. The hull of the boat cracks and groans under the weight of water. The chain by which it is tied sags and grows taut with a rusty clattering. The voice of the river rises: it fills the room. The bed is like a boat. They are swept along side by side by a giddy current—hung in mid-air like a soaring bird. The night grows ever more dark, the void more empty. Ada weeps, Christophe loses consciousness: both are swept down under the flowing waters of the night. . . .

Night. . . . Death. . . . Why wake to life again? . . .

The light of the dawning day peeps through the dripping panes. The spark of life glows once more in their languorous bodies. He awakes. Ada's eyes are looking at him. A whole life passes in a few moments: days of sin, greatness, and peace . . .

"Where am I? And am I two? Do I still exist? I am no longer conscious of being. All about me is the infinite: I have the soul of a statue, with large tranquil eyes, filled with Olympian peace. . . ."

They fall back into the world of sleep. And the familiar sounds of the dawn, the distant bells, a passing boat, oars dripping water, footsteps on the road, all caress without disturbing their happy sleep, reminding them that they are alive, and making them delight in the savor of their happiness. . . .

The puffing of the steamer outside the window brought Christophe from his torpor. They had agreed to leave at seven so as to return to the town in time for their usual occupations. He whispered:

"Do you hear?"

She did not open her eyes; she smiled, she put out her lips, she tried to kiss him and then let her head fall back on his shoulder. . . . Through the window panes he saw the funnel of the steamer slip by against the sky, he saw the empty deck, and clouds of smoke. Once more he slipped into dreaminess. . . .

An hour passed without his knowing it. He heard it strike and started in astonishment.

"Ada! . . ." he whispered to the girl. "Ada!" he said again. "It's eight o'clock."

Her eyes were still closed: she frowned and pouted pettishly.

"Oh! let me sleep!" she said.

She sighed wearily and turned her back on him and went to sleep once more.

He began to dream. His blood ran bravely, calmly through him. His limpid senses received the smallest impressions simply and freshly. He rejoiced in his strength and youth. Unwittingly he was proud of being a man. He smiled in his happiness, and felt himself alone: alone as he had always been, more lonely even but without sadness, in a divine solitude. No more fever. No more shadows. Nature could freely cast her reflection upon his soul in its serenity. Lying on his back, facing the window, his eyes gazing deep into the dazzling air with its luminous mists, he smiled:

"How good it is to live! . . ."

To live! . . . A boat passed. . . . The thought suddenly of those who were no longer alive, of a boat gone by on which they were together: he—she. . . . She? . . . Not that one, sleeping by his side.—She, the only she, the beloved, the poor little woman who was dead.—But is it that one? How came she there? How did they come to this room? He looks at her, he does not know her: she is a stranger to him: yesterday morning she did not exist for him. What does he know of her?—He knows that she is not clever. He knows that she is not good. He knows that she is not even beautiful with her face spiritless and bloated with sleep, her low forehead, her mouth open in breathing, her swollen dried lips pouting like a fish. He knows that he does not love her. And he is filled with a bitter sorrow when he thinks that he kissed those strange lips, in the first moment with her, that he has taken this beautiful body for which he cares nothing on the first night of their meeting,—and that she whom he loved, he watched her live and die by his side and never dared touch her hair with his lips, that he will never know the perfume of her being. Nothing more. All is crumbled away. The earth has taken all from him. And he never defended what was his. . . .

And while he leaned over the innocent sleeper and scanned her face, and looked at her with eyes of unkindness, she felt his eyes upon her. Uneasy under his scrutiny she made a great effort to raise her heavy lids and to smile: and she said, stammering a little like a waking child:

"Don't look at me. I'm ugly. . . ."

She fell back at once, weighed down with sleep, smiled once more, murmured.

"Oh! I'm so . . . so sleepy! . . ." and went off again into her dreams.

He could not help laughing: he kissed her childish lips more tenderly. He watched the girl sleeping for a moment longer, and got up quietly. She gave a comfortable sigh when he was gone. He tried not to wake her as he dressed, though there was no danger of that: and when he had done he sat in the chair near the window and watched the steaming smoking river which looked as though it were covered with ice: and he fell into a brown study in which there hovered music, pastoral, melancholy.

From time to time she half opened her eyes and looked at him vaguely, took a second or two, smiled at him, and passed from one sleep to another. She asked him the time.

"A quarter to nine."

Half asleep she pondered:

"What! Can it be a quarter to nine?"

At half-past nine she stretched, sighed, and said that she was going to get up.

It was ten o'clock before she stirred. She was petulant.

"Striking again! . . . The clock is fast! . . ." He laughed and went and sat on the bed by her side. She put her arms round his neck and told him her dreams. He did not listen very attentively and interrupted her with little love words. But she made him be silent and went on very seriously, as though she were telling something of the highest importance:

"She was at dinner: the Grand Duke was there: Myrrha was a Newfoundland dog. . . . No, a frizzy sheep who waited at table. . . . Ada had discovered a method of rising from the earth, of walking, dancing, and lying down in the air. You see it was quite simple: you had only to do . . . thus . . . thus . . . and it was done. . . ."

Christophe laughed at her. She laughed too, though a little ruffled at his laughing. She shrugged her shoulders.

"Ah! you don't understand! . . ."

They breakfasted on the bed from the same cup, with the same spoon.

At last she got up: she threw off the bedclothes and slipped down from the bed. Then she sat down to recover her breath and looked at her feet. Finally she clapped her hands and told him to go out: and as he was in no hurry about it she took him by the shoulders and thrust him out of the door and then locked it.

After she had dawdled, looked over and stretched each of her handsome limbs, she sang, as she washed, a sentimental *Lied* in fourteen couplets, threw water at Christophe's face—he was outside drumming on the window—and as they left she plucked the last rose in the garden and then they took the steamer. The mist was not yet gone: but the sun shone through it: they floated through a creamy light. Ada sat at the stern with Christophe: she was sleepy and a little sulky: she grumbled about the light in her eyes, and said that she would have a headache all day. And as Christophe did not take her complaints seriously enough she returned into morose silence. Her eyes were hardly opened and in them was the funny gravity of children who have just woke up. But at the next landing-stage an elegant lady came and sat not far from her, and she grew lively at once: she talked eagerly to Christophe about things sentimental and distinguished. She had resumed with him the ceremonious *Sie*.

Christophe was thinking about what she could say to her employer by way of excuse for her lateness. She was hardly at all concerned about it.

"Bah! It's not the first time."

"The first time that . . . what?"

"That I have been late," she said, put out by the question.

He dared not ask her what had caused her lateness.

"What will you tell her?"

"That my mother is ill, dead . . . how do I know?"

He was hurt by her talking so lightly.

"I don't want you to lie."

She took offense:

"First of all, I never lie. . . . And then, I cannot very well tell her . . ."

He asked her half in jest, half in earnest:

"Why not?"

She laughed, shrugged, and said that he was coarse and ill-bred, and that she had already asked him not to use the *Du* to her.

"Haven't I the right?"

"Certainly not."

"After what has happened?"

"Nothing has happened."

She looked at him a little defiantly and laughed: and although she was joking, he felt most strongly that it would not have cost her much to say it seriously and almost to believe it. But some pleasant memory tickled her: for she burst out laughing and looked at Christophe and kissed him loudly without any concern for the people about, who did not seem to be in the least surprised by it.

Now on all his excursions he was accompanied by shop-girls and clerks: he did not like their vulgarity, and used to try to lose them: but Ada out of contrariness was no longer disposed for wandering in the woods. When it rained or for some other reason they did not leave the town he would take her to the theater, or the museum, or the *Thiergarten:*

for she insisted on being seen with him. She even wanted him to go to church with her; but he was so absurdly sincere that he would not set foot inside a church since he had lost his belief—(on some other excuse he had resigned his position as organist)—and at the same time, unknown to himself, remained much too religious not to think Ada's proposal sacrilegious.

He used to go to her rooms in the evening. Myrrha would be there, for she lived in the same house. Myrrha was not at all resentful against him: she would hold out her soft hand caressingly, and talk of trivial and improper things and then slip away discreetly. The two women had never seemed to be such friends as since they had had small reason for being so: they were always together. Ada had no secrets from Myrrha: she told her everything: Myrrha listened to everything: they seemed to be equally pleased with it all.

Christophe was ill at ease in the company of the two women. Their friendship, their strange conversations, their freedom of manner, the crude way in which Myrrha especially viewed and spoke of things—(not so much in his presence, however, as when he was not there, but Ada used to repeat her sayings to him)—their indiscreet and impertinent curiosity, which was forever turned upon subjects that were silly or basely sensual, the whole equivocal and rather animal atmosphere oppressed him terribly, though it interested him: for he knew nothing like it. He was at sea in the conversations of the two little beasts, who talked of dress, and made silly jokes, and laughed in an inept way with their eyes shining with delight when they were off on the track of some spicy story. He was more at ease when Myrrha left them. When the two women were together it was like being in a foreign country without knowing the language. It was impossible to make himself understood: they did not even listen: they poked fun at the foreigner.

When he was alone with Ada they went on speaking different languages: but at least they did make some attempt to understand each other. To tell the truth, the more he understood her, the less he understood her. She was the first woman he had known. For if poor Sabine was a woman he had known, he had known nothing of her: she had always remained for him a phantom of his heart. Ada took upon herself to make him make up for lost time. In his turn he tried to solve the riddle of woman: an enigma which perhaps is no enigma except for those who seek some meaning in it.

Ada was without intelligence: that was the least of her faults. Christophe would have commended her for it, if she had approved it herself. But although she was occupied only with stupidities, she claimed to have some knowledge of the things of the spirit: and she judged everything with complete assurance. She would talk about music, and explain to Christophe things which he knew perfectly, and would pronounce absolute judgment and sentence. It was useless to try to convince her: she had pretensions and susceptibilities in everything; she gave herself airs, she was obstinate, vain: she would not—she could not understand anything. Why would she not accept that she could understand nothing? He loved her so much better when she was content with being just what she was, simply, with her own qualities and failings, instead of trying to impose on others and herself!

In fact, she was little concerned with thought. She was concerned with eating, drinking, singing, dancing, crying, laughing, sleeping: she wanted to be happy: and that would have been all right if she had succeeded. But although she had every gift for it: she was greedy, lazy, sensual, and frankly egoistic in a way that revolted and amused Christophe: although she had almost all the vices which make life pleasant for their fortunate possessor, if not for their friends— (and even then does not a happy face, at least if it be pretty, shed happiness on all those who come near it?)—in spite of so many reasons for being satisfied with life and herself Ada was not even clever enough for that. The pretty, robust girl, fresh, hearty, healthy-looking, endowed with abundant spirits and fierce appetites, was anxious about her health. She bemoaned her weakness, while she ate enough for four. She was always sorry for herself: she could not drag herself along, she could not breathe, she had a headache, feet-ache, her eyes ached, her stomach ached, her soul ached. She was afraid of everything, and madly superstitious, and saw omens everywhere: at meals the crossing of knives and forks, the number of the guests, the upsetting of a salt-cellar: then there must be a whole ritual to turn aside misfortune. Out walking she would count the crows, and never failed to watch which side they flew to: she would anxiously watch the road at her feet, and when a spider crossed her path in the morning she would cry out aloud: then she would wish to go home and there would be no other means of not interrupting the walk than to persuade her that it was after twelve, and so the omen was one of hope rather than of evil. She was afraid of her dreams: she would recount them at length to Christophe; for hours she would try to recollect some detail that she had forgotten; she never spared him one; absurdities piled one on the other, strange marriages, deaths, dressmakers' prices, burlesque, and sometimes, obscene things. He had to listen to her and give her his advice. Often she would be for a whole day under the obsession of her inept fancies.

She would find life ill-ordered, she would see things and people rawly and overwhelm Christophe with her jeremiads: and it seemed hardly worth while to have broken away from the gloomy middle-class people with whom he lived to find once more the eternal enemy: the *"trauriger ungriechischer Hypochondrist."*

But suddenly in the midst of her sulks and grumblings, she would become gay, noisy, exaggerated: there was no more dealing with her gaiety than with her moroseness: she would burst out laughing for no reason and seem as though she were never going to stop: she would rush across the fields, play mad tricks and childish pranks, take a delight in doing silly things, in mixing with the earth, and dirty things, and the beasts, and the spiders, and worms, in teasing them, and hurting them, and making them eat each other: the cats eat the birds, the fowls the worms, the ants the spiders, not from any wickedness, or perhaps from an altogether unconscious instinct for evil, from curiosity, or from having nothing better to do. She seemed to be driven always to say stupid things, to repeat senseless words again and again, to irritate Christophe, to exasperate him, set his nerves on edge, and make him almost beside himself. And her coquetry as soon as anybody—no matter who—appeared on the road! . . . Then she would talk excitedly, laugh noisily, make faces, draw attention to herself: she would assume an affected mincing gait. Christophe would have a horrible presentiment that she was going to plunge into serious discussion.— And, indeed, she would do so. She would become sentimental, uncontrolledly, just as she did everything: she would unbosom herself in a loud voice. Christophe would suffer and long to beat her. Least of all could he forgive her her lack of sincerity. He did not yet know that sincerity is a gift as rare as intelligence or beauty and that it cannot justly be expected of everybody. He could not bear a lie: and Ada gave him lies in full measure. She was always lying, quite calmly, in spite of evidence to the contrary. She had that astounding faculty for forgetting what is displeasing to them—or even what has been pleasing to them—which those women possess who live from moment to moment.

And, in spite of everything, they loved each other with all their hearts. Ada was as sincere as Christophe in her love. Their love was none the less true for not being based on intellectual sympathy: it had nothing in common with base passion. It was the beautiful love of youth: it was sensual, but not vulgar, because it was altogether youthful: it was naïve, almost chaste, purged by the ingenuous ardor of pleasure. Although Ada was not, by a long way, so ignorant as Christophe, yet she had still the divine privilege of youth of soul and body, that freshness of the senses, limpid and vivid as a running stream, which almost gives the illusion of purity and through life is never replaced. Egoistic, commonplace, insincere in her ordinary life,—love made her simple, true, almost good: she understood in love the joy that is to be found in self-forgetfulness. Christophe saw this with delight: and he would gladly have died for her. Who can tell all the absurd and touching illusions that a loving heart brings to its love! And the natural illusion of the lover was magnified an hundredfold in Christophe by the power of illusion which is born in the artist. Ada's smile held profound meanings for him: an affectionate word was the proof of the goodness of her heart. He loved in her all that is good and beautiful in the universe. He called her his own, his soul, his life. They wept together over their love.

Pleasure was not the only bond between them: there was an indefinable poetry of memories and dreams,—their own? or those of the men and women who had loved before them, who had been before them,—in them? . . . Without a word, perhaps without knowing it, they preserved the fascination of the first moments of their meeting in the woods, the first days, the first nights together: those hours of sleep in each other's arms, still, unthinking, sinking down into a flood of love and silent joy. Swift fancies, visions, dumb thoughts, titillating, and making them go pale, and their hearts sink under their desire, bringing all about them a buzzing as of bees. A fine light, and tender. . . . Their hearts sink and beat no more, borne down in excess of sweetness. Silence, languor, and fever, the mysterious weary smile of the earth quivering under the first sunlight of spring. . . . So fresh a love in two young creatures is like an April morning. Like April it must pass. Youth of the heart is like an early feast of sunshine.

Nothing could have brought Christophe closer to Ada in his love than the way in which he was judged by others.

The day after their first meeting it was known all over the town. Ada made no attempt to cover up the adventure, and rather plumed herself on her conquest. Christophe would have liked more discretion: but he felt that the curiosity of the people was upon him: and as he did not wish to seem to fly from it, he threw in his lot with Ada. The little town buzzed with tattle. Christophe's colleagues in the orchestra paid him sly compliments to which he did not reply, because he would not allow any meddling with his affairs. The respectable people of the town judged his conduct very severely. He lost his music lessons with certain families. With others, the mothers thought that they must now be present at the daughters' lessons, watching with suspicious eyes, as though

Christophe were intending to carry off the precious darlings. The young ladies were supposed to know nothing. Naturally they knew everything: and while they were cold towards Christophe for his lack of taste, they were longing to have further details. It was only among the small tradespeople, and the shop people, that Christophe was popular: but not for long: he was just as annoyed by their approval as by the condemnation of the rest: and being unable to do anything against that condemnation, he took steps not to keep their approval: there was no difficulty about that. He was furious with the general indiscretion.

The most indignant of all with him were Justus Euler and the Vogels. They took Christophe's misconduct as a personal outrage. They had not made any serious plans concerning him: they distrusted—especially Frau Vogel—these artistic temperaments. But as they were naturally discontented and always inclined to think themselves persecuted by fate, they persuaded themselves that they had counted on the marriage of Christophe and Rosa; as soon as they were quite certain that such a marriage would never come to pass, they saw in it the mark of the usual ill luck. Logically, if fate were responsible for their miscalculation, Christophe could not be: but the Vogels' logic was that which gave them the greatest opportunity for finding reasons for being sorry for themselves. So they decided that if Christophe had misconducted himself it was not so much for his own pleasure as to give offense to them. They were scandalized. Very religious, moral, and oozing domestic virtue, they were of those to whom the sins of the flesh are the most shameful, the most serious, almost the only sins, because they are the only dreadful sins—(it is obvious that respectable people are never likely to be tempted to steal or murder). —And so Christophe seemed to them absolutely wicked, and they changed their demeanor towards him. They were icy towards him and turned away as they passed him. Christophe, who was in no particular need of their conversation, shrugged his shoulders at all the fuss. He pretended not to notice Amalia's insolence: who, while she affected contemptuously to avoid him, did all that she could to make him fall in with her so that she might tell him all that was rankling in her.

Christophe was only touched by Rosa's attitude. The girl condemned him more harshly even than his family. Not that this new love of Christophe's seemed to her to destroy her last chances of being loved by him: she knew that she had no chance left—(although perhaps she went on hoping: she always hoped). —But she had made an idol of Christophe: and that idol had crumbled away. It was the worst sorrow for her . . . yes, a sorrow more cruel to the innocence and honesty of her heart, than being disdained and forgotten by him. Brought up puritanically, with a narrow code of morality, in which she believed passionately, what she had heard about Christophe had not only brought her to despair but had broken her heart. She had suffered already when he was in love with Sabine: she had begun then to lose some of her illusions about her hero. That Christophe could love so commonplace a creature seemed to her inexplicable and inglorious. But at least that love was pure, and Sabine was not unworthy of it. And in the end death had passed over it and sanctified it. . . . But that at once Christophe should love another woman,—and such a woman!—was base, and odious! She took upon herself the defense of the dead woman against him. She could not forgive him for having forgotten her. . . . Alas! He was thinking of her more than she: but she never thought that in a passionate heart there might be room for two sentiments at once: she thought it impossible to be faithful to the past without sacrifice of the present. Pure and cold, she had no idea of life or of Christophe: everything in her eyes was pure, narrow, submissive to duty, like herself. Modest of soul, modest of herself, she had only one source of pride: purity: she demanded it of herself and of others. She could not forgive Christophe for having so lowered himself, and she would never forgive him.

Christophe tried to talk to her, though not to explain himself—(what could he say to her? what could he say to a little puritanical and naïve girl?).—He would have liked to assure her that he was her friend, that he wished for her esteem, and had still the right to it. He wished to prevent her absurdly estranging herself from him.—But Rosa avoided him in stern silence: he felt that she despised him.

He was both sorry and angry. He felt that he did not deserve such contempt: and yet in the end he was bowled over by it: and thought himself guilty. Of all the reproaches cast against him the most bitter came from himself when he thought of Sabine. He tormented himself.

"Oh! God, how is it possible? What sort of creature am I? . . ."

But he could not resist the stream that bore him on. He thought that life is criminal: and he closed his eyes so as to live without seeing it. He had so great a need to live, and be happy, and love, and believe! . . . No: there was nothing despicable in his love! He knew that it was impossible to be very wise, or intelligent, or even very happy in his love for Ada: but what was there in it that could be called vile? Suppose—(he forced the idea on himself)—that Ada were not a woman of any great moral worth, how was the love that he had for her the less pure for that? Love is in the lover, not in

the beloved. Everything is worthy of the lover, everything is worthy of love. To the pure all is pure. All is pure in the strong and the healthy of mind. Love, which adorns certain birds with their loveliest colors, calls forth from the souls that are true all that is most noble in them. The desire to show to the beloved only what is worthy makes the lover take pleasure only in those thoughts and actions which are in harmony with the beautiful image fashioned by love. And the waters of youth in which the soul is bathed, the blessed radiance of strength and joy, are beautiful and health-giving, making the heart great.

That his friends misunderstood him filled him with bitterness. But the worst trial of all was that his mother was beginning to be unhappy about it.

The good creature was far from sharing the narrow views of the Vogels. She had seen real sorrows too near ever to try to invent others. Humble, broken by life, having received little joy from it, and having asked even less, resigned to everything that happened, without even trying to understand it, she was careful not to judge or censure others: she thought she had no right. She thought herself too stupid to pretend that they were wrong when they did not think as she did: it would have seemed ridiculous to try to impose on others the inflexible rules of her morality and belief. Besides that, her morality and her belief were purely instinctive: pious and pure in herself she closed her eyes to the conduct of others, with the indulgence of her class for certain faults and certain weaknesses. That had been one of the complaints that her father-in-law, Jean Michel, had lodged against her: she did not sufficiently distinguish between those who were honorable and those who were not: she was not afraid of stopping in the street or the market-place to shake hands and talk with young women, notorious in the neighborhood, whom a respectable woman ought to pretend to ignore. She left it to God to distinguish between good and evil, to punish or to forgive. From others she asked only a little of that affectionate sympathy which is so necessary to soften the ways of life. If people were only kind she asked no more.

But since she had lived with the Vogels a change had come about in her. The disparaging temper of the family had found her an easier prey because she was crushed and had no strength to resist. Amalia had taken her in hand: and from morning to night when they were working together alone, and Amalia did all the talking, Louisa, broken and passive, unconsciously assumed the habit of judging and criticizing everything. Frau Vogel did not fail to tell her what she thought of Christophe's conduct. Louisa's calmness irritated her. She thought it indecent of Louisa to be so little concerned about what put him beyond the pale: she was not satisfied until she had upset her altogether. Christophe saw it. Louisa dared not reproach him: but every day she made little timid remarks, uneasy, insistent: and when he lost patience and replied sharply, she said no more: but still he could see the trouble in her eyes: and when he came home sometimes he could see that she had been weeping. He knew his mother too well not to be absolutely certain that her uneasiness did not come from herself.—And he knew well whence it came.

He determined to make an end of it. One evening when Louisa was unable to hold back her tears and had got up from the table in the middle of supper without Christophe being able to discover what was the matter, he rushed downstairs four steps at a time and knocked at the Vogels' door. He was boiling with rage. He was not only angry about Frau Vogel's treatment of his mother: he had to

avenge himself for her having turned Rosa against him, for her bickering against Sabine, for all that he had had to put up with at her hands for months. For months he had borne his pent-up feelings against her and now made haste to let them loose.

He burst in on Frau Vogel and in a voice that he tried to keep calm, though it was trembling with fury, he asked her what she had told his mother to bring her to such a state.

Amalia took it very badly: she replied that she would say what she pleased, and was responsible to no one for her actions—to him least of all. And seizing the opportunity to deliver the speech which she had prepared, she added that if Louisa was unhappy he had to go no further for the cause of it than his own conduct, which was a shame to himself and a scandal to everybody else.

Christophe was only waiting for her onslaught to strike out. He shouted angrily that his conduct was his own affair, that he did not care a rap whether it pleased Frau Vogel or not, that if she wished to complain of it she must do so to him, and that she could say to him whatever she liked: that rested with her, but he *forbade* her—(did she hear?)—*forbade* her to say anything to his mother: it was cowardly and mean so to attack a poor sick old woman.

Frau Vogel cried loudly. Never had any one dared to speak to her in such a manner. She said that she was not to be lectured by a rapscallion,—and in her own house, too!—And she treated him with abuse.

The others came running up on the noise of the quarrel,—except Vogel, who fled from anything that might upset his health. Old Euler was called to witness by the indignant Amalia and sternly bade Christophe in future to refrain from speaking to or visiting them. He said that they did not need him to tell them what they ought to do, that they did their duty and would always do it.

Christophe declared that he would go and would never again set foot in their house. However, he did not go until he had relieved his feelings by telling them what he had still to say about their famous Duty, which had become to him a personal enemy. He said that their Duty was the sort of thing to make him love vice. It was people like them who discouraged good, by insisting on making it unpleasant. It was their fault that so many find delight by contrast among those who are dishonest, but amiable and laughter-loving. It was a profanation of the name of duty to apply it to everything, to the most stupid tasks, to trivial things, with a stiff and arrogant severity which ends by darkening and poisoning life. Duty, he said, was exceptional: it should be kept for moments of real sacrifice, and not used to lend the lover of its name to ill-humor and the desire to be disagreeable to others. There was no reason, because they were stupid enough or ungracious enough to be sad, to want everybody else to be so too and to impose on everybody their decrepit way of living. . . . The first of all virtues is joy. Virtue must be happy, free, and unconstrained. He who does good must give pleasure to himself. But this perpetual upstart Duty, this pedagogic tyranny, this peevishness, this futile discussion, this acrid, puerile quibbling, this ungraciousness, this charmless life, without politeness, without silence, this mean-spirited pessimism, which lets slip nothing that can make existence poorer than it is, this vainglorious unintelligence, which finds it easier to despise others than to understand them, all this middle-class morality, without greatness, without largeness, without happiness, without beauty, all these things are odious and hurtful: they make vice appear more human than virtue.

So thought Christophe: and in his desire to hurt those who had wounded him, he did not see that he was being as unjust as those of whom he spoke.

No doubt these unfortunate people were almost as he saw them. But it was not their fault: it was the fault of their ungracious life, which had made their faces, their doings, and their thoughts ungracious. They had suffered the deformation of misery—not that great misery which swoops down and slays or forges anew—but the misery of ever recurring ill-fortune, that small misery which trickles down drop by drop from the first day to the last. . . . Sad, indeed! For beneath these rough exteriors what treasures in reserve are there, of uprightness, of kindness, of silent heroism! . . . The whole strength of a people, all the sap of the future.

Christophe was not wrong in thinking duty exceptional. But love is so no less. Everything is exceptional. Everything that is of worth has no worse enemy— not the evil (the vices are of worth)— but the habitual. The mortal enemy of the soul is the daily wear and tear.

Ada was beginning to weary of it. She was not clever enough to find new food for her love in an abundant nature like that of Christophe. Her senses and her vanity had extracted from it all the pleasure they could find in it. There was left her only the pleasure of destroying it. She had that secret instinct common to so many women, even good women, to so many men, even clever men, who are not creative either of art, or of children, or of pure action,—no matter what: of life—and yet have too much life in apathy and resignation to bear with their uselessness. They desire others to be as useless as themselves and do their best to make them so. Sometimes they do so in spite of themselves: and when they become aware of their criminal desire they hotly thrust it back. But often they hug it to themselves: and they set themselves according to their strength—some modestly in their own intimate circle—others largely with vast audiences—to destroy everything that has life, everything that loves life, everything that deserves life. The critic who takes upon himself to diminish the stature of great men and great thoughts—and the girl who amuses herself with dragging down her lovers, are both mischievous beasts of the same kind.—But the second is the pleasanter of the two.

Ada then would have liked to corrupt Christophe a little, to humiliate him. In truth, she was not strong enough. More intelligence was needed, even in corruption. She felt that: and it was not the least of her rankling feelings against Christophe that her love could do him no harm. She did not admit the desire that was in her to do him harm: perhaps she would have done him none if she had been able. But it annoyed her that she could not do it. It is to fail in love for a woman not to leave her the illusion of her power for good or evil over her lover: to do that must inevitably be to impel her irresistibly to the test of it. Christophe paid no attention to it. When Ada asked him jokingly:

"Would you leave your music for me?"

(Although she had no wish for him to do so.)

He replied frankly:

"No, my dear: neither you nor anybody else can do anything against that. I shall always make music."

"And you say you love?" cried she, put out.

She hated his music—the more so because she did not understand it, and it was impossible for her to find a means of coming to grips with this invisible enemy and so to wound Christophe in his passion. If she tried to talk of it contemptuously, or scornfully to judge Christophe's compositions, he would shout with laughter; and in spite of her exasperation Ada would relapse into silence: for she saw that she was being ridiculous.

But if there was nothing to be done in that direction, she had discovered another weak spot in Christophe, one more easy of access: his moral faith. In spite of his squabble with the Vogels, and in spite of the intoxication of his adolescence, Christophe had preserved an instinctive modesty, a need of purity, of which he was entirely unconscious. At first it struck Ada, attracted and charmed her, then made her impatient and irritable, and finally, being the woman she was, she detested it. She did not make a frontal attack. She would ask insidiously:

"Do you love me?"

"Of course!"

"How much do you love me?"

"As much as it is possible to love."

"That is not much . . . after all! . . . What would you do for me?"

"Whatever you like."

"Would you do something dishonest?"

"That would be a queer way of loving."

"That is not what I asked. Would you?"

"It is not necessary."

"But if I wished it?"

"You would be wrong."

"Perhaps. . . . Would you do it?"

He tried to kiss her. But she thrust him away.

"Would you do it? Yes or no?"

"No, my dear."

She turned her back on him and was furious.

"You do not love me. You do not know what love is."

"That is quite possible," he said good-humoredly. He knew that, like anybody else, he was capable in a moment of passion of committing some folly, perhaps something dishonest, and—who knows?—even more: but he would have thought shame of himself if he had boasted of it in cold blood, and certainly it would be dangerous to confess it to Ada. Some instinct warned him that the beloved foe was lying in ambush, and taking stock of his smallest remark: he would not give her any weapon against him.

She would return to the charge again, and ask him:

"Do you love me because you love me, or because I love you?"

"Because I love you."

"Then if I did not love you, you would still love me?"

"Yes."

"And if I loved some one else you would still love me?"

"Ah! I don't know about that. . . . I don't think so. . . . In any case you would be the last person to whom I should say so."

"How would it be changed?"

"Many things would be changed. Myself, perhaps. You, certainly."

"And if I changed, what would it matter?"

"All the difference in the world. I love you as you are. If you become another creature I can't promise to love you."

"You do not love, you do not love! What is the use of all this quibbling? You love or you do not love. If you love me you ought to love me just as I am, whatever I do, always."

"That would be to love you like an animal."

"I want to be loved like that."

"Then you have made a mistake," said he jokingly. "I am not the sort of man you want. I would like to be, but I cannot. And I will not."

"You are very proud of your intelligence! You love your intelligence more than you do me."

"But I love you, you wretch, more than you love yourself. The more beautiful and the more good you are, the more I love you."

"You are a schoolmaster," she said with asperity.

"What would you? I love what is beautiful. Anything ugly disgusts me."

"Even in me?"

"Especially in you."

She drummed angrily with her foot.

"I will not be judged."

"Then complain of what I judge you to be, and of what I love in you," said he tenderly to appease her.

She let him take her in his arms, and deigned to smile, and let him kiss her. But in a moment when he thought she had forgotten she asked uneasily:

"What do you think ugly in me?"

He would not tell her: he replied cowardly:

"I don't think anything ugly in you."

She thought for a moment, smiled, and said:

"Just a moment, Christli: you say that you do not like lying?"

"I despise it."

"You are right," she said. "I despise it too. I am of a good conscience. I never lie."

He stared at her: she was sincere. Her unconsciousness disarmed him.

"Then," she went on, putting her arms about his neck, "why would you be cross with me if I loved someone else and told you so?"

"Don't tease me."

"I'm not teasing: I am not saying that I do love some one else: I am saying that I do not. . . . But if I did love some one later on . . ."

"Well, don't let us think of it."

"But I want to think of it. . . . You would not be angry with me? You could not be angry with me?"

"I should not be angry with you. I should leave you. That is all."

"Leave me? Why? If I still loved you. . . . ?"

"While you loved some one else?"

"Of course. It happens sometimes."

"Well, it will not happen with us."

"Why?"

"Because as soon as you love some one else, I shall love you no longer, my dear, never, never again."

"But just now you said perhaps. . . . Ah! you see you do not love me!"

"Well then: all the better for you."

"Because . . . ?"

"Because if I loved you when you loved someone else it might turn out badly for you, me, and him."

"Then! . . . Now you are mad. Then I am condemned to stay with you all my life?"

"Be calm. You are free. You shall leave me when you like. Only it will not be *au revoir:* it will be good-bye."

"But if I still love you?"

"When people love, they sacrifice themselves to each other."

"Well, then . . . sacrifice yourself!"

He could not help laughing at her egoism: and she laughed too.

"The sacrifice of one only," he said, "means the love of one only."

"Not at all. It means the love of both. I shall not love you much longer if you do not sacrifice yourself for me. And think, Christli, how much you will love me, when you have sacrificed yourself, and how happy you will be."

They laughed and were glad to have a change from the seriousness of the disagreement.

He laughed and looked at her. At heart, as she said, she had no desire to leave Christophe at present: if he irritated her and often bored her she knew

the worth of such devotion as his: and she loved no one else. She talked so for fun, partly because she knew he disliked it, partly because she took pleasure in playing with equivocal and unclean thoughts like a child which delights to mess about with dirty water. He knew this. He did not mind. But he was tired of these unwholesome discussions, of the silent struggle against this uncertain and uneasy creature whom he loved, who perhaps loved him: he was tired from the effort that he had to make to deceive himself about her, sometimes tired almost to tears. He would think: "Why, why is she like this? Why are people like this? How second-rate life is!" . . . At the same time he would smile as he saw her pretty face above him, her blue eyes, her flower-like complexion, her laughing, chattering lips, foolish a little, half open to reveal the brilliance of her tongue and her white teeth. Their lips would almost touch: and he would look at her as from a distance, a great distance, as from another world: he would see her going farther and farther from him, vanishing in a mist. . . . And then he would lose sight of her. He could hear her no more. He would fall into a sort of smiling oblivion in which he thought of his music, his dreams, a thousand things foreign to Ada. . . . Ah! beautiful music! . . . so sad, so mortally sad! and yet kind, loving. . . . Ah! how good it is! . . . It is that, it is that. . . . Nothing else is true. . . .

She would shake his arm. A voice would cry:

"Eh, what's the matter with you? You are mad, quite mad. Why do you look at me like that? Why don't you answer?"

Once more he would see the eyes looking at him. Who was it? . . . Ah! yes. . . . He would sigh.

She would watch him. She would try to discover what he was thinking of. She did not understand: but she felt that it was useless: that she could not keep hold of him, that there was always a door by which he could escape. She would conceal her irritation.

"Why are you crying?" she asked him once as he returned from one of his strange journeys into another life.

He drew his hands across his eyes. He felt that they were wet.

"I do not know," he said.

"Why don't you answer? Three times you have said the same thing."

"What do you want?" he asked gently.

She went back to her absurd discussions. He waved his hand wearily.

"Yes," she said. "I've done. Only a word more!" And off she started again.

Christophe shook himself angrily.

"Will you keep your dirtiness to yourself!"

"I was only joking."

"Find cleaner subjects, then!"

"Tell me why, then. Tell me why you don't like it."

"Why? You can't argue as to why a dump-heap smells. It does smell, and that is all! I hold my nose and go away."

He went away, furious: and he strode along taking in great breaths of the cold air.

But she would begin again, once, twice, ten times. She would bring forward every possible subject that could shock him and offend his conscience.

He thought it was only a morbid jest of a neurasthenic girl, amusing herself by annoying him. He would shrug his shoulders or pretend not to hear her: he would not take her seriously. But sometimes he would long to throw her out of the window: for neurasthenia and the neurasthenics were very little to his taste . . .

But ten minutes away from her were enough to make him forget everything that had annoyed him. He would return to Ada with a fresh store of hopes and new illusions. He loved her. Love is a

perpetual act of faith. Whether God exist or no is a small matter: we believe, because we believe. We love because we love: there is no need of reasons! . . .

After Christophe's quarrel with the Vogels it became impossible for them to stay in the house, and Louisa had to seek another lodging for herself and her son.

One day Christophe's younger brother Ernest, of whom they had not heard for a long time, suddenly turned up. He was out of work, having been dismissed in turn from all the situations he had procured: his purse was empty and his health ruined: and so he had thought it would be as well to re-establish himself in his mother's house.

Ernest was not on bad terms with either of his brothers: they thought very little of him and he knew it: but he did not bear any grudge against them, for he did not care. They had no ill-feeling against him. It was not worth the trouble. Everything they said to him slipped off his back without leaving a mark. He just smiled with his sly eyes, tried to look contrite, thought of something else, agreed, thanked them, and in the end always managed to extort money from one or other of them. In spite of himself Christophe was fond of the pleasant mortal who, like himself, and more than himself, resembled their father Melchior in features. Tall and strong like Christophe, he had regular features, a frank expression, a straight nose, a laughing mouth, fine teeth, and endearing manners. When even Christophe saw him he was disarmed and could not deliver half the reproaches that he had prepared: in his heart he had a sort of motherly indulgence for the handsome boy who was of his blood, and physically at all events did him credit. He did not believe him to be bad: and Ernest was not a fool. Without culture, he was not without brains: he was even not incapable of taking an interest in the things of the mind. He enjoyed listening to music: and without understanding his brother's compositions he would listen to them with interest. Christophe, who did not receive too much sympathy from his family, had been glad to see him at some of his concerts.

But Ernest's chief talent was the knowledge that he possessed of the character of his two brothers, and his skill in making use of his knowledge. It was no use Christophe knowing Ernest's egoism and indifference: it was no use his seeing that Ernest never thought of his mother or himself except when he had need of them: he was always taken in by his affectionate ways and very rarely did he refuse him anything. He much preferred him to his other brother Rodolphe, who was orderly and correct, assiduous in his business, strictly moral, never asked for money, and never gave any either, visited his mother regularly every Sunday, stayed an hour, and only talked about himself, boasting about himself, his firm, and everything that concerned him, never asking about the others, and taking no interest in them, and going away when the hour was up, quite satisfied with having done his duty. Christophe could not bear him. He always arranged to be out when Rodolphe came. Rodolphe was jealous of him: he despised artists, and Christophe's success really hurt him, though he did not fail to turn his small fame to account in the commercial circles in which he moved: but he never said a word about it either to his mother or to Christophe: he pretended to ignore it. On the other hand, he never ignored the least of the unpleasant things that happened to Christophe. Christophe despised such pettiness, and pretended not to notice it: but it would really have hurt him to know, though he never thought about it, that much of the unpleasant information that Rodolphe had about him came from Ernest. The

young rascal fed the differences between Christophe and Rodolphe: no doubt he recognized Christophe's superiority and perhaps even sympathized a little ironically with his candor. But he took good care to turn it to account: and while he despised Rodolphe's ill-feeling he exploited it shamefully. He flattered his vanity and jealousy, accepted his rebukes deferentially and kept him primed with the scandalous gossip of the town, especially with everything concerning Christophe,—of which he was always marvelously informed. So he attained his ends, and Rodolphe, in spite of his avarice, allowed Ernest to despoil him just as Christophe did.

So Ernest made use and a mock of them both, impartially. And so both of them loved him.

In spite of his tricks Ernest was in a pitiful condition when he turned up at his mother's house. He had come from Munich, where he had found and, as usual, almost immediately lost a situation. He had had to travel the best part of the way on foot, through storms of rain, sleeping God knows where. He was covered with mud, ragged, looking like a beggar, and coughing miserably. Louisa was upset and Christophe ran to him in alarm when they saw him come in. Ernest, whose tears flowed easily, did not fail to make use of the effect he had produced: and there was a general reconciliation: all three wept in each other's arms.

Christophe gave up his room: they warmed the bed, and laid the invalid in it, who seemed to be on the point of death. Louisa and Christophe sat by his bedside and took it in turns to watch by him. They called in a doctor, procured medicines, made a good fire in the room, and gave him special food.

Then they had to clothe him from head to foot: linen, shoes, clothes, everything new. Ernest left himself in their hands. Louisa and Christophe sweated to squeeze the money from their expenditure. They were very straitened at the moment: the removal, the new lodgings, which were dearer though just as uncomfortable, fewer lessons for Christophe and more expenses. They could just make both ends meet. They managed somehow. No doubt Christophe could have applied to Rodolphe, who was more in a position to help Ernest, but he would not: he made it a point of honor to help his brother alone. He thought himself obliged to do so as the eldest,—and because he was Christophe. Hot with shame he had to accept, to declare his willingness to accept an offer which he had indignantly rejected a fortnight before,—a proposal from an agent of an unknown wealthy amateur who wanted to buy a musical composition for publication under his own name. Louisa took work out, mending linen. They hid their sacrifice from each other: they lied about the money they brought home.

When Ernest was convalescent and sitting huddled up by the fire, he confessed one day between his fits of coughing that he had a few debts.—They were paid. No one reproached him. That would not have been kind to an invalid and a prodigal son who had repented and returned home. For Ernest seemed to have been changed by adversity and sickness. With tears in his eyes he spoke of his past misdeeds: and Louisa kissed him and told him to think no more of them. He was fond: he had always been able to get round his mother by his demonstrations of affection: Christophe had once been a little jealous of him. Now he thought it natural that the youngest and the weakest son should be the most loved. In spite of the small difference in their ages he regarded him almost as a son rather than as a brother. Ernest showed great respect for him: sometimes he would allude to the burdens that

Christophe was taking upon himself, and to his sacrifice of money: but Christophe would not let him go on, and Ernest would content himself with showing his gratitude in his eyes humbly and affectionately. He would argue with the advice that Christophe gave him: and he would seem disposed to change his way of living and to work seriously as soon as he was well again.

He recovered: but had a long convalescence. The doctor declared that his health, which he had abused, needed to be fostered. So he stayed on in his mother's house, sharing Christophe's bed, eating heartily the bread that his brother earned, and the little dainty dishes that Louisa prepared for him. He never spoke of going. Louisa and Christophe never mentioned it either. They were too happy to have found again the son and the brother they loved.

Little by little in the long evenings that he spent with Ernest Christophe began to talk intimately to him. He needed to confide in somebody. Ernest was clever: he had a quick mind and understood—or seemed to understand—on a hint only. There was pleasure in talking to him. And yet Christophe dared not tell him about what lay nearest to his heart: his love. He was kept back by a sort of modesty. Ernest, who knew all about it, never let it appear that he knew.

One day when Ernest was quite well again he went in the sunny afternoon and lounged along the Rhine. As he passed a noisy inn a little way out of the town, where there were drinking and dancing on Sundays, he saw Christophe sitting and Ada and Myrrha, who were making a great noise. Christophe saw him too, and blushed. Ernest was discreet and passed on without acknowledging him.

Christophe was much embarrassed by the encounter: it made him more keenly conscious of the company in which he was: it hurt him that his brother should have seen him then: not only because it made him lose the right of judging Ernest's conduct, but because he had a very lofty, very naïve, and rather archaic notion of his duties as an elder brother which would have seemed absurd to many people: he thought that in failing in that duty, as he was doing, he was lowered in his own eyes.

In the evening when they were together in their room, he waited for Ernest to allude to what had happened. But Ernest prudently said nothing and waited also. Then while they were undressing Christophe decided to speak about his love. He was so ill at ease that he dared not look at Ernest: and in his shyness he assumed a gruff way of speaking. Ernest did not help him out: he was silent and did not look at him, though he watched him all the same: and he missed none of the humor of Christophe's awkwardness and clumsy words. Christophe hardly dared pronounce Ada's name: and the portrait that he drew of her would have done just as well for any woman who was loved. But he spoke of his love: little by little he was carried away by the flood of tenderness that filled his heart: he said how good it was to love, how wretched he had been before he had found that light in the darkness, and that life was nothing without a dear, deep-seated love. His brother listened gravely: he replied tactfully, and asked no questions: but a warm handshake showed that he was of Christophe's way of thinking. They exchanged ideas concerning love and life. Christophe was happy at being so well understood. They exchanged a brotherly embrace before they went to sleep.

Christophe grew accustomed to confiding his love to Ernest, though always shyly and reservedly. Ernest's discretion reassured him. He let him know his uneasiness about Ada: but he never blamed her: he blamed himself: and with tears in

his eyes he would declare that he could not live if he were to lose her.

He did not forget to tell Ada about Ernest: he praised his wit and his good looks.

Ernest never approached Christophe with a request to be introduced to Ada: but he would shut himself up in his room and sadly refuse to go out, saying that he did not know anybody. Christophe would think ill of himself on Sundays for going on his excursions with Ada, while his brother stayed at home. And yet he hated not to be alone with his beloved: he accused himself of selfishness and proposed that Ernest should come with them.

The introduction took place at Ada's door, on the landing. Ernest and Ada bowed politely. Ada came out, followed by her inseparable Myrrha, who when she saw Ernest gave a little cry of surprise. Ernest smiled, went up to Myrrha, and kissed her: she seemed to take it as a matter of course.

"What! You know each other?" asked Christophe in astonishment.

"Why, yes!" said Myrrha, laughing.

"Since when?"

"Oh, a long time!"

"And you knew?" asked Christophe, turning to Ada. "Why did you not tell me?"

"Do you think I know all Myrrha's lovers?" said Ada, shrugging her shoulders.

Myrrha took up the word and pretended in fun to be angry. Christophe could not find out any more about it. He was depressed. It seemed to him that Ernest and Myrrha and Ada had been lacking in honesty, although indeed he could not have brought any lie up against them: but it was difficult to believe that Myrrha, who had no secrets from Ada, had made a mystery of this, and that Ernest and Ada were not already acquainted with each other. He watched them. But they only exchanged a few trivial words and Ernest only paid attention to Myrrha all the rest of the day. Ada only spoke to Christophe: and she was much more amiable to him than usual.

From that time on Ernest always joined them. Christophe could have done without him: but he dared not say so. He had no other motive for wanting to leave his brother out than his shame in having him for boon companion. He had no suspicion of him. Ernest gave him no cause for it: he seemed to be in love with Myrrha and was always reserved and polite with Ada, and even affected to avoid her in a way that was a little out of place: it was as though he wished to show his brother's mistress a little of the respect he showed to himself. Ada was not surprised by it and was none the less careful.

They went on long excursions together. The two brothers would walk on in front. Ada and Myrrha, laughing and whispering, would follow a few yards behind. They would stop in the middle of the road and talk. Christophe and Ernest would stop and wait for them. Christophe would lose patience and go on: but soon he would turn back annoyed and irritated, by hearing Ernest talking and laughing with the two young women. He would want to know what they were saying: but when they came up with him their conversation would stop.

"What are you three always plotting together?" he would ask.

They would reply with some joke. They had a secret understanding like thieves at a fair.

Christophe had a sharp quarrel with Ada. They had been cross with each other all day. Strange to say, Ada had not assumed her air of offended dignity, to which she usually resorted in such cases, so as to avenge herself, by making

herself as intolerably tiresome as usual. Now she simply pretended to ignore Christophe's existence and she was in excellent spirits with the other two. It was as though in her heart she was not put out at all by the quarrel.

Christophe, on the other hand, longed to make peace: he was more in love than ever. His tenderness was now mingled with a feeling of gratitude for all the good things love had brought him, and regret for the hours he had wasted in stupid argument and angry thoughts— and the unreasoning fear, the mysterious idea that their love was nearing its end. Sadly he looked at Ada's pretty face and she pretended not to see him while she was laughing with the others: and the sight of her woke in him so many dear memories, of great love, of sincere intimacy.—Her face had sometimes—it had now—so much goodness in it, a smile so pure, that Christophe asked himself why things were not better between them, why they spoiled their happiness with their whimsies, why she would insist on forgetting their bright hours, and denying and combating all that was good and honest in her—what strange satisfaction she could find in spoiling, and smudging, if only in thought, the purity of their love. He was conscious of an immense need of believing in the object of his love, and he tried once more to bring back his illusions. He accused himself of injustice: he was remorseful for the thoughts that he attributed to her, and of his lack of charity.

He went to her and tried to talk to her: she answered him with a few curt words: she had no desire for a reconciliation with him. He insisted: he begged her to listen to him for a moment away from the others. She followed him ungraciously. When they were a few yards away so that neither Myrrha nor Ernest could see them, he took her hands and begged her pardon, and knelt at her feet in the dead leaves of the wood. He told her that he could not go on living so at loggerheads with her: that he found no pleasure in the walk, or the fine day: that he could enjoy nothing, and could not even breathe, knowing that she detested him: he needed her love. Yes: he was often unjust, violent, disagreeable: he begged her to forgive him: it was the fault of his love, he could not bear anything second-rate in her, nothing that was altogether unworthy of her and their memories of their dear past. He reminded her of it all, of their first meeting, their first days together: he said that he loved her just as much, that he would always love her, that she should not go away from him! She was everything to him. . . .

Ada listened to him, smiling, uneasy, almost softened. She looked at him with kind eyes, eyes that said that they loved each other, and that she was no longer angry. They kissed, and holding each other close they went into the leafless woods. She thought Christophe good and gentle, and was grateful to him for his tender words: but she did not relinquish the naughty whims that were in her mind. But she hesitated, she did not cling to them so tightly: and yet she did not abandon what she had planned to do. Why? Who can say? . . . Because she had vowed what she would do?—Who knows? Perhaps she thought it more entertaining to deceive her lover that day, to prove to him, to prove to herself her freedom. She had no thought of losing him: she did not wish for that. She thought herself more sure of him than ever.

They reached a clearing in the forest. There were two paths. Christophe took one. Ernest declared that the other led more quickly to the top of the hill whither they were going. Ada agreed with him. Christophe, who knew the way, having often been there, maintained

that they were wrong. They did not yield. Then they agreed to try it: and each wagered that he would arrive first. Ada went with Ernest. Myrrha accompanied Christophe: she pretended that she was sure that he was right: and she added, "As usual." Christophe had taken the game seriously: and as he never liked to lose, he walked quickly, too quickly for Myrrha's liking, for she was in much less of a hurry than he.

"Don't be in a hurry, my friend," she said, in her quiet, ironic voice, "we shall get there first."

He was a little sorry.

"True," he said, "I am going a little too fast: there is no need."

He slackened his pace.

"But I know them," he went on. "I am sure they will run so as to be there before us."

Myrrha burst out laughing.

"Oh! no," she said. "Oh! no: don't you worry about that."

She hung on his arm and pressed close to him. She was a little shorter than Christophe, and as they walked she raised her soft eyes to his. She was really pretty and alluring. He hardly recognized her: the change was extraordinary. Usually her face was rather pale and puffy: but the smallest excitement, a merry thought, or the desire to please, was enough to make her worn expression vanish, and her cheeks go pink, and the little wrinkles in her eyelids round and below her eyes disappear, and her eyes flash, and her whole face take on a youth, a life, a spiritual quality that never was in Ada's. Christophe was surprised by this metamorphosis, and turned his eyes away from hers: he was a little uneasy at being alone with her. She embarrassed him and prevented him from dreaming as he pleased: he did not listen to what she said, he did not answer her, or if he did it was only at random: he was thinking—he wished to think only of

Ada. He thought of the kindness in her eyes, her smile, her kiss: and his heart was filled with love. Myrrha wanted to make him admire the beauty of the trees with their little branches against the clear sky. . . . Yes: it was all beautiful: the clouds were gone, Ada had returned to him, he had succeeded in breaking the ice that lay between them: they loved once more: near or far, they were one. He sighed with relief: how light the air was! Ada had come back to him. . . . Everything brought her to mind. . . . It was a little damp: would she not be cold? . . . The lovely trees were powdered with hoar-frost: what a pity she should not see them! . . . But he remembered the wager, and hurried on: he was concerned only with not losing the way. He shouted joyfully as they reached the goal:

"We are first!"

He waved his hat gleefully. Myrrha watched him and smiled.

The place where they stood was a high, steep rock in the middle of the woods. From this flat summit with its fringe of nut-trees and little stunted oaks they could see, over the wooded slopes, the tops of the pines bathed in a purple mist, and the long ribbon of the Rhine in the blue valley. Not a bird called. Not a voice. Not a breath of air. A still, calm winter's day, its chilliness faintly warmed by the pale beams of a misty sun. Now and then in the distance there came the sharp whistle of a train in the valley. Christophe stood at the edge of the rock and looked down at the countryside. Myrrha watched Christophe.

He turned to her amiably:

"Well! The lazy things. I told them so! . . . Well: we must wait for them. . . ."

He lay stretched out in the sun on the cracked earth.

"Yes. Let us wait . . ." said Myrrha, taking off her hat.

In her voice there was something so quizzical that he raised his head and looked at her.

"What is it?" she asked quietly.

"What did you say?"

"I said: Let us wait. It was no use making me run so fast."

"True."

They waited lying on the rough ground. Myrrha hummed a tune. Christophe took it up for a few phrases. But he stopped every now and then to listen.

"I think I can hear them."

Myrrha went on singing.

"Do stop for a moment."

Myrrha stopped.

"No. It is nothing."

She went on with her song.

Christophe could not stay still.

"Perhaps they have lost their way."

"Lost? They could not. Ernest knows all the paths."

A fantastic idea passed through Christophe's mind.

"Perhaps they arrived first, and went away before we came!"

Myrrha was lying on her back and looking at the sun. She was seized with a wild burst of laughter in the middle of her song and all but choked. Christophe insisted. He wanted to go down to the station, saying that their friends would be there already. Myrrha at last made up her mind to move.

"You would be certain to lose them! . . . There was never any talk about the station. We were to meet here."

He sat down by her side. She was amused by his eagerness. He was conscious of the irony in her gaze as she looked at him. He began to be seriously troubled—to be anxious about them: he did not suspect them. He got up once more. He spoke of going down into the woods again and looking for them, calling to them. Myrrha gave a little chuckle: she took from her pocket a needle, scissors, and thread: and she calmly undid and sewed in again the feathers in her hat: she seemed to have established herself for the day.

"No, no, silly," she said. "If they wanted to come do you think they would not come of their own accord?"

There was a catch at his heart. He turned towards her: she did not look at him: she was busy with her work. He went up to her.

"Myrrha!" he said.

"Eh?" she replied without stopping. He knelt now to look more nearly at her.

"Myrrha!" he repeated.

"Well?" she asked, raising her eyes from her work and looking at him with a smile. "What is it?"

She had a mocking expression as she saw his downcast face.

"Myrrha!" he asked, choking, "tell me what you think . . ."

She shrugged her shoulders, smiled, and went on working.

He caught her hands and took away the hat at which she was sewing.

"Leave off, leave off, and tell me. . . ."

She looked squarely at him and waited. She saw that Christophe's lips were trembling.

"You think," he said in a low voice, "that Ernest and Ada . . . ?"

She smiled.

"Oh! well!"

He started back angrily.

"No! No! It is impossible! You don't think that! . . . No! No!"

She put her hands on his shoulders and rocked with laughter.

"How dense you are, how dense, my dear!"

He shook her violently.

"Don't laugh! Why do you laugh? You would not laugh if it were true. You love Ernest. . . ."

She went on laughing and drew him to her and kissed him. In spite of himself he returned her kiss. But when he felt her lips on his, her lips, still warm with his

brother's kisses, he flung her away from him and held her face away from his own: he asked:

"You knew it? It was arranged between you?"

She said "Yes," and laughed.

Christophe did not cry out, he made no movement of anger. He opened his mouth as though he could not breathe: he closed his eyes and clutched at his breast with his hands: his heart was bursting. Then he lay down on the ground with his face buried in his hands and he was shaken by a crisis of disgust and despair like a child.

Myrrha, who was not very soft-hearted, was sorry for him: involuntarily she was filled with motherly compassion, and leaned over him, and spoke affectionately to him, and tried to make him sniff at her smelling-bottle. But he thrust her away in horror and got up so sharply that she was afraid. He had neither strength nor desire for revenge. He looked at her with his face twisted with grief.

"You drab," he said in despair. "You do not know the harm you have done. . . ."

She tried to hold him back. He fled through the woods, spitting out his disgust with such ignomiy, with such muddy hearts, with such incestuous sharing as that to which they had tried to bring him. He wept, he trembled: he sobbed with disgust. He was filled with horror, of them all, of himself, of his body and soul. A storm of contempt broke loose in him: it had long been brewing: sooner or later there had to come the reaction against the base thoughts, the degrading compromises, the stale and pestilential atmosphere in which he had been living for months: but the need of loving, of deceiving himself about the woman he loved, had postponed the crisis as long as possible. Suddenly it burst upon him: and it was better so.

There was a great gust of wind of a biting purity, an icy breeze which swept away the miasma. Disgust in one swoop had killed his love for Ada.

If Ada thought more firmly to establish her domination over Christophe by such an act, that proved once more her gross inappreciation of her lover. Jealousy which binds souls that are besmirched could only revolt a nature like Christophe's, young, proud, and pure. But what he could not forgive, what he never would forgive, was that the betrayal was not the outcome of passion in Ada, hardly even of one of those absurd and degrading though often irresistible caprices to which the reason of a woman is sometimes hard put to it not to surrender. No—he understood now,—it was in her a secret desire to degrade him, to humiliate him, to punish him for his moral resistance, for his inimical faith, to lower him to the common level, to bring him to her feet, to prove to herself her own power for evil. And he asked himself with horror: what is this impulse towards dirtiness, which is in the majority of human beings—this desire to besmirch the purity of themselves and others,—these swinish souls, who take a delight in rolling in filth, and are happy when not one inch of their skins is left clean! . . .

Ada waited two days for Christophe to return to her. Then she began to be anxious, and sent him a tender note in which she made no allusion to what had happened. Christophe did not even reply. He hated Ada so profoundly that no words could express his hatred. He had cut her out of his life. She no longer existed for him.

Christophe was free of Ada, but he was not free of himself. In vain did he try to return into illusion and to take up again the calm and chaste strength of the past. We cannot return to the past. We

have to go onward: it is useless to turn back, save only to see the places by which we have passed, the distant smoke from the roofs under which we have slept, dying away on the horizon in the mists of memory. But nothing so distances us from the soul that we had as a few months of passion. The road takes a sudden turn: the country is changed: it is as though we were saying good-bye for the last time to all that we are leaving behind.

Christophe could not yield to it. He held out his arms to the past: he strove desperately to bring to life again the soul that had been his, lonely and resigned. But it was gone. Passion itself is not so dangerous as the ruins that it heaps up and leaves behind. In vain did Christophe not love, in vain—for a moment—did he despise love: he bore the marks of its talons: his whole being was steeped in it: there was in his heart a void which must be filled. With that terrible need of tenderness and pleasure which devours men and women when they have once tasted it, some other passion was needed, were it only the contrary passion, the passion of contempt, of proud purity, of faith in virtue.—They were not enough, they were not enough to stay his hunger: they were only the food of a moment. His life consisted of a succession of violent reactions—leaps from one extreme to the other. Sometimes he would bend his passion to rules inhumanly ascetic: not eating, drinking water, wearing himself out with walking, heavy tasks, and so not sleeping, denying himself every sort of pleasure. Sometimes he would persuade himself that strength is the true morality for people like himself: and he would plunge into the quest of joy. In either case he was unhappy. He could no longer be alone. He could no longer not be alone.

The only thing that could have saved him would have been to find a true friendship,—Rosa's perhaps: he could have taken refuge in that. But the rupture was complete between the two families. They no longer met. Only once had Christophe seen Rosa. She was just coming out from Mass. He had hesitated to bow to her: and when she saw him she had made a movement towards him: but when he had tried to go to her through the stream of the devout walking down the steps, she had turned her eyes away: and when he approached her she bowed coldly and passed on. In the girl's heart he felt intense, icy contempt. And he did not feel that she still loved him and would have liked to tell him so: but she had come to think of her love as a fault and foolishness: she thought Christophe bad and corrupt, and further from her than ever. So they were lost to each other forever. And perhaps it was as well for both of them. In spite of her goodness, she was not near enough to life to be able to understand him. In spite of his need of affection and respect he would have stifled in a commonplace and confined existence, without joy, without sorrow, without air. They would both have suffered. The unfortunate occurrence which cut them apart was, when all was told, perhaps, fortunate as often happens—as always happens—to those who are strong and endure.

But at the moment it was a great sorrow and a great misfortune for them. Especially for Christophe. Such virtuous intolerance, such narrowness of soul, which sometimes seems to deprive those who have the most of them of all intelligence, and those who are most good of kindness, irritated him, hurt him, and flung him back in protest into a freer life.

During his loafing with Ada in the beer gardens of the neighborhood he had made acquaintance with several good fellows—Bohemians, whose carelessness and freedom of manners had not been altogether distasteful to him. One of them, Friedemann, a musician like himself, an organist, a man of thirty, was not without intelligence, and was good at his work, but he was incurably lazy and rather than make the slightest effort to be more than mediocre, he would have died of hunger, though not, perhaps, of thirst. He comforted himself in his indolence by speaking ill of those who lived energetically, God knows why: and his sallies, rather heavy for the most part, generally made people laugh. Having more liberty than his companions, he was not afraid,—though timidly, and with winks and nods and suggestive remarks,—to sneer at those who held positions: he was even capable of not having ready-made opinions about music, and of having a sly fling at the forged reputations of the great men of the day. He had no mercy upon women either: when he was making his jokes he loved to repeat the old saying of some misogynist monk about them, and Christophe enjoyed its bitterness just then more than anybody:

"Femina mors animae."

In his state of upheaval Christophe found some distraction in talking to Friedemann. He judged him, he could not long take pleasure in this vulgar bantering wit: his mockery and perpetual denial became irritating before long and he felt the impotence of it all: but it did soothe his exasperation with the self-sufficient stupidity of the Philistines. While he heartily despised his companion, Christophe could not do without him. They were continually seen together sitting with the unclassed and doubtful people of Freidemann's acquaintance, who were even more worthless than himself. They used to play, and harangue, and drink the whole evening. Christophe would suddenly wake up in the midst of the dreadful smell of food and tobacco:

he would look at the people about him with strange eyes: he would not recognize them: he would think in agony:

"Where am I? Who are these people? What have I to do with them?"

Their remarks and their laughter would make him sick. But he could not bring himself to leave them: he was afraid of going home and of being left alone face to face with his soul, his desires, and remorse. He was going to the dogs: he knew it: he was doing it deliberately,—with cruel clarity he saw in Friedemann the degraded image of what he was—of what he would be one day: and he was passing through a phase of such disheartenedness and disgust that instead of being brought to himself by such a menace, it actually brought him low.

He would have gone to the dogs, if he could. Fortunately, like all creatures of his kind, he had a spring, a succor against destruction which others do not possess: his strength, his instinct for life, his instinct against letting himself perish, an instinct more intelligent than his intelligence, and stronger than his will. And also, unknown to himself, he had the strange curiosity of the artist, that passionate, impersonal quality, which is in every creature really endowed with creative power. In vain did he love, suffer, give himself utterly to all his passions: he saw them. They were in him but they were not himself. A myriad of little souls moved obscurely in him towards a fixed point unknown, yet certain, just like the planetary worlds which are drawn through space into a mysterious abyss. That perpetual state of unconscious action and reaction was shown especially in those giddy moments when sleep came over his daily life, and from the depths of sleep and the night rose the multiform face of Being with its sphinx-like gaze. For a year Christophe had been obsessed with dreams in which in a second of time he felt clearly with perfect illusion that he *was* at one and the same time several different creatures, often far removed from each other by countries, worlds, centuries. In his waking state Christophe was still under his hallucination and uneasiness, though he could not remember what had caused it. It was like the weariness left by some fixed idea that is gone, though traces of it are left and there is no understanding it. But while his soul was so troublously struggling through the network of the days, another soul, eager and serene, was watching all his desperate efforts. He did not see it: but it cast over him the reflection of its hidden light. That soul was joyously greedy to feel everything, to suffer everything, to observe and understand men, women, the earth, life, desires, passions, thoughts, even those that were torturing, even those that were mediocre, even those that were vile: and it was enough to lend them a little of its light, to save Christophe from destruction. It made him feel—he did not know how—that he was not altogether alone. That love of being and of knowing everything, that second soul, raised a rampart against his destroying passions.

But if it was enough to keep his head above water, it did not allow him to climb out of it unaided. He could not succeed in seeing clearly into himself, and mastering himself, and regaining possession of himself. Work was impossible for him. He was passing through an intellectual crisis: the most fruitful of his life: all his future life was germinating in it: but that inner wealth for the time being only showed itself in extravagance: and the immediate effect of such superabundance was not different from that of the flattest sterility. Christophe was submerged by his life. All his powers had shot up and grown too fast, all at once, suddenly. Only his will had not grown with them: and it was dismayed by such a throng of monsters. His personality was cracking in every part. Of his earthquake, this inner cataclysm, others saw nothing. Christophe himself could see only his impotence to will, to create, to be. Desires, instincts, thoughts issued one after another like clouds of sulphur from the fissures of a volcano: and he was forever asking himself: And now, what will come out? What will become of me? Will it always be so? or is this the end of all? Shall I be nothing, always?"

And now there sprang up in him his hereditary fires, the vices of those who had gone before him.—He got drunk. He would return home smelling of wine, laughing, in a state of collapse.

Poor Louisa would look at him, sigh, say nothing, and pray.

But one evening when he was coming out of an inn by the gates of the town he saw, a few yards in front of him on the road, the droll shadow of his uncle Gottfried, with his pack on his back. The little man had not been home for months, and his periods of absence were growing longer and longer. Christophe hailed him gleefully. Gottfried, bending under his load, turned round: he looked at Christophe, who was making extravagant gestures, and sat down on a milestone to wait for him. Christophe came up to him with a beaming face, skipping along, and shook his uncle's hand with great demonstrations of affection. Gottfried took a long look at him and then he said:

"Good-day, Melchior."

Christophe thought his uncle had made a mistake, and burst out laughing.

"The poor man is breaking up," he thought; "he is losing his memory."

Indeed, Gottfried did look old, shriveled, shrunken, and dried: his breathing came short and painfully. Christophe

went on talking. Gottfried took his pack on his shoulders again and went on in silence. They went home together, Christophe gesticulating and talking at the top of his voice, Gottfried coughing and saying nothing. And when Christophe questioned him, Gottfried still called him Melchior. And then Christophe asked him:

"What do you mean by calling me Melchior? My name is Christophe, you know. Have you forgotten my name?"

Gottfried did not stop. He raised his eyes toward Christophe and looked at him, shook his head, and said coldly:

"No. You are Melchior: I know you."

Christophe stopped dumbfounded. Gottfried trotted along: Christophe followed him without a word. He was sobered. As they passed the door of a café he went up to the dark panes of glass, in which the gas-jets of the entrance and the empty streets were reflected, and he looked at himself: he recognized Melchior. He went home crushed.

He spent the night—a night of anguish—in examining himself, in soul-searching. He understood now. Yes: he recognized the instincts and vices that had come to light in him: they horrified him. He thought of that dark watching by the body of Melchior, of all that he had sworn to do, and, surveying his life since then, he knew that he had failed to keep his vows. What had he done in the year? What had he done for his God, for his art, for his soul? What had he done for eternity? There was not a day that had not been wasted, botched, besmirched. Not a single piece of work, not a thought, not an effort of enduring quality. A chaos of desires destructive of each other. Wind, dust, nothing. . . . What did his intentions avail him? He had fulfilled none of them. He had done exactly the opposite of what he had intended. He had become what he had no wish to be: that was the balance-sheet of his life.

He did not go to bed. About six in the morning it was still dark,—he heard Gottfried getting ready to depart.—For Gottfried had had no intentions of staying on. As he was passing the town he had come as usual to embrace his sister and nephew: but he had announced that he would go on next morning.

Christophe went downstairs. Gottfried saw his pale face and his eyes hollow with a night of torment. He smiled fondly at him and asked him to go a little of the way with him. They set out together before dawn. They had no need to talk: they understood each other. As they passed the cemetery Gottfried said:

"Shall we go in?"

When he came to the place he never failed to pay a visit to Jean Michel and Melchior. Christophe had not been there for a year. Gottfried knelt by Melchior's grave and said:

"Let us pray that they may sleep well and not come to torment us."

His thought was a mixture of strange superstitions and sound sense: sometimes it surprised Christophe: but now it was only too clear to him. They said no more until they left the cemetery.

When they had closed the creaking gate, and were walking along the wall through the cold fields, waking from slumber, by the little path which led them under the cypress trees from which the snow was dropping, Christophe began to weep.

"Oh! uncle," he said, "how wretched I am!"

He dared not speak of his experience in love, from an odd fear of embarrassing or hurting Gottfried: but he spoke of his shame, his mediocrity, his cowardice, his broken vows.

"What am I to do, uncle? I have tried, I have struggled: and after a year I am no further on than before. Worse: I have gone back. I am good for nothing. I am good for nothing! I have ruined my life. I am perjured! . . ."

They were walking up the hill above the town. Gottfried said kindly:

"Not for the last time, my boy. We do not do what we will to do. We will and we live: two things. You must be comforted. The great thing is, you see, never to give up willing and living. The rest does not depend on us."

Christophe repeated desperately:

"I have perjured myself."

"Do you hear?" said Gottfried.

(The cocks were crowing in all the countryside.)

"They, too, are crowing for another who is perjured. They crow for every one of us, every morning."

"A day will come," said Christophe bitterly, "when they will no longer crow for me. . . . A day to which there is no tomorrow. And what shall I have made of my life?"

"There is always a tomorrow," said Gottfried.

"But what can one do, if willing is no use?"

"Watch and pray."

"I do not believe."

Gottfried smiled.

"You would not be alive if you did not believe. Every one believes. Pray."

"Pray to what?"

Gottfried pointed to the sun appearing on the horizon, red and frozen.

"Be reverent before the dawning day. Do not think of what will be in a year, or in ten years. Think of today. Leave your theories. All theories, you see, even those of virtue, are bad, foolish, mischievous. Do not abuse life. Live in today. Be reverent towards each day. Love it, respect it, do not sully it, do not hinder it from coming to flower. Love it even when it is gray and sad like today. Do not be anxious. See. It is winter now. Everything is asleep. The good earth will awake again. You have only to be good and patient like the earth. Be reverent. Wait. If you are good, all will go well. If you are not, if you are weak, if you do not succeed, well, you must be happy in that. No doubt it is the best you can do. So, then, why *will?* Why be angry because of what you cannot do? We all have to do what we can. . . . *Als ich kann.*"

"It is not enough," said Christophe, making a face.

Gottfried laughed pleasantly.

"It is more than anybody does. You are a vain fellow. You want to be a hero. That is why you do such silly things. . . . A hero! . . . I don't quite know what that is: but, you see, I imagine that a hero is a man who does what he can. The others do not do it."

"Oh!" sighed Christophe. "Then what is the good of living? It is not worth while. And yet there are people who say: 'He who wills can!' " . . .

Gottfried laughed again softly.

"Yes? . . . Oh! well, they are liars, my friend. Or they do not will anything much. . . ."

They had reached the top of the hill. They embraced affectionately. The little peddler went on, treading wearily. Christophe stayed there, lost in thought, and watched him go. He repeated his uncle's saying:

"*Als ich kann* (The best I can)."

And he smiled, thinking:

"Yes. . . . All the same. . . . It is enough."

He returned to the town. The frozen snow crackled under his feet. The bitter winter wind made the bare branches of the stunted trees on the hill shiver. It reddened his cheeks, and made his skin tingle, and set his blood racing. The red roofs of the town below were smiling under the brilliant, cold sun. The air was strong and harsh. The frozen earth seemed to rejoice in bitter gladness. And Christophe's heart was like that. He thought:

"I, too, shall wake again."

There were still tears in his eyes. He dried them with the back of his hand, and laughed to see the sun dipping down behind a veil of mist. The clouds, heavy with snow, were floating over the town, lashed by the squall. He laughed at them. The wind blew icily. . . .

"Blow, blow! . . . Do what you will with me. Bear me with you! . . . I know now where I am going."

THE LIFE AND WORKS OF
ROMAIN ROLLAND

By HENRI PETIT

ROMAIN EDME PAUL-EMILE ROLLAND was born at Clamecy on January 29, 1866, to Emile Rolland—son, grandson, and great-grandson of notaries—and Antoinette-Marie Courot—daughter of a notary and granddaughter of an iron-master. (It was fortunate for literature that he escaped a notary's career with so many among his ancestors.) When he was less than a year old, he was left out in the cold by a young maid, and through this single mishap his health suffered permanent damage. He was left with weakened bronchial tubes and a tendency to breathlessness; for the remainder of his life he lived under the shadow of death.

His mother watched over him with tender care. While Romain Rolland owed a great deal to his father, he was primarily his mother's son. She was a gifted, sensitive woman who passed on to him a feeling for music and a direct understanding of everything pertaining to thought and feeling. Under her care, the boy grew up a little withdrawn from children of his own age, a child already ordained for some exceptional mission, privileged as a result of his frailness and also more receptive intellectually. He might easily have become a priest. No mind has ever responded more completely or more naturally to every intel-

lectual stimulus; he learned quite effortlessly, more, perhaps, than his teachers at the school in Clamecy realized. As a young humanist, he was exposed to all the classical culture accessible to an exceptionally gifted young mind.

His mother risked the family's future to give Romain every possible chance. Since Romain's health was too poor for his mother to send him to a lycée in Paris as a boarder, the whole family had to move to Paris, whatever the cost or difficulties. Everything was for Romain. His father had no option but to sell his practice, ending the official career that had made him a person of importance. In Paris he took a minor position at a bank. He was destined to be poor and so was the whole family. But Romain would be able to study for the baccalaureate examination at the Lycée Louis le Grand without being deprived of his mother's protection or the privacy of family life. His father came to Paris, then his sister Madeleine and his maternal grandfather, Edme, a cultivated, reserved man who made a tremendous sacrifice in giving up his provincial peace and the companionship of his friends to avoid being separated from his family.

Behind all these sacrifices, there was a great deal of passion and something more—a sort of fierce confidence. How loved little Romain must have been, even at this early age! And how admirable is the family's reliance on the qualities of a youngster of fourteen! It is understandable that Romain Rolland came to see life as "the final outcome of the experiments of a family or a race."

His father, mother, grandfather, and sister certainly bore some responsibility for the great cycles into which Romain Rolland's works fall—*Tragédies de la foi* (*Tragedies of Faith,* 1909) and *Théâtre de la Révolution* (*Plays of the Revolution,* 1909) *Vies d'hommes illustrés* (Lives of Famous Men), the vast symphonic poems of *Jean-Christophe* (1904–1912) and *L'Ame Enchantée* (*The Soul Enchanted,* 1922–1933), the set of great musical studies, the series of books of action and combat, the massive Journal, four fifths of which is still unpublished, and the correspondence, a monumental collection of his letters possibly without intellectual equal in history. Romain Rolland was a man with an untrammeled, absolutely independent mind, taking all risks alone, relying on no one but himself. But he also was a product of the intellectual and spiritual life of a great family—the Rolland-Breugnon family.

Rolland learned a great deal in those hothouses of learning, where so many others withered and lost their souls. Though physically delicate, he had a wonderfully robust mind—a mind that was orderly and receptive, never allowing his keen powers of observation, good taste, creativity, or freedom of judgment to be stifled. His early letters, his first writings before and after he entered the Ecole Normale Supérieure, already display a strange maturity. Even as a schoolboy, in fact, Romain Rolland was already a master. He took to humanism as though it were his natural element. He studied history, music, and the history of music. But he might just as well have chosen the history of painting, philosophy, or the theater. Whatever the subject, he had an amazing facility that was, almost paradoxically, completely free of superficiality. Students often bury themselves in a single course of study and slave away stubbornly or desperately, like plowhorses in a stony field, but Rolland behaved like a great scholar right from the start, expanding the scope of his research as the fancy took him.

He qualified as a senior history teacher, and at the age of twenty-three won an appointment to teach in Rome. There, for two years, he studied the world—and not only the Roman world of antiquity or the Renaissance. Malwida von Meysenburg, a great-hearted woman already in her seventies, offered the youth a wealth of experience. She introduced him to friends from every part of Europe; she brought him out of his academic shell, and gave him entry to all the spiritual courts, from the Italian Renaissance to the Wagnerian Valhalla at Bayreuth. He was already intoxicated with music, and he wrote his first dramas. His dramas and musings gave substance to his first ideas of the musical novel *Jean Cristophe,* a book that no one can read or reread today without being moved.

At twenty-five Rolland had the knowledge and the fire for greatness. Emotionally he had reached maturity, and he was already full of powerful feeling for his fellow man. His talent, too, was fully developed. However, his intense mental activity had worn down his body, and on his return to Paris, he applied for a year's leave of absence. Although he was supposed to rest, he never stopped writing or planning new works. In October of 1892, he married Clotilde Bréal, the daughter of the great philologist Michel Bréal, who taught at the Collège de France. The newlyweds soon left for Rome, where Romain Rolland collected material that he was to use during the next two years in writing his thesis for his doctorate in literature. He presented his thesis brilliantly in 1895, and was appointed to the faculty of the Ecole Normale Supérieure as a lecturer on the history of art. At his first lecture, his students applauded their new lecturer, and over the years he established himself as an excellent teacher who never followed the beaten track. Unfortunately, however, continuous teaching turned out to be too great a physical strain upon him.

During this period, Rolland wrote a series of remarkable plays in rapid succession, including *Saint-Louis* (1897), *Aërt* (1898), *Le Triomphe de la Raison* (*The Triumph of Reason,* 1899), published together under the common title *Tragedies of Faith, Les Loups* (*The Wolves,* 1898), *Danton* (1900), *Le 14 Juillet* (1902), *Le Temps viendra* (*The Time Will Come,* 1903). At the time, no theater or company was able to stage and act these dramas properly. The public had too long been fed on poor vaudeville and cheap melodrama, and for many years Romain Rolland could not find a stage worthy of him. It was a time in which many people thought they were theater lovers, but ostracized both Romain Rolland and Paul Claudel, who could have created, between them, a great period of dramatic production.

In 1901, Rolland went through the painful experience of divorce. "I must part from the woman I loved and still love now," he wrote to his friend Louis Gillet, "because we are neither of us willing to give up our objectives in life for one another, and these objectives are totally divergent." He became at this time as he was always to be from then on— sorrowful, heroic, full of brotherliness. Six days after the letter to Gillet he wrote at length to his beloved Sofia, a woman who was already a friend and remained a sister in heart and mind for many years:

This is the time of year when I have a great deal of reading to do for my various activities. I absorb an incredible number of books. Every day I take in several works, four or five artists' biographies. I still have no time to do any writing for myself, but I am calm; there is no hurry. I may die tomorrow, yet I behave as though I were going to live for fifty years. At the moment I am engaged, not in writing books, but in broadening my personality, rebuilding its foundations which had grown a little shaky and letting more light and air into all the rooms in my house on every floor. I am renovating and expanding my view of the world. I shall start out again when I have reached a new stage in my development and feel a different man. This year has already changed and matured so many things in me. While waiting for action, I am enjoying the pleasure of contemplating vast periods of history. I feel that I am myself centuries old, breaking out of the confines of my life and effortlessly becoming one with the general laws of the world. The power that history gives the mind is truly amazing—that of assimilating the best features of hundreds of human lives in the space of a few hours and of selecting from among the greatest ones, whose achievements were due to years and years of suffering, joy, action, and passion. To take in the centuries at a glance, to eliminate both time and space—what joyous freedom for the soul! It floats untrammeled on a boundless sea, drawing deep breaths, expanding as the horizon expands round it.

Anyone who has read *Jean-Christophe* will, in the light of the ambitious program, be able to discover the many sources of Romain Rolland's great musical novel—and not only this novel, but the *Lives of Famous Men* and much of his other work.

When the letter to Sofia was written, Rolland was only thirty-five. He had reached his full stature. His humanism was enriched and transformed by his readings in history—the living history of great artists, which he studied for his lectures and for his own benefit. He read as much as any scholar has ever read, and everything he gleaned from his reading was fuel to the fire and life of his mind; his vast culture was like a murmuring forest through which his soul wandered freely. There was nothing bookish about him. He might have given himself up to professional ambition and striven fiercely for the literary success that had so far eluded him, but he had loftier dreams. He had returned to his parents' home, where he led a life as austere as he had when he was preparing to sit for the entrance examination for school and he worked even harder. Thus began a long period of learning—in both the human and the artistic sphere—which made him a brother of all mankind.

In 1898, Charles Péguy, the Parisian author and publisher, had subsidized a fine edition of Rolland's *Wolves*. Five years later, in the *Cahiers de la Quinzaine*, Péguy published *Vie de Beethoven* (*Life of Beethoven*), the first of Rolland's biographies of famous men.

The Life of Beethoven, with its expressive fervor, lyrical and epical in turn, was Romain Rolland's prelude to his monumental study of Beethoven's life and works, *Beethoven: Les Grandes époques créatrices* (*Beethoven the Creator*, 1928). In 1910, in *Notre Jeunesse*, Péguy described the emotions aroused by the earlier, shorter book: "It was suddenly, instantaneously, in a revelation, in the sight of all the world, with sudden accord and by general consensus not only the beginning of Romain Rolland's literary fortune and the literary fortune of the *Cahiers,* but infinitely more than the beginning of a literary fortune—a sudden moral revelation, a presentiment laid bare and revealed, the revelation, explosion, sudden communication of a great moral fortune." The word "revelation" appears several times in this short passage, but it seems to resound a hundred times, as though its echo were borne on the wings of a hurricane. This was perhaps the only way of expressing the shattering effect of this spiritual event, a triumph of the soul.

For Romain Rolland there was to be no more of the obscurity in which great souls develop—and in which they are in danger of breaking up on the rocks of despair. From now on he had a host of admirers and friends, people who did not always understand him but expected a great deal of him and who sometimes tried to hedge him round with their own tastes and preferences.

Earlier, in 1903 there was published in the *Cahiers de la Quinzaine* "Le Théâtre du peuple, essai d'esthétique d'un Théâtre nouveau" ("The People's Theater") Rolland's argument can be summarized in a single sentence: "What is required is the elevation of the Theater by and for the People, the foundation of a new art for a new world."

Jean-Christophe began to appear in February 1904, again in the *Cahiers de la Quinzaine*. Subscribers to the magazine were fortunate. Péguy sent them "L'Aube" ("Dawn") on the 2nd and "Le Matin" ("Morning") on the 16th. Next came "L'Adolescent" ("Youth") in January 1905, and "La Révolte" ("Revolt") at the end of 1906. In March 1908, they received "La Foire sur la place" ("The Market Place"), a declaration of war on all impostors in literature and art. "Antoinette" appeared in the same year, then "Dans la Maison" ("The House") in 1909, "Les Amies" ("Love and

Friendship") early in 1911, and "Le Buisson ardent" ("The Burning Bush") in November of the same year. The tenth and final part, "La Nouvelle journée" ("The New Dawn") completed the cycle in October 1912.

Jean-Christophe belongs with *Lives of Famous Men.* It is itself a biography of a famous man, recounted by a creative mind freed from the precise, sometimes narrow data of reality. The hero is a true child of Europe, unconfined by any frontier. Like Beethoven or Bach, his soul soon transcends the frontiers of the little homeland that cradled his infancy. He is imbued with musical genius—and of all the arts music is without any doubt the closest to the universal spirit.

Romain Rolland refused to be fettered by this great work. In 1905, he published his two biographies of Michelangelo; in 1908, his two great series of articles *Musiciens d'aujourd'hui* (*Musicians of Today*) and *Musiciens d'autrefois* (*Some Musicians of Former Days*). Jean-Christophe would certainly be wrong to suppose himself unique; there were great musicians before him and there would be others after him.

In 1909, Romain Rolland published the first collection of his plays about the Revolution, *Théâtre de la Révolution.* The following year saw the publication of *Handel,* one of his finest, most scholarly books on music. In 1911, his biography of Tolstoy appeared and in 1913, the first complete edition of the *Tragedies of Faith.* (It is worth noting here that several plays in Rolland's best vein are still unpublished today.) We can see Romain Rolland, so greatly favored by the gods, trying to pay his debt by communicating to his fellow man the great fiery passion that he so rightly compared to a burning bush. He retired from teaching in 1912, but was already conducting an enormous correspondence and kept a diary fully and regularly. In 1913, the Académie

Française awarded him its highest prize in literature.

Romain Rolland had no sooner won fame than he became afraid of it. He was on his guard. He felt there were too many people at his heels; he did not want to be "in vogue." He tended rather to browbeat the admirers who had remained faithful to him, as a way of discouraging them; and they did not always understand that he refused to be fettered. In *Le Périple,* one of the first great posthumously published works, we read "Perhaps this instinct of vital reaction was responsible to some extent for the sudden apparition of my *Colas Breugnon* early in April, 1913." And again, "Once Christophe had died at last, I looked round quickly for another, broader human form in which I could cloak myself. Colas was the first one that came to hand. It had been waiting for a long time. In four or five months of frenzied brainwork the outline was filled." He was about to "undertake complete review of the social and moral values of the day." Surely he could not have made it any plainer—"I was preparing to make a break."

But the break occurred in a different way. It was more tragic, more spectacular, and also more painful. Its results affected the remaining forty years of Romain Rolland's life. His life, works, friendships, and influence were all cut in two by World War I. After this tragedy, he remained the same warm-hearted, open-minded universalist, but the light of his face had changed.

For many years Romain Rolland had been spending his summer holidays in Switzerland in attempts to improve his poor health. In June 1914, he went there planning to spend the whole summer at Vevey. He was forty-eight years old. His age group had never been called up. In addition, a new law exempted him from military duty as a graduate of the Ecole Normale Supérieure who agreed to remain in the teaching profession for ten years. Although he had anticipated war throughout all the ten years spent in writing the ten volumes of *Jean-Christophe,* it caught him unaware when it came.

This was probably due to the fact that for the past six months he had let himself be caught up in a dream of love. On August 1, 1914, he wrote in his Journal these shattering lines, which explain all his subsequent behavior. "For anyone like us, incapable of racial hatred, having as high a regard for the nation we are fighting as for the one we are defending, aware of the stupid, criminal folly of this war and conscious of our inner world of thought, beauty, and goodness that longs to blossom forth, is it not most horrible to be forced to massacre it for a monstrous cause?" Two days later he struck the same note of poignant, lucid grief. "I am overwhelmed. I wish I were dead. It is horrible to live in the midst of this demented humanity and to stand by helplessly while civilization goes bankrupt. This European war is the greatest catastrophe in history for many centuries, the ruin of our most sacred trust in human brotherhood."

The point could be further stressed with additional quotations and evidence —but what would be the point? Time has done its work. Most of Romain Rolland's enemies are dead; time has eroded the prejudices of those others who at the time could not or would not understand that his appeal to the conscience of the world did not damage the cause of France at war. The wonder is that some people, generally sincere and fair, could ever have made such a mistake. They had supposed that, in order to defeat Germany, all the hatred of which France was capable had to be mobilized in full force. Romain Rolland's sixteen articles published in the *Journal de Genève* from September 1914, to September 1915, and republished in book form as *Au-dessus de la mêlée* (*Above the Battle*) in November 1915, seemed anti-French to them, destroying the morale of fighting France by depriving her of hatred. But most of those who inveighed against Romain Rolland at the time were misled by his most treacherous detractors. They had been led to believe that Rolland, leaving his country in wartime—"deserting"—was arrogantly playing the aloof bystander in his Swiss mountain retreat by claiming to be "above the battle." Nothing could be further from the truth; the very article that bears this ambiguous title begins with the unforgettable, completely committed words; "O heroic youth of the world. With what lavish joy it is shedding its blood onto the hungry earth."

During the first part of the war Romain Rolland was nobly dreaming of a sort of general crusade of the world's intellectuals, even among the belligerent nations—perhaps among them first of all—to humanize war as far as possible, to protect works of art and centers of advanced civilization, to repatriate civilian prisoners, and the like. He himself set an example of effective charitable activity by giving up the best part of his time to the International Prisoners of War Agency, founded in Geneva under the auspices of the International Red Cross.

In 1919, *Les Précurseurs* (*The Forerunners*) was published, a series of articles and studies in the same vein as *Above the Battle,* but written with more audacity and greater logical force. *Colas Breugnon* also came out. Its gaiety and outspoken vigor, its vitality welling up from deep Burgundian roots surprised, amazed, and delighted readers who were emerging from the long trials of war. In 1913, when the work was scheduled for publication, there was apparently a prudery of the eyes and ears, "prudery of ideas even more than of words," as Rolland wrote. He admitted that at the time some of his best friends begged him, for the sake of the reputation of *Jean-Chris-tophe,* not to publish this book, which is so full of robust vigor and has been so successful since it appeared.

In May 1919, Romain Rolland returned to France, where his mother was seriously ill; she died a few days after his arrival. It was at this same time that *Liluli* appeared; it was followed a few months later by *Pierre et Luce* and then *Clérambault,* the story of a man fighting virtually on his own against everything that impels nations to go to war.

In April 1921, Romain Rolland took up residence in Switzerland again. The great seven-volume cycle of *The Soul Enchanted* began to appear in 1922, and was completed in 1933. Like *Jean-Chris-tophe,* it is a lyrical epic, making full use of all resources of romantic art. Here again we find "sympathy and love of truth" in the description of types of human beings. The great study of Mahatma Gandhi was published in 1923. Between 1925 and 1928, Rolland added three new plays to his *Plays of the Revolution* and in 1927, he began work on his monumental study, *Beethoven the Cre-ator.*

In 1929, Romain Rolland made the acquaintance of the woman who gave him so much help and wonderful devotion during the remaining years of his life. He married her in 1934.

More and more deeply convinced that no frontiers, not even those of civilization or culture, should cut us off from great thinkers and profound doctrines, Romain Rolland made a study of Indian thought, assisted by his sister Madeleine Rolland. It resulted in the three fine volumes of the *Essai sur la mystique et*

l'action de l'Inde vivante (Prophets of the New India), consisting of *La Vie de Ramakrishna* (1929), *La Vie de Vive-kananda* and *L'Evangile universel* (both 1930). In 1935, he published two important collections of political and social studies: *Quinze ans de combat* (1919–1934) *(Fifteen Years of Combat),* a true sequel to *The Forerunners* but much broader in scope; and *Par la Revolution, la Paix* (Peace through Revolution). The following year, he published a collection of writings comprising four magnificent essays on Shakespeare and studies of the Eulenspiegel legend, Gobineau, Goethe, Renan, Spitteler, Hugo, Tolstoy, and Lenin. It is a first-class collection, but has remained somewhat obscured by Rol-land's other works.

In 1937, he settled at Vézelay. There he worked hard, surrounded once again by the beautiful light he had known in childhood; though grander, the country was of the same kind as Brèves and Clamecy. He started on his memoirs (1866–1900) based on his Journal. He wrote a new play, *Robespierre.* He continued his great study of Beethoven. He returned to *Le Voyage Intérieur, Le Périple.* In 1944 he published *Péguy,* the great work in two volumes in which he did lavish justice to his old ally. No other study of the editor of the *Cahiers,* the poet who wrote of Joan of Arc, Chartres, and Eve, is at once so painstaking, accurate, and generous. At last, Péguy was given his rightful place with the understanding and insight he deserved. Until the very end, Romain Rolland retained a prodigious capacity for work and for charity, as well as a tremendous presence. He died December 30, 1944, a month before his seventy-ninth birthday.

Henri Petit, journalist, literary critic, and novelist, was winner of the academic and literary Grand Prix of the Académie Française in 1957 and 1965.
Translated by Annie Jackson.

THE 1915 PRIZE

By GUNNAR AHLSTRÖM

It was the year 1914. The horizon of Alfred Nobel's little neutral country was beginning to darken. The lights of the lighthouses along the Baltic and North Sea coasts were going out. Church bells rang as in the ancient days of war. Defenses were mobilized and brought up to strength by the addition of a militia consisting of forty-year-old civilians in makeshift uniforms, whose military incompetence and goodwill were touching. There was one concession to history: the soldiers wore the three-cornered hats of the time of Charles II. The enemy was equally traditional. It was Russia, the eternal Russia of the Czars, whose political aspirations and spying activities in Scandinavia had shaken public opinion. The Cossack armies drove into East Prussia. The cannon thundered at Tannenberg. The protestations of innocence circulated by German propaganda were very effective and touched a sensitive spot with many pro-Germans.

In these circumstances, what was to be done about the Nobel Prize? Even before war had been declared, it had been decided to postpone the awarding of the Prize until June of 1915. This was a perfectly practical measure of convenience. The change of date was in answer to a request which had been made more and more pressingly, year after year, that the Nobel celebrations should take place at a more hospitable time of year than the tenth of December with its winter gloom: there were dreams of a public holiday in the open air during the most beautiful weather of the whole Nordic year.

The Nobel Committee had taken the usual steps with regard to the candidacies which had been sent in by January 30, 1914, in accordance with the statutes. There were twenty-four candidacies, of which a few were new ones, others were repetitions of old ones, and none was particularly sensational. After the usual deliberations, recommendations were concentrated on the Swiss writer Carl Spitteler, who had been formally proposed some time before by highly qualified authorities. The report, dated October 16, had been drawn up by a professor of history of the University of Uppsala, who was politically minded and very famous. He had made some preliminary reservations, in a reasonable and objective spirit of neutrality. "At the time in which we are living, the Academy cannot help but feel the exceptionally heavy weight of responsibility implicit in the choice of a laureate: there is the risk that this choice might provoke fresh outbursts of that fury which could vent itself against our own country because of a misunderstanding as to the task assumed by the Academy, which would hardly be surprising at the present time."

The events of the autumn of 1914 accentuated the force of the argument. It was thought that the times were hardly propitious for celebrating the reconciliation of peoples. A manifestation of this kind could easily have been mistaken for the cruelest irony. For little Sweden it was more becoming to remain in the background and not become entangled in the fighting of the great powers. This was the opinion that prevailed. The 1914 Prize was held in reserve, and later it was decided to use it for the benefit of the Nobel Library.

Had the right action been taken? Opinion was divided. In various circles, the Swedish Academy was accused of having failed in its duties. It should not have given in to the war in such cowardly fashion; it should have refused to recognize the war's barbarous omnipotence; in the name of peace and by way of protest, it would have been more dignified to have distributed the prizes in the usual way. The country of Linnaeus and Berzelius owed it to herself to brandish the torch in the face of the darkness that had swept over the world. The little kingdom of the North which had been spared the horrors of war ought to profit by its privileged position to prepare for the day when the clamor of arms would be silent. In the world of culture, neutrality must be transformed into something of positive value.

For years, for decades, the peaceful country districts of Sweden had been the object of discreet German infiltration: some opinions were haloed in sympathetic pro-German sentimentality. The edge of this propaganda turned against the merits of French civilization with remarkable effectiveness, through skilful playing on rivalries. France was depicted as the meeting place of decadent and undisciplined individualists. Her literature was cheap, philosophy superficial, and art was reduced to Toulouse-Lautrec and portraits of black-gloved women languishing with their elbows on café tables.

Romain Rolland was in honor bound, at this difficult moment, to patiently present a sober and convincing picture through his literary works which would contradict the distortions of this kind of cliché. His writing vouched for the existence of a France full of burning consciences and integrity of spirit. It is true that the feelings which inspired him were on a level far above the average, but the groups of enthusiasts who were brought together by the periodical in which he published, *Cahiers de la Quinzaine*, certainly lived on the same level, and were none the less French for all that. With a pure heart, he defined certain standards of the cultural heritage of his country, which elsewhere had become blurred: clarity of thought, spirit of sacrifice, and strength of convictions. One may be allowed to formulate the melancholy paradox that perhaps no other French writer rendered greater service to his country on an international basis than this flouted idealist, the outcast in Geneva.

In Sweden, Romain Rolland's books served as a rallying point for the friends of France and the Allies. People were excited by *Jean-Christophe*, which gave the lie to the forces of hatred and war that were particularly violent after Germany's initial victories. Several articles from *Above the Battle*, were published in Stockholm in the *Dagens Nyheter*, the most important mouthpiece of Swedish liberalism. Among the solitary writer's Swedish correspondents were Selma Lagerlöf and especially a pen friend of long standing, Ellen Key, whose feminist ideas were combined with a solid knowledge of European literature. After the declaration of war in 1914, a series of translations of Romain Rolland's works appeared in Sweden, starting with *Jean-Christophe*, soon to be followed by *Plays of the Revolution* and his books on Beethoven and Tolstoy.

This is the background of the candidacy of Romain Rolland. He was proposed for the Nobel Prize for Literature in 1915, by the literary historian of Uppsala, Henrik Schück, better known for his universal erudition than for his political activity. The candidacy was treated explicitly and in detail, in the opinion of the Committee. The writer was judged to be too full of contradictions and, even from the artistic point of view, too uneven. The rejection, however, was not unanimous. Influential voices were eloquent in support of a different view. Romain Rolland's enthusiastic partisans pointed out that he was greatly superior to the Spaniard Pérez Galdós, who was the officially recommended candidate for that year.

The circumstances, and the strength of a neutrality the preservation of which required a great deal of tact, resulted in the 1915 Prize also being reserved for a later date.

The following year the discussions were resumed, intensified by new arguments and new propositions. It was becoming unthinkable that the Prize should go on being withheld from one year to the next. Even though the guns continued to thunder, the Swedish Academy was bound to do its duty in the spirit of idealism of the late Alfred Nobel.

Public opinion was coming round in favor of Romain Rolland. His candidacy was now receiving support from several directions; from people who were not at all in the habit of engaging spontaneously in discussions which were likely to be somewhat heated. Finally, on November 9, a decision was taken on the simultaneous and relatively Solomonian awarding of the Prizes of 1914 and 1915: one went to Romain Rolland, the other to the Swedish writer, Verner von Heidenstam. The latter's distinction remained a national affair; that of Romain Rolland belonged to world literature and for this reason was subjected to the judgment of the international literary world.

"The Academy dares to hope that you will deign to accept this homage, which will be applauded by all the independent minds of the intelligent world"—this from the letter which the Swedish minister handed to Romain Rolland. In the author's posthumous diary, *Journal of the War Years,* one may follow his reactions to the announcement of this astonishing piece of news, which was first communicated telegraphically by the Ministry of Foreign Affairs in Stockholm to the author in exile in Geneva. His first action was to renounce the award which, on the one hand, might encroach on his liberty and on the other might draw fresh persecution upon him. But that Wednesday, November 15, was nevertheless a day of very sweet satisfaction. His confidential friend of the solitary years at Sierre, P.-J. Jouve, has given us a description of that day: "A small group of exiles, like the narrow and pious church of friendship, was gathered round him in his room; they represented his numerous friends throughout the world, and they were rather conscious of this. In the hotel's old eighteenth-century drawing room, Romain Rolland sat down at the piano: music, the supreme oblivion of heart and spirit. To us, it was a profound greeting from the soul, from the great fraternal souls of musicians, gathered around one of their children."

Romain Rolland accepted his Prize money in order to give it to the Red Cross and the French welfare organizations. In fact, France was particularly in his mind at that moment. Among those who had congratulated him, there was a group of Allied soldiers interned in Switzerland. It was to them that he revealed the reasons for his gratitude: "It is not on me, but on our country that this distinction has been conferred: and it is for this reason that I accept it, and I feel happy to think that it can contribute towards spreading the ideas which have made France loved throughout the world."

He expressed similar thoughts in the letter of thanks which he addressed to the Swedish Academy. In it one hears the voice of a man scorned for many years by his compatriots, who speaks proudly in the name of his country: "The high consideration which you have bestowed on my work of thirty years makes me feel proud of my country, to whom I offer it in homage: for it is to my country that I owe the best of my idealism and my indestructible faith in fraternal humanity. I am merely the too-weak interpreter and faithful servant of the spirit of reason, of tolerance, and of pity, which is the heritage of Montaigne, of Voltaire, and of the French philosophers of the eighteenth century. May you be thanked for the new strength which your respected suffrage brings, in this hour of bloodshed, to the hopes which we place in the wisdom of the future and in a reconciled Europe, in spite of the tragedies of the present."

During these dark years there were no Nobel celebrations, nor did anyone think of inviting the laureate to Stockholm. But he kept up relations with the Academy and, in a fine gesture of gratitude, offered them the bulky manuscript of *Jean-Christophe*. The Academy still owns it although, in pious memory of the author, it has been deposited in the Romain Rolland archives which were founded in Paris after World War II. There also is to be found the laureate's diploma, in which the award of the Prize is described in these terms: "As a tribute to the lofty idealism of his literary production and to the sympathy and truth with which he has described diverse human types."

Translated by Camilla Sykes.

Bertrand Russell

1950

"In recognition of his varied and

significant writings, in which he

champions humanitarian ideals and

freedom of thought"

Illustrated by *JAU. K. SCOB*

PRESENTATION ADDRESS

By *ANDERS ÖSTERLING*

PERMANENT SECRETARY
OF THE SWEDISH ACADEMY

———————

THE GREAT WORK on Western philosophy which Bertrand Russell brought out in 1946, that is, at the age of seventy-four, contains numerous characteristic reflections giving us an idea of how he himself might like us to regard his long and arduous life. In one place, speaking of the pre-Socratic philosophers, he says, "In studying a philosopher, the right attitude is neither reverence nor contempt, but first a kind of hypothetical sympathy, until it is possible to know what it feels like to believe in his theories, and only then a revival of the critical attitude, which should resemble, as far as possible, the state of mind of a person abandoning opinions which he has hitherto held."

And in another place in the same work he writes, "It is not good either to forget the questions that philosophy asks, or to persuade ourselves that we have found indubitable answers to them. To teach how to live without certainty, and yet without being paralyzed by hesitation, is perhaps the chief thing that philosophy, in our age, can still do."

With his superior intellect, Russell has, throughout half a century, been at the center of public debate, watchful and always ready for battle, as active as ever to this very day, having behind him a life of writing of most imposing scope. His works in the sciences concerned with human knowledge and mathematical logic are epoch-making and have been compared to Newton's fundamental results in mechanics. Yet it is not these achievements in special branches of science that the Nobel Prize is primarily meant to recognize. What is important, from our point of view, is that Russell has so extensively addressed his books to a public of laymen, and, in doing so, has been so eminently successful in keeping alive the interest in general philosophy.

[255]

His whole life's work is a stimulating defense of the reality of common sense. As a philosopher he pursues the line from the classical English empiricism, from Locke and Hume. His attitude toward the idealistic dogmas is a most independent one and quite frequently one of opposition. The great philosophical systems evolved on the Continent he regards, so to speak, from the chilly, windswept, and distinctive perspective of the English Channel. With his keen and sound good sense, his clear style, and his wit in the midst of seriousness, he has in his work evinced those characteristics which are found among only the elite of authors. Time does not permit even the briefest survey of his works in this area, which are fascinating also from a purely literary point of view. It may suffice to mention such books as the *History of Western Philosophy* (1946), *Human Knowledge* (1948), *Sceptical Essays* (1948), and the sketch "My Mental Development" (in *The Philosophy of Bertrand Russell,* 1951); but to these should be added a great number of equally important books on practically all the problems which the present development of society involves.

Russell's views and opinions have been influenced by varied factors and cannot easily be summarized. His famous family typifies the Whig tradition in English politics. His grandfather was the Victorian statesman John Russell. Familiar from an early age with the ideas of Liberalism, he was soon confronted by the problems of rising socialism and since then he has, as an independent critic, weighed the advantages and disadvantages of this form of society. He has consistently and earnestly warned us of the dangers of the new bureaucracy. He has defended the right of the individual against collectivism, and he views industrial civilization as a growing threat to humanity's chances of simple happiness and joy in living. After his visit to the Soviet Union in 1920 he strongly and resolutely opposed himself to Communism. On the other hand, during a subsequent journey in China, he was very much attracted by the calm and peaceable frame of mind of China's cultivated classes and recommended it as an example to a West ravaged by wild aggression.

Much in Russell's writings excites protest. Unlike many other philosophers, he regards this as one of the natural and urgent tasks of an author. Of course, his rationalism does not solve all troublesome problems and cannot be used as a panacea, even if the philosopher willingly writes out the prescription. Unfortunately, there are—and obviously always will be —obscure forces which evade intellectual analysis and refuse to submit to control. Thus, even if Russell's work has, from a purely practical point of view, met with but little success in an age which has seen two world wars—even if it may look as if, in the main, his ideas have been bitterly repudiated—we must nevertheless admire the unwavering valor of this rebellious teller of the truth and the sort of dry, fiery strength and gay buoyancy with which he presents his convictions, which are never dictated by opportunism but are often directly unpopular. To read the philosopher Russell often gives very much the same pleasure as to listen to the outspoken hero in a Shaw comedy, when in loud and cheerful tones he throws out his bold retorts and keen arguments.

In conclusion, Russell's philosophy may be said in the best sense to fulfill just those desires and intentions that Alfred Nobel had in mind when he instituted his Prizes. There are quite striking similarities between their outlooks on life. Both of them are at the same time skeptics and utopians, both take a gloomy view of the contemporary world, yet both hold fast to a belief in the possibility of achieving logical standards for human behavior. The Swedish Academy believes that it acts in the spirit of Nobel's intention when, on the occasion of the fiftieth anniversary of the Foundation, it wishes to honor Bertrand Russell as one of our time's brilliant spokesmen of rationality and humanity, as a fearless champion of free speech and free thought in the West.

My lord — Exactly two hundred years ago Jean Jacques Rousseau was awarded the prize offered by the Academy of Dijon for his famous answer to the question of "whether the arts and sciences have contributed to improve morals." Rousseau answered "No," and this answer —which may not have been a very serious one—in any case had most serious consequences. The Academy of Dijon had no revolutionary aims. This is true also of the Swedish Academy, which has now chosen to reward you for your philosophical works just because they are undoubtedly of service to moral civilization and, in addition, most eminently answer to the spirit of Nobel's intentions. We honor you as a brilliant champion of humanity and free thought, and it is a pleasure for us to see you here on the occasion of the fiftieth anniversary of the Nobel Foundation. With these words I request you to receive from the hands of His Majesty the King the Nobel Prize for Literature for 1950.

There was no formal Acceptance Speech by Russell.

ADAPTATION: AN AUTOBIOGRAPHICAL EPITOME

By BERTRAND RUSSELL

For those who are too young to remember the world before 1914, it must be difficult to imagine the contrast for a man of my age between childhood memories and the world of the present day. I try, though with indifferent success, to accustom myself to a world of crumbling empires, Communism, atom bombs, Asian self-assertion, and aristocratic downfall. In this strange insecure world where no one knows whether he will be alive tomorrow, and where ancient states vanish like morning mists, it is not easy for those who, in youth, were accustomed to ancient solidities to believe that what they are now experiencing is a reality and not a transient nightmare. Very little remains of institutions and ways of life that when I was a child appeared as indestructible as granite. I grew up in an atmosphere impregnated with tradition. My parents died before I can remember, and I was brought up by my grandparents. My grandfather was born in the early days of the French Revolution and was in Parliament while Napoleon was still Emperor. As a Whig who followed Fox, he thought the English hostility to the French Revolution and Napoleon excessive, and he visited the exiled Emperor in Elba. It was he who, in 1832, introduced the Reform Bill which started England on the road toward democracy. He was Prime Minister during the Mexican War and during the revolutions of 1848. In common with the whole Russell family, he inherited the peculiar brand of aristocratic liberalism which characterized the Revolution of 1688 in which his ancestor played an important part. I was taught a kind of theoretic republicanism which was prepared to tolerate a monarch so long as he recognized that he was an employee of the people and subject to dismissal if he proved unsatisfactory. My grandfather, who was no respecter of persons, used to explain this point of view to Queen Victoria, and she was not altogether sympathetic. She did, however, give him the house in Richmond Park in which I spent all my youth. I imbibed certain political principles and expectations, and have on the whole retained the former in spite of being compelled to reject the latter. There was to be ordered progress throughout the world, no revolutions, a gradual cessation of war, and an extension of parliamentary government to all those unfortunate regions which did not yet enjoy it. My grandmother used to laugh about a conversation she had had with the Russian Ambassador. She said to him, "Perhaps some day you will have a parliament in Russia," and he replied, "God forbid, my dear Lady John." The Russian Ambassador of today might give the same answer if he changed the first word. The hopes of that period seem now a little absurd. There was to be democracy, but it was assumed that the people would always be ready to follow the advice of wise and experienced aristocrats. There was to be a disappearance of imperialism, but the subject races in Asia and Africa, whom the British would voluntarily cease to govern, would have learned the advantage of a bicameral legislature composed of Whigs and Tories in about equal numbers, and would reproduce in torrid zones the parliamentary duels of Disraeli and Gladstone which were at their most brilliant at the time when I imbibed my dominant political prejudices. The idea of any insecurity to British power never entered anybody's head. Britannia ruled the waves, and that was that. There was, it is true, Bismarck, whom I was taught to consider a rascal; but it was thought that the civilizing influences of Goethe and Schiller would prevent the Germans from being permanently led into wrong paths by this uncivilized farmer. It was true also that there had been violence in the not-so-distant past. The French in their Revolution had committed excesses which one must deplore, while urging, at the same time, that reactionaries had grossly exaggerated them and that they would not have occurred at all but for the foolish hostility of the rest of Europe to progressive opinions in France. It might perhaps be admitted also that Cromwell had gone too far in cutting off the king's head but, broadly speaking, anything done against kings was to be applauded—unless, indeed, it were done by priests, like Becket, in which case one sided with the king. The atmosphere in the house was one of puritan piety and austerity. There were family prayers at eight o'clock every morning. Although there were eight servants, food was always of Spartan simplicity, and even what there was, if it was at all nice, was considered too good for children. For instance, if there was apple tart and rice pudding, I was only allowed the rice pudding. Cold baths all the year round were insisted upon, and I had to practice the piano from seven-thirty to eight every morning although the fires were not yet lit. My grandmother never allowed herself to sit in an armchair until the evening. Alcohol and tobacco were viewed with disfavor although stern convention compelled them to serve a little wine to guests. Only virtue was prized, virtue at the expense of intellect, health, happiness, and every mundane good.

I rebelled against this atmosphere first in the name of intellect. I was a solitary, shy, priggish youth. I had no experience of the social pleasures of boyhood and did not miss them. But I liked mathematics, and mathematics was suspect because it has no ethical content. I came also to disagree with the theological opinions of my family, and as I grew up I became increasingly interested in philosophy, of which they profoundly disapproved. Every time the subject came up they repeated with unfailing regularity, "What is mind? No matter. What is matter? Never mind." After some fifty or sixty repetitions, this remark ceased to amuse me.

When at the age of eighteen I went up to Cambridge, I found myself suddenly and almost bewilderingly among people who spoke the sort of language that was natural to me. If I said anything that I really thought they neither stared at me as if I were a lunatic nor denounced me as if I were a criminal. I had been compelled to live in a morbid atmosphere where an unwholesome kind of morality was encouraged to such an extent as to paralyze intelligence. And to find myself in a world where intelligence was valued and clear thinking was thought to be a good thing caused me an intoxicating delight. It is sometimes said that those who have had an unconventional education will find a difficulty in adjusting themselves to the world. I had no such experience. The environment in which I found myself at Cambridge fitted me like a glove. In the course of my first term I made lifelong friends and I never again had to endure the almost unbearable loneliness of my adolescent years. My first three years at Cambridge were given to mathematics and my fourth year to philosophy. I came in time to think ill of the philosophy that I had been taught, but the learning of it was a delight and it opened to me new and fascinating problems which I hoped to be able to solve. I was especially attracted to problems concerning the foundations of mathematics. I wished to believe that some knowledge is certain and I thought that the best hope of finding certain knowledge was in mathematics. At the same time it was obvious to me that the proofs of mathematical propositions which my teachers had offered me were fallacious. I hoped that better proofs were forthcoming. Subsequent study showed me that my hopes were partly justified. But it took me nearly twenty years to find all the justification that seemed possible and even that fell far short of my youthful hopes.

When I had finished my student years at Cambridge, I had to decide whether to devote my life to philosophy or to politics. Politics had been the habitual pursuit of my family since the sixteenth century, and to think of anything else was viewed as a kind of treachery to my ancestors. Everything was done to show

that my path would be smooth if I chose politics. John Morley, who was Irish Secretary, offered me a post. Lord Dufferin, who was British Ambassador in Paris, gave me a job at our Embassy there. My family brought pressure to bear upon me in every way they could think of. For a time I hesitated, but in the end the lure of philosophy proved irresistible. This was my first experience of conflict, and I found it painful. I have since had so much conflict that many people have supposed that I must like it. I should, however, have much preferred to live at peace with everybody. But over and over again profound convictions have forced me into disagreements, even where I least desired them. After I had decided on philosophy, however, everything went smoothly for a long time. I lived mainly in an academic atmosphere where the pursuit of philosophy was not regarded as an eccentric folly. All went well until 1914. But when the First World War broke out, I thought it was a folly and a crime on the part of every one of the Powers involved on both sides. I hoped that England might remain neutral and, when this did not happen, I continued to protest. I found myself isolated from most of my former friends and, what I minded even more, estranged from the current of the national life. I had to fall back upon sources of strength that I hardly knew myself to possess. But something, that if I had been religious I should have called the Voice of God, compelled me to persist. Neither then nor later did I think *all* war wrong. It was *that* war, not all war, that I condemned. The Second World War I thought necessary, not because I had changed my opinions on war, but because the circumstances were different. In fact all that made the Second War necessary was an outcome of the First War. We owe to the First War and its aftermath Russian Communism, Italian Fascism and German Nazism. We owe to the First War the creation of a chaotic unstable world where there is every reason to fear that the Second World War was not the last, where there is the vast horror of Russian Communism to be combatted, where Germany, France and what used to be the Austro-Hungarian Empire have all fallen lower in the scale of civilization, where there is every prospect of chaos in Asia and Africa, where the prospect of vast and horrible carnage inspires daily and hourly terror. All these evils have sprung with the inevitability of Greek tragedy out of the First World War. Consider by way of contrast what would have happened if Britain had remained neutral in that war. The war would have been short. It would have ended in victory for Germany. America would not have been dragged in. Britain would have remained strong and prosperous. Germany would not have been driven into Nazism; Russia, though it would have had a revolution, would in all likelihood have not had the Communist Revolution, since it could not in a short war have been reduced to the condition of utter chaos which prevailed in 1917. The Kaiser's Germany, although war propaganda on our side represented it as atrocious, was in fact only swashbuckling and a little absurd. I had lived in the Kaiser's Germany and I knew that progressive forces in that country were very strong and had every prospect of ultimate success. There was more freedom in the Kaiser's Germany than there is now in any country outside Britain and Scandinavia. We were told at the time that it was a war for freedom, a war for democracy and a war against militarism. As a result of that war freedom has vastly diminished and militarism has vastly increased. As for democracy, its future is still in doubt. I cannot think that the world would now be in anything like the bad state in which it is if English neutral-

ity in the First War had allowed a quick victory to Germany. On these grounds I have never thought that I was mistaken in the line that I took at that time. I also do not regret having attempted throughout the war years to persuade people that the Germans were less wicked than official propaganda represented them as being, for a great deal of the subsequent evil resulted from the severity of the Treaty of Versailles and this severity would not have been possible but for the moral horror with which Germany was viewed. The Second World War was a totally different matter. Very largely as a result of our follies, Nazi Germany had to be fought if human life was to remain tolerable. If the Russians seek world dominion it is to be feared that war with them will be supposed equally necessary. But all this dreadful sequence is an outcome of the mistakes of 1914 and would not have occurred if those mistakes had been avoided.

The end of the First War was not the end of my isolation, but, on the contrary, the prelude to an even more complete isolation (except from close personal friends) which was due to my failure to applaud the new revolutionary government of Russia. When the Russian Revolution first broke out I welcomed it as did almost everybody else, including the British Embassy in Petrograd (as it then was). It was difficult at a distance to follow the confused events of 1918 and 1919 and I did not know what to think of the Bolsheviks. But in 1920 I went to Russia, had long talks with Lenin and other prominent men, and saw as much as I could of what was going on. I came to the conclusion that everything that was being done and everything that was being intended was totally contrary to what any person of a liberal outlook would desire. I thought the regime already hateful and certain to become more so. I found the source of evil in a contempt for liberty and democracy which was a natural outcome of fanaticism. It was thought by radicals in those days that one ought to support the Russian Revolution whatever it might be doing, since it was opposed by reactionaries, and criticism of it played into their hands. I felt the force of this argument and was for some time in doubt as to what I ought to do. But in the end I decided in favor of what seemed to me to be the truth. I stated publicly that I thought the Bolshevik regime abominable, and I have never seen any reason to change this opinion. In this I differed from almost all the friends that I had acquired since 1914. Most people still hated me for having opposed the war, and the minority, who did not hate me on this ground, denounced me for not praising the Bolsheviks.

My visit to Russia in 1920 was a turning point in my life. During the time that I was there I felt a gradually increasing horror which became an almost intolerable oppression. The country seemed to me one vast prison in which the jailers were cruel bigots. When I found my friends applauding these men as liberators and regarding the regime that they were creating as a paradise, I wondered in a bewildered manner whether it was my friends or I that were mad. But the habit of following my own judgment rather than that of others had grown strong in me during the war years. And as a matter of historical dynamics it seemed obvious that revolutionary ardor must develop into imperialism as it had done in the French Revolution. When I finally decided to say what I thought of the Bolsheviks my former political friends, including very many who have since come to my opinion, denounced me as a lackey of the *bourgeoisie*. But reactionaries did not notice what I said and continued to describe me in print as a "lily-livered Bolshie swine." And so I

succeeded in getting the worst of both worlds.

All this would have been more painful than it was if I had not, just at that moment, had occasion to go to China where I spent a year in great happiness away from the European turmoil. Since that time, although I have had occasional conflicts, they have been more external and less painful than those connected with the war and the Bolsheviks.

After I returned from China in 1921 I became absorbed for a number of years in parenthood and attendant problems of education. I did not like conventional education but I thought what is called "progressive education" in most schools deficient on the purely scholastic side. It seemed to me, and still seems, that in a technically complex civilization such as ours a man cannot play an important part unless in youth he has had a very considerable dose of sheer instruction. I could not find any school at that time that seemed to me satisfactory, so I tried starting a school of my own. But a school is an administrative enterprise and I found myself deficient in skill as an administrator. The school, therefore, was a failure. But fortunately about this time I found another school which had recently become excellent. I wrote two books on education and spent a lot of time thinking about it but, as anyone might have expected, I was better at talking than at doing. I am not a believer in complete freedom during childhood. I think children need a fixed routine, though there should be days when it is not carried out. I think also that, if a person when adult is to be able to fit into a society, he must learn while still young that he is not the center of the universe and that his wishes are often not the most important factor in a situation. I think also that the encouragement of originality without technical skill, which is practiced in many progressive schools, is a mistake. There are some things that I like very much in progressive education, especially freedom of speech, and freedom to explore the facts of life, and the absence of a silly kind of morality which is more shocked by the utterance of a swear word than by an unkind action. But I think that those who have rebelled against an unwise discipline have often gone too far in forgetting that some discipline is necessary. This applies more especially to the acquisition of knowledge.

Age and experience have not had as much effect upon my opinions as no doubt they ought to have had, but I have come to realize that freedom is a principle to which there are very important limitations of which those in education are in a certain sense typical. What people will do in given circumstances depends enormously upon their habits; and good habits are not acquired without discipline. Most of us go through life without stealing, but many centuries of police discipline have gone into producing this abstention which now seems natural. If children are taught nothing about manners they will snatch each other's food and the older children will get all the titbits. In international affairs it will not be by prolonging interstate anarchy that the world will be brought back to a tolerable condition, but by the rule of international law, which will never prevail unless backed by international force. In the economic sphere the old doctrine of *laissez faire* is not now held by any practical men, although a few dreamers still hanker after it. As the world grows fuller, regulation becomes more necessary. No doubt this is regrettable. The world of the *Odyssey* is attractive. One sails from island to island and always finds a lovely lady ready to receive one. But nowadays immigration quotas interfere with this sort of life. It

was all very well for Odysseus, who was only one, but if a hundred million Chinese had descended upon Calypso's island, life would have become rather difficult. The broad rule is a simple one: that men should be free in what only concerns themselves, but that they should not be free when they are tempted to aggression against others. But although the broad rule is simple, the carrying out of it in detail is very complex, and so the problem of the proper limitations on human freedom remains.

Although I have been much occupied with the world and the vast events that have taken place during my lifetime, I have always thought of myself as primarily an abstract philosopher. I have tried to extend the exact and demonstrative methods of mathematics and science into regions traditionally given over to vague speculation. I like precision. I like sharp outlines. I hate misty vagueness. For some reason which I do not profess to understand, this has caused large sections of the public to think of me as a cold person destitute of passion. It seems to be supposed that whoever feels any passion must enjoy self-deception and choose to live in a fool's paradise on the ground that no other sort of paradise is attainable. I cannot sympathize with this point of view. The more I am interested in anything, the more I wish to know the truth about it, however unpleasant the truth may be. When I first became interested in philosophy, I hoped that I should find in it some satisfaction for my thwarted desire for a religion. For a time, I found a sort of cold comfort in Plato's eternal world of ideas. But in the end I thought this was nonsense and I have found in philosophy no satisfaction whatever for the impulse toward religious belief. In this sense I have found philosophy disappointing, but as a clarifier I have found it quite the opposite. Many things which, when I was young, were matters of taste or conjecture have become exact and scientific. In this I rejoice and in so far as I have been able to contribute to the result I feel that my work in philosophy has been worth doing.

But in such a world as we now have to live in, it grows increasingly difficult to concentrate on abstract matters. The everyday world presses in upon the philosopher and his ivory tower begins to crumble. The future of mankind more and more absorbs my thoughts. I grew up in the full flood of Victorian optimism, and although the easy cheerfulness of that time is no longer possible, something remains with me of the hopefulness that then was easy. It is now no longer easy. It demands a certain fortitude and a certain capacity to look beyond the moment to a more distant future. But I remain convinced, whatever dark times may lie before us, that mankind will emerge, that the habit of mutual forbearance, which now seems lost, will be recovered, and that the reign of brutal violence will not last forever. Mankind has to learn some new lessons of which the necessity is due to increase of skill without increase of wisdom. Moral and intellectual requirements are inextricably intertwined. Evil passions make men incapable of seeing the truth, and false beliefs afford excuses for evil passions. If the world is to emerge, it requires both clear thinking and kindly feeling. It may be that neither will be learned except through utmost disaster. I hope this is not the case. I hope that something less painful can teach wisdom. But by whatever arduous road, I am convinced that the new wisdom which the new world requires will be learned sooner or later, and that the best part of human history lies in the future, not in the past.

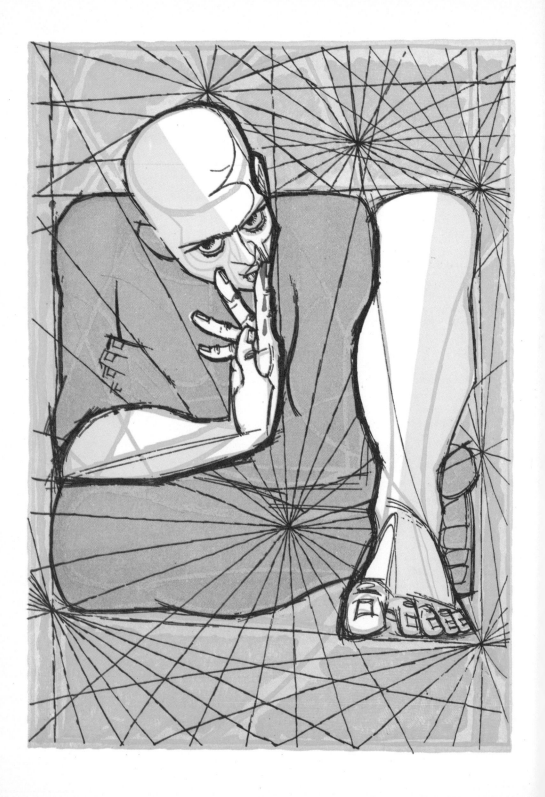

WHY I AM NOT A CHRISTIAN

By BERTRAND RUSSELL

Perhaps it would be as well, first of all, to try to make out what one means by the word *Christian*. It is used these days in a very loose sense by a great many people. Some people mean no more by it than a person who attempts to live a good life. In that sense I suppose there would be Christians in all sects and creeds; but I do not think that that is the proper sense of the word, if only because it would imply that all the people who are not Christians—all the Buddhists, Confucians, Mohammedans, and so on—are not trying to live a good life. I do not mean by a Christian any person who tries to live decently according to his lights. I think that you must have a certain amount of definite belief before you have a right to call yourself a Christian. The word does not have quite such a full-blooded meaning now as it had in the times of St. Augustine and St. Thomas Aquinas. In those days, if a man said that he was a Christian it was known what he meant. You accepted a whole collection of creeds which were set out with great precision, and every single syllable of those creeds you believed with the whole strength of your convictions.

What Is a Christian?

Nowadays it is not quite that. We have to be a little more vague in our meaning of Christianity. I think, however, that there are two different items which are quite essential to anybody calling himself a Christian. The first is one of a dogmatic nature—namely, that you must believe in God and immortality. If you do not believe in those two things, I do not think that you can properly call yourself a Christian. Then, further than that, as the name implies, you must have some kind of belief about Christ. The Mohammedans, for instance, also believe in God and in immortality, and yet they would not call themselves Christians. I think you must have at the very lowest the belief that Christ was, if not divine, at least the best and wisest of men. If you are not going to believe that much about Christ, I do not think you have any right to call yourself a Christian. Of course, there is another sense, which you find in *Whitaker's Almanack* and in geography books, where the population of the world is said to be divided into Christians, Mohammedans, Buddhists, fetish worshipers, and so on; and in that sense we are all Christians. The geography books count us all in, but that is a purely geographical sense, which I suppose we can ignore. Therefore I take it that when I tell you why I am not a Christian I have to tell you two different things: first, why I do not believe in God and in immortality; and, secondly, why I do not think that Christ was the best and wisest of men, although I grant him a very high degree of moral goodness.

But for the successful efforts of unbelievers in the past, I could not take so elastic a definition of Christianity as that. As I said before, in olden days it had a much more full-blooded sense. For instance, it included the belief in hell. Belief in eternal hell-fire was an essential item of Christian belief until pretty recent times. In this country, as you know, it ceased to be an essential item because of a decision of the Privy Council, and from that decision the Archbishop of Canterbury and the Archbishop of York dissented; but in this country our religion is settled by Act of Parliament, and therefore the Privy Council was able to override their Graces and hell was no longer necessary to a Christian. Consequently I shall not insist that a Christian must believe in hell.

The Existence of God

To come to this question of the existence of God: it is a large and serious question, and if I were to attempt to deal with it in any adequate manner I should have to keep you here until Kingdom Come, so that you will have to excuse me if I deal with it in a somewhat summary fashion. You know, of course, that the Catholic Church has laid it down as a dogma that the existence of God can be proved by the unaided reason. That is a somewhat curious dogma, but it is one of their dogmas. They had to introduce it because at one time the freethinkers adopted the habit of saying that there were such and such arguments which mere reason might urge against the existence of God, but of course they knew as a matter of faith that God did exist. The arguments and the reasons were set out at great length, and the Catholic Church felt that they must stop it. Therefore they

laid it down that the existence of God can be proved by the unaided reason and they had to set up what they considered were arguments to prove it. There are, of course, a number of them, but I shall take only a few.

The First-cause Argument

Perhaps the simplest and easiest to understand is the argument of the First Cause. (It is maintained that everything we see in this world has a cause, and as you go back in the chain of causes further and further you must come to a First Cause, and to that First Cause you give the name of God.) That argument, I suppose, does not carry very much weight nowadays, because, in the first place, cause is not quite what it used to be. The philosophers and the men of science have got going on cause, and it has not anything like the vitality it used to have; but, apart from that, you can see that the argument that there must be a First Cause is one that cannot have any validity. I may say that when I was a young man and was debating these questions very seriously in my mind, I for a long time accepted the argument of the First Cause, until one day, at the age of eighteen, I read John Stuart Mill's Autobiography, and I there found this sentence: "My father taught me that the question 'Who made me?' cannot be answered, since it immediately suggests the further question 'Who made God?'" That very simple sentence showed me, as I still think, the fallacy in the argument of the First Cause. If everything must have a cause, then God must have a cause. If there can be anything without a cause, it may just as well be the world as God, so that there cannot be any validity in that argument. It is exactly of the same nature as the Hindu's view, that the world rested upon an elephant and the elephant rested upon a tortoise; and when they said, "How about the tortoise?" the Indian said, "Suppose we change the subject." The argument is really no better than that. There is no reason why the world could not have come into being without a cause; nor, on the other hand, is there any reason why it should not have always existed. There is no reason to suppose that the world had a beginning at all. The idea that things must have a beginning is really due to the poverty of our imagination. Therefore, perhaps, I need not waste any more time upon the argument about the First Cause.

The Natural-law Argument

Then there is a very common argument from natural law. That was a favorite argument all through the eighteenth century, especially under the influence of Sir Isaac Newton and his cosmogony. People observed the planets going around the sun according to the law of gravitation, and they thought that God had given a behest to these planets to move in that particular fashion, and that was why they did so. That was, of course, a convenient and simple explanation that saved them the trouble of looking any further for explanations of the law of gravitation. Nowadays we explain the law of gravitation in a somewhat complicated fashion that Einstein has introduced. I do not propose to give you a lecture on the law of gravitation, as interpreted by Einstein, because that again would take some time; at any rate, you no longer have the sort of natural law that you had in the Newtonian system, where, for some reason that nobody could understand, nature behaved in a uniform fashion. We now find that a great many things we thought were natural laws are really human conventions. You know that even in the remotest depths of stellar space there are still three

feet to a yard. That is, no doubt, a very remarkable fact, but you would hardly call it a law of nature. And a great many things that have been regarded as laws of nature are of that kind. On the other hand, where you can get down to any knowledge of what atoms actually do, you will find they are much less subject to law than people thought, and that the laws at which you arrive are statistical averages of just the sort that would emerge from chance. There is, as we all know, a law that if you throw dice you will get double sixes only about once in thirty-six times, and we do not regard that as evidence that the fall of the dice is regulated by design; on the contrary, if the double sixes came every time we should think that there was design. The laws of nature are of that sort as regards a great many of them. They are statistical averages such as would emerge from the laws of chance; and that makes this whole business of natural law much less impressive than it formerly was. Quite apart from that, which represents the momentary state of science that may change tomorrow, the whole idea that natural laws imply a lawgiver is due to a confusion between natural and human laws. Human laws are behests commanding you to behave a certain way, in which way you may choose to behave, or you may choose not to behave; but natural laws are a description of how things do in fact behave, and being a mere description of what they in fact do, you cannot argue that there must be somebody who told them to do that, because even supposing that there were, you are then faced with the question "Why did God issue just those natural laws and no others?" If you say that he did it simply from his own good pleasure, and without any reason, you then find that there is something which is not subject to law, and so your train of natural law is interrupted. If you say, as more orthodox theologians do, that in all the laws which God issues he had a reason for giving those laws rather than others—the reason, of course, being to create the best universe, although you would never think it to look at it—if there were a reason for the laws which God gave, then God himself was subject to law, and therefore you do not get any advantage by introducing God as an intermediary. You have really a law outside and anterior to the divine edicts, and God does not serve your purpose, because he is not the ultimate lawgiver. In short, this whole argument about natural law no longer has anything like the strength that it used to have. I am traveling on in time in my review of the arguments. The arguments that are used for the existence of God change their character as time goes on. They were at first hard intellectual arguments embodying certain quite definite fallacies. As we come to modern times they become less respectable intellectually and more and more affected by a kind of moralizing vagueness.

The Argument from Design

The next step in this process brings us to the argument from design. You all know the argument from design: everything in the world is made just so that we can manage to live in the world, and if the world was ever so little different, we could not manage to live in it. That is the argument from design. It sometimes takes a rather curious form; for instance, it is argued that rabbits have white tails in order to be easy to shoot. I do not know how rabbits would view that application. It is an easy argument to parody. You all know Voltaire's remark, that obviously the nose was designed to be such as to fit spectacles. That sort of parody has turned out to be not nearly so wide of the mark as it might have seemed in the eighteenth century, because since the time of Darwin we understand much better why living creatures are adapted to their environment. It is not that their environment was made to be suitable to them but that they grew to be suitable to it, and that is the basis of adaptation. There is no evidence of design about it.

When you come to look into this argument from design, it is a most astonishing thing that people can believe that this world, with all the things that are in it, with all its defects, should be the best that omnipotence and omniscience have been able to produce in millions of years. I really cannot believe it. Do you think that, if you were granted omnipotence and omniscience and millions of years in which to perfect your world, you could produce nothing better than the Ku Klux Klan or the Fascists? Moreover, if you accept the ordinary laws of science, you have to suppose that human life and life in general on this planet will die out in due course: it is a stage in the decay of the solar system; at a certain stage of decay you get the sort of conditions of temperature and so forth which are suitable to protoplasm, and there is life for a short time in the life of the whole solar system. You see in the moon the sort of thing to which the earth is tending—something dead, cold, and lifeless.

I am told that that sort of view is depressing, and people will sometimes tell you that if they believed that, they would not be able to go on living. Do not believe it; it is all nonsense. Nobody really worries much about what is going to happen millions of years hence. Even if they think they are worrying much about that, they are really deceiving themselves. They are worried about something much more mundane, or it may merely be a bad digestion; but nobody is really seriously rendered unhappy by the thought of something that is going to happen to this world millions and millions of years hence. Therefore, although it is of course a gloomy view to suppose that life will die out—at least I suppose we may say so, although sometimes when I contemplate the things that people do with their lives I think it is almost a consolation—it is not such as to render life miserable. It merely makes you turn your attention to other things.

The Moral Arguments for Deity

Now we reach one stage further in what I shall call the intellectual descent that the Theists have made in their argumentations, and we come to what are called the moral arguments for the existence of God. You all know, of course, that there used to be in the old days three intellectual arguments for the existence of God, all of which were disposed of by Immanuel Kant in the *Critique of Pure Reason;* but no sooner had he disposed of those arguments than he invented a new one, a moral argument, and that quite convinced him. He was like many people: in intellectual matters he was skeptical, but in moral matters he believed implicitly in the maxims that he had imbibed at his mother's knee. That illustrates what the psychoanalysts so much emphasize—the immensely stronger hold upon us that our very early associations have than those of later times.

Kant, as I say, invented a new moral argument for the existence of God, and that in varying forms was extremely popular during the nineteenth century. It has all sorts of forms. One form is to say that there would be no right or wrong unless God existed. I am not for the moment concerned with whether there is a difference between right and wrong, or whether there is not: that is another question. The point I am concerned with is that, if you are quite sure there is a difference between right and wrong, you are then in this situation: Is that differ-

ence due to God's fiat or is it not? If it is due to God's fiat, then for God himself there is no difference between right and wrong, and it is no longer a significant statement to say that God is good. If you are going to say, as theologians do, that God is good, you must then say that right and wrong have some meaning which is independent of God's fiat, because God's fiats are good and not bad independently of the mere fact that he made them. If you are going to say that, you will then have to say that it is not only through God that right and wrong came into being, but that they are in their essence logically anterior to God. You could, of course, if you liked, say that there was a superior deity who gave orders to the God who made this world, or could take up the line that some of the gnostics took up—a line which I often thought was a very plausible one—that as a matter of fact this world that we know was made by the devil at a moment when God was not looking. There is a good deal to be said for that, and I am not concerned to refute it.

The Argument for the Remedying of Injustice

Then there is another very curious form of moral argument, which is this: they say that the existence of God is required in order to bring justice into the world. In the part of this universe that we know there is great injustice, and often the good suffer, and often the wicked prosper, and one hardly knows which of those is the more annoying; but if you are going to have justice in the universe as a whole you have to suppose a future life to redress the balance of life here on earth. So they say that there must be a God, and there must be heaven and hell in order that in the long run there may be justice. That is a very curious argument. If you looked at the matter from a scientific point of view, you would say, "After all, I know only this world. I do not know about the rest of the universe, but so far as one can argue at all on probabilities one would say that probably this world is a fair sample, and if there is injustice here the odds are that there is injustice elsewhere also." Supposing you got a crate of oranges that you opened, and you found all the top layer of oranges bad, you would not argue, "The underneath ones must be good, so as to redress the balance." You would say, "Probably the whole lot is a bad consignment"; and that is really what a scientific person would argue about the universe. He would say, "Here we find in this world a great deal of injustice, and so far as that goes that is a reason for supposing that justice does not rule in the world; and therefore so far as it goes it affords a moral argument against deity and not in favor of one." Of course I know that the sort of intellectual arguments that I have been talking to you about are not what really moves people. What really moves people to believe in God is not any intellectual argument at all. Most people believe in God because they have been taught from early infancy to do it, and that is the main reason.

Then I think that the next most powerful reason is the wish for safety, a sort of feeling that there is a big brother who will look after you. That plays a very profound part in influencing people's desire for a belief in God.

The Character of Christ

I now want to say a few words upon a topic which I often think is not quite sufficiently dealt with by Rationalists, and that is the question whether Christ was the best and the wisest of men. It is generally taken for granted that we

should all agree that that was so. I do not myself. I think that there are a good many points upon which I agree with Christ a great deal more than the professing Christians do. I do not know that I could go with Him all the way, but I could go with Him much further than most professing Christians can. You will remember that He said, "Resist not evil: but whosoever shall smite thee on thy right cheek, turn to him the other also." That is not a new precept or a new principle. It was used by Lao-tse and Buddha some 500 or 600 years before Christ, but it is not a principle which as a matter of fact Christians accept. I have no doubt that the present Prime Minister,* for instance, is a most sincere Christian, but I should not advise any of you to go and smite him on one cheek. I think you might find that he thought this text was intended in a figurative sense.

Then there is another point which I consider excellent. You will remember that Christ said, "Judge not lest ye be judged." That principle I do not think you would find was popular in the law courts of Christian countries. I have known in my time quite a number of judges who were very earnest Christians, and none of them felt that they were acting contrary to Christian principles in what they did. Then Christ says, "Give to him that asketh of thee, and from him that would borrow of thee turn not thou away." That is a very good principle. Your Chairman has reminded you that we are not here to talk politics, but I cannot help observing that the last general election was fought on the question of how desirable it was to turn away from him that would borrow of thee, so that one must assume that the Liberals and Conservatives of this country are composed of people who do not agree

---

* Stanley Baldwin.

with the teaching of Christ, because they certainly did very emphatically turn away on that occasion.

Then there is one other maxim of Christ which I think has a great deal in it, but I do not find that it is very popular among some of our Christian friends. He says, "If thou wilt be perfect, go and sell that which thou hast, and give to the poor." That is a very excellent maxim, but, as I say, it is not much practiced. All these, I think, are good maxims, although they are a little difficult to live up to. I do not profess to live up to them myself; but then, after all, it is not quite the same thing as for a Christian.

Defects in Christ's Teaching

Having granted the excellence of these maxims, I come to certain points in which I do not believe that one can grant either the superlative wisdom or the superlative goodness of Christ as depicted in the Gospels; and here I may say that one is not concerned with the historical question. Historically it is quite doubtful whether Christ ever existed at all, and if He did we do not know anything about Him, so that I am not concerned with the historical question, which is a very difficult one. I am concerned with Christ as He appears in the Gospels, taking the Gospel narrative as it stands, and there one does find some things that do not seem to be very wise. For one thing, He certainly thought that His second coming would occur in clouds of glory before the death of all the people who were living at that time. There are a great many texts that prove that. He says, for instance, "Ye shall not have gone over the cities of Israel till the Son of Man be come." Then He says, "There are some standing here which shall not taste death till the Son of Man comes into His kingdom"; and there are a lot of places where it is

quite clear that He believed that His second coming would happen during the lifetime of many then living. That was the belief of His earlier followers, and it was the basis of a good deal of His moral teaching. When He said, "Take no thought for the morrow," and things of that sort, it was very largely because He thought that the second coming was going to be very soon, and that all ordinary mundane affairs did not count. I have, as a matter of fact, known some Christians who did believe that the second coming was imminent. I knew a parson who frightened his congregation terribly by telling them that the second coming was very imminent indeed, but they were much consoled when they found that he was planting trees in his garden. The early Christians did really believe it, and they did abstain from such things as planting trees in their gardens, because they did accept from Christ the belief that the second coming was imminent. In that respect, clearly He was not so wise as some other people have been, and He was certainly not superlatively wise.

The Moral Problem

Then you come to moral questions. There is one very serious defect to my mind in Christ's moral character, and that is that He believed in hell. I do not myself feel that any person who is really profoundly humane can believe in everlasting punishment. Christ certainly as depicted in the Gospels did believe in everlasting punishment, and one does find repeatedly a vindictive fury against those people who would not listen to His preaching—an attitude which is not uncommon with preachers, but which does somewhat detract from superlative excellence. You do not, for instance, find that attitude in Socrates. You find him quite bland and urbane toward the people who would not listen to him; and it is, to my mind, far more worthy of a sage to take that line than to take the line of indignation. You probably all remember the sort of things that Socrates was saying when he was dying, and the sort of things that he generally did say to people who did not agree with him.

You will find that in the Gospels Christ said, "Ye serpents, ye generation of vipers, how can ye escape the damnation of hell." That was said to people who did not like His preaching. It is not really to my mind quite the best tone, and there are a great many of these things about hell. There is, of course, the familiar text about the sin against the Holy Ghost: "Whosoever speaketh against the Holy Ghost it shall not be forgiven him neither in this World nor in the world to come." That text has caused an unspeakable amount of misery in the world, for all sorts of people have imagined that they have committed the sin against the Holy Ghost, and thought that it would not be forgiven them either in this world or in the world to come. I really do not think that a person with a proper degree of kindliness in his nature would have put fears and terrors of that sort into the world.

Then Christ says, "The Son of Man shall send forth His angels, and they shall gather out of His kingdom all things that offend, and them which do iniquity, and shall cast them into a furnace of fire; there shall be wailing and gnashing of teeth"; and He goes on about the wailing and gnashing of teeth. It comes in one verse after another, and it is quite manifest to the reader that there is a certain pleasure in contemplating wailing and gnashing of teeth, or else it would not occur so often. Then you all, of course, remember about the sheep and the goats; how at the second coming He is going to divide the sheep from the goats, and He is going to say to the goats, "Depart from me, ye cursed, into everlasting fire." He continues, "And these shall go away into everlasting fire." Then He says again, "If thy hand offend thee, cut it off; it is better for thee to enter into life maimed, than having two hands to go into hell, into the fire that never shall be quenched; where the worm dieth not and the fire is not quenched." He repeats that again and again also. I must say that I think all this doctrine, that hell-fire is a punishment for sin, is a doctrine of cruelty. It is a doctrine that put cruelty into the world and gave the world generations of cruel torture; and the Christ of the Gospels, if you could take Him as His chroniclers represent Him, would certainly have to be considered partly responsible for that.

There are other things of less importance. There is the instance of the Gadarene swine, where it certainly was not very kind to the pigs to put the devils into them and make them rush down the hill to the sea. You must remember that He was omnipotent, and He could have made the devils simply go away; but He chose to send them into the pigs. Then there is the curious story of the fig tree, which always rather puzzled me. You remember what happened about the fig tree. "He was hungry; and seeing a fig tree afar off having leaves, He came if haply He might find anything thereon; and when He came to it He found nothing but leaves, for the time of figs was not yet. And Jesus answered and said unto it: 'No man eat fruit of thee hereafter for ever' . . . and Peter . . . saith unto Him: 'Master, behold the fig tree which thou cursedst is withered away.' " This is a very curious story, because it was not the right time of year for figs, and you really could not blame the tree. I cannot myself feel that either in the matter of wisdom or in the matter of virtue Christ stands quite as high as some other people known to history. I think I should put

Buddha and Socrates above Him in those respects.

The Emotional Factor

As I said before, I do not think that the real reason why people accept religion has anything to do with argumentation. They accept religion on emotional grounds. One is often told that it is a very wrong thing to attack religion, because religion makes men virtuous. So I am told; I have not noticed it. You know, of course, the parody of that argument in Samuel Butler's book, *Erewhon Revisited*. You will remember that in *Erewhon* there is a certain Higgs who arrives in a remote country, and after spending some time there he escapes from that country in a balloon. Twenty years later he comes back to that country and finds a new religion in which he is worshiped under the name of the "Sun Child," and it is said that he ascended into heaven. He finds that the Feast of the Ascension is about to be celebrated, and he hears Professors Hanky and Panky say to each other that they never set eyes on the man Higgs, and they hope they never will; but they are the high priests of the religion of the Sun Child. He is very indignant, and he comes up to them, and he says, "I am going to expose all this humbug and tell the people of Erewhon that it was only I, the man Higgs, and I went up in a balloon." He was told, "You must not do that, because all the morals of this country are bound round this myth, and if they once know that you did not ascend into heaven they will all become wicked"; and so he is persuaded of that and he goes quietly away.

That is the idea—that we should all be wicked if we did not hold to the Christian religion. It seems to me that the people who have held to it have been for the most part extremely wicked. You find

this curious fact, that the more intense has been the religion of any period and the more profound has been the dogmatic belief, the greater has been the cruelty and the worse has been the state of affairs. In the so-called ages of faith, when men really did believe the Christian religion in all its completeness, there was the Inquisition, with its tortures; there were millions of unfortunate women burned as witches; and there was every kind of cruelty practiced upon all sorts of people in the name of religion.

You find as you look around the world that every single bit of progress in humane feeling, every improvement in the criminal law, every step toward the diminution of war, every step toward better treatment of the colored races, or every mitigation of slavery, every moral progress that there has been in the world, has been consistently opposed by the organized churches of the world. I say quite deliberately that the Christian religion, as organized in its churches, has been and still is the principal enemy of moral progress in the world.

How the Churches Have Retarded Progress

You may think that I am going too far when I say that that is still so. I do not think that I am. Take one fact. You will bear with me if I mention it. It is not a pleasant fact, but the churches compel one to mention facts that are not pleasant. Supposing that in this world that we live in today an inexperienced girl is married to a syphilitic man; in that case the Catholic Church says, "This is an indissoluble sacrament. You must endure celibacy or stay together. And if you stay together, you must not use birth control to prevent the birth of syphilitic children." Nobody whose natural sympathies have not been warped by dogma, or whose moral nature was not absolutely dead to all sense of suffering, could maintain that it is right and proper that that state of things should continue.

That is only an example. There are a great many ways in which, at the present moment, the church, by its insistence upon what it chooses to call morality, inflicts upon all sorts of people undeserved and unnecessary suffering. And of course, as we know, it is in its major part an opponent still of progress and of improvement in all the ways that diminish suffering in the world, because it has chosen to label as morality a certain narrow set of rules of conduct which have nothing to do with human happiness; and when you say that this or that ought to be done because it would make for human happiness, they think that has nothing to do with the matter at all. "What has human happiness to do with morals? The object of morals is not to make people happy."

Fear, the Foundation of Religion

Religion is based, I think, primarily and mainly upon fear. It is partly the terror of the unknown and partly, as I have said, the wish to feel that you have a kind of elder brother who will stand by you in all your troubles and disputes. Fear is the basis of the whole thing—fear of the mysterious, fear of defeat, fear of death. Fear is the parent of cruelty, and therefore it is no wonder if cruelty and religion have gone hand in hand. It is because fear is at the basis of those two things. In this world we can now begin a little to understand things, and a little to master them by help of science, which has forced its way step by step against the Christian religion, against the churches, and against the opposition of all the old precepts. Science can help us

to get over this craven fear in which mankind has lived for so many generations. Science can teach us, and I think our own hearts can teach us, no longer to look around for imaginary supports, no longer to invent allies in the sky, but rather to look to our own efforts here below to make this world a fit place to live in, instead of the sort of place that the churches in all these centuries have made it.

What We Must Do

We want to stand upon our own feet and look fair and square at the world— its good facts, its bad facts, its beauties, and its ugliness; see the world as it is and be not afraid of it. Conquer the world by intelligence and not merely by being slavishly subdued by the terror that comes from it. The whole conception of God is a conception derived from the ancient Oriental despotisms. It is a conception quite unworthy of free men. When you hear people in church debasing themselves and saying that they are miserable sinners, and all the rest of it, it seems contemptible and not worthy of self-respecting human beings. We ought to stand up and look the world frankly in the face. We ought to make the best we can of the world, and if it is not so good as we wish, after all it will still be better than what these others have made of it in all these ages. A good world needs knowledge, kindliness, and courage; it does not need a regretful hankering after the past or a fettering of the free intelligence by the words uttered long ago by ignorant men. It needs a fearless outlook and a free intelligence. It needs hope for the future, not looking back all the time toward a past that is dead, which we trust will be far surpassed by the future that our intelligence can create.

SCEPTICAL ESSAYS

By BERTRAND RUSSELL

[A Selection]

Introduction:
On the Value of Scepticism

I wish to propose for the reader's favorable consideration a doctrine which may, I fear, appear wildly paradoxical and subversive. The doctrine in question is this: that it is undesirable to believe a proposition when there is no ground whatever for supposing it true. I must, of course, admit that if such an opinion became common it would completely transform our social life and our political system; since both are at present faultless, this must weigh against it. I am also aware (what is more serious) that it would tend to diminish the incomes of clairvoyants, bookmakers, bishops and others who live on the irrational hopes of those who have done nothing to deserve good fortune here or hereafter. In spite of these grave arguments, I maintain that a case can be made out for my paradox, and I shall try to set it forth.

First of all, I wish to guard myself against being thought to take up an extreme position. I am a British Whig, with a British love of compromise and moderation. A story is told of Pyrrho, the founder of Pyrrhonism (which was the old name for scepticism). He maintained that we never know enough to be sure that one course of action is wiser than another. In his youth, when he was taking his constitutional one afternoon, he saw his teacher in philosophy (from whom he had imbibed his principles) with his head stuck in a ditch, unable to get out. After contemplating him for some time, he walked on, maintaining that there was no sufficient ground for thinking he would do any good by pulling the old man out. Others, less sceptical, effected a rescue, and blamed Pyrrho for his heartlessness. But his teacher, true to his principles, praised him for his consistency. Now I do not advocate such heroic scepticism as that. I am prepared to admit the ordinary beliefs of common sense, in practice if not in theory. I am prepared to admit any well-established result of science, not as certainly true, but as sufficiently probable to afford a basis for rational action. If it is announced that there is to be an eclipse of the moon on such-and-such a date, I think it worth while to look and see whether it is taking place. Pyrrho would have thought otherwise. On this ground, I feel justified in claiming that I advocate a middle position.

There are matters about which those who have investigated them are agreed; the dates of eclipses may serve as an illustration. There are other matters about which experts are not agreed. Even when the experts all agree, they may well be mistaken. Einstein's view as to the magnitude of the deflection of light by gravitation would have been rejected by all experts twenty years ago, yet it proved to be right. Nevertheless the opinion of experts, when it is unanimous, must be accepted by non-experts as more likely to be right than the opposite opinion. The scepticism that I advocate amounts only to this: (1) that when the experts are agreed, the opposite opinion cannot be held to be certain; (2) that when they are not agreed, no opinion can be regarded as certain by a non-expert; and (3) that when they all hold that no sufficient grounds for a positive opinion exist, the ordinary man would do well to suspend his judgment.

These propositions may seem mild, yet, if accepted, they would absolutely revolutionize human life.

The opinions for which people are willing to fight and persecute all belong to one of the three classes which this scepticism condemns. When there are rational grounds for an opinion, people are content to set them forth and wait for them to operate. In such cases, people do not hold their opinions with passion; they hold them calmly, and set forth their reasons quietly. The opinions that are held with passion are always those for which no good ground exists; indeed the passion is the measure of the holder's lack of rational conviction. Opinions in politics and religion are almost always held passionately. Except in China, a man is thought a poor creature unless he has strong opinions on such matters; people hate sceptics far more than they hate the passionate advocates of opinions hostile to their own. It is thought that the claims of practical life demand opinions on such questions, and that, if we became more rational, social existence would be impossible. I believe the opposite of this, and will try to make it clear why I have this belief.

Take the question of unemployment in the years after 1920. One party held that it was due to the wickedness of trade unions, another that it was due to the confusion on the Continent. A third party, while admitting that these causes played a part, attributed most of the trouble to the policy of the Bank of England in trying to increase the value of the pound sterling. This third party, I am given to understand, contained most of the experts, but no one else. Politicians do not find any attractions in a view which does not lend itself to party declamation, and ordinary mortals prefer views which attribute misfortune to the machinations of their enemies. Consequently people fight for and against quite irrelevant measures, while the few who have a rational opinion are not listened to because they do not minister to any one's passions. To produce converts, it would have been necessary to persuade people that the Bank of England is wicked. To convert Labor, it would have been necessary to show that directors of the Bank of England are hostile to trade unionism; to convert the Bishop of London, it would have been necessary to show that they are "immoral." It would be thought to follow that their views on currency are mistaken.

Let us take another illustration. It is often said that socialism is contrary to human nature, and this assertion is denied by socialists with the same heat with which it is made by their opponents. The late Dr. Rivers, whose death cannot be sufficiently deplored, discussed this question in a lecture at University College, published in his posthumous book on *Psychology and Politics*. This is the only discussion of this topic known to me that can lay claim to be scientific. It sets forth certain anthropological data which show that socialism is not contrary to human nature in Melanesia; it then points out that we do not know whether human nature is the same in Melanesia as in

Europe; and it concludes that the only way of finding out whether socialism is contrary to European human nature is to try it. It is interesting that on the basis of this conclusion he was willing to become a Labor candidate. But he would certainly not have added to the heat and passion in which political controversies are usually enveloped.

I will now venture on a topic which people find even more difficulty in treating dispassionately, namely marriage customs. The bulk of the population of every country is persuaded that all marriage customs other than its own are immoral, and that those who combat this view only do so in order to justify their own loose lives. In India, the re-marriage of widows is traditionally regarded as a thing too horrible to contemplate. In Catholic countries, divorce is thought very wicked, but some failure of conjugal fidelity is tolerated, at least in men. In America, divorce is easy, but extra-conjugal relations are condemned with the utmost severity. Mohammedans believe in polygamy, which we think degrading. All these differing opinions are held with extreme vehemence, and very cruel persecutions are inflicted upon those who contravene them. Yet no one in any of the various countries makes the slightest attempt to show that the custom of his own country contributes more to human happiness than the custom of others.

When we open any scientific treatise on the subject, such as (for example) Westermarck's *History of Human Marriage,* we find an atmosphere extraordinarily different from that of popular prejudice. We find that every kind of custom has existed, many of them such as we should have supposed repugnant to human nature. We think we can understand polygamy, as a custom forced upon women by male oppressors. But what are we to say of the Tibetan custom, accord-ing to which one woman has several husbands? Yet travelers in Tibet assure us that family life there is at least as harmonious as in Europe. A little of such reading must soon reduce any candid person to complete scepticism, since there seem to be no data enabling us to say that one marriage custom is better or worse than another. Almost all involve cruelty and intolerance towards offenders against the local code, but otherwise they have nothing in common. It seems that sin is geographical. From this conclusion, it is only a small step to the further conclusion that the notion of "sin" is illusory, and that the cruelty habitually practiced in punishing it is unnecessary. It is just this conclusion which is so unwelcome to many minds, since the infliction of cruelty with a good conscience is a delight to moralists. That is why they invented Hell.

Nationalism is of course an extreme example of fervent belief concerning doubtful matters. I think it may be safely said that any scientific historian, writing now a history of the Great War, is bound to make statements which, if made during the war, would have exposed him to imprisonment in every one of the belligerent countries on both sides. Again with the exception of China, there is no country where people tolerate the truth about themselves; at ordinary times, the truth is only thought ill-mannered, but in war-time it is thought criminal. Opposing systems of violent belief are built up, the falsehood of which is evident from the fact that they are only believed by those who share the same national bias. But the application of reason to these systems of belief is thought as wicked as the application of reason to religious dogmas was formerly thought. When people are challenged as to why scepticism in such matters should be wicked, the only answer is that myths help to win wars, so that a rational nation would be killed rather than kill. The view that there is something shameful in saving one's skin by wholesale slander of foreigners is one which, so far as I know, has hitherto found no supporters among professional moralists outside the ranks of the Quakers. If it is suggested that a rational nation would find ways of keeping out of wars altogether, the answer is usually mere abuse.

What would be the effect of a spread of rational scepticism? Human events spring from passions, which generate systems of attendant myths. Psycho-analysts have studied the individual manifestations of this process in lunatics, certified and uncertified. A man who has suffered some humiliation invents a theory that he is King of England, and develops all kinds of ingenious explanations of the fact that he is not treated with that respect which his exalted position demands. In this case, his delusion is one with which his neighbors do not sympathize, so they lock him up. But if, instead of asserting only his own greatness, he asserts the greatness of his nation or his class or his creed, he wins hosts of adherents, and becomes a political or religious leader, even if, to the impartial outsider, his views seem just as absurd as those found in asylums. In this way a collective insanity grows up, which follows laws very similar to those of individual insanity. Every one knows that it is dangerous to dispute with a lunatic who thinks he is King of England; but as he is isolated, he can be overpowered. When a whole nation shares a delusion, its anger is of the same kind as that of an individual lunatic if its pretensions are disputed, but nothing short of war can compel it to submit to reason.

The part played by intellectual factors in human behavior is a matter as to which there is much disagreement among psychologists. There are two quite distinct questions: (1) how far are beliefs operative as causes of actions? (2) how far are beliefs derived from logically adequate evidence, or capable of being so derived? On both questions, psychologists are agreed in giving a much smaller place to the intellectual factors than the plain man would give, but within this general agreement there is room for considerable differences of degree. Let us take the two questions in succession.

(1) How far are beliefs operative as causes of action? Let us not discuss the question theoretically, but let us take an ordinary day of an ordinary man's life. He begins by getting up in the morning, probably from force of habit, without the intervention of any belief. He eats his breakfast, catches his train, reads his newspaper, and goes to his office, all from force of habit. There was a time in the past when he formed these habits, and in the choice of the office, at least, belief played a part. He probably believed, at the time, that the job offered him there was as good as he was likely to get. In most men, belief plays a part in the original choice of a career, and therefore, derivatively, in all that is entailed by this choice.

At the office, if he is an underling, he may continue to act merely from habit, without active volition, and without the explicit intervention of belief. It might be thought that, if he adds up columns of figures, he believes the arithmetical rules which he employs. But that would be an error; these rules are mere habits of his body, like those of a tennis player. They were acquired in youth, not from an intellectual belief that they corresponded to the truth, but to please the schoolmaster, just as a dog learns to sit on its hind legs and beg for food. I do not say that all education is of this sort, but certainly most learning of the three R's is.

If, however, our friend is a partner or

director, he may be called upon during his day to make difficult decisions of policy. In these decisions it is probable that belief will play a part. He believes that some things will go up and others will go down, that so-and-so is a sound man, and such-and-such on the verge of bankruptcy. On these beliefs he acts. It is just because he is called upon to act on beliefs rather than mere habits that he is considered such a much greater man than a mere clerk, and is able to get so much more money—provided his beliefs are true.

In his home-life there will be much the same proportion of occasions when belief is a cause of action. At ordinary times, his behavior to his wife and children will be governed by habit, or by instinct modified by habit. On great occasions— when he proposes marriage, when he decides what school to send his son to, or when he finds reason to suspect his wife of unfaithfulness—he cannot be guided wholly by habit. In proposing marriage he may be guided by mere instinct, or he may be influenced by the belief that the lady is rich. If he is guided by instinct, he no doubt believes that the lady possesses every virtue, and this may seem to him to be a cause of his action, but in fact it is merely another effect of the instinct which alone suffices to account for his action. In choosing a school for his son, he probably proceeds in much the same way as in making difficult business decisions; here belief usually plays an important part. If evidence comes into his possession showing that his wife has been unfaithful, his behavior is likely to be purely instinctive, but the instinct is set in operation by a belief, which is the first cause of everything that follows.

Thus although beliefs are not directly responsible for more than a small part of our actions, the actions for which they are responsible are among the most im-

portant, and largely determine the general structure of our lives. In particular, our religious and political actions are associated with beliefs.

(2) I come now to our second question, which is itself twofold: (a) how far are beliefs in fact based upon evidence? (b) how far is it possible or desirable that they should be?

(a) The extent to which beliefs are based upon evidence is very much less than believers suppose. Take the kind of action which is most nearly rational: the investment of money by a rich City man. You will often find that his view (say) on the question whether the French franc will go up or down depends upon his political sympathies, and yet is so strongly held that he is prepared to risk money on it. In bankruptcies it often appears that some sentimental factor was the original cause of ruin. Political opinions are hardly ever based upon evidence, except in the case of civil servants, who are forbidden to give utterance to them. There are of course exceptions. In the tariff reform controversy which began twenty-five years ago, most manufacturers supported the side that would increase their own incomes, showing that their opinions were really based on evidence, however little their utterances would have led one to suppose so. We have here a complication. Freudians have accustomed us to "rationalizing," i.e. the process of inventing what seem to ourselves rational grounds for a decision or opinion that is in fact quite irrational. But there is, especially in English-speaking countries, a converse process which may be called "irrationalizing." A shrewd man will sum up, more or less subconsciously, the pros and cons of a question from a selfish point of view. (Unselfish considerations seldom weigh subconsciously except where one's children are concerned.) Having come to a sound egoistic decision by the help of the unconscious, a man proceeds to invent, or adopt from others, a set of high-sounding phrases showing how he is pursuing the public good at immense personal sacrifice. Anybody who believes that these phrases give his real reasons must suppose him quite incapable of judging evidence, since the supposed public good is not going to result from his action. In this case a man appears less rational than he is; what is still more curious, the irrational part of him is conscious and the rational part unconscious. It is this trait in our characters that has made the English and Americans so successful.

Shrewdness, when it is genuine, belongs more to the unconscious than to the conscious part of our nature. It is, I suppose, the main quality required for success in business. From a moral point of view, it is a humble quality, since it is always selfish; yet it suffices to keep men from the worst crimes. If the Germans had had it, they would not have adopted the unlimited submarine campaign. If the French had had it, they would not have behaved as they did in the Ruhr. If Napoleon had had it, he would not have gone to war again after the Treaty of Amiens. It may be laid down as a general rule to which there are few exceptions that, when people are mistaken as to what is to their own interest, the course that they believe to be wise is more harmful to others than the course that really is wise. Therefore anything that makes people better judges of their own interest does good. There are innumerable examples of men making fortunes because, on moral grounds, they did something which they believed to be contrary to their own interests. For instance, among early Quakers there were a number of shopkeepers who adopted the practice of asking no more for their goods than they were willing to accept, instead of bargaining with each cus-

tomer, as everybody else did. They adopted this practice because they held it to be a lie to ask more than they would take. But the convenience to customers was so great that everybody came to their shops, and they grew rich. (I forget where I read this, but if my memory serves me it was in some reliable source.) The same policy *might* have been adopted from shrewdness, but in fact no one was sufficiently shrewd. Our unconscious is more malevolent than it pays us to be; therefore the people who do most completely what is in fact to their interest are those who deliberately, on moral grounds, do what they believe to be against their interest. Next to them come the people who try to think out rationally and consciously what is to their own interest, eliminating as far as possible the influence of passion. Third come the people who have instinctive shrewdness. Last of all come the people whose malevolence overbalances their shrewdness, making them pursue the ruin of others in ways that lead to their own ruin. This last class embraces 90 per cent of the population of Europe.

I may seem to have digressed somewhat from my topic, but it was necessary to disentangle unconscious reason, which is called shrewdness, from the conscious variety. The ordinary methods of education have practically no effect upon the unconscious, so that shrewdness cannot be taught by our present technique. Morality, also, except where it consists of mere habit, seems incapable of being taught by present methods; at any rate I have never noticed any beneficent effect upon those who are exposed to frequent exhortations. Therefore on our present lines any deliberate improvement must be brought about by intellectual means. We do not know how to teach people to be shrewd or virtuous, but we do know, within limits, how to teach them to be rational: it is only necessary to reverse the practice of education authorities in every particular. We may hereafter learn to create virtue by manipulating the ductless glands and stimulating or restraining their secretions. But for the present it is easier to create rationality than virtue—meaning by "rationality" a scientific habit of mind in forecasting the effects of our actions.

(b) This brings me to the question: How far could or should men's actions be rational? Let us take "should" first. There are very definite limits, to my mind, within which rationality should be confined; some of the most important departments of life are ruined by the invasion of reason. Leibniz in his old age told a correspondent that he had only once asked a lady to marry him, and that was when he was fifty. "Fortunately," he added, "the lady asked time to consider. This gave me also time to consider, and I withdrew the offer." Doubtless his conduct was very rational, but I cannot say that I admire it.

Shakespeare puts "the lunatic, the lover, and the poet" together, as being "of imagination all compact." The problem is to keep the lover and the poet, without the lunatic. I will give an illustration. In 1919 I saw *The Trojan Women* acted at the Old Vic. There is an unbearably pathetic scene where Astyanax is put to death by the Greeks for fear he should grow up into a second Hector. There was hardly a dry eye in the theater, and the audience found the cruelty of the Greeks in the play hardly credible. Yet those very people who wept were, at that very moment, practicing that very cruelty on a scale which the imagination of Euripides could have never contemplated. They had lately voted (most of them) for a Government which prolonged the blockade of Germany after the armistice, and imposed the blockade of Russia. It was known that these blockades caused the death of immense numbers of children,

but it was felt desirable to diminish the population of enemy countries: the children, like Astyanax, might grow up to emulate their fathers. Euripides the poet awakened the lover in the imagination of the audience; but lover and poet were forgotten at the door of the theater, and the lunatic (in the shape of the homicidal maniac) controlled the political actions of these men and women who thought themselves kind and virtuous.

Is it possible to preserve the lover and the poet without preserving the lunatic? In each of us, all three exist in varying degrees. Are they so bound up together that when the one is brought under control the others perish? I do not believe it. I believe that there is in each of us a certain energy which must find vent in actions not inspired by reason, but may find vent in art, in passionate love, or in passionate hate, according to circumstances. Respectability, regularity, and routine—the whole cast-iron discipline of a modern industrial society—have atrophied the artistic impulse, and imprisoned love so that it can no longer be generous and free and creative, but must be either stuffy or furtive. Control has been applied to the very things which should be free, while envy, cruelty, and hate sprawl at large with the blessing of nearly the whole bench of Bishops. Our instinctive apparatus consists of two parts—the one tending to further our own life and that of our descendants, the other tending to thwart the lives of supposed rivals. The first includes the joy of life, and love, and art, which is psychologically an offshoot of love. The second includes competition, patriotism, and war. Conventional morality does everything to suppress the first and encourage the second. True morality would do the exact opposite. Our dealings with those whom we love may be safely left to instinct; it is our dealings with those whom we hate that ought to be brought under the dominion of reason. In the modern world, those whom we effectively hate are distant groups, especially foreign nations. We conceive them abstractly, and deceive ourselves into the belief that acts which are really embodiments of hatred are done from love of justice or some such lofty motive. Only a large measure of scepticism can tear away the veils which hide this truth from us. Having achieved that, we could begin to build a new morality, not based on envy and restriction, but on the wish for a full life and the realization that other human beings are a help and not a hindrance when once the madness of envy has been cured. This is not a Utopian hope; it was partially realized in Elizabethan England. It could be realized tomorrow if men would learn to pursue their own happiness rather than the misery of others. This is no impossibly austere morality yet its adoption would turn our earth into a paradise.

Dreams and Facts

I

The influence of our wishes upon our beliefs is a matter of common knowledge and observation, yet the nature of this influence is very generally misconceived. It is customary to suppose that the bulk of our beliefs are derived from some rational ground, and that desire is only an occasional disturbing force. The exact opposite of this would be nearer the truth: the great mass of beliefs by which we are supported in our daily life is merely the bodying forth of desire, corrected here and there, at isolated points, by the rude shock of fact. Man is essentially a dreamer, wakened sometimes for a moment by some peculiarly obtrusive element in the outer world, but lapsing again quickly into the happy somnolence of imagination. Freud has shown how largely our dreams at night are the pictured fulfilment of our wishes; he has, with an equal measure of truth, said the same of day-dreams; and he might have included the day-dreams which we call beliefs.

There are three ways by which this non-rational origin of our convictions can be demonstrated: there is the way of psychoanalysis, which, starting from an understanding of the insane and the hysterical, gradually makes it plain how little, in essence, these victims of malady differ from ordinary healthy people; then there is the way of the sceptical philosopher, showing how feeble is the rational evidence for even our most cherished beliefs; and finally there is the way of common observation of men. It is only the last of these three that I propose to consider.

The lowest savages, as they have become known through the labors of anthropologists, are not found groping in conscious ignorance amid phenomena that they are aware of not understanding. On the contrary, they have innumerable beliefs, so firmly held as to control all their more important actions. They believe that by eating the flesh of an animal or a warrior it is possible to acquire the virtues possessed by the victim when alive. Many of them believe that to pronounce the name of their chief is such sacrilege as to bring instant death; they even go so far as to alter all words in which his name occurs as one of the syllables; for example, if we had a king named John, we should speak of a jonquil as (say) a George-quil, and of a dungeon as a dun-george. When they advance to agriculture, and weather becomes important for the food supply, they believe that magical incantations or the kindling of small fires will cause rain to come or the sun to burn brightly. They believe that when a man is slain his blood, or ghost, pursues the slayer to obtain vengeance, but can be misled by a simple disguise such as painting the face red or putting on mourning.[1] The first half of this belief has obviously originated from those who feared murder, the second from those who had committed it.

Nor are irrational beliefs confined to savages. A great majority of the human race have religious opinions different from our own, and therefore groundless. People interested in politics, with the exception of politicians, have passionate convictions upon innumerable questions which must appear incapable of rational decision to any unprejudiced person. Voluntary workers in a contested election always believe that their side will win, no matter what reason there may be for expecting defeat. There can be no doubt that, in the autumn of 1914, the immense majority of the German nation felt absolutely certain of victory for Germany. In this case fact has intruded and dispelled the dream. But if, by some means, all non-German historians could be prevented from writing during the next hundred years, the dream would reinstate itself: the early triumphs would be remembered, while the ultimate disaster would be forgotten.

Politeness is the practice of respecting that part of a man's beliefs which is specially concerned with his own merits or those of his group. Every man, wherever he goes, is encompassed by a cloud of comforting convictions, which move with him like flies on a summer day. Some of these convictions are personal to himself: they tell him of his virtues and excellencies, the affection of his friends and the respect of his acquaintances, the rosy prospect of his career, and his unflagging energy in spite of delicate health. Next come convictions of the superior

excellence of his family: how his father had that unbending rectitude which is now so rare, and brought up his children with a strictness beyond what is to be found among modern parents; how his sons are carrying all before them in school games, and his daughter is not the sort of girl to make an imprudent marriage. Then there are beliefs about his class, which, according to his station, is the best socially, or the most intelligent, or the most deserving morally, of the classes in the community—though all are agreed that the first of these merits is more desirable than the second, and the second than the third. Concerning his nation, also, almost every man cherishes comfortable delusions. "Foreign nations, I am sorry to say, do as they do do." So said Mr. Podsnap, giving expression, in these words, to one of the deepest sentiments of the human heart. Finally we come to the theories that exalt mankind in general, either absolutely or in comparison with the "brute creation." Men have souls, though animals have not; Man is the "rational animal"; any peculiarly cruel or unnatural action is called "brutal" or "bestial" (although such actions are in fact distinctively human);[2] God made Man in His own image, and the welfare of Man is the ultimate purpose of the universe.

We have thus a hierarchy of comforting beliefs: those private to the individual, those which he shares with his family, those common to his class or his nation, and finally those that are equally delightful to all mankind. If we desire good relations with a man, we must respect these beliefs; we do not, therefore, speak of a man to his face as we should behind his back. The difference increases as his remoteness from ourselves grows greater. In speaking to a brother, we have

---

[1] See the chapter on "The Mark of Cain" in Frazer's *Folk-lore in the Old Testament*.

[2] Compare Mark Twain's *Mysterious Stranger*.

no need of conscious politeness as regards his parents. The need of politeness is at its maximum in speaking with foreigners, and is so irksome as to be paralyzing to those who are only accustomed to compatriots. I remember once suggesting to an untraveled American that possibly there were a few small points in which the British Constitution compared favorably with that of the United States. He instantly fell into a towering passion; having never heard such an opinion before, he could not imagine that anyone seriously entertained it. We had both failed in politeness, and the result was disaster.

But the results of failure in politeness, however bad from the point of view of a social occasion, are admirable from the point of view of dispelling myths. There are two ways in which our natural beliefs are corrected: one the contact with fact, as when we mistake a poisonous fungus for a mushroom and suffer pain in consequence; the other, when our beliefs conflict, not directly with objective fact, but with the opposite beliefs of other men. One man thinks it lawful to eat pork, but not beef; another, beef but not pork. The usual result of this difference of opinion has been bloodshed; but gradually there is beginning to be a rationalist opinion that perhaps neither is really sinful. Modesty, the correlative of politeness, consists in pretending not to think better of ourselves and our belongings than of the man we are speaking to and his belongings. It is only in China that this art is thoroughly understood. I am told that, if you ask a Chinese mandarin after the health of his wife and children, he will reply: "That contemptible slut and her verminous brood are, as your Magnificence deigns to be informed, in the enjoyment of rude health."[1] But

such elaboration demands a dignified and leisurely existence; it is impossible in the swift but important contacts of business or politics. Step by step, relations with other human beings dispel the myths of all but the most successful. Personal conceit is dispelled by brothers, family conceit by schoolfellows, class conceit by politics, national conceit by defeat in war or commerce. But human conceit remains, and in this region, so far as the effect of social intercourse is concerned, the myth-making faculty has free play. Against this form of delusion, a partial corrective is found in Science; but the corrective can never be more than partial, for without some credulity Science itself would crumble and collapse.

II

Men's personal and group dreams may be ludicrous, but their collective human dreams, to us who cannot pass outside the circle of humanity, are pathetic. The universe as astronomy reveals it is very vast. How much there may be beyond what our telescopes show, we cannot tell; but what we can know is of unimaginable immensity. In the visible world, the Milky Way is a tiny fragment; within this fragment, the solar system is an infinitesimal speck, and of this speck our planet is a microscopic dot. On this dot, tiny lumps of impure carbon and water, of complicated structure, with somewhat unusual physical and chemical properties, crawl about for a few years, until they are dissolved again into the elements of which they are compounded. They divide their time between labor designed to postpone the moment of dissolution for themselves and frantic struggles to hasten it for others of their kind. Natural convulsions periodically destroy some thousands or millions of them, and disease prematurely sweeps away many more. These events are considered to be

[1] This was written before I came to know China. It would not be true of the China that I saw (in 1920).

misfortunes; but when men succeed in inflicting similar destruction by their own efforts, they rejoice, and give thanks to God. In the life of the solar system, the period during which the existence of man will have been physically possible is a minute portion of the whole; but there is some reason to hope that even before this period is ended man will have set a term to his own existence by his efforts at mutual annihilation. Such is man's life viewed from the outside.

But such a view of life, we are told, is intolerable, and would destroy the instinctive energy by which men persist. The way of escape that they have found is through religion and philosophy. However alien and indifferent the outer world may seem, we are assured by our comforters that there is harmony beneath the apparent conflict. All the long development from the original nebula is supposed to lead up to man as the culmination of the process. *Hamlet* is a very well-known play, yet few readers would have any recollection of the part of the First Sailor, which consists of the four words: "God bless you, sir." But suppose a society of men whose sole business in life was to act this part; suppose them isolated from contact with the Hamlets, Horatios, and even Guildensterns: would they not invent systems of literary criticism according to which the four words of the First Sailor were the kernel of the whole drama? Would they not punish with ignominy or exile any one of their number who should suggest that other parts were possibly of equal importance? And the life of mankind takes up a much smaller proportion of the universe than the First Sailor's speech does of *Hamlet,* but we cannot listen behind the scenes to the rest of the play, and we know very little of its characters or plot.

When we think of mankind, we think primarily of ourself as its representative; we therefore think well of mankind, and consider its preservation important. Mr. Jones, the Noncomformist grocer, is sure that he deserves eternal life, and that a universe which refused it to him would be intolerably bad. But when he thinks of Mr. Robinson, his Anglican competitor, who mixes sand with his sugar and is lax about Sunday, he feels that the universe might well carry charity too far. To complete his happiness, there is need of hell-fire for Mr. Robinson; in this way, the cosmic importance of man is preserved, but the vital distinction between friends and enemies is not obliterated by a weak universal benevolence. Mr. Robinson holds the same view with the parts inverted, and general happiness results.

In the days before Copernicus there was no need of philosophic subtlety to maintain the anthropocentric view of the world. The heavens visibly revolved about the earth, and on the earth man had dominion over all the beasts of the field. But when the earth lost its central position, man, too, was deposed from his eminence, and it became necessary to invent a metaphysic to correct the "crudities" of science. This task was achieved by those who are called "idealists," who maintain that the world of matter is unreal appearance, while the reality is Mind or Spirit—transcending the mind or spirit of the philosopher as he transcends common men. So far from there being no place like home, these thinkers assure us that every place is like home. In all our best, that is, in all those tasks which we share with the philosopher in question, we are at one with the universe. Hegel assures us that the universe resembles the Prussian State of his day; his English followers consider it more analogous to a bi-cameral plutocratic democracy. The reasons offered for these views are carefully camouflaged so as to conceal even from their authors the connection with human wishes: they are derived, nominally, from such dry sources as logic and the analysis of propositions. But the influence of wishes is shown by the fallacies committed, which all tend in one direction. When a man adds up an account, he is much more likely to make a mistake in his favor than to his detriment; and when a man reasons, he is more apt to incur fallacies which favor his wishes than such as thwart them. And so it comes that, in the study of nominally abstract thinkers, it is their mistakes that give the key to their personality.

Many may contend that, even if the systems men have invented are untrue, they are harmless and comforting, and should be left undisturbed. But they are in fact not harmless, and the comfort they bring is dearly bought by the preventable misery which they lead men to tolerate. The evils of life spring partly from natural causes, partly from men's hostility to each other. In former times, competition and war were necessary for the securing of food, which could only be obtained by the victors. Now, owing to the mastery of natural forces which science has begun to give, there would be more comfort and happiness for all if all devoted themselves to the conquest of Nature rather than of each other. The representation of Nature as a friend, and sometimes as even an ally in our struggles with other men, obscures the true position of man in the world, and diverts his energies from the pursuit of scientific power, which is the only fight that can bring long-continued well-being to the human race.

Apart from all the utilitarian arguments, the search for a happiness based upon untrue beliefs is neither very noble nor very glorious. There is a stark joy in the unflinching perception of our true place in the world, and a more vivid drama than any that is possible to those who hide behind the enclosing walls of myth. There are "perilous seas" in the world of thought, which can only be sailed by those who are willing to face their own physical powerlessness. And above all, there is liberation from the tyranny of Fear, which blots out the light of day and keeps men grovelling and cruel. No man is liberated from fear who dare not see his place in the world as it is; no man can achieve the greatness of which he is capable until he has allowed himself to see his own littleness.

Is Science Superstitious?

Modern life is built on science in two respects. On the one hand, we all depend upon scientific inventions and discoveries for our daily bread and for our comforts and amusements. On the other hand, certain habits of mind, connected with a scientific outlook, have spread gradually during the past three centuries from a few men of genius to large sections of the population. These two operations of science are bound up together when we consider sufficiently long periods, but either might exist without the other for several centuries. Until near the end of the eighteenth century the scientific habit of mind did not greatly affect daily life, since it had not led to the great inventions that revolutionized industrial technique. On the other hand, the manner of life produced by science can be taken over by populations which have only certain practical rudiments of scientific knowledge; such populations can make and utilize machines invented elsewhere, and can even make minor improvements in them. If the collective intelligence of mankind were to degenerate, the kind of technique and daily life which science has produced would nevertheless survive, in all probability, for many generations. But it would not survive forever, because, if seriously disturbed by a cataclysm, it could not be reconstructed.

The scientific outlook, therefore, is a matter of importance to mankind, either for good or evil. But the scientific outlook itself is twofold, like the artistic outlook. The creator and the appreciator are different people and require quite different habits of mind. The scientific creator, like every other, is apt to be inspired by passions to which he gives an intellectualist expression amounting to an undemonstrated faith, without which he would probably achieve little. The appreciator does not need this kind of faith; he can see things in proportion and make necessary reservations, and may regard the creator as a crude and barbaric person in comparison with himself. As civilization becomes more diffused and more traditional, there is a tendency for the habits of mind of the appreciator to conquer those who might be creators, with the result that the civilization in question becomes Byzantine and retrospective. Something of this sort seems to be beginning to happen in science. The simple faith which upheld the pioneers is decaying at the center. Outlying nations, such as the Russians, the Japanese, and the Young Chinese, still welcome science with seventeenth-century fervor; so do the bulk of the populations of Western nations. But the high priests begin to weary of the worship to which they are officially dedicated. The pious young Luther reverenced a free-thinking Pope, who allowed oxen to be sacrificed to Jupiter on the Capitol to promote his recovery from illness. So in our day those remote from centers of culture have a reverence for science which its augurs no longer feel. The "scientific" materialism of the Bolsheviks, like early German Protestantism, is an attempt to preserve the old piety in a form which both friends and foes believe to be new. But their fiery belief in the verbal inspiration of Newton has only accelerated the spread of scientific scepticism among the "bourgeois"

scientists of the West. Science, as an activity recognized and encouraged by the State, has become politically conservative, except where, as in Tennessee, the State has remained pre-scientific. The fundamental faith of most men of science in the present day is in the importance of preserving the *status quo*. Consequently they are very willing to claim for science no more than its due, and to concede much of the claims of other conservative forces, such as religion.

They are faced, however, with a great difficulty. While the men of science are in the main conservative, science is still the chief agent of rapid change in the world. The emotions produced by the change in Asia, in Africa, and among the industrial populations of Europe are often displeasing to those who have a conservative outlook. Hence arises a hesitation as to the value of science which has contributed to the scepticism of the High Priests. If it stood alone, it might be unimportant. But it is reinforced by genuine intellectual difficulties which, if they prove insuperable, are likely to bring the era of scientific discovery to a close. I do not mean that this will happen suddenly. Russia and Asia may continue for another century to entertain the scientific faith which the West is losing. But sooner or later, if the logical case against this faith is irrefutable, it will convince men who, for whatever reason, may be momentarily weary; and, once convinced, they will find it impossible to recapture the old glad confidence. The case against the scientific *credo* deserves, therefore, to be examined with all care.

When I speak of the scientific *credo*, I am not speaking merely of what is logically implied in the view that, in the main, science is true; I am speaking of something more enthusiastic and less rational—namely, the system of beliefs and emotions which lead a man to become a great scientific discoverer. The question is: Can such beliefs and emotions survive among men who have the intellectual powers without which scientific discovery is impossible?

Two very interesting recent books will help us to see the nature of the problem. The books I mean are: Burtt's *Metaphysical Foundations of Modern Science* (1924) and Whitehead's *Science and the Modern World* (1926). Each of these criticizes the system of ideas which the modern world owes to Copernicus, Kepler, Galileo, and Newton—the former almost wholly from an historical standpoint, the latter both historically and logically. Dr. Whitehead's book is the more important, because it is not merely critical, but constructive, and aims at supplying an intellectually satisfying basis for future science, which is to be at the same time emotionally satisfying to the extra-scientific aspirations of mankind. I cannot accept the logical arguments advanced by Dr. Whitehead in favor of what may be called the pleasant parts of his theory: while admitting the need of an intellectual reconstruction of scientific concepts, I incline to the view that the new concepts will be just as disagreeable to our non-intellectual emotions as the old ones, and will therefore be accepted only by those who have a strong emotional bias in favor of science. But let us see what the argument is.

There is, to begin with, the historical aspect. "There can be no living science," says Dr. Whitehead, "unless there is a widespread instinctive conviction in the existence of an *order of things,* and, in particular, of an *order of Nature.*" Science could only have been created by men who already had this belief, and therefore the original sources of the belief must have been pre-scientific. Other elements also went to make up the complex mentality required for the rise of science. The Greek view of life, he maintains, was predominantly dramatic, and

therefore tended to emphasize the end rather than the beginning: this was a drawback from the point of view of science. On the other hand, Greek tragedy contributed the idea of Fate, which facilitated the view that events are rendered necessary by natural laws. "Fate in Greek Tragedy becomes the order of Nature in modern thought." The necessitarian view was reinforced by Roman law. The Roman Government, unlike the Oriental despot, acted (in theory at least) not arbitrarily, but in accordance with rules previously laid down. Similarly, Christianity conceived God as acting in accordance with laws, though they were laws which God Himself had made. All this facilitated the rise of the conception of Natural Law, which is one essential ingredient in scientific mentality.

The non-scientific beliefs which inspired the work of sixteenth- and seventeenth-century pioneers are admirably set forth by Dr. Burtt, with the aid of many little-known original sources. It appears, for example, that Kepler's inspiration was, in part, a sort of Zoroastrian sun-worship which he adopted at a critical period of his youth. "It was primarily by such considerations as the deification of the sun and its proper placing at the center of the universe that Kepler in the years of his adolescent fervor and warm imagination was induced to accept the new system." Throughout the Renaissance there is a certain hostility to Christianity, based primarily upon admiration for Pagan antiquity; it did not dare to express itself openly as a rule, but led, for example, to a revival of astrology, which the Church condemned as involving physical determinism. The revolt against Christianity was associated with superstition quite as much as with science—sometimes, as in Kepler's case, with both in intimate union.

But there is another ingredient, equally essential, but absent in the Middle Ages, and not common in antiquity—namely, an interest in "irreducible and stubborn facts." Curiosity about facts is found before the Renaissance in individuals—for example, the Emperor Frederick II and Roger Bacon; but at the Renaissance it suddenly becomes common among intelligent people. In Montaigne one finds it without the interest in Natural Law; consequently Montaigne was not a man of science. A peculiar blend of general and particular interests is involved in the pursuit of science; the particular is studied in the hope that it may throw light upon the general. In the Middle Ages it was thought that, theoretically, the particular could be deduced from general principles; in the Renaissance these general principles fell into disrepute, and the passion for historical antiquity produced a strong interest in particular occurrences. This interest, operating upon minds trained by the Greek, Roman, and scholastic traditions, produced at last the mental atmosphere which made Kepler and Galileo possible. But naturally something of this atmosphere surrounds their work, and has traveled with it down to their present-day successors. "Science has never shaken off its origin in the historical revolt of the later Renaissance. It has remained predominantly an anti-rationalistic movement, based upon a naïve faith. What reasoning it has wanted has been borrowed from mathematics, which is a surviving relic of Greek rationalism, following the deductive method. Science repudiates philosophy. In other words, it has never cared to justify its faith or to explain its meaning, and has remained blandly indifferent to its refutation by Hume."

Can science survive when we separate it from the superstitions which nourished its infancy? The indifference of science to philosophy has been due, of course, to its amazing success; it has increased the sense of human power, and has therefore

been on the whole agreeable, in spite of its occasional conflicts with theological orthodoxy. But in quite recent times science has been driven by its own problems to take an interest in philosophy. This is especially true of the theory of relativity, with its merging of space and time into the single space-time order of events. But it is true also of the theory of quanta, with its apparent need of discontinuous motion. Also, in another sphere, physiology and bio-chemistry are making inroads on psychology which threaten philosophy in a vital spot; Dr. Watson's Behaviorism is the spear-head of this attack, which, while it involves the opposite of respect for philosophic tradition, nevertheless necessarily rests upon a new philosophy of its own. For such reasons science and philosophy can no longer preserve an armed neutrality, but must be either friends or foes. They cannot be friends unless science can pass the examination which philosophy must set as to its premises. If they cannot be friends, they can only destroy each other; it is no longer possible that either alone can remain master of the field.

Dr. Whitehead offers two things, with a view to the philosophical justification of science. On the one hand, he presents certain new concepts, by means of which the physics of relativity and quanta can be built up in a way which is more satisfying intellectually than any that results from piecemeal amendments to the old conception of solid matter. This part of his work, though not yet developed with the fullness that we may hope to see, lies within science as broadly conceived, and is capable of justification by the usual methods which lead us to prefer one theoretical interpretation of a set of facts to another. It is technically difficult, and I shall say no more about it. From our present point of view, the important aspect of Dr. Whitehead's work is its more philosophical portion. He not only offers us a better science, but a philosophy which is to make that science rational, in a sense in which traditional science has not been rational since the time of Hume. This philosophy is, in the main, very similar to that of Bergson. The difficulty which I feel here is that, in so far as Dr. Whitehead's new concepts can be embodied in formulae which can be submitted to the ordinary scientific or logical tests, they do not seem to involve his philosophy; his philosophy, therefore, must be accepted on its intrinsic merits. We must not accept it merely on the ground that, if true, it justifies science, for the question at issue is whether science can be justified. We must examine directly whether it seems to us to be true in fact; and here we find ourselves beset with all the old perplexities.

I will take only one point, but it is a crucial one. Bergson, as everyone knows, regards the past as surviving in memory, and also holds that nothing is ever really forgotten; on these points it would seem that Dr. Whitehead agrees with him. Now this is all very well as a poetic way of speaking, but it cannot (I should have thought) be accepted as a scientifically accurate way of stating the facts. If I recollect some past event—say my arrival in China—it is a mere figure of speech to say that I am arriving in China over again. Certain words or images occur when I recollect, and are related to what I am recollecting, both causally and by a certain similarity, often little more than a similarity of logical structure. The scientific problem of the relation of a recollection to a past event remains intact, even if we choose to say that the recollection consists of a survival of the past event. For, if we say this, we must nevertheless admit that the event has changed in the interval, and we shall be faced with the scientific problem of finding the laws according to which it changes. Whether we call the recollection a new event or

the old event greatly changed can make no difference to the scientific problem.

The great scandals in the philosophy of science ever since the time of Hume have been causality and induction. We all believe in both, but Hume made it appear that our belief is a blind faith for which no rational ground can be assigned. Dr. Whitehead believes that his philosophy affords an answer to Hume. So did Kant. I find myself unable to accept either answer. And yet, in common with everyone else, I cannot help believing that there must be an answer. This state of affairs is profoundly unsatisfactory, and becomes more so as science becomes more entangled with philosophy. We must hope that an answer will be found; but I am quite unable to believe that it has been found.

Science as it exists at present is partly agreeable, partly disagreeable. It is agreeable through the power which it gives us of manipulating our environment, and to a small but important minority it is agreeable because it affords intellectual satisfactions. It is disagreeable because, however we may seek to disguise the fact, it assumes a determinism which involves, theoretically, the power of predicting human actions; in this respect it seems to lessen human power. Naturally people wish to keep the pleasant aspect of science without the unpleasant aspect; but so far the attempts to do so have broken down. If we emphasize the fact that our belief is causality and induction is irrational, we must infer that we do not know science to be true, and that it may at any moment cease to give us the control over the environment for the sake of which we like it. This alternative, however, is purely theoretical; it is not one which a modern man can adopt in practice. If, on the other hand, we admit the claims of scientific method, we cannot avoid the conclusion that causality and induction are applicable to human volitions as much as to anything else. All that has happened during the twentieth century in physics, physiology, and psychology goes to strengthen this conclusion. The outcome seems to be that, though the rational justification of science is theoretically inadequate, there is no method of securing what is pleasant in science without what is unpleasant. We can do so, of course, by refusing to face the logic of the situation; but, if so, we shall dry up the impulse to scientific discovery at its source, which is the desire to understand the world. It is to be hoped that the future will offer some more satisfactory solution of this tangled problem.

Can Men Be Rational?

I am in the habit of thinking of myself as a Rationalist; and a Rationalist, I suppose, must be one who wishes men to be rational. But in these days rationality has received many hard knocks, so that it is difficult to know what one means by it, or whether, if that were known, it is something which human beings can achieve. The question of the definition of rationality has two sides, theoretical and practical: what is a rational opinion? and what is rational conduct? Pragmatism emphasizes the irrationality of opinion, and psycho-analysis emphasizes the irrationality of conduct. Both have led many people to the view that there is no such thing as an ideal of rationality to which opinion and conduct might with advantage conform. It would seem to follow that, if you and I hold different opinions, it is useless to appeal to argument, or to seek the arbitrament of an impartial outsider; there is nothing for us to do but to fight it out, by the methods of rhetoric, advertisement, or warfare, according to the degree of our financial and military

strength. I believe such an outlook to be very dangerous, and, in the long run, fatal to civilization. I shall, therefore, endeavor to show that the ideal of rationality remains unaffected by the ideas that have been thought fatal to it, and that it retains all the importance it was formerly believed to have as a guide to thought and life.

To begin with rationality in opinion: I should define it merely as the habit of taking account of all relevant evidence in arriving at a belief. Where certainty is unattainable, a rational man will give most weight to the most probable opinion, while retaining others, which have an appreciable probability, in his mind as hypotheses which subsequent evidence may show to be preferable. This, of course, assumes that it is possible in many cases to ascertain facts and probabilities by an objective method—i.e., a method which will lead any two careful people to the same result. This is often questioned. It is said by many that the only function of intellect is to facilitate the satisfaction of the individual's desires and needs. The Plebs Text-Books Committee, in their *Outline of Psychology* (p. 68), say: *"The intellect is above all things an instrument of partiality. Its function is to secure that those actions which are beneficial to the individual or the species shall be performed,* and that those actions which are less beneficial shall be inhibited."* (Italics in the original.)

But the same authors, in the same book (p. 123), state, again in italics: *"The faith of the Marxian differs profoundly from religious faith; the latter is based only on desire and tradition; the former is grounded on the scientific analysis of objective reality."* This seems inconsistent with what they say about the intellect, unless, indeed, they mean to suggest that it is not intellect which has led them to adopt the Marxian faith. In any case, since they admit that "scientific analysis of objective reality" is possible, they must admit that it is possible to have opinions which are rational in an objective sense.

More erudite authors who advocate an irrationalist point of view, such as the pragmatist philosophers, are not to be caught out so easily. They maintain that there is no such thing as objective fact to which our opinions must conform if they are to be true. For them opinions are merely weapons in the struggle for existence, and those which help a man to survive are to be called "true." This view was prevalent in Japan in the sixth century A.D., when Buddhism first reached that country. The Government, being in doubt as to the truth of the new religion, ordered one of the courtiers to adopt it experimentally; if he prospered more than the others, the religion was to be adopted universally. This is the method (with modifications to suit modern times) which the pragmatists advocate in regard to all religious controversies; and yet I have not heard of any who have announced their conversion to the Jewish faith, although it seems to lead to prosperity more rapidly than any other.

In spite of the pragmatist's definition of "truth," however, he has always, in ordinary life, a quite different standard for the less refined questions which arise in practical affairs. A pragmatist on a jury in a murder case will weigh the evidence exactly as any other man will, whereas if he adopted his professed criterion he ought to consider whom among the population it would be most profitable to hang. That man would be, by definition, guilty of the murder, since belief in his guilt would be more useful, and therefore more "true," than belief in the guilt of anyone else. I am afraid such practical pragmatism does sometimes occur; I have heard of "frame-ups" in America and Russia which answered this

description. But in such cases all possible efforts after concealment are made, and if they fail there is a scandal. This effort after concealment shows that even policemen believe in objective truth in the case of a criminal trial. It is this kind of objective truth—a very mundane and pedestrian affair—that is sought in science. It is this kind also that is sought in religion so long as people hope to find it. It is only when people have given up the hope of proving that religion is true in a straight-forward sense that they set to work to prove that it is "true" in some new-fangled sense. It may be laid down broadly that irrationalism, i.e. disbelief in objective fact, arises almost always from the desire to assert something for which there is no evidence, or to deny something for which there is very good evidence. But the belief in objective fact always persists as regards particular practical questions, such as investments or engaging servants. And if fact can be made the test of the truth of our beliefs anywhere, it should be the test everywhere, leading to agnosticism wherever it cannot be applied.

The above considerations are, of course, very inadequate to their theme. The question of the objectivity of fact has been rendered difficult by the obfuscations of philosophers, with which I have attempted to deal elsewhere in a more thoroughgoing fashion. For the present I shall assume that there are facts, that some facts can be known, and that in regard to certain others a degree of probability can be ascertained in relation to facts which can be known. Our beliefs are, however, often contrary to fact; even when we only hold that something is probable on the evidence, it may be that we ought to hold it to be improbable on the same evidence. The theoretical part of rationality, then, will consist in basing our beliefs as regards matters of fact upon evidence rather than upon wishes, prejudices, or traditions. According to the subject-matter, a rational man will be the same as one who is judicial or one who is scientific.

There are some who think that psychoanalysis has shown the impossibility of being rational in our beliefs, by pointing out the strange and almost lunatic origin of many people's cherished convictions. I have a very high respect for psychoanalysis, and I believe that it can be enormously useful. But the popular mind has somewhat lost sight of the purpose which has mainly inspired Freud and his followers. Their method is primarily one of therapeutics, a way of curing hysteria and various kinds of insanity. During the war psycho-analysis proved to be far the most potent treatment for war-neuroses. Rivers's *Instinct and the Unconscious,* which is largely based upon experience of "shell-shock" patients, gives a beautiful analysis of the morbid effects of fear when it cannot be straightforwardly indulged. These effects, of course, are largely nonintellectual; they include various kinds of paralysis, and all sorts of apparently physical ailments. With these, for the moment, we are not concerned; it is intellectual derangements that form our theme. It is found that many of the delusions of lunatics result from instinctive obstructions, and can be cured by purely mental means—i.e. by making the patient bring to mind facts of which he had repressed the memory. This kind of treatment, and the outlook which inspires it, pre-suppose an ideal of sanity, from which the patient has departed, and to which he is to be brought back by making him conscious of all the relevant facts, including those which he most wishes to forget. This is the exact opposite of that lazy acquiescence in irrationality which is sometimes urged by those who only know that psycho-analysis has shown the prevalence of irrational beliefs, and who forget or ignore that its

purpose is to diminish this prevalence by a definite method of medical treatment. A closely similar method can cure the irrationalities of those who are not recognized lunatics, provided they will submit to treatment by a practitioner free from their delusions. Presidents, Cabinet Ministers, and Eminent Persons, however, seldom fulfil this condition, and therefore remain uncured.

So far, we have been considering only the theoretical side of rationality. The practical side, to which we must now turn our attention, is more difficult. Differences of opinion on practical questions spring from two sources: first, differences between the desires of the disputants; secondly, differences in their estimates of the means for realizing their desires. Differences of the second kind are really theoretical, and only derivatively practical. For example, some authorities hold that our first line of defense should consist of battleships, others that it should consist of aeroplanes. Here there is no difference as regards the end proposed, namely, national defense, but only as to the means. The argument can therefore be conducted in a purely scientific manner, since the disagreement which causes the dispute is only as to facts, present or future, certain or probable. To all such cases the kind of rationality which I called theoretical applies, in spite of the fact that a practical issue is involved.

There is, however, in many cases which appear to come under this head a complication which is very important in practice. A man who desires to act in a certain way will persuade himself that by so acting he will achieve some end which he considers good, even when, if he had no such desire, he would see no reason for such a belief. And he will judge quite differently as to matters of fact and as to probabilities from the way in which a man with contrary desires will judge.

Gamblers, as everyone knows, are full of irrational beliefs as to systems which *must* lead them to win in the long run. People who take an interest in politics persuade themselves that the leaders of their party would never be guilty of the knavish tricks practiced by opposing politicians. Men who like administration think that it is good for the populace to be treated like a herd of sheep, men who like tobacco say that it soothes the nerves, and men who like alcohol say that it stimulates wit. The bias produced by such causes falsifies men's judgments as to facts in a way which is very hard to avoid. Even a learned scientific article about the effects of alcohol on the nervous system will generally betray by internal evidence whether the author is or is not a teetotaller; in either case he has a tendency to see the facts in the way that would justify his own practice. In politics and religion such considerations become very important. Most men think that in framing their political opinions they are actuated by desire for the public good; but nine times out of ten a man's politics can be predicted from the way in which he makes his living. This has led some people to maintain, and many more to believe practically, that in such matters it is impossible to be objective, and that no method is possible except a tug-of-war between classes with opposite bias.

It is just in such matters, however, that psycho-analysis is particularly useful, since it enables man to become aware of a bias which has hitherto been unconscious. It gives a technique for seeing ourselves as others see us, and a reason for supposing that this view of ourselves is less unjust than we are inclined to think. Combined with a training in the scientific outlook, this method could, if it were widely taught, enable people to be infinitely more rational than they are at present as regards all their beliefs about matters of fact, and about the probable effect of any proposed action. And if men did not disagree about such matters, the disagreements which might survive would almost certainly be found capable of amicable adjustment.

There remains, however, a residuum which cannot be treated by purely intellectual methods. The desires of one man do not by any means harmonize completely with those of another. Two competitors on the Stock Exchange might be in complete agreement as to what would be the effect of this or that action, but this would not produce practical harmony, since each wishes to grow rich at the expense of the other. Yet even here rationality is capable of preventing most of the harm that might otherwise occur. We call a man irrational when he acts in a passion, when he cuts off his nose to spite his face. He is irrational because he forgets that, by indulging the desire which he happens to feel most strongly at the moment, he will thwart other desires which in the long run are more important to him. If men were rational, they would take a more correct view of their own interest than they do at present; and if all men acted from enlightened self-interest the world would be a paradise in comparison with what it is. I do not maintain that there is nothing better than self-interest as a motive to action; but I do maintain that self-interest, like altruism, is better when it is enlightened than when it is unenlightened. In an ordered community it is very rarely to a man's interest to do anything which is very harmful to others. The less rational a man is, the oftener he will fail to perceive how what injures others also injures him, because hatred or envy will blind him. Therefore, although I do not pretend that enlightened self-interest is the highest morality, I do maintain that, if it became common, it would make the world an immeasurably better place than it is.

Rationality in practice may be defined

as the habit of remembering all our relevant desires, and not only the one which happens at the moment to be strongest. Like rationality in opinion, it is a matter of degree. Complete rationality is no doubt an unattainable ideal, but so long as we continue to classify some men as lunatics it is clear that we think some men more rational than others. I believe that all solid progress in the world consists of an increase in rationality, both practical and theoretical. To preach an altruistic morality appears to me somewhat useless, because it will appeal only to those who already have altruistic desires. But to preach rationality is somewhat different, since rationality helps us to realize our own desires on the whole, whatever they may be. A man is rational in proportion as his intelligence informs and controls his desires. I believe that the control of our acts by our intelligence is ultimately what is of most importance, and what alone will make social life remain possible as science increases the means at our disposal for injuring each other. Education, the press, politics, religion—in a word, all the great forces in the world—are at present on the side of irrationality; they are in the hands of men who flatter King Demos in order to lead him astray. The remedy does not lie in anything heroically cataclysmic, but in the efforts of individuals towards a more sane and balanced view of our relations to our neighbors and to the world. It is to intelligence, increasingly wide-spread, that we must look for the solution of the ills from which our world is suffering.

Philosophy in the Twentieth Century

Ever since the end of the Middle Ages philosophy has steadily declined in social and political importance. William of Ockham, one of the greatest of mediaeval philosophers, was hired by the Kaiser to write pamphlets against the Pope; in those days many burning questions were bound up with disputes in the schools. The advances of philosophy in the seventeenth century were more or less connected with political opposition to the Catholic Church; Malebranche, it is true, was a priest, but priests are not now allowed to accept his philosophy. The disciples of Locke in eighteenth-century France, and the Benthamites in nineteenth-century England, were for the most part extreme Radicals in politics, and created the modern bourgeois liberal outlook. But the correlation between philosophical and political opinions grows less definite as we advance. Hume was a Tory in politics, though an extreme Radical in philosophy. Only in Russia, which remained mediaeval till the Revolution, has any clear connection of philosophy and politics survived. Bolsheviks are materialists, while Whites are idealists. In Tibet the connection is even closer; the second official in the State is called the "metaphysician in chief." Elsewhere philosophy is no longer held in such high esteem.

Academic philosophy, throughout the twentieth century, has been mainly divided into three groups. The first consists of the adherents of the classical German philosophy, usually Kant, but sometimes Hegel. The second consists of the pragmatists and Bergson. The third consists of those who attach themselves to the sciences, believing that philosophy has no special brand of truth and no peculiar method of arriving at it; these men, for convenience, may be called realists, though in fact there are many among them to whom this name is not strictly applicable. The distinction between the different schools is not sharp, and individuals belong partly to one, partly to another. William James may be regarded as almost the founder of both realism and pragmatism. Dr. Whitehead's recent books employ the methods of realists in defense of a more or less Bergsonian metaphysic. Many philosophers, not without a considerable show of reason, regard Einstein's doctrines as affording a scientific basis for Kant's belief in the subjectivity of time and space. The distinctions in fact are thus less clear than the distinctions in logic. Nevertheless the distinctions in logic are useful as affording a framework for the classification of opinions.

German idealism, throughout the twentieth century, has been on the defensive. The new books that have been recognized as important by others than professors have represented newer schools, and a person who judged by book reviews might imagine that these schools had now the upper hand. But in fact most teachers of philosophy, in Germany, France, and Great Britain, though perhaps not America, still adhere to the classical tradition. It is certainly much easier for a young man to get a post if he belongs to this party than if he does not. Its opponents made an attempt to show that it shared the wickedness of everything German, and was in some way responsible for the invasion of Belgium.[1] But its adherents were too eminent and respectable for this line of attack to be successful. Two of them, Émile Boutroux and Bernard Bosanquet, were until their deaths the official spokesmen of French and British philosophy respectively at international congresses. Religion and conservatism look mainly to this school for defense against heresy and revolution. They have the strength and weakness of those who stand for the *status quo:* the strength that comes of tradition, and the weakness that comes of lack of fresh thought.

_____
[1] See e.g. Santayana's *Egotism in German Philosophy.*

In the English-speaking world, this position was only acquired just before the beginning of the twentieth century. I began the serious study of philosophy in the year 1893, the year which saw the publication of Mr. Bradley's *Appearance and Reality.* Mr. Bradley was one of those who had had to fight to win proper recognition of German philosophy in England, and his attitude was very far from that of one who defends a traditional orthodoxy. To me, as to most of my contemporaries, his *Logic* and his *Appearance and Reality* made a profound appeal. I still regard these books with the greatest respect, though I have long ceased to agree with their doctrines.

The outlook of Hegelianism is characterized by the belief that logic alone can tell us a great deal about the real world. Mr. Bradley shares this belief; he contends that the world as it seems to be is self-contradictory, and therefore illusory, while the real world, since it must be logically self-consistent, is bound to have certain characteristics of a surprising kind. It cannot be in time and space, it cannot contain a variety of interrelated things, it cannot contain separate selves, or even that degree of division between subject and object which is involved in knowing. It consists therefore of a single Absolute, timelessly engaged in something more analogous to feeling than to thinking or willing. Our sublunary world is all illusion, and what seems to happen in it does not really matter. This doctrine ought to destroy morality, but morality is temperamental and defies logic. Hegelians in fact urge as their basic moral principle that we ought to behave as if the Hegelian philosophy were true; but they do not notice that if it were true it would not matter how we behave.

The attack upon this philosophy came from two sides. On the one side were the logicians, who pointed to fallacies in

Hegel, and contended that relations and plurality, space and time, are in fact not self-contradictory. On the other side were those who disliked the regimentation and orderliness involved in a world created by logic; of these the chief were William James and Bergson. The two lines of attack were not logically inconsistent, except in some of their accidental manifestations, but they were temperamentally different, and were inspired by different kinds of knowledge. Moreover their appeal was quite different; the appeal of the one was academic, that of the other was human. The academic appeal argued that Hegelianism was false: the human appeal argued that it was disagreeable. Naturally the latter had more popular success.

In the English-speaking world, the greatest influence in the overthrow of German idealism was William James— not as he appears in his *Psychology,* but as he came to be known through the series of small books which were published in the last years of his life and after his death. In an article published in *Mind* so long ago as 1884, reprinted in the posthumous volume *Essays in Radical Empiricism,* he sets out his temperamental bias with extraordinary charm:—

Since we are in the main not sceptics, we might go on and frankly confess to each other the motives for our several faiths. I frankly confess mine—I cannot but think that at bottom they are of an aesthetic and not of a logical sort. The "through-and-through" universe seems to suffocate me with its infallible impeccable all-pervasiveness. Its necessity, with no possibilities; its relations, with no subjects, make me feel as if I had entered into a contract with no reserved rights, or rather as if I had to live in a large seaside boarding-house with no private

bedroom in which I might take refuge from the society of the place. I am distinctly aware, moreover, that the old quarrel of sinner and pharisee has something to do with the matter. Certainly, to my personal knowledge, all Hegelians are not prigs, but I somehow feel as if all prigs ought to end, if developed, by becoming Hegelians. There is a story of two clergymen asked by mistake to conduct the same funeral. One came first and had got no further than "I am the Resurrection and the Life" when the other entered. *"I* am the Resurrection and the Life," cried the latter. The "through-and-through" philosophy, as it actually exists, reminds many of us of that clergyman. It seems too buttoned-up and white-chokered and clean-shaven a thing to speak for the vast slow-breathing unconscious Kosmos with its dread abysses and its unknown tides.

I think it may be wagered that no one except William James has ever lived who would have thought of comparing Hegelianism to a seaside boarding-house. In 1884 this article had no effect, because Hegelianism was still on the upgrade, and philosophers had not learned to admit that their temperaments had anything to do with their opinions. In 1912 (the date of the reprint) the atmosphere had changed through many causes—among others the influence of William James upon his pupils. I cannot claim to have known him more than superficially except from his writings, but it seems to me that one may distinguish three strands in his nature, all of which contributed to form his outlook. Last in time but first in its philosophical manifestations was the influence of his training in physiology and medicine, which gave him a scientific and slightly materialistic bias as compared to purely literary philosophers who derived their inspiration from Plato, Aristotle, and Hegel. This strand dominates his *Psychology* except in a few crucial passages, such as his discussion of free will. The second element in his philosophical make-up was a mystical and religious bias inherited from his father and shared with his brother. This inspired the *Will to Believe* and his interest in psychical research. Thirdly, there was an attempt, made with all the earnestness of a New England conscience, to exterminate the natural fastidiousness which he also shared with his brother, and replace it by democratic sentiment à la Walt Whitman. The fastidiousness is visible in the above quotation, where he expresses horror of a boarding-house with no private bedroom (which Whitman would have loved). The wish to be democratic is visible in the claim that he is a sinner, not a pharisee. Certainly he was not a pharisee, but he probably committed as few sins as any man who ever lived. On this point he fell short of his usual modesty.

The best people usually owe their excellence to a combination of qualities which might have been supposed incompatible, and so it was in the case of James, whose importance was greater than was thought by most of his contemporaries. He advocated pragmatism as a method of presenting religious hopes as scientific hypotheses, and he adopted the revolutionary view that there is no such thing as "consciousness," as a way of overcoming the opposition between mind and matter without giving predominance to either. In these two parts of his philosophy he had different allies: Schiller and Bergson as regards the former, the new realists as regards the latter. Only Dewey, among eminent men, was with him on both issues. The two parts have different histories and affiliations, and must be considered separately.

James's *Will to Believe* dates from 1897; his *Pragmatism* from 1907. Schiller's *Humanism* and Dewey's *Studies in Logical Theory* both date from 1903. Throughout the early years of the twentieth century the philosophical world was excited about pragmatism; then Bergson outbid it in appealing to the same tastes. The three founders of pragmatism differ greatly *inter se;* we may distinguish James, Schiller, and Dewey as respectively its religious, literary, and scientific protagonists—for, though James was many-sided, it was chiefly his religious side which found an outlet in pragmatism. But let us ignore these differences and try to present the doctrine as a unity.

The basis of the doctrine is a certain kind of scepticism. Traditional philosophy professed to be able to prove the fundamental doctrines of religion; its opponents professed to be able to disprove them, or at least, like Spencer, to prove that they could not be proved. It seemed, however, that if they could not be proved, they also could not be disproved. And this appeared to be the case with many doctrines which such men as Spencer regarded as unshakable: causality, the reign of law, the general trustworthiness of memory, the validity of induction, and so on. All these, from a purely rational point of view, should be embraced in the agnostic's suspense of judgment, since, so far as we can see, they are radically incapable of proof or disproof. James argued that, as practical men, we cannot remain in doubt on these issues if we are to survive. We must assume, for instance, that the sort of food which has nourished us in the past will not poison us in the future. Sometimes we are mistaken, and die. The test of a belief is not conformity with "fact," since we can never reach the facts concerned; the test is its success in promoting life and the achievement of our desires. From this point of view, as James tried to show in *The Varieties of Religious Experience,* religious beliefs often pass the test, and are therefore to be called "true." It is in no other sense—so he contends—that the most accredited theories of science can be called "true": they work in practice, and that is all we know about it.

As applied to the general hypotheses of science and religion, there is a great deal to be said for this view. Given a careful definition of what is meant by "working," and a proviso that the cases concerned are those where we do not really know the truth, there is no need to quarrel with the doctrine in this region. But let us take humbler examples, where real truth is not so hard to obtain. Suppose you see a flash of lightning, you may expect to hear thunder, or you may judge that the flash was too distant for the thunder to be audible, or you may not think about the matter at all. This last is usually the most sensible course, but let us suppose that you adopt one of the other two. When you hear the thunder, your belief is verified or refused, not by any advantage or disadvantage it has brought you, but by a "fact," the sensation of hearing thunder. Pragmatists attend mainly to beliefs which are incapable of being verified by any facts that come within our experience. Most of our everyday beliefs about mundane affairs—e.g. that so-and-so's address is such-and-such—are capable of verification within our experience, and in these cases the pragmatist's criterion is unnecessary. In many cases, like the above instance of the thunder, it is quite inapplicable, since the true belief has no practical advantage over the false one, and neither is as advantageous as thinking about something else. It is a common defect of philosophers to like "grand" examples rather than such as come from ordinary daily life.

Although pragmatism may not contain ultimate philosophical truth, it has certain important merits. First, it realizes that the truth that *we* can attain to is merely human truth, fallible and changeable like everything human. What lies outside the cycle of human occurrences is not truth, but fact (of certain kinds). Truth is a property of beliefs, and beliefs are psychical events. Moreover their relation to facts does not have the schematic simplicity which logic assumes; to have pointed this out is a second merit in pragmatism. Beliefs are vague and complex, pointing not to one precise fact, but to several vague regions of fact. Beliefs, therefore, unlike the schematic propositions of logic, are not sharply opposed as true or false, but are a blur of truth and falsehood; they are of varying shades of gray, never white or black. People who speak with reverence to the "Truth" would do better to speak about Fact, and to realize that the reverend qualities to which they pay homage are not to be found in human beliefs. There are practical as well as theoretical advantages in this, since people persecute each other because they believe that they know the "Truth." Speaking psycho-analytically, it may be laid down that any "great ideal" which people mention with awe is really an excuse for inflicting pain on their enemies. Good wine needs no bush, and good morals need no bated breath.

In practice, however, pragmatism has a more sinister side. The truth, it says, is what pays in the way of beliefs. Now a belief may be made to pay through the operation of the criminal law. In the seventeenth century, Catholicism paid in Catholic countries and Protestantism in Protestant countries. Energetic people can manufacture "truth" by getting hold of the Government and persecuting opinions other than their own. These consequences flow from an exaggeration into which pragmatism has fallen. Granted that, as pragmatists point out, truth is a matter of degree, and is a property of purely human occurrences, namely beliefs, it still does not follow that the degree of truth possessed by a belief depends upon purely human conditions. In increasing the degree of truth in our beliefs, we are approximating to an ideal, and the ideal is determined by Fact, which is only within our control to a certain very limited extent, as regards some of the minor circumstances on or near the surface of a certain planet. The theory of the pragmatist is derived from the practice of the advertiser, who, by saying repeatedly that his pills are worth a guinea a box, makes people willing to give sixpence a box for them, and thus makes his assertion more nearly true than if it had been made with less confidence. Such instances of man-made truth are interesting, but their scope is very limited. By exaggerating their scope, people become involved in an orgy of propaganda, which is ultimately brought to an abrupt end by hard facts in the shape of war, pestilence, and famine. The recent history of Europe is an object-lesson of the falsehood of pragmatism in this form.

It is a curious thing that Bergson should have been hailed as an ally by the pragmatists, since, on the face of it, his philosophy is the exact antithesis to theirs. While pragmatists teach that utility is the test of truth, Bergson teaches, on the contrary, that our intellect, having been fashioned by practical needs, ignores all the aspects of the world which it does not pay to notice, and is in fact an obstacle to the apprehension of truth. We have, he thinks, a faculty called "intuition" which we can use if we take the trouble, and which will enable us to know, in theory at least, everything past and present, though apparently not the future. But since it would be inconvenient to be troubled with so much knowledge, we have developed a brain, the function of which is to forget. But for the brain, we should remember everything; owing to its sieve-like operations, we usually remember only what is useful, and that all wrong. Utility, for Bergson, is the source of error, while truth is arrived at by a mystic contemplation from which all thought of practical advantage is absent. Nevertheless Bergson, like the pragmatists, prefers action to reason, Othello to Hamlet; he thinks it better to kill Desdemona by intuition than to let the King live because of intellect. It is this that makes pragmatists regard him as an ally.

Bergson's *Données Immédiates de la Conscience* was published in 1889, and his *Matière et Mémoire* in 1896. But his great reputation began with *L'Evolution Créatrice*, published in 1907—not that this book was better than the others, but that it contained less argument and more rhetoric, so that it had more persuasive effect. This book contains, from beginning to end, no argument, and therefore no bad argument; it contains merely a poetical picture appealing to the fancy. There is nothing in it to help us to a conclusion as to whether the philosophy which it advocates is true or false; this question, which might be thought not unimportant, Bergson has left to others. But according to his own theories he is right in this, since truth is to be attained by intuition, not by intellect, and is therefore not a matter of argument.

A great part of Bergson's philosophy is merely traditional mysticism expressed in slightly novel language. The doctrine of interpenetration, according to which different things are not really separate, but are merely so conceived by the analytic intellect, is to be found in every mystic, eastern or western, from Parmenides to Mr. Bradley. Bergson has given an air of novelty to this doctrine by means of two devices. First, he connects "intuition" with the instincts of animals;

he suggests that intuition is what enables the solitary wasp Ammophila to sting the larva in which it lays its eggs exactly so as to paralyze it without killing it. (The instance is unfortunate, since Dr. and Mrs. Peckham have shown that this poor wasp is no more unerring than a mere man of science with his blundering intellect.) This gives a flavor of modern science to his doctrines, and enables him to adduce zoological instances which make the unwary think that his views are based upon the latest results of biological research. Secondly, he gives the name "space" to the separateness of things as they appear to the analytic intellect, and the name "time" or "duration" to their interpenetration as revealed to intuition. This enables him to say many new things about "space" and "time," which sound very profound and original when they are supposed to be about what is ordinarily meant by those words. "Matter," being that which is in "space," is of course a fiction created by the intellect, and is seen to be such as soon as we place ourselves at the point of view of intuition.

In this part of his philosophy, apart from phraseology, Bergson has added nothing to Plotinus. The invention of the phraseology certainly shows great ability, but it is that of the company-promoter rather than the philosopher. It is not this part of his philosophy, however, which has won him his wide popularity. He owes that to his doctrine of the *élan vital* and real becoming. His great and remarkable innovation is to have combined mysticism with a belief in the reality of time and progress. It is worth while to see how he achieved this feat.

Traditional mysticism has been contemplative, convinced of the unreality of time, and essentially a lazy man's philosophy. The psychological prelude to the mystic illumination is the "dark night of the soul," which arises when a man is hopelessly balked in his practical activi-

ties, or for some reason suddenly loses interest in them. Activity being thus ruled out, he takes to contemplation. It is law of our being that, whenever it is in any way possible, we adopt such beliefs as will preserve our self-respect. Psychoanalytic literature is full of grotesque examples of this law. Accordingly the man who has been driven to contemplation presently discovers that contemplation is the true end of life, and that the real world is hidden from those who are immersed in mundane activities. From this basis the remaining doctrines of traditional mysticism can be deduced. Lao-Tze, perhaps the first of the great mystics, wrote his book (so tradition avers) at a custom-house while he was waiting to have his baggage examined;[1] and, as might be expected, it is full of the doctrine that action is futile.

But Bergson sought to adapt mysticism to those who believe in activity and "life," who believe in the reality of progress and are in no way disillusioned about our existence here below. The mystic is usually a temperamentally active man forced into inaction; the vitalist is a temperamentally inactive man with a romantic admiration for action. Before 1914 the world was full of such people, "Heartbreak House" people. Their temperamental basis is boredom and scepticism, leading to love of excitement and longing for an irrational faith—a faith which they found ultimately in the belief that it was their duty to make other people kill each other. But in 1907 they had not this outlet, and Bergson provided a good substitute.

Bergson's view is sometimes expressed in language which might mislead, because things which he regards as illusory are occasionally mentioned in a way which suggests that they are real. But

_____

[1] The chief argument against this tradition is that the book is not very long.

when we avoid these possibilities of mis-understanding, I think his doctrine of time is as follows. Time is not a series of separate moments or events, but a con-tinuous growth, in which the future can-not be foreseen because it is genuinely new and therefore unimaginable. Every-thing that really happens persists, like the successive rings in the growth of a tree. (This is not his illustration.) Thus the world is perpetually growing fuller and richer. Everything that has happened persists in the pure memory of intuition, as opposed to the pseudo-memory of the brain. This persistence is "duration," while the impulse to new creation is the *"élan vital."* To recover the pure memory of intuition is a matter of self-discipline. We are not told how to do it, but one suspects something not unlike the prac-tices of Yogis.

If one might venture to apply to Berg-son's philosophy so vulgar a thing as logic, certain difficulties would appear in this philosophy of change. Bergson is never tired of pouring scorn upon the mathematician for regarding time as a series, whose parts are mutually external. But if there is indeed genuine novelty in the world, as he insists (and without this feature his philosophy loses its attractive qualities), and if whatever really comes into the world persists (which is the simple essence of his doctrine of dura-tion), then the sum-total of existence at any earlier time is part of the sum-total at any later time. Total states of the world at various times form a series in virtue of this relation of whole and part, and this series has all the properties that the mathematician wants and that Berg-son professes to have banished. If the new elements which are added in later states of the world are not external to the old elements, there is no genuine novelty, creative evolution has created nothing, and we are back in the system of Plotinus. Of course Bergson's answer to

this dilemma is that what happens is "growth," in which everything changes and yet remains the same. This concep-tion, however, is a mystery, which the profane cannot hope to fathom. At bot-tom, Bergson's appeal is to mystical faith, not to reason; but into the regions where faith is above logic we cannot follow him.

Meanwhile, from many directions, a philosophy grew up which is often de-scribed as "realism," but is really char-acterized by analysis as a method and pluralism as a metaphysic. It is not necessarily realistic, since it is, in some forms, compatible with Berkleian ideal-ism. It is not compatible with Kantian or Hegelian idealism, because it rejects the logic upon which those systems are based. It tends more and more to the adoption and development of James's view, that the fundamental stuff of the world is neither mental nor material, but something simpler and more funda-mental, out of which both mind and matter are constructed.

In the nineties, James was almost the only eminent figure, except among the very old, that stood out against German idealism. Schiller and Dewey had not yet begun to make themselves felt, and even James was regarded as a psychologist who need not be taken very seriously in philosophy. But with the year 1900 a revolt against German idealism began, not from a pragmatist point of view, but from a severely technical standpoint. In Germany, apart from the admirable works of Frege (which begin in 1879, but were not read until recent years), Husserl's *Logische Untersuchungen,* a monumental work published in 1900, soon began to exert a great effect. Meinong's *Ueber Annahmen* (1902) and *Gegenstandstheorie und Psychologie* (1904) were influential in the same direction. In England, G. E. Moore and I began to advocate similar views. His article on *The Nature of Judgment* was published in 1899; his *Principia Ethica* in 1903. My *Philosophy of Leibniz* appeared in 1900, and *Principles of Mathematics* in 1903. In France, the same kind of philosophy was vigorously championed by Couturat. In America, William James's radical empiricism (without his pragmatism) was blended with the new logic to produce a radically new philosophy, that of the *New Realists,* somewhat later in date, but more revolutionary, than the European works mentioned above, although Mach's *Analyse der Empfindungen* had anticipated part of its teaching.

The new philosophy which was thus inaugurated has not yet reached a final form, and is still in some respects immature. Moreover, there is a very considerable measure of disagreement among its various advocates. It is in parts somewhat abstruse. For these reasons, it is impossible to do more than set forth some of its salient features.

The first characteristic of the new philosophy is that it abandons the claim to a special philosophic method or a peculiar brand of knowledge to be obtained by its means. It regards philosophy as essentially one with science, differing from the special sciences merely by the generality of its problems, and by the fact that it is concerned with the formation of hypotheses where empirical evidence is still lacking. It conceives that all knowledge is scientific knowledge, to be ascertained and proved by the methods of science. It does not aim, as previous philosophy has usually done, at statements about the universe as a whole, nor at the construction of a comprehensive system. It believes, on the basis of its logic, that there is no reason to deny the apparently piecemeal and higgledy-piggledy nature of the world. It does not regard the world as "organic," in the sense that, from any part adequately understood, the whole

could be inferred as the skeleton of an extinct monster can be inferred from a single bone. In particular, it does not attempt, as German idealism did, to deduce the nature of the world as a whole from the nature of knowledge. It regards knowledge as a natural fact like another, with no mystic significance and no cosmic importance.

The new philosophy had originally three main sources: theory of knowledge, logic, and the principles of mathematics. Ever since Kant, knowledge had been conceived as an interaction, in which the thing known was modified by our knowledge of it, and therefore always had certain characteristics due to our knowledge. It was also held (though not by Kant) to be logically impossible for a thing to exist without being known. Therefore the properties acquired through being known were properties which everything must have. In this way, it was contended, we can discover a great deal about the real world by merely studying the conditions of knowledge. The new philosophy maintained, on the contrary, that knowledge, as a rule, makes no difference to what is known, and that there is not the slightest reason why there should not be things which are not known to any mind. Consequently theory of knowledge ceases to be a magic key to open the door to the mysteries of the universe, and we are thrown back upon the plodding investigations of science.

In logic, similarly, atomism replaced the "organic" view. It had been maintained that everything is affected in its intrinsic nature by its relations to everything else, so that a thorough knowledge of one thing would involve a thorough knowledge of the whole universe. The new logic maintained that the intrinsic character of a thing does not logically enable us to deduce its relations to other things. An example will make the point clear. Leibniz maintains somewhere (and in this he agrees with modern idealists) that if a man is in Europe and his wife dies in India, there is an intrinsic change in the man at the moment of his wife's death. Common sense would say that there is no intrinsic change in the man until he hears of his bereavement. This view is adopted by the new philosophy; its consequences are more far-reaching than they might appear to be at first sight.

The principles of mathematics have always had an important relation to philosophy. Mathematics apparently contains *a priori* knowledge of a high degree of certainty, and most philosophy aspires to *a priori* knowledge. Ever since Zeno the Eleatic, philosophers of an idealistic cast have sought to throw discredit on mathematics by manufacturing contradictions which were designed to show that mathematicians had not arrived at real metaphysical truth, and that the philosophers were able to supply a better brand. There is a great deal of this in Kant, and still more in Hegel. During the nineteenth century, the mathematicians destroyed this part of Kant's philosophy. Lobatchevski, by inventing non-Euclidean geometry, undermined the mathematical argument of Kant's transcendental aesthetic. Weierstrass proved that continuity does not involve infinitesimals; Georg Cantor invented a theory of continuity and a theory of infinity which did away with all the old paradoxes upon which philosophers had battened. Frege showed that arithmetic follows from logic, which Kant had denied. All these results were obtained by ordinary mathematical methods, and were as indubitable as the multiplication table. Philosophers met the situation by not reading the authors concerned. Only the new philosophy assimilated the new results, and thereby won an easy argumentative victory over the partisans of continued ignorance.

The new philosophy is not merely critical. It is constructive, but as science is constructive, bit by bit and tentatively. It has a special technical method of construction, namely, mathematical logic, a new branch of mathematics, much more akin to philosophy than any of the traditional branches. Mathematical logic makes it possible, as it never was before, to see what is the outcome, for philosophy, of a given body of scientific doctrine, what entities must be assumed, and what relations between them. The philosophy of mathematics and physics has made immense advances by the help of this method; part of the outcome for physics has been set forth by Dr. Whitehead in three recent works.[1] There is reason to hope that the method will prove equally fruitful in other fields, but it is too technical to be set forth here.

A good deal of modern pluralist philosophy has been inspired by the logical analysis of propositions. At first this method was applied with too much respect for grammar; Meinong, for example, maintained that, since we can say truly "the round square does not exist," there must be such an object as the round square, although it must be a nonexistent object. The present writer was at first not exempt from this kind of reasoning, but discovered in 1905 how to escape from it by means of the theory of "descriptions," from which it appears that the round square is not mentioned when we say "the round square does not exist." It may seem absurd to spend time on such a ridiculous topic as the round square, but such topics often afford the

---

[1] *The Principles of Natural Knowledge,* 1919; *The Concept of Nature,* 1920; *The Principle of Relativity,* 1922. All published by the Cambridge University Press.

best tests of logical theories. Most logical theories are condemned by the fact that they lead to absurdities; therefore the logician must be aware of absurdities and on the lookout for them. Many laboratory experiments would seem trivial to anyone who did not know their relevance, and absurdities are the experiments of the logician.

From preoccupation with the logical analysis of propositions, the new philosophy had at first a strong tincture of Platonic and medieval realism; it regarded abstracts as having the same kind of existence that concretes have. From this view, as its logic perfected itself, it became gradually more free. What remains is not such as to shock common sense.

Although pure mathematics was more concerned than any other science in the first beginnings of the new philosophy, the most important influence in the present day is physics. This has come about chiefly through the work of Einstein, which has fundamentally altered our notions of space, time, and matter. This is not the place for an explanation of the theory of relativity, but a few words on some of its philosophical consequences are unavoidable.

Two specially important items in the theory of relativity, from the philosophical point of view, are: (1) that there is not a single all-embracing time in which all the events in the universe have their place; (2) that the conventional or subjective part in our observation of physical phenomena, though much greater than was formerly supposed, can be eliminated by means of a certain mathematical method known as the tensor calculus. I shall say nothing on this latter topic, as it is intolerably technical.

As regards time, it must be understood, to begin with, that we are not dealing with a philosophical speculation, but with a theory necessitated by experimental results and embodied in mathematical formulae. There is the same sort of difference between the two as there is between the theories of Montesquieu and the American Constitution. What emerges is this: that while the events that happen to a given piece of matter have a definite time-order from the point of view of an observer who shares its motion, events which happen to pieces of matter in different places have not always a definite time-order. To be precise: if a light-signal is sent from the earth to the sun, and reflected back to the earth, it will return to the earth about sixteen minutes after it was sent out. The events which happen on the earth during those sixteen minutes are neither earlier nor later than the arrival of the light-signal at the sun. If we imagine observers moving in all possible ways with respect to the earth and the sun, observing the events on the earth during those sixteen minutes, and also the arrival of the light-signal at the sun; if we assume that all these observers allow for the velocity of light and employ perfectly accurate chronometers; then some of these observers will judge any given event on earth during those sixteen minutes to be earlier than the arrival of the light-signal at the sun, some will judge it to be simultaneous, and some will judge it to be later. All are equally right or equally wrong. From the impersonal standpoint of physics, the events on earth during those sixteen minutes are neither earlier nor later than the arrival of the light-signal at the sun, nor yet simultaneous with it. We cannot say that an event A in one piece of matter is definitely earlier than an event B in another unless light can travel from A to B, starting when the earlier event happens (according to A's time), and arriving before the later event happens (according to B's time). Otherwise the apparent time-order of the two events will vary according to the observer, and will therefore not represent any physical fact.

If velocities comparable with that of light were common in our experience, it is probable that the physical world would have seemed too complicated to be tackled by scientific methods, so that we should have been content with medicine-men down to the present day. But if physics *had* been discovered, it would have had to be the physics of Einstein, because Newtonian physics would have been obviously inapplicable. Radio-active substances send out particles which move very nearly with the velocity of light, and the behavior of these particles would be unintelligible without the new physics of relativity. There is no doubt that the old physics is faulty, and from a philosophical point of view it is no excuse to say that the fault is "only a little one." We have to make up our minds to the fact that, within certain limits, there is no definite time-order between events which happen in different places. This is the fact which has led to the introduction of the single manifold called "space-time" instead of the two separate manifolds called "space" and "time." The time that we have been regarding as cosmic is really "local time," a time bound up with the motion of the earth with as little claim to universality as that of a ship which does not alter its clocks in crossing the Atlantic.

When we consider the part that time plays in all our common notions, it becomes evident that our outlook would be profoundly changed if we really imaginatively realized what the physicists have done. Take the notion of "progress": if the time-order is arbitrary, there will be progress or retrogression according to the convention adopted in measuring time. The notion of distance in space is of course also affected: two observers who employ every possible device for ensuring accuracy will arrive at different estimates of the distance between two places, if the observers are in rapid relative motion. It is obvious that the very idea of distance has become vague, because distance must be between material things, not points of empty space (which are fictions); and it must be the distance at a given time, because the distance between any two bodies is continually changing; and a given time is a subjective notion, dependent upon the way the observer is traveling. We can no longer speak of a body at a given time, but must speak simply of an event. Between two events there is, quite independently of any observer, a certain relation called the "interval" between them. This interval will be differently analyzed by different observers into a spatial and a temporal component, but this analysis has no objective validity. The interval is an objective physical fact, but its separation into spatial and temporal elements is not.

It is obvious that our old comfortable notion of "solid matter" cannot survive. A piece of matter is nothing but a series of events obeying certain laws. The conception of matter arose at a time when philosophers had no doubts as to the validity of the conception of "substance." Matter was substance which was in space and time, mind was substance which was in time only. The notion of substance grew more shadowy in metaphysics as time went on, but it survived in physics because it did no harm—until relativity was invented. Substance, traditionally, was a notion compounded of two elements. First, a substance had the logical property that it could only occur as subject in a proposition, not as predicate. Secondly, it was something that persisted through time, or, in the case of God, was outside time altogether. These two properties had no necessary connection, but this was not perceived because physics taught that bits of matter are immortal and theology taught that the soul is immortal. Both, therefore, were thought to have both the characteristics of substance. Now, however, physics compels us to regard evanescent events as substances in the logical sense, i.e. as subjects which cannot be predicates. A piece of matter which we took to be a single persistent entity, is really a string of entities, like the apparently persistent objects in a cinema. And there is no reason why we should not say the same of a mind: the persistent ego seems as fictitious as the permanent atom. Both are only strings of events having certain interesting relations to each other.

Modern physics enables us to give body to the suggestion of Mach and James, that the "stuff" of the mental and physical worlds is the same. "Solid matter" was obviously very different from thoughts and also from the persistent ego. But if matter and the ego are both only convenient aggregations of events, it is much less difficult to imagine them composed out of the same materials. Moreover, what has hitherto seemed one of the most marked peculiarities of mind, namely subjectivity, or the possession of a point of view, has now invaded physics, and is found not to involve mind: photographic cameras in different places may photograph the "same" event, but they will photograph it differently. Even chronometers and measuring-rods become subjective in modern physics; what they directly record is not a physical fact, but their relation to a physical fact. Thus physics and psychology have approached each other, and the old dualism of mind and matter has broken down.

It is perhaps worth while to point out that modern physics knows nothing of

"force" in the old or popular sense of that word. We used to think that the sun exerted a "force" on the earth. Now we think that space-time, in the neighborhood of the sun, is so shaped that the earth finds it less trouble to move as it does than in any other way. The great principle of modern physics is the "principle of least action," that in going from one place to another a body always chooses the route which involves least action. (Action is a technical term, but its meaning need not concern us at present.) Newspapers and certain writers who wish to be thought forceful are fond of the word "dynamic." There is nothing "dynamic" in dynamics, which, on the contrary, finds everything deducible from a law of universal laziness. And there is no such thing as one body "controlling" the movements of another. The universe of modern science is much more like that of Lao-Tze than that of those who prate of "great laws" and "natural forces."

The modern philosophy of pluralism and realism has, in some ways, less to offer than earlier philosophies. In the Middle Ages, philosophy was the handmaid of theology; to this day, they come under one heading in booksellers' catalogues. It has been generally regarded as the business of philosophy to prove the great truths of religion. The new realism does not profess to be able to prove them, or even to disprove them. It aims only at clarifying the fundamental ideas of the sciences, and synthesizing the different sciences in a single comprehensive view of that fragment of the world that science has succeeded in exploring. It does not know what lies beyond; it possesses no talisman for transforming ignorance into knowledge. It offers intellectual delights to those who value them, but it does not attempt to flatter human conceit as most philosophies do. If it is dry and technical, it lays the blame on the universe, which has chosen to work in a mathematical way rather than as poets or mystics might have desired. Perhaps this is regrettable, but a mathematician can hardly be expected to regret it.

Machines and the Emotions

Will machines destroy emotions, or will emotions destroy machines? This question was suggested long ago by Samuel Butler in *Erewhon,* but it is growing more and more actual as the empire of machinery is enlarged.

At first sight, it is not obvious why there should be any opposition between machines and emotions. Every normal boy loves machines; the bigger and more powerful they are, the more he loves them. Nations which have a long tradition of artistic excellence, like the Japanese, are captivated by Western mechanical methods as soon as they come across them, and long only to imitate us as quickly as possible. Nothing annoys an educated and traveled Asiatic so much as to hear praise of "the wisdom of the East" or the traditional virtues of Asiatic civilization. He feels as a boy would feel who was told to play with dolls instead of toy automobiles. And like a boy, he would prefer a real automobile to a toy one, not realizing that it may run over him.

In the West, when machinery was new, there was the same delight in it, except on the part of a few poets and aesthetes. The nineteenth century considered itself superior to its predecessors chiefly because of its mechanical progress. Peacock, in its early years, makes fun of the "steam intellect society" because he is a literary man, to whom the Greek and Latin authors represent civilization; but he is conscious of being out of touch with the prevailing tendencies of

his time. Rousseau's disciples with the return to Nature, the Lake Poets with their medievalism, William Morris with his *News from Nowhere* (a country where it is always June and everybody is engaged in haymaking), all represent a purely sentimental and essentially reactionary opposition to machinery. Samuel Butler was the first man to apprehend intellectually the non-sentimental case against machines, but in him it may have been no more than a *jeu d'esprit*—certainly it was not a deeply held conviction. Since his day numbers of people in the most mechanized nations have been tending to adopt in earnest a view similar to that of the Erewhonians; this view, that is to say, has been latent or explicit in the attitude of many rebels against existing industrial methods.

Machines are worshiped because they are beautiful, and valued because they confer power; they are hated because they are hideous, and loathed because they impose slavery. Do not let us suppose that one of these attitudes is "right" and the other "wrong," any more than it would be right to maintain that men have heads but wrong to maintain that they have feet, though we can easily imagine Lilliputians disputing this question concerning Gulliver. A machine is like a Djinn in the Arabian Nights: beautiful and beneficent to its master, but hideous and terrible to his enemies. But in our day nothing is allowed to show itself with such naked simplicity. The master of the machine, it is true, lives at a distance from it, where he cannot hear its noise or see its unsightly heaps of slag or smell its noxious fumes; if he ever sees it, the occasion is before it is installed in use, when he can admire its force or its delicate precision without being troubled by dust and heat. But when he is challenged to consider the machine from the point of view of those who have to live with it and work it, he has a ready answer. He can point out that, owing to its operations, these men can purchase more goods—often vastly more—than their great-grandfathers could. It follows that they must be happier than their great-grandfathers—if we are to accept an assumption which is made by almost everyone.

The assumption is, that the possession of material commodities is what makes men happy. It is thought that a man who has two rooms and two beds and two loaves must be twice as happy as a man who has one room and one bed and one loaf. In a word, it is thought that happiness is proportional to income. A few people, not always quite sincerely, challenge this idea in the name of religion or morality; but they are glad if they increase their income by the eloquence of their preaching. It is not from a moral or religious point of view that I wish to challenge it; it is from the point of view of psychology and observation of life. If happiness is proportional to income, the case for machinery is unanswerable; if not the whole question remains to be examined.

Men have physical needs, and they have emotions. While physical needs are unsatisfied, they take first place; but when they are satisfied, emotions unconnected with them become important in deciding whether a man is to be happy or unhappy. In modern industrial communities there are many men, women, and children whose bare physical needs are not adequately supplied; as regards them, I do not deny that the first requisite for happiness is an increase of income. But they are a minority, and it would not be difficult to give the bare necessaries of life to all of them. It is not of them that I wish to speak, but of those who have more than is necessary to support existence—not only those who have much more, but also those who have only a little more.

Why do we, in fact, almost all of us, desire to increase our incomes? It may seem, at first sight, as though material goods were what we desire. But, in fact, we desire these mainly in order to impress our neighbors. When a man moves into a larger house in a more genteel quarter, he reflects that "better" people will call on his wife, and some unprosperous cronies of former days can be dropped. When he sends his son to a good school or an expensive university, he consoles himself for the heavy fees by thoughts of the social kudos to be gained. In every big city, whether of Europe or of America, houses in some districts are more expensive than equally good houses in other districts, merely because they are more fashionable. One of the most powerful of all our passions is the desire to be admired and respected. As things stand, admiration and respect are given to the man who seems to be rich. This is the chief reason why people wish to be rich. The actual goods purchased by their money play quite a secondary part. Take, for example, a millionaire who cannot tell one picture from another, but has acquired a gallery of old masters by the help of experts. The only pleasure he derives from his pictures is the thought that others know how much they have cost; he would derive more direct enjoyment from sentimental chromos out of Christmas numbers, but he would not obtain the same satisfaction for his vanity.

All this might be different, and has been different in many societies. In aristocratic epochs, men have been admired for their birth. In some circles in Paris, men are admired for their artistic or literary excellence, strange as it may seem. In a German university, a man may actually be admired for his learning. In India saints are admired; in China, sages. The study of these differing societies shows the correctness of our analysis, for in all of them we find a large percentage of men who are indifferent to money so long as they have enough to keep alive on, but are keenly desirous of the merits by which, in their environment, respect is to be won.

The importance of these facts lies in this, that the modern desire for wealth is not inherent in human nature, and could be destroyed by different social institutions. If, by law, we all had exactly the same income, we should have to seek some other way of being superior to our neighbors, and most of our present craving for material possessions would cease. Moreover, since this craving is in the nature of a competition, it only brings happiness when we outdistance a rival, to whom it brings correlative pain. A general increase of wealth gives no competitive advantage, and therefore brings no competitive happiness. There is, of course, *some* pleasure derived from the actual enjoyment of goods purchased, but, as we have seen, this is a very small part of what makes us desire wealth. And in so far as our desire is competitive, no increase of human happiness as a whole comes from increase of wealth, whether general or particular.

If we are to argue that machinery increases happiness, therefore, the increase of material prosperity which it brings cannot weigh very heavily in its favor, except in so far as it may be used to prevent absolute destitution. But there is no inherent reason why it should be so used. Destitution can be prevented without machinery where the population is stationary; of this France may serve as an example, since there is very little destitution and much less machinery than in America, England, or pre-war Germany. Conversely, there may be much destitution where there is much machinery; of this we have examples in the industrial areas of England a hundred years ago and of Japan at the present day. The pre-

vention of destitution does not depend upon machines, but upon quite other factors—partly density of population, and partly political conditions. And apart from prevention of destitution, the value of increasing wealth is not very great.

Meanwhile, machines deprive us of two things which are certainly important ingredients of human happiness, namely, spontaneity and variety. Machines have their own pace, and their own insistent demands: a man who has an expensive plant must keep it working. The great trouble with the machine, from the point of view of the emotions, is its *regularity*. And, of course, conversely, the great objection to the emotions, from the point of view of the machine, is their *irregularity*. As the machine dominates the thoughts of people who consider themselves "serious," the highest praise they can give to a man is to suggest that he has the qualities of a machine—that he is reliable, punctual, exact, etc. And an "irregular" life has come to be synonymous with a bad life. Against this point of view Bergson's philosophy was a protest—not, to my mind, wholly sound from an intellectual point of view, but inspired by a wholesome dread of seeing men turned more and more into machines.

In life, as opposed to thought, the rebellion of our instincts against enslavement to mechanism has hitherto taken a most unfortunate direction. The impulse to war has always existed since men took to living in societies, but it did not, in the past have the same intensity or virulence as it has in our day. In the eighteenth century, England and France had innumerable wars, and contended for the hegemony of the world; but they liked and respected each other the whole time. Officer prisoners joined in the social life of their captors, and were honored guests at their dinner-parties. At the beginning of our war with Holland in 1665, a man came home from Africa with atrocity stories about the Dutch there; we [the British] persuaded ourselves that his story was false, punished him, and published the Dutch denial. In the late war we should have knighted him, and imprisoned anyone who threw doubt on his veracity. The greater ferocity of modern war is attributable to machines, which operate in three different ways. First, they make it possible to have larger armies. Secondly, they facilitate a cheap Press, which flourishes by appealing to men's baser passions. Thirdly—and this is the point that concerns us—they starve the anarchic, spontaneous side of human nature, which works underground, producing an obscure discontent, to which the thought of war appeals as affording possible relief. It is a mistake to attribute a vast upheaval like the late war merely to the machinations of politicians. In Russia, perhaps, such an explanation would have been adequate; that is one reason why Russia fought half-heartedly, and made a revolution to secure peace. But in England, Germany, and the United States (in 1917), no Government could have withstood the popular demand for war. A popular demand of this sort must have an instinctive basis, and for my part I believe that the modern increase in warlike instinct is attributable to the dissatisfaction (mostly unconscious) caused by the regularity, monotony, and tameness of modern life.

It is obvious that we cannot deal with this situation by abolishing machinery. Such a measure would be reactionary, and is in any case impracticable. The only way of avoiding the evils at present associated with machinery is to provide breaks in the monotony, with every encouragement to high adventure during the intervals. Many men would cease to desire war if they had opportunities to risk their lives in Alpine climbing; one of the ablest and most vigorous workers for peace that it has been my good fortune to

know habitually spent his summer climbing the most dangerous peaks in the Alps. If every working man had a month in the year during which, if he chose, he could be taught to work an aeroplane, or encouraged to hunt for sapphires in the Sahara, or otherwise enabled to engage in some dangerous and exciting pursuit involving quick personal initiative, the popular love of war would become confined to women and invalids. I confess I know no method of making these classes pacific, but I am convinced that a scientific psychology would find a method if it undertook the task in earnest.

Machines have altered our way of life, but not our instincts. Consequently there is maladjustment. The whole psychology of the emotions and instincts is as yet in its infancy; a beginning has been made by psycho-analysis, but only a beginning. What we may accept from psycho-analysis is the fact that people will, in action, pursue various ends which they do not *consciously* desire, and will have an attendant set of quite irrational beliefs which enable them to pursue these ends without knowing that they are doing so. But orthodox psycho-analysis has unduly simplified our unconscious purposes, which are numerous, and differ from one person to another. It is to be hoped that social and political phenomena will soon come to be understood from this point of view, and will thus throw light on average human nature.

Moral self-control, and external prohibition of harmful acts, are not adequate methods of dealing with our anarchic instincts. The reason they are inadequate is that these instincts are capable of as many disguises as the Devil in medieval legend, and some of these disguises deceive even the elect. The only adequate method is to discover what are the needs of our instinctive nature, and then to search for the least harmful way of satisfying them. Since spontaneity is what is most thwarted by machines, the only thing that can be *provided* is opportunity; the use made of opportunity must be left to the initiative of the individual. No doubt considerable expense would be involved; but it would not be comparable to the expense of war. Understanding of human nature must be the basis of any real improvement in human life. Science has done wonders in mastering the laws of the physical world, but our own nature is much less understood, as yet, than the nature of stars and electrons. When science learns to understand human nature, it will be able to bring a happiness into our lives which machines and the physical sciences have failed to create.

The Harm That Good Men Do

A hundred years ago there lived a philosopher named Jeremy Bentham, who was universally recognized to be a very wicked man. I remember to this day the first time that I came across his name when I was a boy. It was in a statement by the Rev. Sydney Smith to the effect that Bentham thought people ought to make soup of their dead grandmothers. This practice appeared to me as undesirable from a culinary as from a moral point of view, and I therefore conceived a bad opinion of Bentham. Long afterwards, I discovered that the statement was one of those reckless lies in which respectable people are wont to indulge in the interests of virtue. I also discovered what was the really serious charge against him. It was no less than this: that he defined a "good" man as a man who does good. This definition, as the reader will perceive at once if he is right-minded, is subversive of all true morality. How much more exalted is the attitude of Kant, who lays it down that a kind action is not virtuous if it springs from affection for the beneficiary, but only if it is inspired by the moral law, which is, of course, just as likely to inspire unkind actions. We know that the exercise of virtue should be its own reward, and it seems to follow that the enduring of it on the part of the patient should be its own punishment. Kant, therefore, is a more sublime moralist than Bentham, and has the suffrages of all those who tell us that they love virtue for its own sake.

It is true that Bentham fulfilled his own definition of a good man: he did much good. The forty middle years of the nineteenth century in England were years of incredibly rapid progress, materially, intellectually, and morally. At the beginning of the period comes the Reform Act, which made Parliament representative of the middle-class, not, as before, of the aristocracy. This Act was the most difficult of the steps towards democracy in England, and was quickly followed by other important reforms, such as the abolition of slavery in Jamaica. At the beginning of the period the penalty for petty theft was death by hanging; very soon the death penalty was confined to those who were guilty of murder or high treason. The Corn Laws, which made food so dear as to cause atrocious poverty, were abolished in 1846. Compulsory education was introduced in 1870. It is the fashion to decry the Victorians, but I wish our age had half as good a record as theirs. This, however, is beside the point. My point is that a very large proportion of the progress during those years must be attributed to the influence of Bentham. There can be no doubt that nine-tenths of the people living in England in the latter part of last century were happier than they would have been if he had never lived. So shallow was his philosophy that he would have regarded this as a vindication of his activities. We, in our more enlightened age, can see that such a view is preposterous; but it may fortify us to review the grounds for rejecting a groveling utilitarianism such as that of Bentham.

II

We all know what we mean by a "good" man. The ideally good man does not drink or smoke, avoids bad language, converses in the presence of men only exactly as he would if there were ladies present, attends church regularly, and holds the correct opinions on all subjects. He has a wholesome horror of wrongdoing, and realizes that it is our painful duty to castigate Sin. He has a still greater horror of wrong thinking, and considers it the business of the authorities to safeguard the young against those who question the wisdom of the views generally accepted by middle-aged successful citizens. Apart from his professional duties, at which he is assiduous, he spends much time in good works: he may encourage patriotism and military training; he may promote industry, sobriety, and virtue among wage-earners and their children by seeing to it that failures in these respects receive due punishment; he may be a trustee of a university and prevent an ill-judged respect for learning from allowing the employment of professors with subversive ideas. Above all, of course, his "morals," in the narrow sense, must be irreproachable.

It may be doubted whether a "good" man, in the above sense, does, on the average, any more good than a "bad" man. I mean by a "bad" man the contrary of what we have been describing. A "bad" man is one who is known to smoke and to drink occasionally, and even to say a bad word when someone treads on his toe. His conversation is not always such as could be printed, and he sometimes spends fine Sundays out-of-doors instead of at church. Some of his opinions are subversive; for instance, he may

think that if you desire peace you should prepare for peace, not for war. Towards wrongdoing he takes a scientific attitude, such as he would take towards his motorcar if it misbehaved; he argues that sermons and prison will no more cure vice than mend a broken tire. In the matter of wrong thinking he is even more perverse. He maintains that what is called "wrong thinking" is simply thinking, and what is called "right thinking" is repeating words like a parrot; this gives him a sympathy with all sorts of undesirable cranks. His activities outside his working hours may consist merely in enjoyment, or, worse still, in stirring up discontent with preventable evils which do not interfere with the comfort of the men in power. And it is even possible that in the matter of "morals" he may not conceal his lapses as carefully as a truly virtuous man would do, defending himself by the perverse contention that it is better to be honest than to pretend to set a good example. A man who fails in any or several of these respects will be thought ill of by the average respectable citizen, and will not be allowed to hold any position conferring authority, such as that of a judge, a magistrate, or a schoolmaster. Such positions are open only to "good" men.

This whole state of affairs is more or less modern. It existed in England during the brief reign of the Puritans in the time of Cromwell, and by them it was transplanted to America. It did not reappear in force in England till after the French Revolution, when it was thought to be a good method of combating Jacobinism (i.e. what we should now call Bolshevism). The life of Wordsworth illustrates the change. In his youth he sympathized with the French Revolution, went to France, wrote good poetry, and had a natural daughter. At this period he was a "bad" man. Then he became "good," abandoned his daughter, adopted correct principles, and wrote bad poetry. Coleridge went through a similar change: when he was wicked he wrote *Kubla Khan,* and when he was good he wrote theology.

It is difficult to think of any instance of a poet who was "good" at the times when he was writing good poetry. Dante was deported for subversive propaganda; Shakespeare, to judge by the Sonnets, would not have been allowed by American immigration officers to land in New York. It is of the essence of a "good" man that he supports the Government; therefore, Milton was good during the reign of Cromwell, and bad before and after; but it was before and after that he wrote his poetry—in fact most of it was written after he had narrowly escaped hanging as a Bolshevik. Donne was virtuous after he became Dean of St. Paul's, but all his poems were written before that time, and on account of them his appointment caused a scandal. Swinburne was wicked in his youth, when he wrote *Songs Before Sunrise* in praise of those who fought for freedom; he was virtuous in his old age, when he wrote savage attacks on the Boers for defending their liberty against wanton aggression. It is needless to multiply examples; enough has been said to suggest that the standards of virtue now prevalent are incompatible with the production of good poetry.

In other directions the same thing is true. We all know that Galileo and Darwin were bad men; Spinoza was thought dreadfully wicked until a hundred years after his death; Descartes went abroad for fear of persecution. Almost all the Renaissance artists were bad men. To come to humbler matters, those who object to preventable mortality are necessarily wicked. I lived in a part of London which is partly very rich, partly very poor; the infant death-rate is abnormally high, and the rich, by corruption and intimidation, control the local government. They use their power to cut down the expenditure on infant welfare and public health and to engage a medical officer at less than the standard rate on condition that he gives only half his time to the work. No one can win the respect of the important local people unless he considers that good dinners for the rich are more important than life for the children of the poor. The corresponding thing is true in every part of the world with which I am acquainted. This suggests that we may simplify our account of what constitutes a good man: a good man is one whose opinions and activities are pleasing to the holders of power.

III

It has been painful to have to dwell upon the bad men who, in the past, have unfortunately achieved eminence. Let us turn to the more agreeable contemplation of the virtuous.

A typically virtuous man was George III. When Pitt wanted him to emancipate the Catholics (who at that time were not allowed to vote), he would not agree, on the ground that to do so would be contrary to his coronation oath. He righteously refused to be misled by the argument that it would do good to emancipate them; the question, for him, was not whether it would do good, but whether it was "right" in the abstract. His interference in politics was largely responsible for the régime which caused America to claim independence; but his interference was always dictated by the most lofty motives. The same may be said of the ex-Kaiser, a deeply religious man, sincerely convinced, until his fall, that God was on his side, and (so far as I know) wholly free from personal vices. Yet it would be hard to name any man of our time who has done more to cause human misery.

Among politicians good men have

their uses, the chief of which is to afford a smoke-screen behind which others can carry on their activities unsuspected. A good man will never suspect his friends of shady actions: this is part of his goodness. A good man will never be suspected by the public of using his goodness to screen villains: this is part of his utility. It is clear that this combination of qualities makes a good man extremely desirable wherever a somewhat narrow-minded public objects to the transference of public funds into the hands of the deserving rich. I am told—though far be it from me to endorse this statement—that at a not very distant period in history there was an American President who was a good man and served this purpose. In England, Whittaker Wright, at the height of his fame, surrounded himself with blameless peers, whose virtue made them incapable of understanding his arithmetic, or of knowing that they did not.

Another of the uses of good men is that any undesirables can be kept out of politics by means of scandals. Ninety-nine out of a hundred commit breaches of the moral law, but in general this fact does not become public. And when in the ninety-ninth case it becomes known in relation to any individual, the one man in the hundred who is genuinely innocent expresses genuine horror, while the other ninety-eight are compelled to follow suit for fear of being suspected. When, therefore, any man of obnoxious opinions ventures into politics, it is only necessary for those who have the preservation of our ancient institutions at heart to keep track of his private activities until they discover something which, if exposed, will ruin his political career. They then have three courses open to them: to make the facts known and cause him to disappear in a cloud of obloquy; or to compel him to retire into private life by threats of exposure; or to derive for themselves a comfortable income by means of blackmail. Of these three courses the first two protect the public, while the third protects those who protect the public. All three, therefore, are to be commended, and all three are only rendered possible through the existence of good men.

Consider, again, such a matter as venereal disease: it is known that this can be almost entirely prevented by suitable precautions taken in advance, but owing to the activities of good men this knowledge is disseminated as little as possible, and all kinds of obstacles are placed in the way of its utilization. Consequently sin still secures its "natural" punishment, and the children are still punished for the sins of the fathers, in accordance with Biblical precept. How dreadful it would be if this were otherwise, for, if sin were no longer punished, there might be people so abandoned as to pretend that it was no longer sin, and if the punishment did not fall also upon the innocent, it would not seem so dreadful. How grateful we ought to be, therefore, to those good men who ensure that the stern laws of retribution decreed by Nature during our days of ignorance can still be made to operate in spite of the impious knowledge rashly acquired by scientists. All right-thinking people know that a bad act is bad quite regardless of the question whether it causes any suffering or not, but since men are not all capable of being guided by the pure moral law, it is highly desirable that suffering should follow from sin in order to secure virtue. Men must be kept in ignorance of all ways of escaping the penalties which were incurred by sinful actions in pre-scientific ages. I shudder when I think how much we should all know about the preservation of mental and physical health if it were not for the protection against this dangerous knowledge which our good men so kindly provide.

Another way in which good men can be useful is by getting themselves murdered. Germany acquired the province of Shantung in China by having the good fortune to have two missionaries murdered there. The Archduke who was murdered at Sarajevo was, I believe, a good man; and how grateful we ought to be to him! If he had not died as he did, we might not have had the war, and then the world would not have been made safe for democracy, nor would militarism have been overthrown, nor should we be now enjoying military despotisms in Spain, Italy, Hungary, Bulgaria, and Russia.

To speak seriously: the standards of "goodness" which are generally recognized by public opinion are not those which are calculated to make the world a happier place. This is due to a variety of causes, of which the chief is tradition, and the next most powerful is the unjust power of dominant classes. Primitive morality seems to have developed out of the notion of taboo; that is to say, it was originally purely superstitious, and forbade certain perfectly harmless acts (such as eating out of the chief's dish) on the supposed ground that they produced disaster by magical means. In this way there came to be prohibitions, which continued to have authority over people's feelings when the supposed reasons for them were forgotten. A considerable part of current morals is still of this sort: certain kinds of conduct produce emotions of horror, quite regardless of the question whether they have bad effects or not. In many cases the conduct which inspires horror is in fact harmful; if this were not the case, the need for a revision of our moral standards would be more generally recognized. Murder, for example, can obviously not be tolerated in a civilized society; yet the origin of the prohibition of murder is purely superstitious. It was thought that the murdered man's blood (or, later, his ghost) demanded vengeance, and might punish not only the guilty man, but any one who showed him kindness. The superstitious character of the prohibition of murder is shown by the fact that it was possible to be purified from blood-guiltiness by certain ritual ceremonies, which were apparently designed, originally, to disguise the murderer so that the ghost would not recognize him. This, at least, is the theory of Sir J. G. Frazer. When we speak of repentance as "washing out" guilt we are using a metaphor derived from the fact that long ago actual washing was used to remove blood-stains. Such notions as "guilt" and "sin" have an emotional background connected with this source in remote antiquity. Even in the case of murder a rational ethic will view the matter differently: it will be concerned with prevention and cure, as in the case of illness, rather than with guilt, punishment, and expiation.

Our current ethic is a curious mixture of superstition and rationalism. Murder is an ancient crime, and we view it through a mist of age-long horror. Forgery is a modern crime, and we view it rationally. We punish forgers, but we do not feel them strange beings set apart, as we do murderers. And we still think in social practice, whatever we may hold in theory, that virtue consists in not doing rather than in doing. The man who abstains from certain acts labeled "sin" is a good man, even though he never does anything to further the welfare of others. This, of course, is not the attitude inculcated in the Gospels: "Love thy neighbor as thyself" is a positive precept. But in all Christian communities the man who obeys this precept is persecuted, suffering at least poverty, usually imprisonment, and sometimes death. The world is full of injustice, and those who profit by injustice are in a position to administer rewards and punishments. The rewards go to those who invent ingenious justifications for inequality, the punishments to those who try to remedy it. I do not know of any country where a man who has a genuine love for his neighbor can long avoid obloquy. In Paris, just before the outbreak of the war, Jean Jaurès, the best citizen of France, was murdered; the murderer was acquitted, on the ground that he had performed a public service. This case was peculiarly dramatic, but the same sort of thing happens everywhere.

Those who defend traditional morality will sometimes admit that it is not perfect, but contend that any criticism will make all morality crumble. This will not be the case if the criticism is based upon something positive and constructive, but only if it is conducted with a view to nothing more than momentary pleasure. To return to Bentham: he advocated, as the basis of morals, "the greatest happiness of the greatest number." A man who acts upon this principle will have a much more arduous life than a man who merely obeys conventional precepts. He will necessarily make himself the champion of the oppressed, and so incur the enmity of the great. He will proclaim facts which the powers that be wish to conceal; he will deny falsehoods designed to alienate sympathy from those who need it. Such a mode of life does not lead to a collapse of genuine morality. Official morality has always been oppressive and negative: it has said "thou shalt not," and has not troubled to investigate the effect of activities not forbidden by the code. Against this kind of morality all the great mystics and religious teachers have protested in vain: their followers ignored their most explicit pronouncements. It seems unlikely, therefore, that any large-scale improvements will come through their methods.

More is to be hoped, I think, from the progress of reason and science. Gradually men will come to realize that a world whose institutions are based upon hatred and injustice is not the one most likely to produce happiness. The late war taught this lesson to a few, and would have taught it to many more if it had ended in a draw. We need a morality based upon love of life, upon pleasure in growth and positive achievement, not upon repression and prohibition. A man should be regarded as "good" if he is happy, expansive, generous, and glad when others are happy; if so, a few peccadilloes should be regarded as of little importance. But a man who acquires a fortune by cruelty and exploitation should be regarded as at present we regard what is called an "immoral" man; and he should be so regarded even if he goes to church regularly and gives a portion of his ill-gotten gains to public objects. To bring this about, it is only necessary to instil a rational attitude towards ethical questions, instead of the mixure of superstition and oppression which still passes muster as "virtue" among important personages. The power of reason is thought small in these days, but I remain an unrepentant rationalist. Reason may be a small force, but it is constant, and works always in one direction, while the forces of unreason destroy one another in futile strife. Therefore every orgy of unreason in the end strengthens the friends of reason, and shows afresh that they are the only true friends of humanity.

The Need for Political Scepticism

One of the peculiarities of the English-speaking world is its immense interest and belief in political parties. A very large percentage of English-speaking people really believe that the ills from which they suffer would be cured if a certain political party were in power. That is a reason for the swing of the pendulum. A man votes for one party and remains miserable; he concludes that it was the other party that was to bring the millennium. By the time he is disenchanted with all parties, he is an old man on the verge of death; his sons retain the belief of his youth, and the seesaw goes on.

I want to suggest that, if we are to do any good in politics, we must view political questions in quite a different way. A party which is to obtain power must, in a democracy, make an appeal to which the majority of the nation responds. For reasons which will appear in the course of the argument, an appeal which is widely successful, with the existing democracy, can hardly fail to be harmful. Therefore no important political party is likely to have a useful program, and if useful measures are to be passed, it must be by means of some other machinery than party government. How to combine any such machinery with democracy is one of the most urgent problems of our time.

There are at present two very different kinds of specialists in political questions. On the one hand there are the practical politicians of all parties; on the other hand there are the experts, mainly civil servants, but also economists, financiers, scientific medical men, etc. Each of these two classes has a special kind of skill. The skill of the politician consists in guessing what people can be brought to *think* advantageous to themselves; the skill of the expert consists in calculating what really *is* advantageous, provided people can be brought to think so. (The proviso is essential, because measures which arouse serious resentment are seldom advantageous, whatever merits they may have otherwise.) The power of the politician, in a democracy, depends upon his adopting the opinions which *seem* right to the average man. It is useless to urge that politicians ought to be high-minded enough to advocate what

enlightened opinion considers good, because if they do they are swept aside for others. Moreover, the intuitive skill that they require in forecasting opinion does not imply any skill whatever in forming their own opinions, so that many of the ablest (from a party-political point of view) will be in a position to advocate, quite honestly, measures which the majority think good, but which experts know to be bad. There is therefore no point in moral exhortations to politicians to be disinterested, except in the crude sense of not taking bribes.

Wherever party politics exist, the appeal of a politician is primarily to a section, while his opponents appeal to an opposite section. His success depends upon turning his section into a majority. A measure which appeals to all sections equally will presumably be common ground between the parties, and will therefore be useless to the party politician. Consequently he concentrates attention upon those measures which are disliked by the section which forms the nucleus of his opponents' supporters. Moreover, a measure, however admirable, is useless to the politician unless he can give reasons for it which will appear convincing to the average man when set forth in a platform speech. We have thus two conditions which must be fulfilled by the measures on which party politicians lay stress: (1) they must seem to favor a section of the nation; (2) the arguments for them must be of the utmost simplicity. Of course this does not apply to a time of war, because then the party conflict is suspended in favor of conflict with the external enemy. In war, the arts of the politician are expended on neutrals, who correspond to the doubtful voter in ordinary politics. The late war showed that, as we should have expected, democracy affords an admirable training for the business of appealing to neutrals. That was one of the main reasons why democracy won the war. It is true it lost the peace; but that is another question.

The special skill of the politician consists in knowing what passions can be most easily aroused, and how to prevent them, when aroused, from being harmful to himself and his associates. There is a Gresham's law in politics as in currency; a man who aims at nobler ends than these will be driven out, except in those rare moments (chiefly revolutions) when idealism finds itself in alliance with some powerful movement of selfish passion. Moreover, since politicians are divided into rival groups, they aim at similarly dividing the nation, unless they have the good fortune to unite it in war against some other nation. They live by "sound and fury, signifying nothing." They cannot pay attention to anything difficult to explain, or to anything not involving division (either between nations or within the nation), or to anything that would diminish the power of politicians as a class.

The expert is a curiously different type. As a rule, he is a man who does not aim at political power. His natural reaction to a political problem is to inquire what would be beneficial rather than what would be popular. In certain directions, he has exceptional technical knowledge. If he is a civil servant or the head of a big business, he has considerable experience of individual men, and may be a shrewd judge as to how they will act. All these are favorable circumstances, which entitle his opinion on his speciality to considerable respect.

He has, however, as a rule, certain correlative defects. His knowledge being specialized, he probably overestimates the importance of his department. If you went successively to a scientific dentist, a scientific oculist, a heart specialist, a lung specialist, a nerve specialist, and so on, they would each give you admirable advice as to how to prevent their particular kind of ailment. If you followed the advice of all, you would find your whole twenty-four hours consumed in preserving your health, and no time left to make any use of your health. The same sort of thing may easily happen with political experts; if all are attended to, there will be no time for the nation to live its ordinary life.

A second defect of the able civil servant results from his having to use the method of persuasion behind the scenes. He will either greatly overestimate the possibility of persuading people to be reasonable, or he will prefer hole-and-corner methods, by which politicians are induced to pass crucial measures without knowing what they are doing. As a rule, he will make the former mistake when he is young and the latter when he is middle-aged.

A third defect of the expert, if regarded as one who is to have executive power, is that he is no judge of popular passions. He usually understands a committee very well, but he seldom understands a mob. Having discovered some measure which all well-informed persons of good will at once see to be desirable, he does not realize that, if it is publicly advocated, certain powerful people who think it will damage themselves can stir up popular feeling to the point where any advocate of the measure in question will be lynched. In America, the magnates, it is said, set detectives on to any man they dislike, and presently, if he is not exceptionally astute, maneuver him into a compromising situation. He must then either change his politics or be denounced throughout the Press as an immoral man. In England, these methods are not yet so well developed, but they probably will be before long. Even where there is nothing sinister, popular passions are often such as to astonish the unwary. Everybody wishes the Government to cut down expenditure in general, but any particular economy is always unpopular, because it throws individuals out of work, and they win sympathy. In China, in the eleventh century, there was a civil servant, Wang An Shih, who, having converted the Emperor, set to work to introduce Socialism. In a rash moment, however, he offended the literati (the Northcliffe Press of that time), was hurled from power, and has been held up to obloquy by every subsequent Chinese historian until modern times.

A fourth defect is connected with this, namely, that experts are apt to undervalue the importance of consent to administrative measures, and to ignore the difficulty of administering an unpopular law. Medical men could, if they had power, devise means which would stamp out infectious diseases, provided their laws were obeyed; but if their laws went much ahead of public opinion, they would be evaded. The ease of administration during the war was due to the fact that people would submit to a great deal in order to win the war, whereas ordinary peace legislation has no object making such a strong appeal.

Hardly any expert allows enough for sheer laziness and indifference. We take some trouble to avoid dangers which are obvious, but very little to avoid those only visible to the expert. We think we like money, and daylight saving saves us many millions a year; yet we never adopted it until we were driven to it as a war-measure. We love our habits more than our income, often more than our life. This seems incredible to a person who has reflected upon the harmfulness of some of our habits.

Probably most experts do not realize that, if they had executive power, their impulses towards tyranny would develop, and they would cease to be the amiable and high-minded men they are at present. Very few people are able to discount the effect of circumstances upon their own characters.

For all these reasons, we cannot escape from the evils of our present politicians by simply handing over the power to civil servants. Nevertheless it seems imperative, in our increasingly complex society, that experts should acquire more influence than they have at present. There is at present a violent conflict between instinctive passions and industrial needs. Our environment, both human and material, has been suddenly changed by industrialism. Our instincts have presumably not changed, and almost nothing has been done to adapt our habits of thought to the altered circumstances. Unwise people who keep beavers in their libraries find that, when wet weather is coming, the beavers build dams out of books, because they used to live on the banks of streams. We are almost equally ill-adapted to our new surroundings. Our education still teaches us to admire the qualities that were biologically useful in the Homeric age, regardless of the fact that they are now harmful and ridiculous. The instinctive appeal of every successful political movement is to envy, rivalry, or hate, never to the need for co-operation. This is inherent in our present political methods, and in conformity with pre-industrial habits. Only a deliberate effort can change men's habits of thought in this respect.

It is a natural propensity to attribute misfortune to someone's malignity. When prices rise, it is due to the profiteer; when wages fall, it is due to the capitalist. Why the capitalist is ineffective when wages rise, and the profiteer when prices fall, the man in the street does not inquire. Nor does he notice that wages and prices rise and fall together. If he is a capitalist, he wants wages to fall and prices to rise; if he is a wage earner, he wants the opposite. When a currency expert tries to explain that profiteers and trade unions and ordinary employers have very little to do with the matter, he irritates everybody, like the man who threw doubt on German atrocities. We do not like to be robbed of an enemy; we want someone to hate when we suffer. It is so depressing to think that we suffer because we are fools; yet, taking mankind in the mass, that is the truth. For this reason, no political party can acquire any driving force except through hatred; it must hold up someone to obloquy. If so-and-so's wickedness is the sole cause of our misery, let us punish so-and-so and we shall be happy. The supreme example of this kind of political thought was the Treaty of Versailles. Yet most people are only seeking some new scapegoat to replace the Germans.

I will illustrate the point by contrasting two books advocating international Socialism, Marx's *Capital* and Salter's *Allied Shipping Control*. (No doubt Sir Arthur Salter does not call himself an international socialist, but he is one none the less.) We may take these two books as representing the politician's and the civil servant's methods, respectively, of advocating economic change. Marx's object was to create a political party which should ultimately overwhelm all others; Salter's object is to influence administrators within the existing system, and to modify public opinion by arguments based upon the general advantage. Marx proves conclusively that under capitalism wage-earners have suffered terrible privations. He does not prove, and does not attempt to prove, that they will suffer less under Communism; that is an assumption implicit in his style and in the ordering of his chapters. Any reader who starts with a proletarian class bias will find himself sharing this assumption as he reads, and will never notice that it is

not proved. Again: Marx emphatically repudiates ethical considerations as having nothing to do with social development, which is supposed to proceed by inexorable economic laws, just as in Ricardo and Malthus. But Ricardo and Malthus thought that the inexorable laws inexorably brought happiness to their class along with misery to wage-earners; while Marx, like Tertullian, had an apocalyptic vision of a future in which his class would enjoy the circuses while the bourgeois would lie howling. Although Marx professed to regard men as neither good nor bad, but merely embodiments of economic forces, he did in fact represent the bourgeois as wicked, and set to work to stimulate a fiery hatred of him in the wage-earner. Marx's *Capital* is in essence, like the Bryce Report, a collection of atrocity stories designed to stimulate martial ardor against the enemy.[1] Very naturally, it also stimulates the martial ardor of the enemy. It thus brings about the class-war which it prophesies. It is through the stimulation of hatred that Marx has proved such a tremendous political force, and through the fact that he has successfully represented capitalists as objects of moral abhorrence.

In Salter's *Allied Shipping Control* we find a diametrically opposite spirit. Salter has the advantage, which Marx had not, of having been for some time concerned in administering a system of international Socialism. This system was brought about, not by the desire to kill capitalists, but by the desire to kill Germans. As, however, the Germans were irrelevant to

---

[1] The theoretical part of *Capital* is analogous to our talk about a "war to end war," a "war for small nations," a "war for democracy," etc. Its sole purpose is to make the reader feel that the hatred stirred up in him is righteous indignation, and may be indulged with benefit to mankind.

economic issues, they are in the background in Salter's book. The economic problem was exactly the same as if the soldiers and munition-workers and those who supplied the raw materials of munitions had been kept in idleness and the remainder of the population had had to do all the work. Or, alternatively, as if it had been suddenly decreed that everybody was to do only half as much work as hitherto. War experience has given us a *technical* solution of this problem, but not a *psychological* solution, because it has not shown how to provide a stimulus to co-operation in peacetime as powerful as hatred and fear of the Germans during the years of war.

Salter says (p. 19):

There is probably no task at this moment which more deserves the attention of professional economists who will approach the problem in a purely scientific spirit, without bias either for or against the principle of State control, than an investigation of the actual results of the war period. The *prima facie* facts with which they would start are indeed so striking as to constitute at least a challenge to the normal economic system. It is true that several factors contributed to the results. . . . An unbiased professional inquiry would assign full weight to these and other factors, but would probably find much still to the credit of the new methods of organization. The success of these methods under the conditions of the war is indeed beyond reasonable dispute. At a moderate estimate, and allowing for the production of persons who were idle before the war, between half and two-thirds of the productive capacity of the country was withdrawn into combatant or other war service. And yet throughout the War Great Britain sustained the whole of her military effort and maintained civilian population at a standard of life which was never intolerably low, and for some periods and for some classes was perhaps as comfortable as in time of peace. She did this without, on balance, drawing any aid from other countries. She imported, on borrowed money, less from America than she supplied, on loaned money, to her Allies. She therefore maintained the whole of the current consumption both of her war effort and her civilian population with a mere remnant of her productive power by means of current production.

Discussing the ordinary commercial system of peace-time, he says:

It was thus of the essence of the peace economic system that it was under no deliberate direction and control. By the exacting criterion of war conditions, however, this system proved to be, at least for those conditions, seriously inadequate and defective. By the new standards it was blind and it was wasteful. It produced too little, it produced the wrong things, and it distributed them to the wrong people. (p. 17)

The system which was gradually built up under the stress of war became, in 1918, in all essentials a complete international Socialism. The Allied Governments jointly were the sole buyer of food and raw material, and the sole judge as to what should be imported, not only into their own countries, but even into those of European neutrals. They controlled production absolutely, because they controlled raw material, and could ration factories as they chose. As regards food they even controlled retail distribution. They fixed prices as well as quantities. Their power was exercised mainly through the Allied Maritime Transport

Council, which, in the end, controlled nearly all the world's available shipping, and was consequently able to dictate the conditions of import and export. The system was thus, in all essentials, one of international Socialism, applied primarily to foreign trade, the very matter which causes the greatest difficulties to political socialists.

The odd thing about this system is that it was introduced without antagonizing the capitalists. It was a necessary feature of wartime politics that at all costs no important section of the population must be antagonized. For instance, at the time of greatest stringency in the shipping position, it was argued that munitions must be cut down rather than food, for fear of discontent in the civilian population. To have alienated the capitalists would have been very dangerous, and in fact the whole transformation was carried out without serious friction. The attitude was not: Such-and-such classes of men are wicked and must be punished. The attitude was: The peace-time system was inefficient, and a new system must be established with a minimum of hardship to all concerned. Under the stress of national danger, consent to measures which the Government considered necessary was not so difficult to obtain as it would be at ordinary times. But even at ordinary times consent would be less difficult if measures were presented from an administrative point of view rather than from that of class-antagonism.

It would appear from the administrative experience of the war that most of the advantages hoped for from Socialism can be obtained by Government control of raw materials, foreign trade, and banking. This point of view has been developed by Lloyd's valuable book on *Stabilization*.[1] It may be taken as a definite advance in the scientific analysis of the

problem, which we owe to the experimentation forced upon civil servants by the war.

One of the most interesting things, from a practical point of view, in Sir Arthur Salter's book is his analysis of the method of international co-operation which was found to work best in practice. It was not the custom for each country separately to consider each question, and then employ diplomatic representatives to secure as much as possible in bargaining with other Powers. The plan adopted was for each question to have its separate international committee of experts, so that the conflicts were not between nations, but between commodities. The wheat commission would fight the coal commission, and so on; but the recommendations of each were the result of deliberation between expert representatives of the different Allies. The position, in fact, was almost one of international syndicalism, except for the paramount authority of the Supreme War Council. The moral is that any successful internationalism must organize separate functions internationally, and not merely have one supreme international body to adjust the claims of conflicting purely national bodies.

Any person reading Salter's book can see at once that such an international government as existed among the Allies during the war would increase the material, mental, and moral welfare of almost the whole population of the globe, if it could be established universally in time of peace. It would not injure business men; indeed, they could easily be promised in perpetuity, as a pension, their average profits for the last three years. It would prevent unemployment, fear of war, destitution, shortage, and over-production. The argument and the method are set forth in Mr. Lloyd's book. Yet, in spite of these obvious and universal advantages, the prospect of

[1] George Allen & Unwin, 1923.

[325]

anything of the sort is, if possible, even more remote than the establishment of universal revolutionary Socialism. The difficulty of revolutionary Socialism is that it rouses too much opposition; the difficulty of the civil servant's Socialism is that it wins too little support. Opposition to a political measure is roused by the fear that oneself will be damaged; support is won by the hope (usually subconscious) that one's enemies will be damaged. Therefore a policy that injures no one wins no support, and a policy that wins much support also rouses fierce opposition.

Industrialism has created a new necessity for world-wide co-operation and a new facility for injuring each other by hostility. But the only kind of appeal that wins any instinctive response in party politics is an appeal to hostile feeling; the men who perceive the need of co-operation are powerless. Until education has been directed for a generation into new channels, and the Press has abandoned incitements to hatred, only harmful policies have any chance of being adopted in practice by our present political methods. But there is no obvious means of altering education and the Press until our political system is altered. From this dilemma there is no issue by means of ordinary action, at any rate for a long time to come. The best that can be hoped, it seems to me, is that we should, as many of us as possible, become political sceptics, rigidly abstaining from belief in the various attractive party programs that are put before us from time to time. Many quite sensible people, from Mr. H. G. Wells downward, believed that the late war was a war to end war. They are now disillusioned. Many quite sensible people believe that the Marxian class war will be a war to end war. If it ever comes, they too will be disillusioned—if any of them survive. A well-intentioned person who believes in any strong political movement

is merely helping to prolong that organized strife which is destroying our civilization. Of course I do not lay this down as an absolute rule: we must be sceptical even of our scepticism. But if a political party has a policy (as most have) which must do much harm on the way to some ultimate good, the call for scepticism is very great, in view of the doubtfulness of all political calculations. We may fairly suspect that, from a psycho-analytic point of view, the harm to be done by the way is what makes the policy really attractive, and the ultimate good is of the nature of a "rationalizing."

Widespread political scepticism is possible; psychologically, it means concentrating our enmity upon politicians, instead of nations or social classes. Since enmity cannot be effective except by the help of politicians, an enmity of which they are the objects may be psychologically satisfying, but cannot be socially harmful. I suggest it as fulfilling the conditions for William James's desideratum, a "moral equivalent for war." True, it would leave politics to obvious scoundrels (i.e. persons whom you and I dislike), but that might be a gain. I read in *The Freeman* of September 26, 1923, a story which may illustrate the usefulness of political scoundrelism. A certain Englishman, having made friends with a Japanese Elder Statesman, asked him why Chinese merchants were honest while those of Japan were not. "Some time ago," he replied, "a period of particularly brilliant corruption set in in Chinese politics, and as far as the Courts were concerned, justice became a mockery. Hence, in order to save the processes of trade from complete chaos and stagnation, the Chinese merchant was compelled to adopt the strictest ethical standards; and since that time his word has been as good as his bond. In Japan, however, the merchant has been under no such compulsion, for we have probably the finest code of legal justice in the world. Hence when you do business with a Japanese, you must take your chances." This story shows that dishonest politicians may do less harm than honest ones.

The conception of an "honest" politician is not altogether a simple one. The most tolerant definition is: one whose political actions are not dictated by a desire to increase his own income. In this sense, Mr. Lloyd George is honest. The next stage would be the man whose political actions are not dictated by desire to secure or preserve his own power any more than by pecuniary motives. In this sense, Lord Grey is an honest politician. The last and most stringent sense is: one who, in his public actions, is not only disinterested, but does not fall very far below the standard of veracity and honor which is taken for granted between acquaintances. In this sense, the late Lord Morley was an honest politician; at least, he was honest always, and a politician until his honesty drove him out of politics. But even a politician who is honest in the highest sense may be very harmful; one may take George III as an illustration. Stupidity and unconscious bias often work more damage than venality. Moreover, an honest politician will not be tolerated by a democracy unless he is very stupid, like the late Duke of Devonshire; because only a very stupid man can honestly share the prejudices of more than half the nation. Therefore any man who is both able and public-spirited must be a hypocrite if he is to succeed in politics; but the hypocrisy will in time destroy his public spirit.

One obvious palliative of the evils of democracy in its present form would be to encourage much more publicity and initiative on the part of civil servants. They ought to have the right, and, on occasion, the duty, to frame Bills in their own names, and set forth publicly the arguments in their favor. Finance and Labor already have international conferences, but they ought to extend this method enormously, and cause an international secretariat to be perpetually considering measures to be simultaneously advocated in different countries. The agricultural interests of the world ought to meet for direct negotiations and adoption of a common policy. And so on. It is neither possible nor desirable to dispense with democratic parliaments, because measures which are to succeed must, after due discussion and the dissemination of considered expert opinions, be such as to commend themselves to the ordinary citizen. But at present, in most matters, the ordinary citizen does not know the considered opinion of experts, and little machinery exists for arriving at their collective or majority opinion. In particular, civil servants are debarred from public advocacy of their views, except in exceptional cases and by non-political methods. If measures were framed by experts after international deliberation, they would cut across party lines, and would be found to involve far less division of opinion than is now taken for granted. I believe, for example, that international finance and international labor, if they could overcome their mutual distrust, could at this moment agree on a program which would take the national Parliaments several years to carry out, and would improve the world immeasurably. In unison, they would be difficult to resist.

The common interests of mankind are numerous and weighty, but our existing political machinery obscures them through the scramble for power between different nations and different parties. A different machinery, requiring no legal or constitutional changes, and not very difficult to create, would undermine the strength of national and party passion, and focus attention upon measures beneficial to all rather than upon those damaging to enemies. I suggest that it is along these lines, rather than by party government at home and foreign-office diplomacy abroad, that an issue is to be found from the present peril to civilization. Knowledge exists, and good will exists; but both remain impotent until they possess the proper organs for making themselves heard.

Freedom Versus Authority in Education

Freedom, in education as in other things, must be a matter of degree. Some freedoms cannot be tolerated. I met a lady once who maintained that no child should ever be forbidden to do anything, because a child ought to develop its nature from within. "How if its nature leads it to swallow pins?" I asked; but I regret to say the answer was mere vituperation. And yet every child, left to itself, will sooner or later swallow pins, or drink poison out of medicine bottles, or fall out of an upper window, or otherwise bring itself to a bad end. At a slightly later age, boys, when they have the opportunity, will go unwashed, overeat, smoke till they are sick, catch chills from sitting in wet feet, and so on—let alone the fact that they will amuse themselves by plaguing elderly gentlemen, who may not all have Elisha's powers of repartee. Therefore one who advocates freedom in education cannot mean that children should do exactly as they please all day long. An element of discipline and authority must exist; the question is as to the amount of it, and the way in which it is to be exercised.

Education may be viewed from many standpoints: that of the State, of the Church, of the schoolmaster, of the parents, or even (though this is usually forgotten) of the child itself. Each of these points of view is partial; each contributes something to the ideal of education, but also contributes elements that are bad. Let us examine them successively, and see what is to be said for and against them.

We will begin with the State, as the most powerful force in deciding what modern education is to be. The interest of the State in education is very recent. It did not exist in antiquity or the Middle Ages; until the Renaissance, education was only valued by the Church. The Renaissance brought an interest in advanced scholarship, leading to the foundation of such institutions as the Collège de France, intended to offset the ecclesiastical Sorbonne. The Reformation, in England and Germany, brought a desire on the part of the State to have some control over universities and grammar schools, to prevent them from remaining hotbeds of "Popery." But this interest soon evaporated. The State took no decisive or continuous part until the quite modern movement for universal compulsory education. Nevertheless the State, now, has more to say to scholastic institutions than have all the other factors combined.

The motives which led to universal compulsory education were various. Its strongest advocates were moved by the feeling that it is in itself desirable to be able to read and write, that an ignorant population is a disgrace to a civilized country, and that democracy is impossible without education. These motives were reinforced by others. It was soon seen that education gave commercial advantages, that it diminished juvenile crime, and that it gave opportunities for regimenting slum populations. Anti-clericals perceived in State education an opportunity of combating the influence of the Church; this motive weighed considerably in England and France. Nationalists, especially after the Franco-Prussian War, considered that universal education would increase the national strength. All these other reasons, however, were at first subsidiary. The main reason for adopting universal education was the feeling that illiteracy was disgraceful.

This institution, once firmly established, was found by the State to be capable of many uses. It makes young people more docile, both for good and evil. It improves manners and diminishes crime; it facilitates common action for public ends; it makes the community more responsive to direction from a center. Without it, democracy cannot exist except as an empty form. But democracy, as conceived by politicians, is a form of *government,* that is to say, it is a method of making people do what their leaders wish under the impression that they are doing what they themselves wish. Accordingly, State education has acquired a certain bias. It teaches the young (so far as it can) to respect existing institutions, to avoid all fundamental criticism of the powers that be, and to regard foreign nations with suspicion and contempt. It increases national solidarity at the expense both of internationalism and of individual development. The damage to individual development comes through the undue stress upon authority. Collective rather than individual emotions are encouraged, and disagreement with prevailing beliefs is severely repressed. Uniformity is desired because it is convenient to the administrator, regardless of the fact that it can only be secured by mental atrophy. So great are the resulting evils that it can be seriously questioned whether universal education has hitherto done good or harm on the balance.

The point of view of the Church as regards education is, in practice, not very different from that of the State. There is,

however, one important divergence: the Church would prefer that the laity should not be educated at all, and only give them instruction when the State insists. The State and the Church both wish to instil beliefs which are likely to be dispelled by free inquiry. But the State creed is easier to instill into a population which can read the newspaper, whereas the Church creed is easier to instill into a wholly illiterate population. State and Church are both hostile to thought, but the Church is also (though now surreptitiously) hostile to instruction. This will pass, and is passing, as the ecclesiastical authorities perfect the technique of giving instruction without stimulating mental activity—a technique in which, long ago, the Jesuits led the way.

The schoolmaster, in the modern world, is seldom allowed a point of view of his own. He is appointed by an education authority, and is "sacked" if he is found to be educating. Apart from this economic motive, the schoolmaster is exposed to temptations of which he is likely to be unconscious. He stands, even more directly than the State and the Church, for discipline; officially he knows what his pupils do not know. Without some element of discipline and authority, it is difficult to keep a class in order. It is easier to punish a boy for showing boredom than it is to be interesting. Moreover, even the best schoolmaster is likely to exaggerate his importance, and to deem it possible and desirable to mold his pupils into the sort of human beings that he thinks they ought to be. Lytton Strachey describes Dr. Arnold walking beside the Lake of Como and meditating on "moral evil." Moral evil, for him, was whatever he wished to change in his boys. The belief that there was a great deal of it in them justified him in the exercise of power, and in conceiving of himself as a ruler whose duty was even more to chasten than to love. This attitude—variously phrased in various ages—is natural to any schoolmaster who is zealous without being on the watch for the deceitful influence of self-importance. Nevertheless the teacher is far the best of the forces concerned in education, and it is primarily to him or her that we must look for progress.

Then again, the schoolmaster wants the credit of his school. This makes him wish to have his boys distinguish themselves in athletic contests and scholarship examinations, which leads to care for a certain selection of superior boys to the exclusion of the others. For the rank and file, the result is bad. It is much better for a boy to play a game badly himself than to watch others playing it well. Mr. H. G. Wells, in his *Life of Sanderson of Oundle,* tells how this really great schoolmaster set his face against everything that left the faculties of the average boy unexercised and uncared-for. When he became headmaster, he found that only certain selected boys were expected to sing in chapel; they were trained as a choir, and the rest listened. Sanderson insisted that all should sing, whether musical or not. In this he was rising above the bias which is natural to a schoolmaster who cares more for his credit than for his boys. Of course, if we all apportioned credit wisely there would be no conflict between these two motives: the school which did best by the boys would get the most credit. But in a busy world spectacular successes will always win credit out of proportion to their real importance, so that some conflict between the two motives is hardly avoidable.

I come now to the point of view of the parent. This differs according to the economic status of the parent: the average wage-earner has desires quite different from those of the average professional man. The average wage-earner wishes to get his children to school as soon as pos-sible, so as to diminish bother at home; he also wishes to get them away as soon as possible, so as to profit by their earnings. When recently the British Government decided to cut down expenditure on education, it proposed that children should not go to school before the age of six, and should not be obliged to stay after the age of thirteen. The former proposal caused such a popular outcry that it had to be dropped: the indignation of worried mothers (recently enfranchised) was irresistible. The latter proposal, lowering the age for leaving school, was not unpopular. Parliamentary candidates advocating better education would get unanimous applause from those who came to meetings, but would find, in canvassing, that unpolitical wage-earners (who are the majority) want their children to be free to get paid work as soon as possible. The exceptions are mainly those who hope that their children may rise in the social scale through better education.

Professional men have quite a different outlook. Their own income depends upon the fact that they have had a better education than the average, and they wish to hand on this advantage to their children. For this object they are willing to make great sacrifices. But in our present competitive society what will be desired by the average parent is not an education which is good in itself, but an education which is better than other people's. This may be facilitated by keeping down the general level, and therefore we cannot expect a professional man to be enthusiastic about facilities for higher education for the children of wage-earners. If everybody who desired it could get a medical education, however poor his parents might be, it is obvious that doctors would earn less than they do, both from increased competition and from the improved health of the community. The same thing applies to the

law, the civil service, and so on. Thus the good things which the professional man desires for his own children he will not desire for the bulk of the population unless he has exceptional public spirit.

The fundamental defect of fathers, in our competitive society, is that they want their children to be a credit to them. This is rooted in instinct, and can only be cured by efforts directed to that end. The defect exists also, though to a lesser degree, in mothers. We all feel instinctively that our children's successes reflect glory upon ourselves, while their failures make us feel shame. Unfortunately, the successes which cause us to swell with pride are often of an undesirable kind. From the dawn of civilization till almost our own time—and still in China and Japan—parents have sacrificed their children's happiness in marriage by deciding whom they were to marry, choosing almost always the richest bride or bridegroom available. In the western world (except partially in France) children have freed themselves from this slavery by rebellion, but parents' instincts have not changed. Neither happiness nor virtue, but worldly success, is what the average father desires for his children. He wants them to be such as he can boast of to his cronies, and this desire largely dominates his efforts for their education.

Authority, if it is to govern education, must rest upon one or several of the powers we have considered: the State, the Church, the schoolmaster, and the parent. We have seen that no one of them can be trusted to care adequately for the child's welfare, since each wishes the child to minister to some end which has nothing to do with its own well-being. The State wants the child to serve for national aggrandizement and the support of the existing form of government. The Church wants the child to serve for increasing the power of the priesthood.

The schoolmaster, in a competitive world, too often regards his school as the State regards the nation, and wants the child to glorify the school. The parent wants the child to glorify the family. The child itself, as an end in itself, as a separate human being with a claim to whatever happiness and well-being may be possible, does not come into these various external purposes, except very partially. Unfortunately, the child lacks the experience required for the guidance of its own life, and is therefore a prey to the sinister interests that batten on its innocence. This is what makes the difficulty of education as a political problem. But let us first see what can be said from the child's own point of view.

It is obvious that most children, if they were left to themselves, would not learn to read or write, and would grow up less adapted than they might be to the circumstances of their lives. There must be educational institutions, and children must be to some extent under authority. But in view of the fact that no authority can be wholly trusted, we must aim at having as little authority as possible, and try to think out ways by which young people's natural desires and impulses can be utilized in education. This is far more possible than is often thought, for, after all, the desire to acquire knowledge is natural to most young people. The traditional pedagogue, possessing knowledge not worth imparting, and devoid of all skill in imparting it, imagined that young people have a native horror of instruction, but in this he was misled by failure to realize his own shortcomings. There is a charming tale of Tchekov's about a man who tried to teach a kitten to catch mice. When it wouldn't run after them, he beat it, with the result that even as an adult cat it cowered with terror in the presence of a mouse. "This is the man," Tchekov adds, "who taught me Latin." Now cats teach their kittens to catch mice, but they wait till the instinct has awakened. Then the kittens agree with their mammas that the knowledge is worth acquiring, so that discipline is not required.

The first two or three years of life have hitherto escaped the domination of the pedagogue, and all authorities are agreed that those are the years in which we learn most. Every child learns to talk by its own efforts. Anyone who has watched an infant knows that the efforts required are very considerable. The child listens intently, watches movements of the lips, practices sounds all day long, and concentrates with amazing ardor. Of course grown-up people encourage it by praise, but it does not occur to them to punish it on days when it learns no new word. All that they provide is opportunity and praise. It is doubtful whether more is required at any stage.

What is necessary is to make the child or young person feel that the knowledge is worth having. Sometimes this is difficult because in fact the knowledge is not worth having. It is also difficult when only a considerable amount of knowledge in any direction is useful, so that at first the pupil tends to be merely bored. In such cases, however, the difficulty is not insuperable. Take, for instance, the teaching of mathematics. Sanderson of Oundle found that almost all his boys were interested in machinery, and he provided them with opportunities for making quite elaborate machines. In the course of this practical work, they came upon the necessity for making calculations, and thus grew interested in mathematics as required for the success of a constructive enterprise on which they were keen. This method is expensive, and involves patient skill on the part of the teacher. But it goes along the lines of the pupil's instinct, and is therefore likely to involve less boredom with more intellectual effort. Effort is natural both to animals and men, but it must be effort for which there is an instinctive stimulus. A football match involves more effort than the treadmill, yet the one is a pleasure and the other a punishment. It is a mistake to suppose that mental effort can rarely be a pleasure; what is true is that certain conditions are required to make it pleasurable, and that, until lately, no attempt was made to create these conditions in education. The chief conditions are: first, a problem of which the solution is desired; secondly, a feeling of hopefulness as to the possibility of obtaining a solution. Consider the way David Copperfield was taught Arithmetic:

Even when the lessons are done, the worst is yet to happen, in the shape of an appalling sum. This is invented for me, and delivered to me orally by Mr. Murdstone, and begins, "If I go into a cheesemonger's shop, and buy five thousand double-Gloucester cheeses at fourpence-halfpenny each, present payment"—at which I see Miss Murdstone secretly overjoyed. I pore over these cheeses without any result or enlightenment until dinner-time; when, having made a mulatto of myself by getting the dirt of the slate into the pores of my skin, I have a slice of bread to help me out with the cheeses, and am considered in disgrace for the rest of the evening.

Obviously the poor boy could not be expected to take any interest in the cheeses, or to have any hope of doing the sum right. If he had wanted a box of a certain size, and had been told to save up his allowance until he could buy enough wood and nails, it would have stimulated his arithmetical powers amazingly.

There should be nothing hypothetical about the sums that a child is asked to do. I remember once reading a young boy's own account of his arithmetic lesson. The governess set the problem: If a horse is worth three times as much as a pony, and the pony is worth £22, what is the horse worth? "Had he been down?" asks the boy. "That makes no difference," says the governess. "Oh, but James (the groom) says it makes a great difference." The power of understanding hypothetical truth is one of the latest developments of logical faculty, and ought not to be expected in the very young. This, however, is a digression, from which we must return to our main theme.

I do not maintain that *all* children can have their intellectual interests aroused by suitable stimuli. Some have much less than average intelligence, and require special treatment. It is very undesirable to combine in one class children whose mental capacities are very different: the cleverer ones will be bored by having things explained that they clearly understand, and the stupider ones will be worried by having things taken for granted that they have not yet grasped. But subjects and methods should be adapted to the intelligence of the pupil. Macaulay was made to learn mathematics at Cambridge, but it is obvious from his letters that it was a sheer waste of time. I was made to learn Latin and Greek, but I resented it, being of opinion that it was silly to learn a language that was no longer spoken. I believe that all the little good I got from years of classical studies I could have got in adult life in a month. After the bare minimum, account should be taken of tastes, and pupils should only be taught what they find interesting. This puts a strain upon teachers, who find it easier to be dull, especially if they are overworked. But the difficulties can be overcome by giving teachers shorter hours and instruction in the art of teaching, which is done at present in training teachers in elementary schools, but not teachers in universities or public schools.

Freedom in education has many aspects. There is first of all freedom to learn or not to learn. Then there is freedom as to what to learn. And in later education there is freedom of opinion. Freedom to learn or not to learn can be only partially conceded in childhood. It is necessary to make sure that all who are not imbecile learn to read and write. How far this can be done by the mere provision of opportunity, only experience can show. But even if opportunity alone suffices, children must have the opportunity thrust upon them. Most of them would rather play out of doors, where the necessary opportunities would be lacking. Later on, it might be left to the choice of young people whether, for instance, they should go to the university; some would wish to do so, others would not. This would make quite as good a principle of selection as any to be got from entrance examinations. Nobody who did not work should be allowed to stay at a university. The rich young men who now waste their time in college are demoralizing others and teaching themselves to be useless. If hard work were exacted as a condition of residence, universities would cease to be attractive to people with a distaste for intellectual pursuits.

Freedom as to what to learn ought to exist far more than at present. I think it is necessary to group subjects by their natural affinities; there are grave disadvantages in the elective system, which leaves a young man free to choose wholly unconnected subjects. If I were organizing education in Utopia, with unlimited funds, I should give every child, at the age of about twelve, some instruction in classics, mathematics, and science. After two years, it ought to be evident where the child's aptitudes lay, and the child's own tastes would be a safe indication, provided there were no "soft options." Consequently I should allow every boy and girl who so desired to specialize from the age of fourteen. At first, the specialization would be very broad, growing gradually more defined as education advanced. The time when it was possible to be universally well-informed is past. An industrious man may know something of history and literature, which requires a knowledge of classical and modern languages. Or he may know some parts of mathematics, or one or two sciences. But the ideal of an "all-round" education is out of date; it has been destroyed by the progress of knowledge.

Freedom of opinion, on the part of both teachers and pupils, is the most important of the various kinds of freedom, and the only one which requires no limitations whatever. In view of the fact that it does not exist, it is worth while to recapitulate the arguments in its favor.

The fundamental argument for freedom of opinion is the doubtfulness of all our beliefs. If we certainly knew the truth, there would be something to be said for teaching it. But in that case it could be taught without invoking authority, by means of its inherent reasonableness. It is not necessary to make a law that no one shall be allowed to teach arithmetic if he holds heretical opinions on the multiplication table, because here the truth is clear, and does not require to be enforced by penalties. When the State intervenes to ensure the teaching of some doctrine, it does so *because* there is no conclusive evidence in favor of that doctrine. The result is that the teaching is not truthful, even if it should happen to be true. In the State of New York, it was till lately illegal to teach that Communism is good; in Soviet Russia, it is illegal to teach that Communism is bad. No doubt one of these opinions is true and one false, but no one knows which. Either New York or Soviet Russia was teaching truth and proscribing falsehood, but neither was teaching truthfully, because each was representing a doubtful proposition as certain.

The difference between truth and truthfulness is important in this connection. Truth is for the gods; from our point of view, it is an ideal, towards which we can approximate, but which we cannot hope to reach. Education should fit us for the nearest possible approach to truth, and to do this it must teach truthfulness. Truthfulness, as I mean it, is the habit of forming our opinions on the evidence, and holding them with that degree of conviction which the evidence warrants. This degree will always fall short of complete certainty, and therefore we must be always ready to admit new evidence against previous beliefs. Moreover, when we act on a belief, we must, if possible, only take such action as will be useful even if our belief is more or less inaccurate; we should avoid actions which are disastrous unless our belief is *exactly* true. In science, an observer states his results along with the "probable error"; but who ever heard of a theologian or a politician stating the probable error in his dogmas, or even admitting that any error is conceivable? That is because in science, where we approach nearest to real knowledge, a man can safely rely on the strength of his case, whereas, where nothing is known, blatant assertion and hypnotism are the usual ways of causing others to share our beliefs. If the fundamentalists thought they had a good case against evolution, they would not make the teaching of it illegal.

The habit of teaching some one orthodoxy, political, religious, or moral, has all kinds of bad effects. To begin with, it excludes from the teaching profession men who combine honesty with intellectual vigor, who are just the men likely to have the best moral and mental effect upon their pupils. I will give three illustrations. First, as to politics: a teacher of economics in America is expected to teach such doctrines as will add to the wealth and power of the very rich; if he does not, he finds it advisable to go elsewhere, like Mr. Laski, formerly of Harvard, now one of the most valuable teachers in the London School of Economics. Second, as to religion: the immense majority of intellectually eminent men disbelieve the Christian religion, but they conceal the fact in public, because they are afraid of losing their incomes. Thus on the most important of all subjects most of the men whose opinions and arguments would be best worth having are condemned to silence. Third, as to morals: Practically all men are unchaste at some time of their lives; clearly those who conceal this fact are worse than those who do not, since they add the guilt of hypocrisy. But it is only to the hypocrites that teaching posts are open. So much for the effects of orthodoxy upon the choice and character of teachers.

I come now to the effect upon the pupils, which I will take under two heads, intellectual and moral. Intellectually, what is stimulating to a young man is a problem of obvious practical importance, as to which he finds that divergent opinions are held. A young man learning economics, for example, ought to hear lectures from individualists and socialists, protectionists and free-traders, inflationists and believers in the gold standard. He ought to be encouraged to read the best books of the various schools, as recommended by those who believe in them. This would teach him to weigh arguments and evidence, to know that no opinion is certainly right, and to judge men by their quality rather than by their consonance with preconceptions. History should be taught not only from the point of view of one's own country, but also from that of foreigners. If history were taught by Frenchmen in England, and by Englishmen in France, there would be no disagreements between the two countries, because each would understand the other's point of view. A young man should learn to think that all questions are open, and that an argument should be followed wherever it leads. The needs of practical life will destroy this attitude all too soon when he begins to earn his living; but until that time he should be encouraged to taste the joys of free speculation.

Morally, also, the teaching of an orthodoxy to the young is very harmful. There is not only the fact that it compels the abler teachers to be hypocrites, and therefore to set a bad moral example. There is also, what is more important, the fact that it encourages intolerance and the bad forms of herd instinct. Edmund Gosse, in his *Father and Son,* relates how, when he was a boy, his father told him he was going to marry again. The boy saw there was something his father was ashamed of, so at last he asked, in accents of horror: "Father, is she a Paedo-Baptist?" And she was. Until that moment, he had believed all Paedo-Baptists to be wicked. So children in Catholic schools believe that Protestants are wicked, children in any school in an English-speaking country believe that atheists are wicked, children in France believe that Germans are wicked, and children in Germany believe that Frenchmen are wicked. When a school accepts as part of its task the teaching of an opinion which cannot be intellectually defended (as practically all schools do), it is compelled to give the impression that those who hold an opposite opinion are wicked, since otherwise it cannot generate the passion required for repelling the assaults of reason. Thus for the sake of orthodoxy the children are rendered uncharitable, intolerant, cruel, and bellicose. This is unavoidable so long as definite opinions are prescribed on politics, morals, and religion.

Finally, arising out of this moral damage to the individual, there is untold damage to society. Wars and persecutions are rife everywhere, and everywhere they are rendered possible by the teaching in the schools. Wellington used to say that the battle of Waterloo was won on the playing-fields of Eton. He might have said with more truth that the war against revolutionary France was instigated in the classrooms of Eton. In our democratic age, Eton has become unimportant; now, it is the ordinary elementary and secondary school that matters. In every country, by means of flag-waving, Empire Day, Fourth-of-July celebrations, Officer's Training Corps, etc., everything is done to give boys a taste for homicide, and girls a conviction that men given to homicide are the most worthy of respect. This whole system of moral degradation to which innocent boys and girls are exposed would become impossible if the authorities allowed freedom of opinion to teachers and pupils.

Regimentation is the source of the evil. Education authorities do not look on children, as religion is supposed to do, as human beings with souls to be saved. They look upon them as material for grandiose social schemes: future "hands" in factories or "bayonets" in war or what not. No man is fit to educate unless he feels each pupil an end in himself, with his own rights and his own personality, not merely a piece in a jig-saw puzzle, or a soldier in a regiment, or a citizen in a State. Reverence for human personality is the beginning of wisdom, in every social question, but above all in education.

Some Prospects: Cheerful and Otherwise

I

There are two ways of writing about the future, the scientific and the Utopian. The scientific way tries to discover what is probable; the Utopian way sets out what the writer would like. In a well-developed science such as astronomy no one would adopt the Utopian method: people do not prophesy eclipses because it would be pleasant if they took place. But in social affairs those who profess to have discovered general laws enabling them to foretell future developments are usually not so scientific as they pretend to be; there must be a great deal of guesswork in any attempt to say what is going to happen to human institutions. We do not know, for instance, what difference may be made by new discoveries. Perhaps people will find out how to go to Mars or Venus. Perhaps almost all our food will be manufactured in chemical laboratories instead of being grown in the fields. To such possibilities there is no end. I shall ignore them, and consider only tendencies which are already well developed. And I shall also assume that our civilization will continue, although this is by no means certain. It may be destroyed by wars, or by a gradual decay such as occurred in the later Roman Empire. But if it survives, it is likely to have certain characteristics, and it is these that I shall be attempting to discover.

In addition to the introduction of machinery, and largely as a result of it, there has been another change: society has become far more organized than it was formerly. Printing, railways, the telegraph, and (now) broadcasting have provided the technical means for large organizations such as a modern State or an international financial business. Public affairs play almost no part in the life of an Indian or Chinese peasant, whereas in England they are a matter of interest to almost every one even in the remotest country districts. This was not the case until recently; one would gather from Jane Austen that the country gentry of her time hardly noticed the Napoleonic wars. I should put as the most important change in modern times the tendency towards closer social organization.

Connected with this is another result of science, namely, the greater unity of the world. Before the sixteenth century, America and the Far East were almost unrelated to Europe; since that time their relations have become continually closer. Augustus in Rome and the Han Emperor in China simultaneously imagined themselves masters of the whole civilized world; nowadays such pleasing illusions are impossible. Practically every part of the world has relations to practically every other part, which may be either friendly or hostile, but are in either case important. The Dalai Lama, after centuries of isolation, found himself courted by both Russians and British; he took refuge from their embarrassing attentions in Peking, where all his suite arrived duly armed with kodaks from America.

From these two premises, of closer social organization and greater unity in the world, it follows that, if our civilization is to develop, there will have to be a central authority to control the whole world. For, if not, causes of dispute will multiply and wars will become more intense owing to the growth of public spirit. The central authority may not be a formal government; I think it likely that it will not be. It is far more likely to be a combination of financiers, who have become persuaded that peace is to their in-terest because money lent to belligerent States is often lost. Or it may be a single dominant State (America), or a group of States (America and the British Empire). But before such a condition is reached, there may be a long period in which the world is virtually divided between America and Russia, the former controlling Western Europe and the self-governing Dominions, the latter controlling all Asia. Two such groups would be strong for defense and weak for attack, so that they might subsist for a century or more. Ultimately, however—I mean at latest some time during the twenty-first century—there must be either a cataclysm or a central authority controlling the whole world. I shall assume that civilized mankind will have enough sense, or that America will have enough power, to prevent a cataclysm involving a return to barbarism. If so, what powers must the central authority possess?

First and foremost, it must be able to decide questions of peace and war, or to ensure that if there is war the side which it favors wins a speedy victory. This end may be secured by financial supremacy alone, without formal political control. As war becomes more scientific it becomes more expensive, so that the leading financiers of the world, if they combined, could decide the issue by giving or withholding loans. And by the sort of pressure which has been brought to bear upon Germany since the Treaty of Versailles they could secure the virtual disarmament of any group that they dislike. In this way, they would gradually come to control all the large armed forces of the world. This is the fundamental condition for the other activities which they would have to undertake.

In addition to revising treaties and intervening in disputes, there are three matters which would have to be decided by the central authority. They are (1) the allocation of territory to the different national States, (2) movements of population across the boundaries of national States, and (3) the rationing of raw materials as between different claimants. Each of these demands a few words.

Questions of territorial allegiance are treated at present with an absurd solemnity which has grown out of the old personal allegiance to a sovereign. If a person in one State gives expression to the opinion that the district in which he lives ought to belong to another State he is guilty of treason, and liable to severe punishment. And yet, in itself, his opinion is as much a legitimate matter of political debate as any other. We do not feel any horror of a citizen of (say) Croydon who holds that Croydon ought to count as part of London. But a citizen of Colombia who holds that his village should belong to Venezuela is regarded by his Government as a monster of iniquity. The central authority will have to prevent the national governments from acting upon such prejudices, and will have to treat territorial readjustments rationally, i.e. mainly by the wishes of the local population, but also in part by economic and cultural considerations.

(2) Movements of population are likely to raise increasingly difficult problems as years go by. It is natural for population to flow from places where wages are low to those where they are high. This is now permitted within a single country, but not throughout a super-national federation such as the British Empire. Asiatic immigration is almost totally prohibited in America and the self-governing Dominions, and European immigration into America is becoming more and more restricted. The forces on both sides in this matter are immensely powerful. They afford a stimulus to Asiatic militarism, and may ultimately cause it to become so strong that it can challenge the white race—say during the next great war between white nations.

Ultimately, if war on a large scale has been eliminated and public health has been immensely improved by medicine and hygiene, it will become essential to the preservation of peace and well-being that the backward nations shall limit the increase of population, as the more civilized nations are already doing. Those who in principle oppose birth control are either incapable of arithmetic or else in favor of war, pestilence, and famine as permanent features of human life. One may assume that the international authority will insist upon freedom to limit births among backward races and classes, and will not, as governments do now, insist that only the intelligent shall have small families.

(3) The last matter, the rationing of raw material, is perhaps the most important of all. Wars are likely to be very largely concerned with raw material; it is notorious what a large part oil, coal, and iron have played in post-war disputes. I am not assuming that raw materials will be rationed justly, but merely that they will be rationed in some way by an authority having irresistible force at its command. I believe that the problem of organizing the world as a single economic and political unit will have to be solved before questions of justice can be tackled successfully. I am an international socialist, but I expect to see internationalism realized sooner than Socialism.

II

Assuming that within the next one hundred and fifty years a central authority is developed, strong enough to reduce all wars to the level of sporadic revolts quickly suppressed, what kind of economic changes are likely to be associated with this development? Will the general level of well-being be increased? Will competition survive, or will production be monopolistic? In the latter case, will the monopolies be in private hands or in those of the State? And will the products of labor be distributed with less injustice than at present?

There are here two different kinds of questions: one is concerned with the forms of economic organization, the other with the principles of distribution. The latter will depend upon political power: every class and every nation always secures as great a share of wealth as it can, and it is ultimately armed force that decides how large this share shall be. Let us first discuss organization, and leave distribution alone for the moment.

A study of history reveals a somewhat humiliating fact about organization. Whenever an increase in the size of organizations has been desirable in the interests of those concerned, it has had to be brought about (with negligible exceptions) by means of force on the part of the stronger. Where voluntary federation was the only available method no unity has been achieved. It was so with ancient Greece in the face of Macedonia, with sixteenth-century Italy in the face of France and Spain, with present-day Europe in the face of America and Asia. I assume, therefore, that the central authority will be brought into being by force, or the threat of force, not by a voluntary organization such as the League of Nations, which will never be strong enough to coerce recalcitrant Great Powers. I think, also, that the power of the central authority will be primarily economic, and will rest upon possession of raw materials combined with control of financial credit. I conceive of it as consisting, in the beginning, of a group of financiers backed, informally, by one or more great States.

It follows that at the basis of the economic structure there will be monopoly.

All the oil supply of the world, for example, will be centrally controlled. It follows that aeroplanes and oil-driven warships will be useless to Powers which conflict with the central authority, unless they can be used to capture an oil-field by a brief raid. The same will apply to other things in less obvious ways. Already at the present day a large proportion of the world's meat supply is controlled by the Big Five in Chicago, who are themselves to some extent controlled by Messrs. J. P. Morgan & Co. From the raw material to the finished commodity there is a long road to travel, and monopoly may intervene at any stage. In the case of oil the natural stage is at the beginning. In other cases, it may be harbors or ships or railways that give the monopolist his opportunity to control. But wherever he intervenes, he is stronger than any of the other parties concerned.

Given monopoly at one stage of a process there will be a tendency to extend the monopoly to earlier and later stages. The growth of economic monopoly is part of the general tendency to increase the organization, which is shown politically in the greater power and size of States. We may therefore confidently expect a continuation of the process of eliminating competition which has been going on throughout the last half-century. It is of course to be assumed that trade unions will continue to diminish competition among wage-earners. The view that while employers are organized wage-earners should be prevented by law from counter-organizing is not one which it will be found long possible to maintain.

Secure peace and adequate control of production ought to lead to a great increase of material comfort, provided it is not all swallowed up by an increase of population. Whether the world, at that stage, is capitalistic or socialistic, we may expect an improvement in the economic position of all classes. But this brings us to our second question, that of distribution.

Assuming a dominant group associated with a dominant nation (or several dominant nations in alliance), it is of course obvious that the dominant group will secure great wealth to itself, and will produce contentment in the population of the dominant nation by conceding to its wage-earners a progressive increase in their earnings. This has been happening in the United States, as it formerly happened in England. So long as there is a rapid increase in the total wealth of a nation it is easy for capitalists to prevent successful socialist propaganda by timely monetary control. And the less fortunate nations can be kept subdued by a system of imperialistic control.

But such a system will probably develop in the direction of democracy, i.e. of Socialism—for Socialism is merely economic democracy in a community which has reached the stage of monopoly in many industries. One may take the political development of England as a parallel. England was unified by the King—a process practically completed by Henry VII after the anarchy of the Wars of the Roses. The royal power was necessary to produce unity, but when unity had been achieved the movement towards democracy began almost at once, and it was found, after the troubles of the seventeenth century, that democracy was compatible with public order. We are now, in the economic sphere, just about at the transition from the Wars of the Roses to Henry VII. When once economic unity, however despotic, has been achieved, the movement towards economic democracy will be immensely strengthened, since it will no longer have to contend with the fear of anarchy. Minorities can only retain power if they have considerable support in public opinion, since they must be loyally served by their armies and navies and civil servants.

Situations will continually arise in which the holders of economic power will find it prudent to make concessions; in the control of affairs they will have to associate with themselves representatives of the less fortunate nations and classes, and this process will probably continue until a completely democratic régime has been established.

Since we have been assuming a central authority which controls the whole world, democracy in regard to this authority would be international democracy, embracing not only the white races, but also the races of Asia and Africa. Asia is developing at present with such extraordinary rapidity that it may well be capable of taking a worthy part in the government of the world by the time such a government comes into existence. Africa is a more difficult problem. But even in Africa the French (who are in this respect our superiors) are achieving remarkable results, and no one can foretell what may be accomplished within the next hundred years. I conclude, therefore, that a system of world-wide Socialism, involving economic justice to all nations and classes, may well become possible not long after the establishment of a central authority. And, if so, the natural operation of political forces is pretty sure to bring it about.

There are, however, other possibilities, which might lead to a perpetuation of caste distinctions. Wherever white men and Negroes live side by side, as in South Africa and the Southern States of America, it has been found possible to combine democracy for white men with a semi-servile condition for the colored population. What stands in the way of this development on a large scale is the objection by Labor to colored immigration in most parts of the English-speaking world. Nevertheless, it remains a possibility to be borne in mind. I shall have something more to say about it later.

III

What is likely to be the development of the family during the next two centuries? We cannot tell, but we can note certain forces at work which are likely, if unchecked, to have certain results. I wish to state, at the outset, that I am not concerned with what I desire, but with what I expect, which is a very different thing. The world has never in the past developed just as I should have wished, and I see no reason to think that it will do so in future.

There are certain things in modern civilized communities which are tending to weaken the family; the chief of them is humanitarian sentiment towards children. More and more, people come to feel that children should not suffer more than can be helped through their parents' misfortunes or even sins. In the Bible the lot of the orphan is always spoken of as very sad, and so no doubt it was; nowadays he suffers little more than other children. There will be a growing tendency for the State or charitable institutions to give fairly adequate care to neglected children, and consequently children will be more and more neglected by unconscientious parents or guardians. Gradually the expense of caring for neglected children out of public funds will become so great that there will be a very strong inducement for all who are not well off to avail themselves of the opportunities for giving their children over to the State; probably this will be done, in the end, as now with schooling, by practically all who are below a certain economic level.

The effects of such a change would be very far-reaching. With parental responsibility removed, marriage would no longer be felt important, and would gradually cease among those classes which left their children to the State. In

civilized countries, the number of children produced under these conditions would probably be very small, and the State would have to fix a payment to mothers at a scale found adequate to produce the number of citizens which it considered desirable. All this is not so very remote; it might easily happen in England before the end of the twentieth century.

If all this happens while the capitalist system and the international anarchy are still in force, the results are likely to be terrible. To begin with, there will be profound division between the proletarians, who will virtually have neither parents nor children, and the well-to-do, who will preserve the family system with inheritance of property. The proletarians, being educated by the State, will be imbued, like the Janissaries in old Turkey, with a passionate militaristic loyalty. The women will be taught that it is their duty to have many children, both to keep down the tariff of State payments for children and to increase the supply of soldiers for killing the population of other countries. With no parental propaganda to counteract that of the State, there will be no limit to the anti-foreign ferocity with which children can be imbued, so that when they grow up they will fight blindly for their masters. Men whose opinions the Government dislikes will be punished by having their children confiscated to the State institutions.

It is thus quite possible that through the joint operation of patriotism and humanitarian feeling for children we may be led, step by step, to the creation of a society profoundly divided into two different castes, the upper retaining marriage and family loyalties, the lower feeling loyalty only to the State. For military reasons the State will secure, by payment, a high birth-rate among the proletarians; hygiene and medicine will secure a low death-rate. War will therefore be the only way of keeping the population of the world within limits, except starvation, which nations will try to avert by fighting. In these circumstances we may expect an era of internecine wars, comparable only to the invasions of Huns and Mongols in the Middle Ages. The only hope will lie in the speedy victory of some one nation or group of nations.

The results of State care of children will be almost diametrically opposite to the above if a world-wide authority has been previously established. In that case the central authority will not permit the children to be taught a militaristic patriotism, and will not permit the various national States to pay for an increase of population beyond what is economically desirable. The children brought up in State institutions will, if the pressure of militaristic necessities is removed, almost certainly be better developed both physically and mentally than the average child is now, and a very rapid progress will therefore become possible.

But even if a central authority exists the effects will be profoundly different if the world remains capitalistic from what they will be if it has adopted Socialism. In the former alternative there will be that division of castes which we spoke of a moment ago, the upper caste retaining the family, the lower substituting the State for the parents. And there will still be need to produce submissiveness in the lower caste, lest it should rebel against the rich. This will involve a low level of culture, and will perhaps lead the rich to encourage breeding among black rather than white or yellow proletarians. The white race may thus gradually become a numerically small aristocracy, and be finally exterminated by a Negro insurrection.

All this may be thought fantastic, in view of the fact that most white nations possess political democracy. I observe,

however, that the democracy everywhere permits the school teaching to be such as furthers the interests of the rich; school teachers are dismissed for being communists, but never for being conservatives. I see no reason to suppose that this will change in the near future. And I think, for such reasons as I have been giving, that if our civilization continues much longer to pursue the interests of the rich, it is doomed. It is because I do not desire the collapse of civilization that I am a socialist.

If we have been right in what was said earlier, the family is likely to die out except in a privileged minority. Therefore if there ceases to be a privileged minority the family may be expected to die out almost completely. Biologically, this seems inevitable. The family is an institution which serves to protect children during their years of helplessness; with ants and bees the community undertakes this task, and there is no family. So, among men, if infant life comes to be safe apart from the protection of parents, family life will gradually disappear. This will make profound changes in men's emotional life, and a great divorce from the art and literature of all previous ages. It will diminish the differences between different people, since parents will no longer educate their children to reproduce their peculiarities. It will make sex-love less interesting and romantic; probably all love-poetry will come to be thought absurd. The romantic elements in human nature will have to find other outlets, such as art, science, politics. (To Disraeli politics was a romantic adventure.) I cannot but think that there will be a real loss in the emotional texture of life; but every increase of safety involves some such loss. Steamers are less romantic than sailing-ships; tax-collectors than highwaymen. Perhaps, in the end, safety will become wearisome, and men will become destructive from sheer boredom. But such possibilities are incalculable.

IV

The tendency of culture in our time is, and will probably continue to be, towards science and away from art and literature. This is due, of course, to the immense practical unity of science. There is a powerful literary tradition, which comes to us from the Renaissance, and is backed by social prestige: a "gentleman" should know some Latin, but need not know how a steam-engine is made. The survival of this tradition, however, tends only to make "gentlemen" less useful than other men. I think we may assume that, before very long, no one will be considered educated unless he knows something of science.

This is all to the good, but what is regrettable is that science seems to be winning its victories at the expense of an impoverishment of our culture in other directions. Art becomes more and more an affair of coteries and a few rich patrons: it is not felt by ordinary men to be important, as it was when it was associated with religion and public life. The money that built St. Paul's might have been used to give our navy the victory over the Dutch, but in the time of Charles II St. Paul's was thought more important. The emotional needs that were formerly satisfied in aesthetically admirable ways are now finding more and more trivial outlets: the dancing and dance-music of our time have, as a rule, no artistic value, except in the Russian ballet, which is imported from a less modern civilization. I am afraid the decay of art is inevitable, and is connected with our more careful and utilitarian way of living as compared with our ancestors.

I imagine that a hundred years hence every fairly educated person will know a good deal of mathematics, a fair amount of biology, and a great deal about how to make machines. Education, except for the few, will become more and more what is called "dynamic," i.e. will teach people to do rather than to think or feel. They will perform all sorts of tasks with extraordinary skill, but will be incapable of considering rationally whether the tasks are worth performing. There will probably be an official caste of thinkers and another of feelers, the former a development of the Royal Society, the latter a federation of the Royal Academy and the Episcopate. The results obtained by the thinkers will be the property of the Government, and they will be revealed only to the War Office, Admiralty, or Air Ministry, as the case may be. Perhaps the Health Ministry will be included, if, in time, it becomes part of its duties to spread disease in enemy countries. The Official Feelers will decide what emotions are to be propagated in schools, theaters, churches, etc., though it will be the business of the Official Thinkers to discover how the desired emotions are to be caused. In view of the cussedness of school-children it will probably be thought desirable that the decisions of the Official Feelers also should be Government secrets. They will, however, be allowed to exhibit pictures or preach sermons which have already been sanctioned by the Board of Elder Censors.

The daily Press, presumably, will be killed by broadcasting. A certain number of weeklies may survive for the expression of minority opinions. But reading may come to be a rare practice, its place being taken by listening to the gramophone, or to whatever better invention takes its place. Similarly, writing will be replaced, in ordinary life, by the dictaphone.

If wars are eliminated and production is organized scientifically, it is probable that four hours' work a day will suffice to keep everybody in comfort. It will be an open question whether to work that amount and enjoy leisure, or to work more and enjoy luxuries; presumably some will choose one course, some the other. The hours of leisure will no doubt be spent by most people in dancing, watching football, and going to the movies. Children will be no anxiety, since the State will care for them; illness will be very rare; old age will be postponed by rejuvenation till a short time before death. It will be a hedonist's paradise, in which almost everyone will find life so tedious as to be scarcely endurable.

In such a world it is to be feared that destructive impulses would become irresistible. R. L. Stevenson's Suicide Club might flourish in it; secret societies devoted to artistic murder might grow up. Life in the past has been kept serious by danger, and interesting by being serious. Without danger, if human nature remained unchanged, life would lose its savor and men would resort to all kinds of decadent vices in the hope of a little excitement.

Is this dilemma inescapable? Are the more somber aspects of life essential to what is best in it? I do not think so. If human nature were unchangeable, as ignorant people still suppose it to be, the situation would indeed be hopeless. But we now know, thanks to psychologists and physiologists, that what passes as "human nature" is at most one-tenth nature, the other nine-tenths being nurture. What is called human nature can be almost completely changed by changes in early education. And these changes could be such as to preserve sufficient seriousness in life without the spice of danger if thought and energy were devoted to that end. Two things are necessary for this purpose: the development of constructive impulses in the young, and opportunities for their existence in adult life.

Hitherto, defense and attack have provided most of what is serious in life. We defend ourselves against poverty, our children against an indifferent world, our country against national enemies; we attack, verbally or physically, those whom we regard as hostile or dangerous. But there are other sources of emotions which are capable of being quite as powerful. The emotions of aesthetic creation or scientific discovery may be as intense and absorbing as the most passionate love. And love itself, though it may be grasping and oppressive, is also capable of being creative. Given the right education, a very large percentage of mankind could find happiness in constructive activities, provided the right kind were available.

And this brings us to our second requisite. There must be scope for constructive initiative, not only for useful work ordered by a superior authority. There must be no barrier to intellectual or artistic creation, nor to human relations of a constructive kind, nor to the suggestion of ways in which human life might be improved. If all this is the case, and education is of the right kind, there will still be room for serious and strenuous living on the part of all those who feel the need of it. In that case, but in that case only, a community organized so as to eliminate the major evils of life as we know it might be stable, because it would be satisfactory to its more energetic members.

This is, I must confess, the matter upon which I feel that our civilization is most likely to go wrong. There is need of much organization, and where there must be so much, there is almost sure to be more than there ought to be. The harm that this will do will be the diminution of opportunities for individual effort. Vast organizations produce a sense of impotence in the individual, leading to a decay of effort. The danger can be averted if it is realized by administrators, but it is of a kind which most administrators are constitutionally incapable of realizing. Into every tidy scheme for arranging the pattern of human life it is necessary to inject a certain dose of anarchism, enough to prevent immobility leading to decay, but not enough to bring about disruption. This is a delicate problem, not theoretically insoluble, but hardly likely to be solved in the rough-and-tumble of practical affairs.

THE LIFE AND WORKS OF

BERTRAND RUSSELL

By E. W. F. TOMLIN

IN THE COURSE of a long and active life, Bertrand Russell enjoyed one advantage denied to the majority of his fellowmen: he was able to follow several careers at the same time. He was mathematician, philosopher, educator, politician, philanthropist, and international peacemaker. Although each of these roles separately would have enabled him to attain eminence, he excelled in them all.

Born into one of Britain's most influential political families, Bertrand Russell, the third Earl Russell, combined the outlook of a radical with that of a Whig aristocrat. He was the contemporary of several generations of famous writers, artists, scholars, and men of action, and he might have belonged to the eighteenth century as easily as to the twentieth. As a child, he was privileged to meet Queen Victoria, Gladstone, Tennyson, and Browning, and later on, he associated with some of the most powerful of world figures including Lenin among others. Had he lived in their time, he might have been the friend of Voltaire, Diderot, d'Alembert, or Holbach, for as a thinker, Russell resembled an encyclopedist or a physiocrat. As a reformer, there was nothing in him of the demagogue. He understood the ordinary

man, though he himself was far from being a man of the people.

Another aspect of Russell's personality has perhaps even greater importance—he was a man of profound sensibility. This linked him not only with the apostles of reason but also with those of feeling. There was something in him of the temperament of Rousseau. From his earliest infancy, he was subject to moods of revery and melancholy. As a man, he displayed great compassion for human misery, coupled with an ardent desire to improve the human condition. The conflict between his altruistic passion and the inflexible principles of his keen intellect was responsible no doubt for some of the turbulence of his personal life: for if Russell was successful in almost all the domains in which he worked, this was by no means always true of his personal relationships. Only in his final and ninth decade did he succeed in finding true domestic peace and fulfilment.

Russell's upbringing and early education throw much light upon his character. He was born on May 18, 1872, at Ravenscroft, near Tintern, in Monmouthshire. His father, Lord Amberley, was the eldest son of Lord John Russell, celebrated for his great Reform

Bill of 1832. His mother came from a family no less aristocratic—the Stanleys of Alderney. Both his parents died when he was too young to preserve more than the vaguest memories of them, and he was brought up by his grandparents, a high-minded and cultivated couple but rigid in outlook. In their home there reigned an atmosphere of "piety and puritan austerity." A cold bath every morning was prescribed all the year round, and at least half an hour of piano practice before the fires were lit. Although there were eight domestic servants, the family meals were of "Spartan simplicity." In recalling this early period, Russell remarked that "only virtue was held in high esteem and this at the expense of intelligence, of health, of happiness, and of all that the world offered in the way of pleasure."

Russell lacked the benefits of school life, with its shared interests and comradeships since he was educated at home by governesses and tutors. When he was eleven years old, he began the study of geometry under his brother's guidance. This was the beginning of a lifelong devotion to mathematics. He always described himself as owing an eternal debt to this discipline, for mathematical speculation seemed to lend some sort of meaning to his life. Through its refined structure he could glimpse a world of eternal truth. Whereas for many young people mathematics is synonymous with torment and constraint, for Russell it became a source of profound exultation. The contemplation of a world of abstract perfection completely absorbed him, and he later described it as the means whereby his thoughts were turned from morbid obsessions and even from suicide.

Mathematics was not Russell's only love. An insatiable reader, he took an increasing interest in both history and literature, and he developed a passion for poetry. Throughout his work, even in the most modest essay, there is evidence of immense erudition, though lightly carried. Like many of the great Victorians, Russell acquired a profound knowledge of the Bible, despite religious doubts that assailed him at about his sixteenth year.

Russell's admission to the University of Cambridge opened not merely a new chapter in his life, but, so to speak, a new book. For the first time he broke with the austerity of his youth. Trinity College, which was to play so important a part in his career, had always attracted teachers and students of intellectual distinction. Among Russell's learned contemporaries were McTaggart, Ward, Sidgwick, Whitehead, Moore, Ramsey, Stout, Broad, and later Wittgenstein. Inspired by the "high seriousness" preached by Matthew Arnold, these thinkers, like the students gathered round them, led a life which today might seem privileged, isolated, or lacking in "engagement." A wide gulf separates that epoch and our present era of television, devotion to sport, cocktail parties, and political demonstrations. So far as university life was concerned, World War I marked the end of an era. The old tradition had maintained something of the atmosphere of the Academy of Plato or the Lyceum of Aristotle. In fact, the intellectual life of that period was, in Whitehead's words, "a daily Platonic dialogue"; and as Russell wrote many years later, "to find myself in a world where intelligence was valued and clear thinking was thought to be a good thing caused me an intoxicating delight."

One colleague and close friend of Russell, G. E. Moore, was a typical representative of this old school. He was a humanist, a brilliant conversationalist, an acute thinker, as well as a man of great personal charm. After dinner at college came the moment for leisurely discussion, and on such occasions Moore was in the habit of engaging in long debates with that picturesque, eccentric, but subtle philosopher, McTaggart. Among other philosophical theses, McTaggart sought to demonstrate unreality of time. Moore took up the challenge. Russell, though working for the mathematical tripos, was so fascinated by this philosophical dialogue that he was drawn to join it. What attracted him above all was Moore's defense of commonsense. It afforded a kind of relief from the refined subtleties of mathematics. In due course, Russell urged Moore to devote himself seriously to philosophy, finding at the same time that he himself was increasingly attracted to that discipline. Even before he entered Cambridge he had studied John Stuart Mill who became for a time his "Pope." (Curiously enough, it was only later that he learned that Mill had been an intimate friend of his parents.) While attracted to Mill's empiricism, Russell remained unshaken in his conviction that mathematical truths were immune from empirical criticism. After taking his degree in 1894, he began to devote himself seriously to philosophical studies. Thereafter, Moore and Russell, despite differences in temperament and outlook, assumed the leadership of a new philosophical school at Cambridge. This school was later to exercise considerable influence upon the Anglo-Saxon world. It is interesting to note that the Vienna Circle, which was later to have an impact on British academic thought, owed much at the outset to Russell.

On leaving Cambridge in 1894, Russell began another and somewhat more active career. True to his family traditions, he took an interest in public affairs. After a short period as Honorary Attaché at the British Embassy in Paris, he married Alys Smith, who belonged to a Quaker family from Philadelphia. During their honeymoon, the couple visited Germany.

Russell, while taking a lively interest in the philosophical thought of that country, found time to study local social and political conditions. On his return home, he delivered a series of lectures in 1895 at the London School of Economics concerning German social democracy, and he published a book on the subject in 1896. This was the first of a long series of critical, and sometimes iconoclastic, works on politics and society. Having been elected a Fellow of Trinity, he visited the United States, where he delivered lectures on geometry at Johns Hopkins and Bryn Mawr. In 1898, he revisited Cambridge and lectured on the philosophy of Leibniz. There followed a vigorous period of speculative activity, during which he laid the foundations of his great work on logic and mathematics.

This huge task, undertaken in collaboration with his friend, the philosopher-mathematician Alfred North Whitehead, was to occupy him, with some interruptions, for nearly ten years. It was not Russell's original intention to compile a purely abstract study, but to examine the nature of mathematics up to the point where the abstract gave way to the concrete, i.e. to the world of biology; and, by contrast, he intended his social studies to lead progressively from the concrete to the abstract. The result of these two intellectual exercises was to be a work of *synthesis*. He took for his model Hegel's *Encyclopedia of the Philosophical Sciences*. Russell never achieved this synthesis, though he was to lay the foundations of it in a brilliant work of his late maturity.

By 1900, Russell had reached the view that mathematics was nothing more than a prolongation or development of logic. He was not the first to come to such a conclusion. Frege, in Germany, and also Peano, had been pursuing speculations in the same direction, though at that period Russell knew nothing of their work. The International Congress of Philosophy, held in Paris in 1900, brought him into contact with a number of Continental logicians and served to broaden his outlook. But his gigantic *Principia Mathematica,* preceded by the *Principles of Mathematics* (1903), was not published in its entirety until 1913. The writing of it entailed such mental strain that there were moments when Russell felt that he was in danger of losing his reason. Baffled by certain contradictory logical propositions, and still more by an apparent contradiction at the heart of logic itself, he was obliged to suspend work for a period of about two years. Few people have read the *Principia* in its entirety, or possess the intellectual capacity to do so. It is certainly a unique product of the human brain, though some of its conclusions are now disputed. The introduction, of which Russell was the sole author, is the only uninterrupted piece of prose in a volume consisting largely of equations based upon a new and recondite symbolism.

But during even this period of intense concentration on mathematics and logic, Russell did not lose his interest in social problems. In 1907, he sought to enter Parliament. This was the first of a series of attempts, all of which proved unsuccessful. At his second try, as a candidate of the Liberal Party, he was openly assailed as an agnostic and a free-thinker. He did not repudiate the charges. During the next few years, and indeed throughout the period of World War I and after, he was repeatedly in trouble with the authorities, both civil and ecclesiastical. His resolute opposition to the war of 1914–1918 not only cost him his post at Cambridge, but resulted in a period of imprisonment, and his library was seized in 1916 after a court case. (It was later repurchased by friends.) In his eighty-ninth year, he was again committed to prison, though for a nominal period, on a charge of incitement to passive resistance in his campaign against nuclear armaments.

Russell put his first period of imprisonment to good use. He devoted part of his time to the compilation of a work of popularization, *An Introduction to Mathematical Philosophy* (1919). Not long before, he had produced one of his most contentious works, *Road to Freedom* (1918), an essay of singular persuasiveness, expounding anarchistic or syndicalistic views which he later modified. Despite his revolutionary opinions, Russell was never attracted to the doctrines of Marxism. In this way, he perhaps showed that he understood the nature of tyranny better than some of his intellectual contemporaries. His hostility to dictatorship of the Right did not lead him, by way of reaction, to an espousal of tyranny of the Left. He saw no reason to suppose that the dictatorship of the proletariat was preferable to that of a single man.

During the period following World War I, Russell's philosophy shed all but the vestiges of its idealism. He now perceived more clearly that both philosophy, as conventionally understood, and abstract logic, as he understood it, had their limitations. He continued to take a close interest in the philosophy of Leibniz, to which he had devoted his first work of pure philosophy. This interest, together with the increasing influence of Moore and Wittgenstein, precipitated something like a new philosophical conversion for Russell, even though it was a temporary one. With a feeling of intellectual liberation he rejoiced in the liberty of "believing that grass was green, and that the sun and the stars existed even when no one was looking at them!" At Oxford, in reply one day to an idealist philosopher who had declared that truth consisted of ideas conceived in the Absolute, Russell replied: "Do you mean to say that if the Absolute ceases to think of the hairs on my head, I shall go bald?"

Despite this change, Russell confessed that he had renounced with difficulty his belief in a "pluralistic timeless world of Platonic ideas." That the theories of Euclid do not afford us information about the real world, and that logic cannot establish any truth with certainty, he was obliged to admit. In the syllogism, the premises must be provided "from the outside." They were simply passed through the logical mill. The syllogism itself was neutral. Despite the *Principia Mathematica*, Russell could never rid himself of the suspicion that logic was by nature contradictory, though he did everything possible to dissipate it. One of his favorite examples was the following. Take the case of a man who declares, in respect of everything he says, "I am lying." We are immediately impelled to ask: "Is he lying when he says this?" If he lies, then he is telling the truth; but if he is telling the truth, then he is lying. Although Russell maintained that such paradoxes were to be explained by "the class of all classes which are not members of themselves," his perplexity remained; for to indulge for a moment in technicalities, the "class of all classes which are not members of themselves" reveals, on examination, precisely the same dilemma. Is *this* class, we may ask, a member of itself? If it is not, then it *is;* but if it is, it is by definition *not.* This sample of Russell's reasoning is given here not as the last word on the subject, but as revealing the kind of logical paradoxes with which he wrestled.

Even so, for Russell a more profound contradiction resulted from a conflict between the natural human desire for certitude, and the admission that all the assertions of physical science were founded upon mathematical hypotheses.

Upon this subject, Russell expressed himself with commendable frankness. He admitted late in life, with regret, that he no longer derived any mystical satisfaction from the contemplation of mathematical truth. The splendid certitude which he had hoped to find in mathematics was lost, and with it the hope of attaining finality and perfection on that plane. In the end, he was obliged to acknowledge that much of philosophy rested on a priori assumptions, and that this was particularly true even of the empirical philosophy he had at one time most admired.

There came a moment, indeed, when both mathematics and commonsense philosophy seemed to provide no satisfactory answer. "The best years of my life were given to the *Principles of Mathematics.* The whole of this effort, in spite of three big volumes, ended inwardly in doubt and bewilderment. As regards metaphysics, when, under the influence of Moore, I first threw off the belief in German idealism, I experienced the delight of believing that the sensible world is real. Bit by bit, chiefly under the influence of physics, this delight had faded, and I have been driven to a position not unlike that of Berkeley, without his God and his Anglican complacency."

In calling him the "passionate skeptic," his first biographer, Alan Wood, summed up Russell's outlook admirably. The passion inspired not merely his aversion to hypocrisy, cruelty, and injustice, but also his latent desire to arrive, in or outside philosophy, at a position beyond the reach of doubt. When, under the influence of Wittgenstein, Russell was obliged to admit that the propositions of mathematics were tautologous, he experienced a sense of desolation almost as deep as when, on the declaration of war in 1914, he realized that it was "impossible to continue to live in a world of abstractions." Russell's entire work reflects his internal torment: the *Angst* of a man condemned to skepticism but unable to face with equanimity the pain which this caused him. He had moments of extreme dejection. Writing late one night in 1931, he declared: "There is darkness without, and when I die there will be darkness within. There is no splendor, no vastness anywhere; only trivality for a moment, and then nothing. Why live in such a world? Why even die?"

There were thus two Russells in permanent conflict—on the one hand, "the passionate skeptic," and on the other, the skeptic who could not complacently accept the limitations of skepticism. For skepticism, considered as an end in itself, seemed incompatible with his faith in the liberty and power of the mind. In one of his most celebrated essays, "A Free Man's Worship" (1902), he expounded a form of stoicism which has been much praised. Nevertheless, the idea of "dignity" implies the idea of value and merit; and value is either a metaphysical concept or a fantasy of the imagination. It is curious to notice that some so-called realists, Russell included, in repudiating the transcendental go so far as to admit criteria which have no apparent rational guarantee. "Without a knowledge of ends," wrote Russell in *Authority and the Individual* (1949), "life becomes dull and insipid." In the same work he remarks that science is neutral, being neither good nor bad, and that our values come from a domain other than that of science. But what, for Russell, is this other domain? We search in vain for the answer in his one systematic treatise on morals, *Human Society in Ethics and Politics* (1954).

The dilemma haunted him permanently. In *Principles of Social Reconstruction* (1916), we come upon this striking passage: "Those who best promote life do not have life for their purpose. They

aim rather at what seems like a gradual incarnation, a bringing into existence of something eternal." In the same year, he wrote to his friend Constance Malleson: "I cannot bear the littleness and enclosing walls of a purely *personal* being . . . In some way I cannot put into words, I feel that some of our thoughts and feelings are just of the moment, but others are part of the eternal world— even if their actual existence is passing, something—some spirit or essence seems to last on, to be part of the real history of the universe, not only of the separate person. Somehow, that is how I want to live, so that as much of life as possible may have that quality of eternity." Well might Gilbert Ryle, in his fine obituary delivered before the Aristotelian Society of London, declare that "Russell was that rare being, a philosopher whose heart was divided between Transcendentalism and Naturalism."

Russell's ideas underwent, as we have seen, considerable modification, but he repeatedly took the view that "beyond philosophy" there was a saving wisdom, a world of values, if only we could descry it. Even in so "realist" a work as *The Scientific Outlook* (1931), he wrote: "I mean by wisdom a right conception of the ends of life. This is something which science in itself does not provide."

Just as the physicist necessarily changes his views from time to time, so the philosopher, whose task it is in part to analyze the "world-view of physics," must modify his opinions, even if this mental adjustment is both violent and painful. In a little book which had an immense success, *The Problems of Philosophy* (1912), Russell outlined his celebrated distinction between "knowledge by acquaintance" and "knowledge by description"—that is to say, immediate knowledge and mediate knowledge. By means of this distinction, Russell intended to suggest, for example, that the notion of a table is directly "given" to us by the *data* of sense, and only indirectly as a physical object (the "cause" of these sense-*data*). Nevertheless, this distinction reveals that we perceive intuitively the existence of immediate knowledge, without which human intelligence would be doomed to permanent frustration. This also implies another element in knowledge, the reality of *personal identity*. For we apprehend the truth, "I know this sense-*data*"; and how could we attain such a truth, or understand its significance without a direct acquaintance with something which we call *ourselves?* With his customary caution, Russell went so far as to suggest that this knowledge of personal identity, though very probable, is still uncertain; and there was a time when, to quote Leslie Paul, Russell "turned the Cartesian doubt upon the Cartesian ego itself."

In a later work, Russell's skepticism was directed toward another aspect of the Cartesian dichotomy, that of nature. If we cast doubt upon our own reality as beings that survive through time, and if we cannot prove that our sense-*data* imply an object which is "given," how can we admit the existence of nature? This led Russell on one occasion to the extreme view that, apart from "prejudice and habit," there is little reason to believe that there exists a world at all; but he might have asked himself how much of commonsense is mere prejudice and habit, and what a scientific "outlook" would amount to in the absence of a world to "view."

Such extreme skepticism, inspired partly by an impish delight in attacking orthodox thought, derived from Russell's attempt to "liquidate" philosophy in the traditional sense. In his book *Our Knowledge of the External World* (1926), he maintained that if we submit a philosophical problem to rigorous analysis, it moves away from philosophy and be-

comes logic. We see here the influence of Wittgenstein and the early Positivists.

In his collection of essays *Mysticism and Logic* (1918), the "mysticism" which Russell opposed to "logic" was, as Collingworth pointed out, traditional metaphysics; and having always associated metaphysics and idealism, Russell was permanently at war with all forms of thought which claimed, in the manner of the idealists, to say more about the world than science can substantiate by its system of verifiable hypotheses. In consequence, Russell attempted to replace all vast and unverifiable generalities by partial, though in principle verifiable, results. This amounted to the abandonment of philosophy in favor of physical science. In an essay entitled "Philosophy's Ulterior Motives" in his *Unpopular Essays* (1950), Russell went so far as to dismiss traditional philosophy as only a particular and temporary stage in the intellectual development of man—a stage that was incompatible with mental maturity. In a more radical manner, he described such philosophy as an ingenious attempt to elaborate chains of fallacious reasoning. In other words, all valid knowledge was scientific knowledge. This is why, Russell claimed, it is reasonable to place in science a measure of trust and confidence. In short, the achievements of science would seem to invalidate the fundamental skepticism to which logic otherwise leads. "Skepticism, though logically impeachable, is psychologically impossible, and there is an element of frivolous insincerity in any philosophy which pretends to accept it." This was the principle established at the outset of Russell's last major work, *Human Knowledge; Its Scope and Limits* (1948). In admitting as an established principle that the validity of scientific knowledge must be accepted, Russell modified his view on the place of logic. Logic, he now claimed, did not form part of philosophy at all. Thus he reaffirmed the view that fragmentary, detailed, and verifiable results, added one to another, must take the place of ancient systems of metaphysics. In his *Analysis of Matter* (1927), he had maintained that all human knowledge is uncertain, inexact, and partial; but, like Descartes and his faith in God, Russell stuck to his belief that science cannot ultimately deceive us.

When this form of reasoning attained its climax, Russell arrived at a position he called "Neutral Monism." Employed for the first time in *The Analysis of Matter,* Russell endeavored to establish the identity between the world of matter and the world of mind, on the assumption that they were two aspects of the same reality; for, in the light of modern physics, both matter and the self are nothing but aggregations or collections of "events." Physics and psychology, hitherto so divergent, now approached each other, uniting to form the single science of psychophysics. And since mind and nature were no longer separate, the problem of how one came to "know" the other amounted to a pseudoproblem. The distinction between the "mental" and the "physical" belonged to the theory of knowledge, not to metaphysics.

While renouncing the idea of a philosophical worldview in the classical sense, Russell tacitly adhered to the conception of the universe which modern science, since the seventeenth century, recognized as a form of orthodoxy. Modern physics, founded on the theory of relativity and on quantum mechanics, was for him simply the New Testament of science, a sequel to the Old Testament established by Galileo, Kepler, Descartes, and Newton. The two Testaments together formed a *Weltanschauung* in direct contrast to that of traditional religion. Hence, in his strictly scientific attitude, Russell remained a kind of fundamentalist. Even thus understood,

physics, especially after Einstein, inevitably lacked that "concrete" character which should exist in a complete science of nature. As Russell wrote in *The Analysis of Matter,* the aim of physics had always been to discover what may be called the "causal structure" of the world. This affirmation suggested that he had renounced the idea of science as revealing the essence of nature, at least as understood since the pre-Socratic philosophers. For the essence of nature was its organic character.

Russell's repudiation of this organic concept marked his rupture with Whitehead; for while Whitehead continued to elaborate a systematic, organic philosophy, Russell, being still attached to the logical atomism of his youth, preserved an instinctive distrust toward philosophies which make use of "the concept of system." It is interesting to note that the *Outline of Philosophy* (1927), perhaps Russell's least successful work, made no mention of the theory of evolution.

Nevertheless, the organic processes of nature, explicable ultimately in physicochemical terms, were surely the very essence of nature, and in consequence they merited a place in the "scientific outlook" on the same level as the abstract or atomistic truths of physics. As Whitehead maintained, the concept of organism implied the notion of *aim,* whereas Russell repudiated teleology. "It is . . . prudent to adopt the mechanistic view as a working hypothesis, to be abandoned only where there is clear evidence against it. As regards biological phenomena, such evidence, so far, is entirely absent." Russell had affirmed that science was ethically neutral, and that our "conclusions" about the value of life must come from "the outside." Once again the two Russells oppose each other. One upholds the identity of science and "knowledge"; the other believes that this identity, analyzed *au fond*, deprives life of significance. In his polemical little work, *Religion and Science* (1935, reissued 1958), the conflict was apparent from one page to another. Knowledge, he declared, following the pragmatic tradition, was simply an instrument for manipulating matter. Later, however, he affirmed that, insofar as religion consisted of a "state of mind" and not of a group of doctrinal beliefs, science could not replace it. There existed an aspect of the religious life, perhaps the most precious of all, which remained independent of the discoveries of science, and which would survive however much our convictions on the nature of the universe might change; the supreme example was shown in the lives of the "greatest among the saints and the mystics." The same conviction illuminated the last pages of *Authority and the Individual* (1949).

In 1927, in collaboration with his second wife, Dora, whom he had married in 1921, Russell founded a school called Beacon Hill, at Telegraph House near Petersfield. This school was designed, at least in theory, to be progressive in every sense, and it naturally gave rise to much hostile criticism. The experiment was his only contribution, in the practical sphere, to the reform of education; though almost all his writings, except those concerned exclusively with logic and mathematics, had a pedagogical impact. In this respect his aim was to elaborate theories concerned with the formation of the personality as a whole. He learned soon enough that progressive education did not mean complete liberty for the children, and there are some sobering reflections in the *Autobiography* on this subject. "To let the children go free," he wrote, "was to establish a reign of terror, in which the strong kept the weak trembling and miserable. A school is like a world: only government can prevent brute violence. And so I found myself, when the children were not at lessons, obliged to supervise them to stop cruelty. Young children in a group cannot be happy without a certain amount of order and routine. Left to amuse themselves, they are bored, and turn to bullying and destruction."

Even so, his experiments in the educational sphere contributed perhaps even more than his incursions into politics to affirm his unshakable belief in democracy: whereas a large number of his contemporaries, Fabians like Shaw and the Webbs, and Catholics like Belloc, were from time to time seduced by the attractions of authoritarianism. In Russell's view, the defense of the state, in all civilized countries, depended as much on the teachers as on the armed forces. The defense of the state was desirable except in totalitarian countries, and the use of education to that end was not reprehensible in itself—it was only reprehensible if the state defended obscurantism and appealed to irrational passions. There was no place for these evils if the state were to be worthy of defense.

Although in 1935, with his divorce from Dora, he severed his connection with the school, Russell continued to take an interest in education. He proved an outstanding teacher. Not merely did he hold chairs in philosophy in a number of countries, but he exercised great influence over thousands of readers by the combination of eloquence and wit in his discursive writings. His travels took him around the world. He knew China, Russia, Japan, Australia, and the United States. In 1948, during an over-water flight to Norway, where he was due to give a lecture on the prevention of war, he was involved in an air crash. Although he was wearing a heavy overcoat at the time, the gallant old man swam for ten minutes before help arrived.

During the Cuban crisis of 1962 which brought the United States and the Soviet close to war, Russell's house, Plas Penrhyn in North Wales, became an important center for international communication. Despite his ninety years, Russell stayed up into the small hours, and sometimes did not go to bed at all, in order to draft telegrams and messages to Khrushchev and to Kennedy, and to reply to the questions of an army of journalists. The fact that he was so much concerned with public affairs, however, did not interrupt his strictly philosophical work. In 1954, he caused a storm in academic circles by his severe criticism of certain tendencies in British linguistic philosophy, which he dismissed as "silly people saying silly things," thereby reducing philosophy to a superficial and unrewarding study. This rumpus exerted an influence outside university circles; it resulted in a flood of letters to *The Times*. In 1949 the great radical was awarded one of the most important honors the British state can confer, the Order of Merit. In spite of his unorthodox opinions, Russell showed, throughout a long career, qualities of integrity, justice, and honesty that earned him the respect of even his most ardent opponents. Admittedly, there were regrettable exceptions. The cancellation of his nomination to a professorship at the City College of New York, in 1940, was an episode casting greater discredit on his critics than on himself. His writings were described as "lubricious, filthy, libidinous, lascivious, depraved, erotic, aphrodisiac, irreverent, narrow-minded and deprived of all moral fiber." That such accusations should have been brought against a man with so generally wholesome an outlook as Russell, at an epoch which witnessed the publication of thousands of works of deliberate salacity, reveals how much hypocrisy and cant had survived from the Victorian era. It is to the credit of a number of distinguished American personalities, among them the veteran philosopher John Dewey, that they resolutely defended the reputation of their distinguished guest; and when later he paid a visit to California, he received a hero's welcome.

Nevertheless, the episode plunged him into severe financial difficulties. Remarking that his "income was less than his income tax," he added with typical gaiety of spirit: "it will be interesting to see how the government will handle this situation." On a careful reading of Russell's work, even the controversial *Marriage and Morals* (1929), one cannot find a single trace of vulgarity, still less any appeal to the baser instincts; and the accusation of narrowness of mind of which some had accused him could only rebound upon his critics.

Of Russell's four marriages, only the last, to an American in 1952, brought him the peace for which he had longed as much in his personal life as in the world. Certainly the *Autobiography*, issued in three volumes from 1967, shows a man who might have left an impression of disillusion and frustration had he died twenty or thirty years earlier. Perhaps the vigorous campaigns with which his name became associated were attempts, at least at the outset, to compensate for a lurking sense of personal inadequacy. For the higher a man rises in the world's eyes, the more he becomes conscious, if he is sincere, of inner failings. The last campaign, however, was dictated by a genuine conviction that the world was on the brink of an abyss, from which only a determined, collective effort might save it. This was the Campaign for Nuclear Disarmament, launched in February 1958, of which he became president. Owing to strained relationships among the leadership, however, Russell left this movement and joined the Committee of 100, whose aim was "civil disobedience against nuclear warfare." On the eve of a sitdown demonstration in Parliament

Square in London, he was arraigned for inciting members of the public to commit breach of the peace; and, having refused in court to be bound over on good behavior, he was sentenced with his wife to prison for two months—a period reduced to two weeks at the plea of his counsel. He was confined to Brixton prison, where he had served his previous sentence, but he spent the time in the hospital. Not long after, he left the Committee of 100 on the plea—he was then over ninety—of pressure of other work directed to similar ends but he was not slow to intervene by telegram or by letter when some international issue seemed to warrant it. In order to further his general opposition to nuclear armaments and to war in general, in 1963 he established the Bertrand Russell Peace Foundation and the Atlantic Peace Foundation.

Somewhat less satisfactory a venture was the part he played in setting up, with a group of intellectuals including Sartre and Simone de Beauvoir, a War Crimes Tribunal to try the United States for crimes committed in Vietnam. More than one government refused permission for the court to be held on its soil, and it finally sat in Stockholm, heard all the evidence in one session, and came to a verdict of guilty without a dissenting voice. This was perhaps Russell's one attempt at international action which came near to bringing his name into discredit, as it certainly revealed an absence of his habitual balanced judgment. (Some would see a similar lack of balance in his handling of the earlier Cuban crisis.)

Even so, his international prestige remained supreme not merely among men of intellect, but among thousands who needed a spokesman capable of making himself heard across national and ideological boundaries. One remarkable example was a desperate appeal for his personal intervention at the time of the Czech crisis. Nor did it go unheeded. Russell, if anyone, demonstrated that the pen was mightier than the sword, but only because his pen was a rapier with an uncommonly powerful thrust.

As Russell moved into his late nineties, he neither gave way to idleness nor showed signs of the approach of senility. As he had wished, he was at work when death overtook him in his ninety-eighth year, on Monday, February 2, 1970, after an attack of influenza. From all over the world there came tributes, and more than one spokesman compared him in stature to Voltaire. All singled out his great moral courage. Even the Vatican, for which Russell had shown no particular affection, remarked through its newspaper *L'Osservatore Romano* on his "unreserved effort in favor of the dignity of man," adding that he was "a mild and terrible, restless and serene protester, compared with whom the young protesters of today are only pale shadows."

E. W. F. Tomlin, an English literary critic, teaches at Oxford University.

THE 1950 PRIZE

By KJELL STRÖMBERG

In 1950 the Swedish Academy had two Nobel Prizes to award, since the one for 1949 had been held in reserve. Everyone expected that one of the two would go to Sir Winston Churchill. The former Prime Minister of Great Britain had just published the third volume of his masterly epic on World War II, and he had several enthusiastic supporters in the Academy itself. Another very prominent candidate was Pär Lagerkvist, the Swedish poet, dramatist, and novelist, who had been proposed that year by all the Scandinavian literary societies. There was no shortage of other distinguished candidates, English, French, and American, some of whom were later to carry off the Prize. Having agreed on William Faulkner for the 1949 Prize, the Swedish Academy made a choice farther afield and awarded its 1950 Prize to an outsider who had been proposed that year for the first time, Bertrand Lord Russell, the English philosopher.

There was general surprise. Since 1928, the year in which Henri Bergson received the Prize, no philosopher had been chosen. The elderly English peer was now nearly eighty. Unlike his French predecessor, he did not show great artistic imagination in his style of writing, but he was very well known and popular as the witty and elegant developer and popularizer of the empirical, humanist philosophy of the great English thinkers of the eighteenth century, Locke, Berkeley, and Hume. He also had an affinity with the no less influential utilitarians of the nineteenth century, Jeremy Bentham, John Stuart Mill, and Herbert Spencer.

We know that Herbert Spencer was particularly appreciated by Alfred Nobel, who would have been gratified to see him receive the first Nobel Prize for Literature, for which he had in fact been a candidate and a very prominent one. No doubt the Swedish Academy, on very good grounds, wanted to mark the fiftieth anniversary of the Nobel institution by paying tardy and discreet homage to the world of ideas represented by Russell as well as by Spencer.

According to the brief published account of the reasons for this choice, the Nobel Prize of 1950 was awarded to Bertrand Russell "in homage to his philosophical work, which is as rich as it is important and which makes him rank as a defender of humanity and the freedom of ideas." The Committee's adviser was a professor of philosophy at Stockholm University, and after a detailed analysis of Russell's vast philosophical, scientific, historical, sociological, and political works, he came to the conclusion that Russell compared favorably with the other "non-literary" writers—Mommsen, Eucken, and Bergson—who had previously been honored with the Nobel

Prize for Literature. If the Swedish Academy wanted to honor the intellectual culture of England in the same way, it could not have chosen a worthier representative than Bertrand Russell.

Anders Österling, the permanent secretary of the Swedish Academy, did not spare his praise in awarding the Prize to the noble lord.

Lord Russell did not make a formal acceptance at the award ceremony but on the following day he gave a public lecture on the current trends in world politics. He reaffirmed his unshakable faith in human intelligence, the only thing capable of making this world in which we live a better one. It should be remembered that this profession of optimistic faith was composed and spoken at the moment when a new struggle with far-reaching repercussions had just broken out—the Korean war.

Translated by Camilla Sykes.